6th EDITION

Basic College Mathematics:
An Applied Approach

Richard N. Aufmann
Palomar College

Vernon C. Barker
Palomar College

Joanne S. Lockwood
Plymouth State College

HOUGHTON MIFFLIN COMPANY

Boston   New York

Senior Sponsoring Editor: Maureen O'Connor
Senior Associate Editor: Dawn M. Nuttall
Project Editor: Christina Lillios
Senior Production/Design Coordinator: Carol Merrigan
Senior Manufacturing Coordinator: Marie Barnes
Editorial Assistant: Lauren Gagliardi

Cover designer: Harold Burch Design, NYC

Photo Credits

Page 1, Matthew Borkoski/Stock, Boston, Inc.; page 61, Will & Deni McIntyre/Photo Researchers, Inc.; page 121, Gary Landsman/The Stock Market; page 167, Oliver LeClerc/Gamma Liaison; page 195, Ben Osborne/TSI; page 227, Jeff Greenberg/Photo Researchers, Inc.; page 281, Bob Daemmrich Photo, Inc.; page 317, Wesley Bocxe/Photo Researchers, Inc.; page 347, Bob Daemmrich Photo, Inc.; page 379, Stacy Pick/Stock, Boston, Inc.; page 429, Robert Brenner/Photo Edit; page 485, Doug Armand/TSI.

Art Credits

Page 39, (table sources) USA TODAY, September 15, 1993 and Craig Carter, *Complete Baseball Record Book—1994* (The Sporting News); page 58, (figure) copyright © 1993, USA TODAY. Reprinted with permission; page 90, (top figure) reprinted by permission of Wall Street Journal, © 1997 Dow Jones & Company, Inc. All rights reserved; page 127, (figure) reprinted courtesy of West Shore Acres Display Garden; page 130, (top figure) copyright © 1993, USA TODAY. Reprinted with permission; page 294, (bottom figure) from *Mathematics Teacher*, Vol. 86, No. 8, p. 629. Reprinted with permission from the *Mathematics Teacher*, copyright 1993 by the National Council of Teachers of Mathematics; page 474, copyright © 1993, USA TODAY. Reprinted with permission.

ISBN Numbers
     Student Text: 0-395-90704-7
     Instructor's Annotated Edition: 0-395-92320-4

   789-WC-02 01

Contents

Contents

3   Decimals   121

4   Ratio and Proportion   167

5   Percents   195

12 Geometry   485

Preface

The sixth edition of *Basic College Mathematics: An Applied Approach* provides mathematically sound and comprehensive coverage of the topics considered essential in a basic college mathematics course. The text has been designed not only to meet the needs of the traditional college student but also to serve the needs of returning students whose mathematical proficiency may have declined during years away from formal education.

In this new edition of *Basic College Mathematics: An Applied Approach,* we have continued to integrate some of the approaches suggested by AMATYC. Each chapter begins with a mathematical vignette in which there may be a historical note, application, or curiosity related to mathematics. At the end of each section there are "Applying the Concepts" exercises that include writing, synthesis, critical thinking, and challenge problems. At the end of each chapter there is a "Focus on Problem Solving" that introduces students to various problem-solving strategies. This is followed by "Projects and Group Activities" that can be used for cooperative learning activities.

One of the main challenges for students is the ability to translate verbal phrases into mathematical expressions. One reason for this difficulty is that students are not exposed to verbal phrases until later in most texts. In *Basic College Mathematics: An Applied Approach,* we introduce verbal phrases for operations as we introduce the operation. For instance, after addition concepts have been presented, we provide exercises that say "Find the sum of…." or "What is 6 more than 7?" In this way, students are constantly confronted with verbal phrases and must make a mathematical connection between the phrase and a mathematical operation.

INSTRUCTIONAL FEATURES

Interactive Approach

Basic College Mathematics: An Applied Approach uses an interactive style that provides a student with an opportunity to try a skill as it is presented. Each section is divided into objectives, and every objective contains one or more sets of matched-pair examples. The first example in each set is worked out; the second example, called "You Try It," is for the student to work. By solving this problem, the student practices concepts as they are presented in the text. There are complete worked-out solutions to these examples in an appendix at the end of the book. By comparing their solution to the solution in the appendix, students are able to obtain immediate feedback on and reinforcement of the concept.

Emphasis on Problem-Solving Strategies

Basic College Mathematics: An Applied Approach features a carefully developed approach to problem solving that emphasizes developing strategies to solve problems. Students are encouraged to develop their own strategies, to draw diagrams, and to write strategies as part of their solution to a problem. In each case, model strategies are presented as guides for students to follow as they attempt the "You Try It" problem. Having students provide strategies is a natural way to incorporate writing into the math curriculum.

Emphasis on Applications

The traditional approach to teaching algebra covers only the straightforward manipulation of numbers and variables and thereby fails to teach students the practical value of algebra. By contrast, *Basic College Mathematics: An Applied Approach* contains an extensive collection of contemporary application problems. Wherever appropriate, the last objective of a section presents applications that require the student to use the skills covered in that section to solve practical problems. This carefully integrated applied approach generates student awareness of the value of algebra as a real-life tool.

Completely Integrated Learning System Organized by Objectives

Each chapter begins with a list of the learning objectives included within that chapter. Each of the objectives is then restated in the chapter to remind the student of the current topic of discussion. The same objectives that organize the text are also used as the structure for exercises, testing programs, and the Computer Tutor. For each objective in the text, there is a corresponding computer tutorial and a corresponding set of test questions.

AN INTERACTIVE APPROACH

Instructors have long realized the need for a text that requires students to use a skill as it is being taught. *Basic College Mathematics: An Applied Approach* uses an interactive technique that meets this need. Every objective, including the one shown on the next page, contains at least one pair of examples. One of the examples is worked. The second example in the pair (You Try It) is not worked so that students may "interact" with the text by solving it. To provide immediate feedback, a complete worked-out solution to this example is provided in the Solutions Section at the end of the book. The benefit of this interactive style is that students can immediately determine whether a new skill has been learned before attempting a homework assignment or moving on to the next skill.

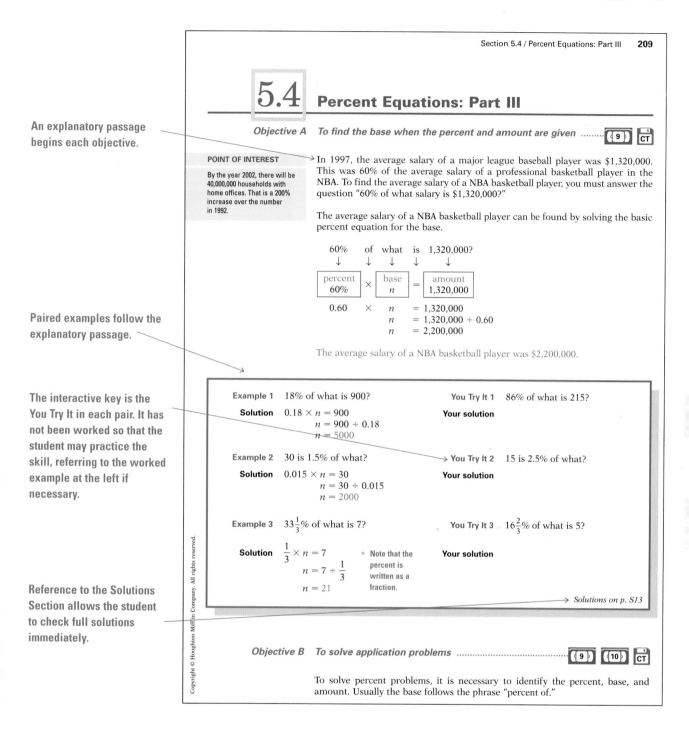

An explanatory passage begins each objective.

Paired examples follow the explanatory passage.

The interactive key is the You Try It in each pair. It has not been worked so that the student may practice the skill, referring to the worked example at the left if necessary.

Reference to the Solutions Section allows the student to check full solutions immediately.

5.4 Percent Equations: Part III

Objective A   *To find the base when the percent and amount are given* ....

POINT OF INTEREST

By the year 2002, there will be 40,000,000 households with home offices. That is a 200% increase over the number in 1992.

In 1997, the average salary of a major league baseball player was $1,320,000. This was 60% of the average salary of a professional basketball player in the NBA. To find the average salary of a NBA basketball player, you must answer the question "60% of what salary is $1,320,000?"

The average salary of a NBA basketball player can be found by solving the basic percent equation for the base.

$$60\% \quad \text{of} \quad \text{what} \quad \text{is} \quad 1{,}320{,}000?$$

$$\boxed{\begin{array}{c}\text{percent}\\60\%\end{array}} \times \boxed{\begin{array}{c}\text{base}\\n\end{array}} = \boxed{\begin{array}{c}\text{amount}\\1{,}320{,}000\end{array}}$$

$$\begin{aligned}0.60 \times n &= 1{,}320{,}000\\ n &= 1{,}320{,}000 \div 0.60\\ n &= 2{,}200{,}000\end{aligned}$$

The average salary of a NBA basketball player was $2,200,000.

Example 1   18% of what is 900?

Solution $0.18 \times n = 900$
$n = 900 \div 0.18$
$n = 5000$

You Try It 1   86% of what is 215?

Your solution

Example 2   30 is 1.5% of what?

Solution $0.015 \times n = 30$
$n = 30 \div 0.015$
$n = 2000$

You Try It 2   15 is 2.5% of what?

Your solution

Example 3 $33\frac{1}{3}\%$ of what is 7?

Solution $\frac{1}{3} \times n = 7$
$n = 7 \div \frac{1}{3}$
$n = 21$

• Note that the percent is written as a fraction.

You Try It 3 $16\frac{2}{3}\%$ of what is 5?

Your solution

Solutions on p. S13

Objective B   *To solve application problems* ....

To solve percent problems, it is necessary to identify the percent, base, and amount. Usually the base follows the phrase "percent of."

AN EMPHASIS ON APPLICATIONS

The traditional teaching approach neglects the difficulties that students have in making the transition from arithmetic to algebra. One of the most troublesome and uncomfortable transitions for the student is from concrete arithmetic to symbolic algebra. *Basic College Mathematics: An Applied Approach* recognizes the formidable task the student faces by introducing variables in a very natural way—through applications of mathematics. A secondary benefit of this approach is that the student becomes aware of the value of algebra as a real-life tool.

The solution of an application problem in *Basic College Mathematics: An Applied Approach* is always accompanied by two parts: **Strategy** and **Solution**. The strategy is a written description of the steps that are necessary to solve the problem; the solution is the implementation of the strategy. This format provides students with a structure for problem solving. It also encourages students to write strategies for solving problems and, in turn, fosters organizing problem-solving strategies in a logical way.

A strategy that the student may use in solving an application problem is stated.

The strategy is used in the solution of the worked example.

Students are encouraged to write a strategy for the application problem they solve.

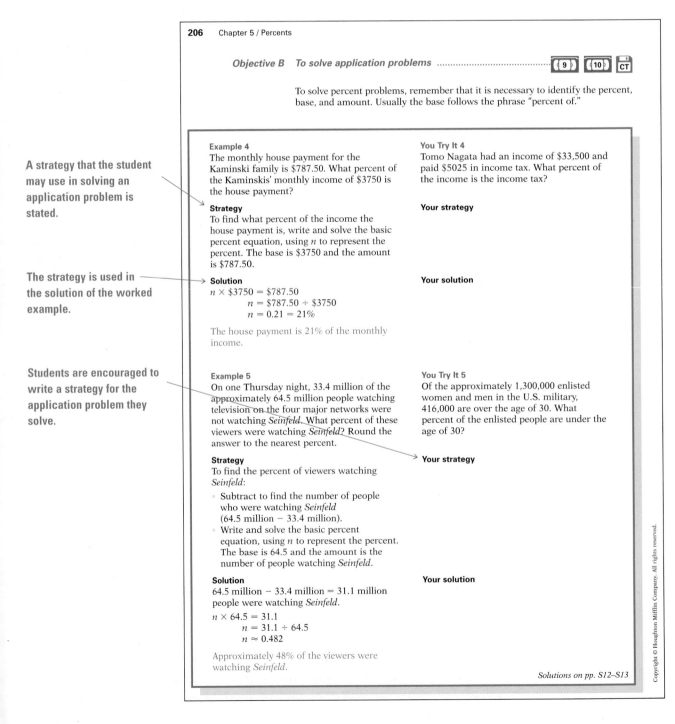

206   Chapter 5 / Percents

Objective B   **To solve application problems** .... (9) (10) CT

To solve percent problems, remember that it is necessary to identify the percent, base, and amount. Usually the base follows the phrase "percent of."

Example 4
The monthly house payment for the Kaminski family is $787.50. What percent of the Kaminskis' monthly income of $3750 is the house payment?

Strategy
To find what percent of the income the house payment is, write and solve the basic percent equation, using n to represent the percent. The base is $3750 and the amount is $787.50.

Solution
$n \times \$3750 = \$787.50$
$n = \$787.50 \div \$3750$
$n = 0.21 = 21\%$

The house payment is 21% of the monthly income.

Example 5
On one Thursday night, 33.4 million of the approximately 64.5 million people watching television on the four major networks were not watching *Seinfeld*. What percent of these viewers were watching *Seinfeld*? Round the answer to the nearest percent.

Strategy
To find the percent of viewers watching *Seinfeld*:
- Subtract to find the number of people who were watching *Seinfeld* (64.5 million − 33.4 million).
- Write and solve the basic percent equation, using n to represent the percent. The base is 64.5 and the amount is the number of people watching *Seinfeld*.

Solution
64.5 million − 33.4 million = 31.1 million people were watching *Seinfeld*.

$n \times 64.5 = 31.1$
$n = 31.1 \div 64.5$
$n \approx 0.482$

Approximately 48% of the viewers were watching *Seinfeld*.

You Try It 4
Tomo Nagata had an income of $33,500 and paid $5025 in income tax. What percent of the income is the income tax?

Your strategy

Your solution

You Try It 5
Of the approximately 1,300,000 enlisted women and men in the U.S. military, 416,000 are over the age of 30. What percent of the enlisted people are under the age of 30?

Your strategy

Your solution

Solutions on pp. S12–S13

OBJECTIVE-SPECIFIC APPROACH

Many mathematics texts are not organized in a manner that facilitates management of learning. Typically, students are left to wander through a maze of apparently unrelated lessons, exercise sets, and tests. *Basic College Mathematics: An Applied Approach* solves this problem by organizing all lessons, exercise sets, computer tutorials, and tests around a carefully constructed hierarchy of objectives. The advantage of this objective-by-objective organization is that it enables the student who is uncertain at any step in the learning process to refer easily to the original presentation and review that material.

The Objective-Specific Approach also gives the instructor greater control over the management of student progress. The Computerized Test Generator and the printed Test Bank are organized by the same objectives as the text. These references are provided with the answers to the test items, thereby allowing the instructor to quickly determine those objectives on which a student may need additional instruction.

The Computer Tutor is also organized around the objectives of the text. As a result, supplemental instruction is available for any objectives that are troublesome for a student.

A numbered objective statement names the topic of each lesson.

Section 5.4 / Percent Equations: Part III   **209**

5.4 Percent Equations: Part III

Objective A   To find the base when the percent and amount are given .... (9) CT

The exercise sets correspond to the objectives in the text.

Section 5.4 / Percent Equations: Part III   **211**

5.4 Exercises

Objective A

Solve. Round to the nearest hundredth.

1. 12% of what is 9?

2. 38% of what is 171?

The answers to the odd-numbered exercises are provided in the Answer Section.

SECTION 5.4

1. 75   3. 50   5. 100   7. 85   9. 1200   11. 19.2   13. 7.5   15. 32   17. 200   19. 80   21. 9
23. 504   25. 108   27. 7122.15   29. The average size of a house in 1977 was 1680 square feet.   31. The selling

The answers to the Chapter Review Exercises, Chapter Test, and the Cumulative Review Exercises show the objective to study if the student incorrectly answers the exercise.

CHAPTER REVIEW

1. 60 [5.2A]   2. 20% [5.3A]   3. 175% [5.1B]   4. 75 [5.4A]   5. $\frac{3}{25}$ [5.1A]   6. 19.36 [5.2A]

7. 150% [5.3A]   8. 504 [5.4A]   9. 0.42 [5.1A]   10. 5.4 [5.2A]   11. 157.5 [5.4A]   12. 0.076 [5.1A]

CHAPTER TEST

1. 0.973 [5.1A]   2. $\frac{5}{6}$ [5.1A]   3. 30% [5.1B]   4. 163% [5.1B]   5. 150% [5.1B]   6. $66\frac{2}{3}$% [5.1B]

7. 50.05 [5.2A]   8. 61.36 [5.2A]   9. 76% of 13 [5.2A]   10. 212% of 12 [5.2A]   11. The company spends

CUMULATIVE REVIEW

1. 4 [1.6B]   2. 240 [2.1A]   3. $10\frac{11}{24}$ [2.4C]   4. $12\frac{41}{48}$ [2.5C]   5. $12\frac{4}{7}$ [2.6B]   6. $\frac{7}{24}$ [2.7B]

7. $\frac{1}{3}$ [2.8B]   8. $\frac{13}{36}$ [2.8C]   9. 3.08 [3.1B]   10. 1.1196 [3.3A]   11. 34.2813 [3.5A]   12. 3.625 [3.6A]

ADDITIONAL LEARNING AIDS

Chapter Opener

The Chapter Opener relates a historical, contemporary, or interesting note about mathematics or its application.

Focus on Problem Solving

At the end of each chapter there is a Focus on Problem Solving, the purpose of which is to introduce the student to various successful problem-solving strategies. Each Focus consists of a problem and an appropriate strategy to solve the problem. Strategies such as guessing, trying to solve a simpler but similar problem, drawing a diagram, and looking for patterns are some of the techniques that are demonstrated.

Projects and Group Activities

The Projects and Group Activities feature can be used as extra credit or cooperative learning activities. The projects cover various aspects of mathematics including the use of calculators, extended applications, additional problem-solving strategies, and other topics related to mathematics.

Chapter Summaries

At the end of each chapter there is a Chapter Summary that includes Key Words and Essential Rules that were covered in the chapter. These chapter summaries provide a single point of reference as the student prepares for a test.

Study Skills

The To the Student Preface on page xxiii provides suggestions for using this text and approaches to creating good study habits. Students are referred to this Preface at appropriate places in the text.

Computer Tutor

This state-of-the-art Tutor is a networkable, interactive, algorithmically driven software package. Features include full-color graphics, a glossary, extensive hints, animated solution steps, and a comprehensive class management system. Written by Dick Aufmann, the tutor and the text are in the same voice.

Glossary

A Glossary at the end of the book includes definitions of terms used in the text.

Margin Notes

There are three types of margin notes in the student text. *Point of Interest* notes interesting sidelights of the topic being discussed. The *Take Note* feature warns students that a procedure may be particularly involved or reminds students that there are certain checks of their work that should be performed. *Calculator Notes* provide suggestions for using a calculator in certain situations. In addition, there are *Instructor Notes* that are printed only in the Instructor's Annotated Edition. These notes provide suggestions for presenting the material or related material that can be used in class.

Index of Applications

The Index of Applications illustrates the power and scope of mathematics and its application. This may help some students see the benefits of mathematics as a tool that is used in everyday experiences.

EXERCISES

End-of-Section Exercises

Basic College Mathematics: An Applied Approach contains more than 6000 exercises. At the end of each section there are exercise sets that are keyed to the corresponding learning objectives. The exercises are carefully developed to ensure that students can apply the concepts in the section to a variety of problem situations. Data Analysis exercises are identified by ◐ . Calculator exercises are identified by ▦ .

Applying the Concepts Exercises

The End-of-Section Exercises are followed by Applying the Concepts Exercises. These sections contain a variety of exercise types, including:

- challenge problems
- problems that require that the student determine if a statement is always true, sometimes true, or never true
- problems that ask students to determine incorrect procedures

Writing Exercises

Within the "Applying the Concepts Exercises," there are Writing Exercises denoted by ∦ . These exercises ask students to write about a topic in the section or to research and report on a related topic.

Chapter Review Exercises

Review Exercises are found at the end of each chapter. These exercises are selected to help the student integrate all of the topics presented in the chapter. The answers to all review exercises are given in the answer section at the end of the book. Along with the answer, there is a reference to the objective that pertains to each exercise.

Chapter Test Exercises

The Chapter Test Exercises are designed to simulate a possible test of the material in the chapter. The answers to all Chapter Test Exercises are given in the answer section at the end of the book. Along with the answer, there is a reference to the objective that pertains to each exercise.

Cumulative Review Exercises

Cumulative Review Exercises, which appear at the end of each chapter (beginning with Chapter 2), help students maintain skills learned in previous chapters. The answers to all Cumulative Review Exercises are given in the answer section. Along with the answer, there is a reference to the objective that pertains to each exercise.

NEW TO THIS EDITION

Scientific notation has been added to Chapter 10, *Rational Numbers*.

The material in Chapter 6, *Applications for Business and Consumers,* has been updated to reflect current interest rates and prices.

In Chapter 7, *Statistics,* we have replaced approximately 90% of all the graphs with contemporary data and situations. In Section 7.4, the mean and median objectives have been combined into a single objective and a discussion of the mode was included. A new objective on box-and-whiskers plots was added to Section 7.4.

We have added some problems that have too much data, thereby requiring the student to select the information needed to solve the problem.

For some exercises, not enough information is given to reach a single answer. Thus, there is more than one answer that satisfies the conditions of the problem.

The skill development exercises were thoroughly reviewed to ensure that there was an adequate representation of various problem types. As a result of this review, we have changed or replaced some drill exercises to include problem types that were missing.

Approximately one-third of all the application problems were changed to reflect current data and trends. New application problems were added to demonstrate to students the variety of problems that require mathematical analysis.

Career notes were added to the chapter opener pages to illustrate to students the diverse ways mathematics is used in the workplace.

We have more than doubled the number of projects and group activities. Some of these projects have suggested Internet sites so that the student may continue to explore a topic.

In response to suggestions by users, the Chapter Review Exercises are no longer categorized by section. Thus there are no organizational clues to students as to the type of skill needed to solve an exercise. The answers to all Chapter Review Exercises are in the answer appendix. Along with the answer, there is a reference to the objective that pertains to each exercise.

SUPPLEMENTS FOR THE INSTRUCTOR

Instructor's Annotated Edition

The Instructor's Annotated Edition is an exact replica of the student text except that answers to all exercises are given in the text. Also, there are Instructor Notes in the margin that offer suggestions for presenting the material in that objective.

Instructor's Resource Manual with Chapter Tests

The Instructor's Resource Manual contains the printed Chapter Tests, which are the first of three sources of testing material. Eight printed tests, four free response and four multiple choice, are provided for each chapter. In addition, there are cumulative tests after Chapters 3, 6, 9, and 12, and a final exam. The Instructor's Resource Manual also includes suggestions for course sequencing and outlines for the answers to the Writing Exercises.

Computerized Test Generator

The Computerized Test Generator is the second source of testing material. The database contains more than 2000 test items. The Test Generator is designed to provide an unlimited number of tests for each chapter, cumulative chapter tests, and a final exam. It is available for Windows and the Macintosh. Both versions also provide **on-line testing** and **gradebook** functions.

Printed Test Bank

The printed Test Bank, the third component of the testing material, is a printout of all items in the Computerized Test Generator. Instructors who do not have access to a computer can use the Test Bank to select items to include on a test being prepared by hand.

Solutions Manual

The Solutions Manual contains worked-out solutions for all end-of-section exercises, Chapter Review Exercises, Chapter Test Exercises, Cumulative Review Exercises, and the Final Exam.

SUPPLEMENTS FOR THE STUDENT

Student Solutions Manual

The Student Solutions Manual contains the complete solutions to all odd-numbered exercises in the text.

Computer Tutor

This new interactive state-of-the art tutorial software was written by Dick Aufmann and therefore is in the same voice as the text. Every objective in the text is supported by the Tutor. Problems are algorithmically generated, solution steps are animated, lessons and problems are presented in a colorful, lively manner and an integrated classroom management system tracks and reports student performance. New features include:

- assessment
- free response problems
- ability to repeat same problem type
- ability to print problems
- syllabus customization
- ability to bookmark

The Computer Tutor can be used in several ways: (1) to cover material the student missed because of an absence; (2) to reinforce instruction on a concept that the student has not yet mastered; (3) to review material in preparation for exams. This tutorial is available for Windows, and there is a version available for the Macintosh.

Within each section of the book, a computer icon appears next to each objective. The icon serves as a reminder that there is a Computer Tutor lesson corresponding to that objective.

Videotapes

Within each section of the text, a videotape icon appears next to an objective for which there is a corresponding video. The icon contains the reference number of the appropriate video. Each video topic is motivated through an application and the necessary mathematics to solve that problem are then presented.

ACKNOWLEDGMENTS

We sincerely wish to thank the following reviewers, who reviewed the manuscript in various stages of development, for their valuable contributions.

Lawrence Chernoff, Miami-Dade Community College, FL

Jeanne Marie Draper

Rose Ann Haw, Mesa Community College, AZ

Rosalie K. Hojegian, Passaic County Community College, NJ

Susan Howey, Harford Community College, MD

Ann Johnson, Community College of Denver, CO

Dr. Barbara Kistler, Lehigh Carbon Community College, PA

Mort E. Mattson, Lansing Community College, MI

Debi McCandrew, Florence-Darlington Technical College, SC

Donna L. McCart, Southern Vermont College

Fadi Nasr, Mt. San Jacinto College, CA

Sister Elizabeth Ogilvie, Horry Georgetown Technical College, SC

Thomas J. Pandolfini, Jr., Johnson & Wales University, RI

Dennis Reissig, Suffolk Community College, Selden, NY

Deana J. Richmond

Jennifer J. Sanders, Bryant & Stratton Business Institute, NY

Alice Stauffer, Slippery Rock University, PA

Desmond Tynan, Holyoke Community College, MA

George Welch, Laredo Community College, TX

Special thanks to Dan Clegg of Palomar College for some of the new application problems.

To the Student

Take an active role in the learning process.

Many students feel that they will never understand math, while others appear to do very well with little effort. Oftentimes what makes the difference is that successful students take an active role in the learning process.

Do the homework.

Attend class regularly.

Participate in class.

Learning mathematics requires your *active* participation. Although doing homework is one way you can actively participate, it is not the only way. First, you must attend class regularly and become an active participant. Second, you must become actively involved with the textbook.

Basic College Mathematics: An Applied Approach was written and designed with you in mind as a participant. Here are some suggestions on how to use the features of this textbook.

Use the features of the text.

There are 12 chapters in this text. Each chapter is divided into sections, and each section is subdivided into learning objectives. Each learning objective is labeled with a letter from A to D.

Read the objective statement.

Read the objective material.

Study the in-text examples.

First, read each objective statement carefully so you will understand the learning goal that is being presented. Next, read the objective material carefully, being sure to note each bold word. These words indicate important concepts that you should familiarize yourself with. Study carefully each in-text example (denoted by an orange arrow), noting the techniques and strategies used to solve the example.

Use the boxed examples.

1. Study the example on the left.

2. Solve the You Try It example.

3. Check your work against the solution in the back of the book.

You will then come to the key learning feature of this text, the *boxed examples*. These examples have been designed to assist you in a very specific way. Notice that in each example box, the example on the left is completely worked out and the "You Try It" example on the right is not. *You* are expected to work the right-hand example (in the space provided) in order to immediately test your understanding of the material you have just studied.

You should study the worked-out example carefully by working through each step presented. This allows you to focus on each step and reinforces the technique for solving that type of problem. You can then use the worked-out example as a model for solving similar problems.

Next, try to solve the "You Try It" example using the problem-solving techniques that you have just studied. When you have completed your solution, check your work by turning to the page in the Appendix where the complete solution can be found. The page number on which the solution appears is printed at the bottom of the example box in the right-hand corner. By checking your solution, you will know immediately whether or not you fully understand the skill you just studied.

Do the exercises.

Check your answers to the odd-numbered exercises.

When you have completed studying an objective, do the exercises in the exercise set that correspond to that objective. The exercises are labeled with the same letter as the objective. Math is a subject that needs to be learned in small sections and practiced continually in order to be mastered. Doing all of the exercises in each exercise set will help you to master the problem-solving techniques necessary for success. As you work through the exercises for an objective, check your answers to the odd-numbered exercises with those in the back of the book.

Read the Chapter Summary.

Do the Chapter Review exercises.

After completing a chapter, read the Chapter Summary. This summary highlights the important topics covered in the chapter. Following the Chapter Summary are a Chapter Review, a Chapter Test, and a Cumulative Review (beginning with Chapter 2). Doing the review exercises is an important way of testing your understanding of the chapter. The answer to each review exercise is given at the back of the book. Each answer to the Chapter Test and Cumulative Review is followed

Check your answers.

Restudy objectives you missed.

by a reference that tells which objective that exercise was taken from. For example, (4.2B) means Section 4.2, Objective B. After checking your answers, restudy any objective that you missed. It may be very helpful to retry some of the exercises for that objective to reinforce your problem-solving techniques.

Do the Chapter Test.

The Chapter Test should be used to prepare for an exam. We suggest that you try the Chapter Test a few days before your actual exam. Take the test in a quiet place and try to complete the test in the same amount of time you will be allowed for your exam. When taking the Chapter Test, practice the strategies of successful test takers: 1) scan the entire test to get a feel for the questions; 2) read the directions carefully; 3) work the problems that are easiest for you first; and perhaps most importantly, 4) try to stay calm.

Check your answers.

Restudy objectives you missed.

When you have completed the Chapter Test, check your answers. If you missed a question, review the material in that objective and rework some of the exercises from that objective. This will strengthen your ability to perform the skills in that objective.

The Cumulative Review allows you to refresh the skills you have learned in previous chapters. This is very important in mathematics. By consistently reviewing previous material, you will retain the skills already learned as you build new ones.

Remember, to be successful: attend class regularly; read the textbook carefully; actively participate in class; work with your textbook using the "You Try It" examples for immediate feedback and reinforcement of each skill; do all the homework assignments; review constantly; and work carefully.

Index of Applications

CHAPTER

1

Whole Numbers

Medical technicians use a petri dish, named after Julius Petri (1852–1921), to count the number of bacteria in a culture. By using whole numbers to count the bacteria at various times, medical technicians help researchers determine the growth rate of the bacteria. By the end of an experiment, there may be millions of bacteria in the dish.

Objectives

Section 1.1
To identify the order relation between two numbers
To write whole numbers in words and in standard form
To write whole numbers in expanded form
To round a whole number to a given place value

Section 1.2
To add whole numbers
To solve application problems

Section 1.3
To subtract whole numbers without borrowing
To subtract whole numbers with borrowing
To solve application problems

Section 1.4
To multiply a number by a single digit
To multiply larger whole numbers
To solve application problems

Section 1.5
To divide by a single digit with no remainder in the quotient
To divide by a single digit with a remainder in the quotient
To divide by larger whole numbers
To solve application problems

Section 1.6
To simplify expressions that contain exponents
To use the Order of Operations Agreement to simplify expressions

Section 1.7
To factor numbers
To find the prime factorization of a number

Family Tree for Numbers

Our number system is called the Hindu-Arabic system because it has its ancestry in India and was refined by the Arabs. But despite the influence of these cultures on our system, there is some evidence that our system may have originated in China around 1400 B.C. That is 34 centuries ago.

The family tree shown here illustrates the most widely believed account of the history of our number system. In the 16th century, with Gutenberg's invention of the printing press, symbols for our numbers started to become standardized.

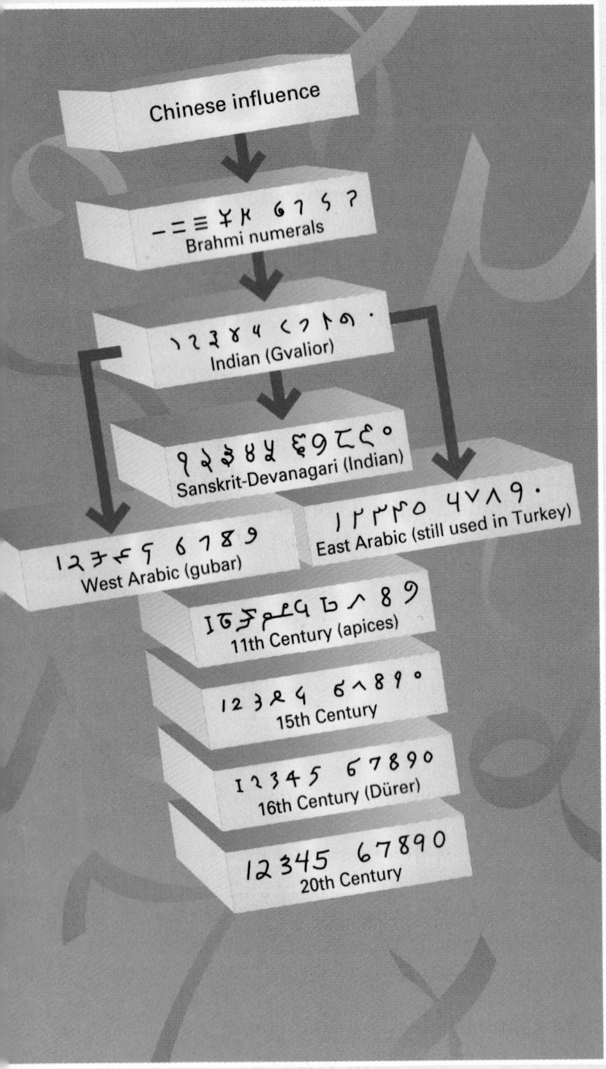

Chinese influence

Brahmi numerals

Indian (Gvalior)

Sanskrit-Devanagari (Indian)

West Arabic (gubar)

East Arabic (still used in Turkey)

11th Century (apices)

15th Century

16th Century (Dürer)

20th Century

1.1 Introduction to Whole Numbers

Objective A   ***To identify the order relation between two numbers*** ....

The **whole numbers** are 0, 1, 2, 3, 4, 5, 6, 7, 8, 9, 10, 11, 12, 13, 14, ...

The three dots mean that the list continues on and on and that there is no largest whole number.

Just as distances are associated with the markings on the edge of a ruler, the whole numbers can be associated with points on a line. This line is called the **number line.** The arrow on the number line indicates that there is no largest whole number.

The Number Line
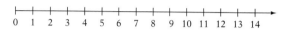

The **graph of a whole number** is shown by placing a heavy dot on the number line directly above the number. Here is the graph of 7 on the number line:

The number line can be used to show the order of whole numbers. A number that appears to the left of a given number is **less than** the given number. The symbol for "is less than" is <. A number that appears to the right of a given number is **greater than** the given number. The symbol for "is greater than" is >.

Four is less than seven.
4 < 7

Twelve is greater than seven.
12 > 7
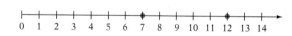

Example 1   Graph 11 on the number line.

Solution
 ├┼┼┼┼┼┼┼┼┼┼┼●┼┼┼►
 0 1 2 3 4 5 6 7 8 9 10 11 12 13 14

Example 2   Place the correct symbol, < or >, between the two numbers.

  a. 39   24
  b. 0   51

Solution   **a.** 39 > 24
  b. 0 < 51

You Try It 1   Graph 9 on the number line.

Your solution
 ├┼┼┼┼┼┼┼┼┼┼┼┼┼┼►
 0 1 2 3 4 5 6 7 8 9 10 11 12 13 14

You Try It 2   Place the correct symbol, < or >, between the two numbers.

  a. 45   29
  b. 27   0

Your solution   **a.**
  b.

Solutions on p. S1

Objective B   *To write whole numbers in words and in standard form* ....

When a whole number is written using the digits 0, 1, 2, 3, 4, 5, 6, 7, 8, and 9, it is said to be in **standard form.** The position of each digit in the number determines the digit's **place value.** The diagram below shows a **place-value chart** naming the first twelve place values. The number 37,462 is in standard form and has been entered in the chart.

In the number 37,462, the position of the digit 3 determines that its place value is ten-thousands.

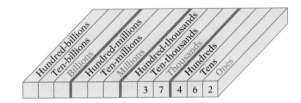

When a number is written in standard form, each group of digits separated by a comma is called a **period.** The number 3,786,451,294 has four periods. The period names are shown in red in the place-value chart above.

To write a number in words, start from the left. Name the number in each period. Then write the period name in place of the comma.

3,786,451,294 is read "three billion seven hundred eighty-six million four hundred fifty-one thousand two hundred ninety-four."

To write a whole number in standard form, write the number named in each period, and replace each period name with a comma.

Four million sixty-two thousand five hundred eighty-four is written 4,062,584. The zero is used as a place holder for the hundred-thousands' place.

Example 3   Write 25,478,083 in words.

Solution   Twenty-five million four hundred seventy-eight thousand eighty-three

You Try It 3   Write 36,462,075 in words.

Your solution

Example 4   Write three hundred three thousand three in standard form.

Solution   303,003

You Try It 4   Write four hundred fifty-two thousand seven in standard form.

Your solution

Solutions on p. S1

Objective C   *To write whole numbers in expanded form* ....

The whole number 26,429 can be written in **expanded form** as

$$20,000 + 6000 + 400 + 20 + 9$$

The place-value chart can be used to find the expanded form of a number.

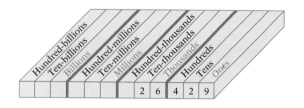

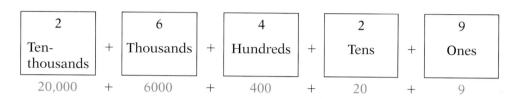

2		6		4		2		9
Ten-thousands	+	Thousands	+	Hundreds	+	Tens	+	Ones
20,000	+	6000	+	400	+	20	+	9

The number 420,806 is written in expanded form below.

Note the effect of having zeros in the number.

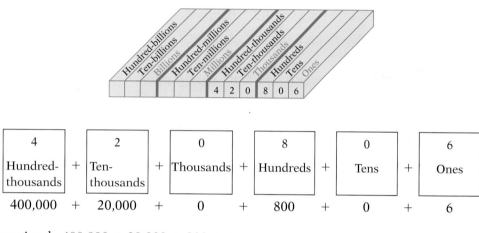

4		2		0		8		0		6
Hundred-thousands	+	Ten-thousands	+	Thousands	+	Hundreds	+	Tens	+	Ones
400,000	+	20,000	+	0	+	800	+	0	+	6

or simply 400,000 + 20,000 + 800 + 6

Example 5 Write 23,859 in expanded form.

Solution 20,000 + 3000 + 800 + 50 + 9

You Try It 5 Write 68,281 in expanded form.

Your solution

Example 6 Write 709,542 in expanded form.

Solution 700,000 + 9000 + 500 + 40 + 2

You Try It 6 Write 109,207 in expanded form.

Your solution

Solutions on p. S1

Objective D *To round a whole number to a given place value* ....

When the distance to the moon is given as 240,000 miles, the number represents an approximation to the true distance. Giving an approximate value for an exact number is called **rounding.** A number is always rounded to a given place value.

37 is closer to 40 than it is to 30. 37 rounded to the nearest ten is 40.

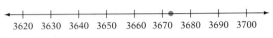

3673 rounded to the nearest ten is 3670. 3673 rounded to the nearest hundred is 3700.

A whole number is rounded to a given place value without using the number line by looking at the first digit to the right of the given place value.

If the digit to the right of the given place value is less than 5, that digit and all digits to the right are replaced by zeros.

➡ Round 13,834 to the nearest hundred.

```
              ┌──── Given place value
              │
        13,834
            └──── 3 < 5
```

13,834 rounded to the nearest hundred is 13,800.

If the digit to the right of the given place value is greater than or equal to 5, increase the digit in the given place value by 1, and replace all other digits to the right by zeros.

➡ Round 386,217 to the nearest ten-thousand.

```
            ┌──── Given place value
            │
       386,217
           └──── 6 > 5
```

386,217 rounded to the nearest ten-thousand is 390,000.

Example 7   Round 525,453 to the nearest ten-thousand.

Solution
```
            ┌──── Given place value
            │
      525,453
           └──── 5 = 5
```

525,453 rounded to the nearest ten-thousand is 530,000.

You Try It 7   Round 368,492 to the nearest ten-thousand.

Your solution

Example 8   Round 1972 to the nearest hundred.

Solution
```
          ┌──── Given place value
          │
      1972
         └──── 7 > 5
```

1972 rounded to the nearest hundred is 2000.

You Try It 8   Round 3962 to the nearest hundred.

Your solution

Solutions on p. S1

1.1 Exercises

TAKE NOTE

To the Student in the front of the book discusses the exercise sets in this textbook.

___

Objective A

Graph the number on the number line.

1. 3

2. 5

3. 9

4. 0

Place the correct symbol, < or >, between the two numbers.

5. 37   49

6. 58   21

7. 101   87

8. 16   5

9. 245   158

10. 2701   2071

11. 0   45

12. 107   0

13. 815   928

___

Objective B

Write the number in words.

14. 2675

15. 3790

16. 42,928

17. 58,473

18. 356,943

19. 498,512

20. 3,697,483

21. 6,842,715

Write the number in standard form.

22. Eighty-five

23. Three hundred fifty-seven

24. Three thousand four hundred fifty-six

25. Sixty-three thousand seven hundred eighty

26. Six hundred nine thousand nine hundred forty-eight

27. Seven million twenty-four thousand seven hundred nine

Objective C

Write the number in expanded form.

28. 5287   **29.** 6295   **30.** 58,943   **31.** 453,921

32. 200,583   **33.** 301,809   **34.** 403,705   **35.** 3,000,642

Objective D

Round the number to the given place value.

36. 926 Tens   **37.** 845 Tens

38. 1439 Hundreds   **39.** 3973 Hundreds

40. 43,607 Thousands   **41.** 52,715 Thousands

42. 647,989 Ten-thousands   **43.** 253,678 Ten-thousands

APPLYING THE CONCEPTS

Answer true or false for Exercise 44a and 44b. If the answer is false, give an example to show that it is false.

44. **a.** If you are given two distinct whole numbers, then one of the numbers is always greater than the other number.
      b. A rounded-off number is always less than its exact value.

45. What is the largest three-digit whole number? What is the smallest five-digit whole number?

46. In the Roman numeral system, IV = 4 and VI = 6. Does the position of the I in this system change the value of the number it represents? Determine the value of IX and XI.

47. If 3846 is rounded off to the nearest ten and then that number is rounded to the nearest hundred, is the result the same as what you get when you round 3846 to the nearest hundred? If not, which of the two methods is correct for rounding to the nearest hundred?

1.2 Addition of Whole Numbers

Objective A *To add whole numbers* ....

Addition is the process of finding the total of two or more numbers.

By counting, we see that the total of $3 and $4 is $7.

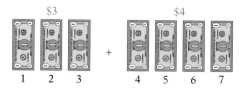

$$\$3 \quad + \quad \$4 \quad = \quad \$7$$

Addend   Addend   Sum

Addition can be illustrated on the number line by using arrows to represent the addends. The size, or magnitude, of a number can be represented on the number line by an arrow.

The number 3 can be represented anywhere on the number line by an arrow that is 3 units in length.

To add on the number line, place the arrows representing the addends head to tail, with the first arrow starting at zero. The sum is represented by an arrow starting at zero and stopping at the tip of the last arrow.

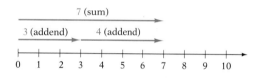

$$3 + 4 = 7$$

More than two numbers can be added on the number line.

$$3 + 2 + 4 = 9$$

Some special properties of addition that are used frequently are given below.

Addition Property of Zero

Zero added to a number does not change the number.

$$4 + 0 = 4$$
$$0 + 7 = 7$$

Commutative Property of Addition

Two numbers can be added in either order; the sum will be the same.

$$4 + 8 = 8 + 4$$
$$12 = 12$$

Associative Property of Addition

Grouping the addition in any order gives the same result. The parentheses are grouping symbols and have the meaning "do the operations inside the parentheses first."

$$(4 + 2) + 3 = 4 + (2 + 3)$$
$$6 \quad + 3 = 4 + \quad 5$$
$$9 = 9$$

The number line is not useful for adding large numbers. The basic addition facts for adding one digit to one digit should be memorized. Addition of larger numbers requires the repeated use of the basic addition facts.

To add large numbers, begin by arranging the numbers vertically, keeping the digits of the same place value in the same column.

➡ Add: 321 + 6472

```
          3 2 1
      + 6 4 7 2
        6 7 9 3
```

• Add the digits in each column.

There are several words or phrases in English that indicate the operation of addition. Here are some examples.

added to	3 added to 5	5 + 3
more than	7 more than 5	5 + 7
the sum of	the sum of 3 and 9	3 + 9
increased by	4 increased by 6	4 + 6
the total of	the total of 8 and 3	8 + 3
plus	5 plus 10	5 + 10

CALCULATOR NOTE

A scientific calculator is a useful tool in mathematical computation. To add 24 + 71 with your calculator, enter the following:

24 $\boxed{+}$ 71 $\boxed{=}$

➡ What is the sum of 24 and 71?

The phrase *the sum of* means to add.

```
    24
  + 71
    95
```

The sum of 24 and 71 is 95.

When the sum of the digits in a column exceeds 9, the addition will involve "carrying."

➡ Add: 487 + 369

```
      1
    4 8 7
  + 3 6 9
        6
```

• Add the ones' column.
$7 + 9 = 16$ (1 ten + 6 ones).
Write the 6 in the ones' column and carry the 1 ten to the tens' column.

```
    1 1
    4 8 7
  + 3 6 9
      5 6
```

• Add the tens' column.
$1 + 8 + 6 = 15$ (1 hundred + 5 tens).
Write the 5 in the tens' column and carry the 1 hundred to the hundreds' column.

```
    1 1
    4 8 7
  + 3 6 9
    8 5 6
```

• Add the hundreds' column.
$1 + 4 + 3 = 8$ (8 hundreds).
Write the 8 in the hundreds' column.

Example 1 Find the total of 17, 103, and 8.

Solution

$$
\begin{array}{r}
{}^{1} \\
17 \\
103 \\
+8 \\
\hline
128
\end{array}
$$

You Try It 1 What is 347 increased by 12,453?

Your solution

Example 2 Add: 89 + 36 + 98

Solution

$$
\begin{array}{r}
{}^{2} \\
89 \\
36 \\
+98 \\
\hline
223
\end{array}
$$

You Try It 2 Add: 95 + 88 + 67

Your solution

Example 3 Add:

$$
\begin{array}{r}
41{,}395 \\
4{,}327 \\
497{,}625 \\
+32{,}991 \\
\hline
\end{array}
$$

Solution

$$
\begin{array}{r}
{}^{1\,1\,2\,\,2\,1} \\
41{,}395 \\
4{,}327 \\
497{,}625 \\
+32{,}991 \\
\hline
576{,}338
\end{array}
$$

You Try It 3 Add:

$$
\begin{array}{r}
392 \\
4{,}079 \\
89{,}035 \\
+4{,}992 \\
\hline
\end{array}
$$

Your solution

Solutions on p. S1

ESTIMATION

Estimation and Calculators

At some places in the text, you will be asked to use your calculator. Effective use of a calculator requires that you estimate the answer to the problem. This helps ensure that you have entered the numbers correctly and pressed the correct keys.

For example, if you use your calculator to find 22,347 + 5896 and the answer in the calculator's display is 131,757,912, you should realize that you have entered some part of the calculation incorrectly. In this case, you pressed ⊠ instead of ⊞ . By estimating the answer to a problem, you can help ensure the accuracy of your calculations. The symbol ≈ is used to denote **approximately equal.**

For example, to estimate the answer to 22,347 + 5896, round each number to the same place value. In this case, we will round to the nearest thousand. Then add.

$$
\begin{array}{r}
22{,}347 \approx 22{,}000 \\
+5{,}896 \approx +6{,}000 \\
\hline
28{,}000
\end{array}
$$

The sum 22,347 + 5896 is approximately 28,000. Knowing this, you would know that 131,757,912 is much too large and is therefore incorrect.

To estimate the sum of two numbers, first round each whole number to the same place value and then add. Compare this answer with the calculator's answer.

Objective B   *To solve application problems* .... 🔲 CT

To solve an application problem, first read the problem carefully. The **Strategy** involves identifying the quantity to be found and planning the steps that are necessary to find that quantity. The **Solution** involves performing each operation stated in the Strategy and writing the answer.

The table below displays the number of snowmobiles registered in four states in 1996.

This information can also be displayed using a bar graph.

State	Number of Snowmobiles
Michigan	270,266
Minnesota	254,510
Wisconsin	193,184
New York	89,617

Source: American Council of Snowmobile Associations

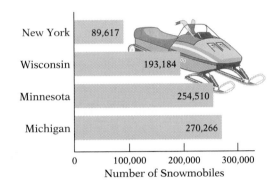

➡ Find the total number of snowmobiles registered in the four states as shown in the table and graph above.

Strategy   To find the total number of snowmobiles registered in the four states, read the table to find the number of snowmobiles registered in each state. Then add the numbers.

Solution
$$
\begin{array}{r}
270,266 \\
254,510 \\
193,184 \\
+ \quad 89,617 \\
\hline
807,577
\end{array}
$$

There were 807,577 snowmobiles registered in the four states in 1996.

Example 4

Your paycheck shows deductions of $225 for savings, $98 for taxes, and $27 for insurance. Find the total of the three deductions.

Strategy

To find the total of the deductions, add the three amounts ($225, $98, and $27).

Solution
$$
\begin{array}{r}
\$225 \\
98 \\
+ \quad 27 \\
\hline
\$350
\end{array}
$$

The total of the three deductions is $350.

You Try It 4

Anna Barrera has a monthly budget of $475 for food, $275 for car expenses, and $120 for entertainment. Find the total amount budgeted for the three items each month.

Your strategy

Your solution

Solution on p. S1

1.2 Exercises

Objective A

Add.

1. 17 + 11	**2.** 25 + 63	**3.** 83 + 42	**4.** 63 + 94
5. 77 + 25	**6.** 63 + 49	**7.** 56 + 98	**8.** 86 + 68
9. 658 + 831	**10.** 842 + 936	**11.** 735 + 93	**12.** 189 + 50
13. 859 + 725	**14.** 637 + 829	**15.** 470 + 749	**16.** 427 + 690
17. 36,925 + 65,392	**18.** 56,772 + 51,239	**19.** 50,873 + 28,453	**20.** 34,872 + 46,079
21. 878 737 + 189	**22.** 768 461 + 669	**23.** 319 348 + 912	**24.** 292 579 + 315
25. 9409 3253 + 7078	**26.** 8188 8020 + 7104	**27.** 2038 2243 + 3139	**28.** 4252 6882 + 5235
29. 67,428 32,171 + 20,971	**30.** 52,801 11,664 + 89,638	**31.** 76,290 43,761 + 87,402	**32.** 43,901 98,301 + 67,943

Add.

33. 20,958 + 3218 + 42

34. 80,973 + 5168 + 29

35. 392 + 37 + 10,924 + 621

36. 694 + 62 + 70,129 + 217

37. 294 + 1029 + 7935 + 65

38. 692 + 2107 + 3196 + 92

39. 97 + 7234 + 69,532 + 276

40. 87 + 1698 + 27,317 + 727

41. What is 9874 plus 4509?

42. What is 7988 plus 5678?

43. What is 3487 increased by 5986?

44. What is 99,567 added to 126,863?

45. What is 23,569 more than 9678?

46. What is 7894 more than 45,872?

47. What is 479 added to 4579?

48. What is 23,902 added to 23,885?

49. Find the total of 659, 55, and 1278.

50. Find the total of 4561, 56, and 2309.

51. Find the sum of 34, 329, 8, and 67,892.

52. Find the sum of 45, 1289, 7, and 32,876.

Estimate by rounding to the nearest hundred. Then use your calculator to add.

53. 1234 + 9780 + 6740

54. 919 + 3642 + 8796

55. 241 + 569 + 390 + 1672

56. 107 + 984 + 1035 + 2904

Estimate by rounding to the nearest thousand. Then use your calculator to add.

57.	**58.**	**59.**	**60.**
32,461	29,036	25,432	66,541
9,844	22,904	62,941	29,365
+ 59,407	+ 7,903	+ 70,390	+ 98,742

Estimate by rounding to the nearest ten-thousand. Then use your calculator to add.

61.	**62.**	**63.**	**64.**
67,421	21,896	281,421	542,698
82,984	4,235	9,874	97,327
66,361	62,544	34,394	7,235
10,792	21,892	526,398	73,667
+ 34,037	+ 1,334	+ 94,631	+ 173,201

Estimate by rounding to the nearest million. Then use your calculator to add.

65.	**66.**	**67.**	**68.**
28,627,052	1,792,085	12,377,491	46,751,070
983,073	29,919,301	3,409,723	6,095,832
+ 3,081,496	+ 3,406,882	7,928,026	280,011
		+ 10,705,682	+ 1,563,897

Objective B   *Application Problems*

69. In 1996, the United States had $290 billion in total trade with Canada, $183 billion with Japan, and $130 billion with Mexico. Find the total amount of these countries' trade with the United States.

70. The attendance at a Friday night San Diego Padres game was 16,542. The attendance at the Saturday night game was 20,763. Find the total attendance for the two games.

71. Dan Marino threw 5 passes for 42 yards in the first quarter, 7 passes for 117 yards in the second quarter, 9 passes for 66 yards in the third quarter, and 8 passes for 82 yards in the fourth quarter. Find the total number of yards Dan Marino gained by passing.

The graph at the right shows the box-office income of several selected Disney productions. Use this information for Exercises 72 to 75.

72. Estimate the total income from the five Disney productions.

73. Find the total income from the five Disney productions.

74. Find the total income from the two productions with the lowest box-office incomes.

75. Does the total income from the two productions with the lowest box-office incomes exceed the income from the production of *Aladdin*?

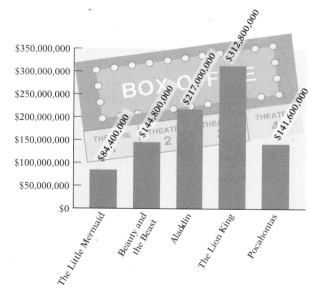

Source: Exhibitor Relations Co. Inc.

76. A student has $2135 in a checking account to be used for the fall semester. During the summer the student makes deposits of $518, $678, and $468.
   a. Find the total amount deposited.
   b. Find the new checking account balance, assuming that there are no withdrawals.

77. The odometer on a moving van reads 68,692. The driver plans to drive 515 miles the first day, 492 miles the second day, and 278 miles the third day.
   a. How many miles will be driven during the three days?
   b. What will the odometer reading be at the end of the trip?

The accompanying table shows the average amount of money all Americans have invested in selected assets and the amounts invested for Americans between the ages of 16 and 34.

	All Americans	Ages 16 to 34
Checking accounts	$487	$375
Savings accounts	3,494	1,155
U.S. Savings Bonds	546	266
Money market	10,911	4,427
Stocks/mutual funds	4,510	1,615
Home equity	43,070	17,184
Retirement	9,016	4,298

78. What is the total average amount for all Americans in checking accounts, savings accounts, and U.S. Savings Bonds?

79. What is the total average amount for Americans ages 16 to 34 in checking accounts, savings accounts, and U.S. Savings Bonds?

80. What is the total average amount for Americans ages 16 to 34 in all categories except home equity and retirement?

81. Is the sum of the average amounts invested in home equity and retirement for all Americans greater than or less than that same sum for Americans between the ages of 16 and 34?

APPLYING THE CONCEPTS

82. How many two-digit numbers are there? How many three-digit numbers are there?

83. If you roll two ordinary six-sided dice and add the two numbers that appear on top, how many different sums are possible?

84. If you add two *different* whole numbers, is the sum always greater than either one of the numbers? If not, give an example.

85. If you add two whole numbers, is the sum always greater than either one of the numbers? If not, give an example. (Compare this with the previous exercise.)

86. Make up a word problem for which the answer is the sum of 34 and 28.

87. Call a number "lucky" if it ends in a 7. How many lucky numbers are less than 100?

1.3 Subtraction of Whole Numbers

Objective A **To subtract whole numbers without borrowing** ....

Subtraction is the process of finding the difference between two numbers.

By counting, we see that the difference between $8 and $5 is $3.

$$\$8 \quad - \quad \$5 \quad = \quad \$3$$

Minuend   Subtrahend   Difference

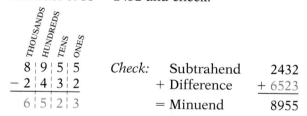

The difference $8 - 5$ can be shown on the number line.

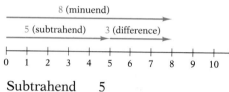

Note from the number line that addition and subtraction are related.

$$
\begin{array}{ll}
 \text{Subtrahend} & 5 \\
+ \text{Difference} & +\,3 \\
\hline
= \text{Minuend} & 8
\end{array}
$$

The fact that the sum of the subtrahend and the difference equals the minuend can be used to check subtraction.

To subtract large numbers, begin by arranging the numbers vertically, keeping the digits that have the same place value in the same column. Then subtract the digits in each column.

➡ Subtract $8955 - 2432$ and check.

$$
\begin{array}{r}
8\,|\,9\,|\,5\,|\,5 \\
-\,2\,|\,4\,|\,3\,|\,2 \\
\hline
6\,|\,5\,|\,2\,|\,3
\end{array}
$$

THOUSANDS HUNDREDS TENS ONES

Check:
$$
\begin{array}{lr}
\text{Subtrahend} & 2432 \\
+ \text{Difference} & +\,6523 \\
\hline
= \text{Minuend} & 8955
\end{array}
$$

Example 1 Subtract $6594 - 3271$ and check.

Solution
$$
\begin{array}{r}
6594 \\
-\,3271 \\
\hline
3323
\end{array}
$$
Check:
$$
\begin{array}{r}
3271 \\
+\,3323 \\
\hline
6594
\end{array}
$$

You Try It 1 Subtract $8925 - 6413$ and check.

Your solution

Example 2 Subtract $15{,}762 - 7541$ and check.

Solution
$$
\begin{array}{r}
15{,}762 \\
-\,7{,}541 \\
\hline
8{,}221
\end{array}
$$
Check:
$$
\begin{array}{r}
7{,}541 \\
+\,8{,}221 \\
\hline
15{,}762
\end{array}
$$

You Try It 2 Subtract $17{,}504 - 9302$ and check.

Your solution

Solutions on p. S1

Objective B *To subtract whole numbers with borrowing* ··························

In all the subtraction problems in the previous objective, for each place value the lower digit was not larger than the upper digit. When the lower digit is larger than the upper digit, subtraction will involve "borrowing."

➡ Subtract: 692 − 378

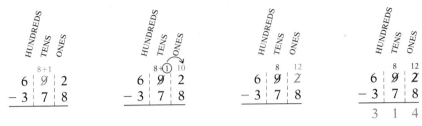

Because 8 > 2, borrowing is necessary. 9 tens = 8 tens + 1 ten.

Borrow 1 ten from the tens' column and write 10 in the ones' column.

Add the borrowed 10 to 2.

Subtract the digits in each column.

The phrases below are used to indicate the operation of subtraction. An example is shown at the right of each phrase.

minus	8 minus 5	8 − 5
less	9 less 3	9 − 3
less than	2 less than 7	7 − 2
the difference between	the difference between 8 and 2	8 − 2
decreased by	5 decreased by 1	5 − 1

➡ Find the difference between 1234 and 485 and check.

From the phrases that indicate subtraction, the difference between 1234 and 485 is 1234 − 485.

$$\begin{array}{r} \overset{214}{1\;2\;3\;4} \\ -\quad 4\;8\;5 \\ \hline 9 \end{array} \qquad \begin{array}{r} \overset{11214}{1\;2\;3\;4} \\ -\quad 4\;8\;5 \\ \hline 4\;9 \end{array} \qquad \begin{array}{r} \overset{0111214}{1\;2\;3\;4} \\ -\quad 4\;8\;5 \\ \hline 7\;4\;9 \end{array}$$

Check:
$$\begin{array}{r} \overset{1\;1}{485} \\ +\;749 \\ \hline 1234 \end{array}$$

Subtraction with a zero in the minuend involves repeated borrowing.

➡ Subtract: 3904 − 1775

$$\begin{array}{r} \overset{810}{3\;9\;0\;4} \\ -\;1\;7\;7\;5 \\ \hline \end{array} \qquad \begin{array}{r} \overset{9}{\overset{81014}{3\;9\;0\;4}} \\ -\;1\;7\;7\;5 \\ \hline \end{array} \qquad \begin{array}{r} \overset{9}{\overset{81014}{3\;9\;0\;4}} \\ -\;1\;7\;7\;5 \\ \hline 2\;1\;2\;9 \end{array}$$

5 > 4
There is a 0 in the tens' column. Borrow 1 hundred (= 10 tens) from the hundreds' column and write 10 in the tens' column.

Borrow 1 ten from the tens' column and add 10 to the 4 in the ones' column.

Subtract the digits in each column.

Example 3   Subtract 4392 − 678 and
check.

Solution

$$
\begin{array}{r}
\overset{3}{\cancel{4}}\ \overset{13}{\cancel{3}}\ \overset{8}{\cancel{9}}\ \overset{12}{\cancel{2}} \\
-\ \ \ 6\ \ 7\ \ 8 \\
\hline
3\ \ 7\ \ 1\ \ 4
\end{array}
$$

Check:
$$
\begin{array}{r}
678 \\
+\ 3714 \\
\hline
4392
\end{array}
$$

You Try It 3   Subtract 3481 − 865 and
check.

Your solution

Example 4   Find 23,954 less than 63,221
and check.

Solution

$$
\begin{array}{r}
\overset{5}{\cancel{6}}\ \overset{12}{\cancel{3}},\overset{11}{\cancel{2}}\ \overset{11}{\cancel{2}}\ \overset{11}{\cancel{1}} \\
-\ 2\ \ 3,9\ \ 5\ \ 4 \\
\hline
3\ \ 9,2\ \ 6\ \ 7
\end{array}
$$

Check:
$$
\begin{array}{r}
23,954 \\
+39,267 \\
\hline
63,221
\end{array}
$$

You Try It 4   Find 54,562 decreased by
14,485 and check.

Your solution

Example 5   Subtract 46,005 − 32,167 and
check.

Solution

$$
\begin{array}{r}
\overset{5}{\cancel{4}}\overset{10}{\cancel{6}},\cancel{0}05 \\
-\ 32,167
\end{array}
$$
• There are two zeros in the minuend. Borrow 1 thousand from the thousands' column and write 10 in the hundreds' column.

$$
\begin{array}{r}
\overset{5}{\cancel{4}}\overset{\overset{9}{10}}{\cancel{6}},\overset{10}{\cancel{0}}\cancel{0}5 \\
-\ 32,167
\end{array}
$$
• Borrow 1 hundred from the hundreds' column and write 10 in the tens' column.

$$
\begin{array}{r}
\overset{5}{\cancel{4}}\overset{\overset{9}{10}}{\cancel{6}},\overset{\overset{9}{10}}{\cancel{0}}\overset{15}{\cancel{0}}\cancel{5} \\
-\ 32,167 \\
\hline
13,838
\end{array}
$$
• Borrow 1 ten from the tens' column and add 10 to the 5 in the ones' column.

Check:
$$
\begin{array}{r}
32,167 \\
+\ 13,838 \\
\hline
46,005
\end{array}
$$

You Try It 5   Subtract 64,003 − 54,936
and check.

Your solution

Solutions on p. S1

ESTIMATION

Estimating the Difference Between Two Whole Numbers

Estimate and then use your calculator to find 323,502 − 28,912.

To estimate the difference between two
numbers, round each number to the same
place value. In this case we will round to
the nearest ten-thousand. Then subtract.
The estimated answer is 290,000.

$$
\begin{array}{r}
323,502 \approx\ \ \ 320,000 \\
-\ \ 28,912 \approx -\ 30,000 \\
\hline
290,000
\end{array}
$$

Now use your calculator to find the exact
result. The exact answer is 294,590.

323502 [−] 28912 [=] 294590

Objective C   To solve application problems .... ◁ 1 ▷ CT

The table at the right shows that western migration has slowed. The table shows the number of U.S. residents who have migrated to the states listed during the years 1995 and 1996. Use the table for Example 6 and You Try It 6.

State	1995	1996
Arizona	100,170	72,465
Colorado	45,546	30,049
Idaho	18,350	11,039
Montana	10,064	5250
New Mexico	11,963	4692
Oregon	33,438	33,386

Source: Analysis of U.S. Census data by Paul Overberg, USA Today, March 21, 1997

Example 6
Find the difference between the numbers of residents who migrated to Arizona in 1995 and 1996.

Strategy
To find the difference, subtract the number of residents who migrated in 1996 (72,465) from the number of residents who migrated in 1995 (100,170).

Solution

$$\begin{array}{r} 100{,}170 \\ -72{,}465 \\ \hline 27{,}705 \end{array}$$

27,705 fewer residents migrated to Arizona in 1996 than in 1995.

You Try It 6
How many more residents migrated to Colorado than to Montana in 1996?

Your strategy

Your solution

Example 7
You had a balance of $815 in your checking account. You then wrote checks in the amount of $112 for taxes, $57 for food, and $39 for shoes. What is your new checking account balance?

Strategy
To find your new checking account balance:
• Add to find the total of the three checks ($112 + $57 + $39).
• Subtract the total of the three checks from the old balance ($815).

Solution

$$\begin{array}{r} 112 \\ 57 \\ +39 \\ \hline 208 \end{array} \text{ total of checks} \qquad \begin{array}{r} 815 \\ -208 \\ \hline 607 \end{array}$$

Your new checking account balance is $607.

You Try It 7
Your total salary is $638. Deductions of $127 for taxes, $18 for insurance, and $35 for savings are taken from your pay. Find your take-home pay.

Your strategy

Your solution

Solutions on p. S1

1.3 Exercises

· ·

Objective A

Subtract.

1. $\begin{array}{r} 9 \\ -\ 5 \\ \hline \end{array}$ **2.** $\begin{array}{r} 8 \\ -\ 7 \\ \hline \end{array}$ **3.** $\begin{array}{r} 8 \\ -\ 4 \\ \hline \end{array}$ **4.** $\begin{array}{r} 7 \\ -\ 3 \\ \hline \end{array}$ **5.** $\begin{array}{r} 10 \\ -\ 0 \\ \hline \end{array}$

6. $\begin{array}{r} 11 \\ -\ 4 \\ \hline \end{array}$ **7.** $\begin{array}{r} 12 \\ -\ 8 \\ \hline \end{array}$ **8.** $\begin{array}{r} 19 \\ -\ 8 \\ \hline \end{array}$ **9.** $\begin{array}{r} 15 \\ -\ 6 \\ \hline \end{array}$ **10.** $\begin{array}{r} 16 \\ -\ 7 \\ \hline \end{array}$

11. $\begin{array}{r} 25 \\ -\ 3 \\ \hline \end{array}$ **12.** $\begin{array}{r} 55 \\ -\ 4 \\ \hline \end{array}$ **13.** $\begin{array}{r} 68 \\ -\ 8 \\ \hline \end{array}$ **14.** $\begin{array}{r} 77 \\ -\ 3 \\ \hline \end{array}$ **15.** $\begin{array}{r} 89 \\ -\ 23 \\ \hline \end{array}$

16. $\begin{array}{r} 54 \\ -\ 21 \\ \hline \end{array}$ **17.** $\begin{array}{r} 88 \\ -\ 57 \\ \hline \end{array}$ **18.** $\begin{array}{r} 1202 \\ -\ 701 \\ \hline \end{array}$ **19.** $\begin{array}{r} 1305 \\ -\ 404 \\ \hline \end{array}$ **20.** $\begin{array}{r} 1763 \\ -\ 801 \\ \hline \end{array}$

21. $\begin{array}{r} 1497 \\ -\ 706 \\ \hline \end{array}$ **22.** $\begin{array}{r} 8974 \\ -\ 3972 \\ \hline \end{array}$ **23.** $\begin{array}{r} 2836 \\ -\ 1711 \\ \hline \end{array}$ **24.** $\begin{array}{r} 8976 \\ -\ 7463 \\ \hline \end{array}$ **25.** $\begin{array}{r} 9273 \\ -\ 6142 \\ \hline \end{array}$

26. $77 - 36$ **27.** $129 - 82$ **28.** $132 - 61$ **29.** $969 - 44$ **30.** $1347 - 103$

31. $4865 - 304$ **32.** $1525 - 702$ **33.** $9999 - 6794$ **34.** $7806 - 3405$ **35.** $8843 - 7621$

36. What is 3795 minus 1092?   **37.** What is 9071 minus 6050?

38. Find the difference between 9763 and 541.   **39.** Find the difference between 6094 and 3072.

40. What is 3701 less than 6932?   **41.** What is 2031 less than 5071?

42. Find 6509 decreased by 3102.   **43.** Find 7994 decreased by 7782.

44. Find 23,907 less 12,705.   **45.** Find 65,986 less 5741.

Objective B

Subtract.

46.   71
        − 18

47.   93
        − 28

48.   47
        − 18

49.   44
        − 27

50.   37
        − 29

51.   50
        − 27

52.   70
        − 33

53.   993
        − 537

54.   250
        − 192

55.   840
        − 783

56.   768
        − 194

57.   770
        − 395

58. 674 − 337

59. 3526 − 387

60. 1712 − 289

61. 4350 − 729

62. 1702 − 948

63. 1607 − 869

64. 5933 − 3754

65. 7293 − 3748

66. 9407 − 2918

67. 3706 − 2957

68. 8605 − 7716

69. 8052 − 2709

70. 80,305 − 9176

71. 70,702 − 4239

72. 10,004 − 9306

73. 80,009 − 63,419

74. 70,618 − 41,213

75. 80,053 − 27,649

76. 70,700 − 21,076

77. 80,800 − 42,023

78.   2600
        − 1972

79.   8400
        − 3762

80.   9003
        − 2471

81.   6004
        − 2392

82.   8202
        − 3916

83.   7050
        − 4137

84.   7015
        − 2973

85.   4207
        − 1624

86.   7005
        − 1796

87.   8003
        − 2735

88.   20,005
        − 9,627

89.   80,004
        − 8,237

90. Find 10,051 less 9027.

91. Find 17,031 less 5792.

92. Find the difference between 1003 and 447.

93. What is 29,874 minus 21,392?

94. What is 29,797 less than 68,005?

95. What is 69,379 less than 70,004?

96. What is 25,432 decreased by 7994?

97. What is 86,701 decreased by 9976?

Estimate by rounding to the nearest ten-thousand. Then use your calculator to subtract.

98.
$$\begin{array}{r} 80,032 \\ -\ 19,605 \\ \hline \end{array}$$

99.
$$\begin{array}{r} 90,765 \\ -\ 60,928 \\ \hline \end{array}$$

100.
$$\begin{array}{r} 32,574 \\ -\ 10,961 \\ \hline \end{array}$$

101.
$$\begin{array}{r} 96,430 \\ -\ 59,762 \\ \hline \end{array}$$

102.
$$\begin{array}{r} 567,423 \\ -\ 208,444 \\ \hline \end{array}$$

103.
$$\begin{array}{r} 300,712 \\ -\ 198,714 \\ \hline \end{array}$$

Objective C   *Application Problems*

104. You have $304 in your checking account. If you write a check for $139, how much is left in your checking account?

105. Sam Akyol buys a Geo Tracker for $15,392. How much did Sam save from a sticker price of $17,871?

106. The tennis coach at a high school purchased a video camera that costs $1079 and made a down payment of $180. Find the amount that remains to be paid.

107. Rod Guerra, an engineer, purchased a used car that cost $5225 and made a down payment of $450. Find the amount that remains to be paid.

108. Merger-related job cuts decreased from 72,083 in 1995 to 42,603 in 1996. What was the decrease in merger-related cuts from 1995 to 1996?

109. In May 1997, the population of the United States was 267,103,163 and the national debt was approximately $5,348,000,000,000. In May 1996, the debt was approximately $5,128,000,000,000. How much did the national debt increase in one year?

110. At the end of a vacation trip, the odometer of your car read 63,459 miles. If the odometer reading at the start of the trip was 62,963, what was the length of the trip?

111. Florida had 20,188,506 acres of wetlands 200 years ago. Today Florida has 10,901,793 acres of wetlands. How many acres of wetlands has Florida lost over the last 200 years?

The table shows the cost of a Ford Escort and the cost of a Chevrolet Cavalier. The table also shows four popular options that are available on these models. Use the table for Exercises 112 and 113.

Source: Consumer Guide, 1997 cars
Signet Reference AE 9241, pages 284, 314

	Ford	Chevrolet
4-door notchback	$11,015	$11,180
Automatic transmission	795	815
CD player	515	652
Cruise control package	495	456
Alloy wheels	265	295

112. What is the difference in cost between the two notchbacks without any additional options?

113. Which of these cars, equipped with all the options listed, costs more?

The graph at the right shows the number of months required to recover all interest and principal from the Social Security fund after a person retires. Use this graph for Exercises 114 and 115.

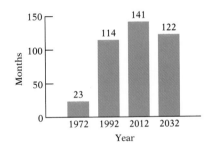

114. How much longer did it take to withdraw principal and interest in 1992 than it did in 1972?

115. How much longer will it take to withdraw principal and interest in 2012 than it did in 1992?

APPLYING THE CONCEPTS

116. Answer true or false.
  a. The phrases "the difference between 9 and 5" and "5 less than 9" mean the same thing.
  b. $9 - (5 - 3) = (9 - 5) - 3$.
  c. Subtraction is an associative operation. *Hint:* See part b of this exercise.

117. Explain how you can check the answer to a subtraction problem.

118. Make up a word problem for which the difference between 15 and 8 is the answer.

1.4 Multiplication of Whole Numbers

Objective A *To multiply a number by a single digit* ....

Six boxes of toasters are ordered. Each box contains eight toasters. How many toasters are ordered?

This problem can be worked by adding 6 eights.

$8 + 8 + 8 + 8 + 8 + 8 = 48$

This problem involves repeated addition of the same number and can be worked by a shorter process called **multiplication.** Multiplication is the repeated addition of the same number.

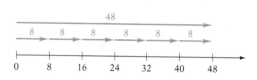

$8 + 8 + 8 + 8 + 8 + 8 = 48$

The numbers that are multiplied are called **factors.** The answer is called the **product.**

or

$$6 \quad \times \quad 8 \qquad = 48$$
Factor Factor   Product

The product of 6×8 can be represented on the number line. The arrow representing the whole number 8 is repeated 6 times. The result is the arrow representing 48.

The times sign "×" is one symbol that is used to mean multiplication. Another common symbol used is a dot placed between the numbers.

$$7 \times 8 = 56 \qquad 7 \cdot 8 = 56$$

As with addition, there are some useful properties of multiplication.

Multiplication Property of Zero

The product of a number and zero is zero.

$0 \times 4 = 0$
$7 \times 0 = 0$

Multiplication Property of One

The product of a number and one is the number.

$1 \times 6 = 6$
$8 \times 1 = 8$

Commutative Property of Multiplication

Two numbers can be multiplied in either order. The product will be the same.

$4 \times 3 = 3 \times 4$
$12 = 12$

Associative Property of Multiplication

Grouping the numbers to be multiplied in any order gives the same result. Do the multiplication inside the parentheses first.

$(4 \times 2) \times 3 = 4 \times (2 \times 3)$
$8 \quad \times 3 = 4 \times \quad 6$
$24 = 24$

The basic facts for multiplying one-digit numbers should be memorized. Multiplication of larger numbers requires the repeated use of the basic multiplication facts.

➡ Multiply: 37 × 4

$$
\begin{array}{r}
\overset{2}{} \\
3\ 7 \\
\times\ \ \ 4 \\
\hline
8 \\
\end{array}
$$

- 4 × 7 = 28 (2 tens + 8 ones).
  Write the 8 in the ones' column and
  carry the 2 to the tens' column.

$$
\begin{array}{r}
\overset{2}{} \\
3\ 7 \\
\times\ \ \ 4 \\
\hline
14\ \ 8 \\
\end{array}
$$

- The 3 in 37 is 3 tens.
  $4 \times 3 \text{ tens} = 12 \text{ tens}$
  Add the carry digit. $+ 2 \text{ tens}$
  $\overline{14 \text{ tens}}$

- Write the 14.

The phrases below are used to indicate the operation of multiplication. An example is shown at the right of each phrase.

times	7 times 3	7 · 3
the product of	the product of 6 and 9	6 · 9
multiplied by	8 multiplied by 2	2 · 8

Example 1   Multiply: 735 × 9

Solution

$$
\begin{array}{r}
\overset{3\ 4}{} \\
735 \\
\times\ \ \ 9 \\
\hline
6615 \\
\end{array}
$$

You Try It 1   Multiply: 648 × 7

Your solution

Solution on p. S2

Objective B   *To multiply larger whole numbers* ....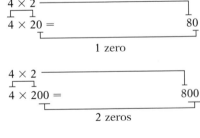

Note the pattern when the following numbers are multiplied.

Multiply the nonzero part of the factors.

Now attach the same number of zeros to the product as the total number of zeros in the factors.

$$
\begin{array}{l}
4 \times 2 \\
4 \times 20 = \hspace{4cm} 80
\end{array}
$$
1 zero

$$
\begin{array}{l}
4 \times 2 \\
4 \times 200 = \hspace{3.5cm} 800
\end{array}
$$
2 zeros

$$
\begin{array}{l}
4 \times\ 2 \\
40 \times 200 = \hspace{3cm} 8000
\end{array}
$$
3 zeros

$$
\begin{array}{l}
12 \times 5 \\
12 \times 5000 = \hspace{2.5cm} 60,000
\end{array}
$$
3 zeros

➡ Find the product of 47 and 23.

Multiply by the ones' digit.	Multiply by the tens' digit.	Add.

$$\begin{array}{r} 47 \\ \times\ 23 \\ \hline 141\ (=47\times3) \end{array}$$

$$\begin{array}{r} 47 \\ \times\ 23 \\ \hline 141 \\ 940\ (=47\times20) \end{array}$$

$$\begin{array}{r} 47 \\ \times\ 23 \\ \hline 141 \\ 940 \\ \hline 1081 \end{array}$$

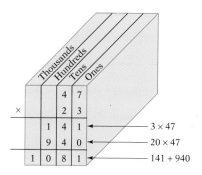

- 3 × 47
- 20 × 47
- 141 + 940

Writing the 0 is optional.

The place-value chart illustrates the placement of the products.

Note the placement of the products when we are multiplying by a factor that contains a zero.

➡ Multiply: 439 × 206

$$\begin{array}{r} 439 \\ \times\ 206 \\ \hline 2634 \\ 000 \quad 0\times439 \\ 878 \\ \hline 90,434 \end{array}$$

When working the problem, we usually write only one zero. Writing this zero ensures the proper placement of the products.

$$\begin{array}{r} 439 \\ \times\ 206 \\ \hline 2634 \\ 8780 \\ \hline 90,434 \end{array}$$

Example 2   Find 829 multiplied by 603.

Solution
$$\begin{array}{r} 829 \\ \times\ 603 \\ \hline 2487 \\ 49740 \\ \hline 499,887 \end{array}$$

You Try It 2   Multiply: 756 × 305

Your solution

Solution on p. S2

ESTIMATION

Estimating the Product of Two Whole Numbers

Estimate and then use your calculator to find 3267 × 389.

To estimate a product, round each number so that all the digits are zero except the first digit. Then multiply. The estimated answer is 1,200,000.

$$\begin{array}{r} 3267 \approx\quad 3000 \\ \times\ 389 \approx\quad \times\ 400 \\ \hline 1,200,000 \end{array}$$

Now use your calculator to find the exact answer. The exact answer is 1,270,863.

3267 ☒ 389 ☐= 1270863

Objective C   To solve application problems ·························

Example 3
An auto mechanic receives a salary of $525 each week. How much does the auto mechanic earn in 4 weeks?

Strategy
To find the mechanic's earnings for 4 weeks, multiply the weekly salary ($525) by the number of weeks (4).

Solution

$$\begin{array}{r} \$525 \\ \times \quad 4 \\ \hline \$2100 \end{array}$$

The mechanic earns $2100 in 4 weeks.

You Try It 3
A new-car dealer receives a shipment of 37 cars each month. Find the number of cars the dealer will receive in 12 months.

Your strategy

Your solution

Example 4
A press operator earns $320 for working a 40-hour week. This week the press operator also worked 7 hours of overtime at $13 an hour. Find the press operator's total pay for the week.

Strategy
To find the press operator's total pay for the week:

- Find the overtime pay by multiplying the hours of overtime (7) by the overtime rate of pay ($13).
- Add the weekly salary ($320) to the overtime pay.

Solution

$$\begin{array}{r} \$13 \\ \times \quad 7 \\ \hline \$91 \text{ overtime pay} \end{array} \qquad \begin{array}{r} \$320 \\ + \quad 91 \\ \hline \$411 \end{array}$$

The press operator earned $411 this week.

You Try It 4
The buyer for Ross Department Store can buy 80 men's suits for $4800. Each sports jacket will cost the store $23. The manager orders 80 men's suits and 25 sports jackets. What is the total cost of the order?

Your strategy

Your solution

Solutions on p. S2

1.4 Exercises

· ·

Objective A

Multiply.

1. $\begin{array}{r} 3 \\ \times\, 4 \\ \hline \end{array}$

2. $\begin{array}{r} 2 \\ \times\, 8 \\ \hline \end{array}$

3. $\begin{array}{r} 5 \\ \times\, 7 \\ \hline \end{array}$

4. $\begin{array}{r} 6 \\ \times\, 4 \\ \hline \end{array}$

5. $\begin{array}{r} 5 \\ \times\, 5 \\ \hline \end{array}$

6. $\begin{array}{r} 7 \\ \times\, 7 \\ \hline \end{array}$

7. $\begin{array}{r} 0 \\ \times\, 7 \\ \hline \end{array}$

8. $\begin{array}{r} 8 \\ \times\, 0 \\ \hline \end{array}$

9. $\begin{array}{r} 8 \\ \times\, 9 \\ \hline \end{array}$

10. $\begin{array}{r} 7 \\ \times\, 6 \\ \hline \end{array}$

11. $\begin{array}{r} 66 \\ \times\, 3 \\ \hline \end{array}$

12. $\begin{array}{r} 70 \\ \times\, 4 \\ \hline \end{array}$

13. $\begin{array}{r} 67 \\ \times\, 5 \\ \hline \end{array}$

14. $\begin{array}{r} 127 \\ \times\, 9 \\ \hline \end{array}$

15. $\begin{array}{r} 623 \\ \times\, 4 \\ \hline \end{array}$

16. $\begin{array}{r} 802 \\ \times\, 5 \\ \hline \end{array}$

17. $\begin{array}{r} 607 \\ \times\, 9 \\ \hline \end{array}$

18. $\begin{array}{r} 300 \\ \times\, 5 \\ \hline \end{array}$

19. $\begin{array}{r} 600 \\ \times\, 7 \\ \hline \end{array}$

20. $\begin{array}{r} 906 \\ \times\, 8 \\ \hline \end{array}$

21. $\begin{array}{r} 703 \\ \times\, 9 \\ \hline \end{array}$

22. $\begin{array}{r} 127 \\ \times\, 5 \\ \hline \end{array}$

23. $\begin{array}{r} 632 \\ \times\, 3 \\ \hline \end{array}$

24. $\begin{array}{r} 559 \\ \times\, 4 \\ \hline \end{array}$

25. $\begin{array}{r} 632 \\ \times\, 8 \\ \hline \end{array}$

26. $\begin{array}{r} 524 \\ \times\, 4 \\ \hline \end{array}$

27. $\begin{array}{r} 337 \\ \times\, 5 \\ \hline \end{array}$

28. $\begin{array}{r} 841 \\ \times\, 6 \\ \hline \end{array}$

29. $\begin{array}{r} 6709 \\ \times\, 7 \\ \hline \end{array}$

30. $\begin{array}{r} 3608 \\ \times\, 5 \\ \hline \end{array}$

31. $\begin{array}{r} 8568 \\ \times\, 7 \\ \hline \end{array}$

32. $\begin{array}{r} 5495 \\ \times\, 4 \\ \hline \end{array}$

33. $\begin{array}{r} 4780 \\ \times\, 4 \\ \hline \end{array}$

34. $\begin{array}{r} 3690 \\ \times\, 5 \\ \hline \end{array}$

35. $\begin{array}{r} 9895 \\ \times\, 2 \\ \hline \end{array}$

36. Find the product of 5, 7, and 4.

37. Find the product of 6, 2, and 9.

38. Find the product of 5304 and 9.

39. Find the product of 458 and 8.

40. What is 3208 multiplied by 7?

41. What is 5009 multiplied by 4?

42. What is 3105 times 6?

43. What is 8957 times 8?

Objective B

Multiply.

44.   16
       $\times\,21$

45.   18
       $\times\,24$

46.   35
       $\times\,26$

47.   27
       $\times\,72$

48.   693
       $\times\,\ 91$

49.   581
       $\times\,\ 72$

50.   419
       $\times\,\ 80$

51.   727
       $\times\,\ 60$

52.   8279
       $\times\,\ \ 46$

53.   9577
       $\times\,\ \ 35$

54.   6938
       $\times\,\ \ 78$

55.   8875
       $\times\,\ \ 67$

56.   7035
       $\times\,\ \ 57$

57.   6702
       $\times\,\ \ 48$

58.   3009
       $\times\,\ \ 35$

59.   6003
       $\times\,\ \ 57$

60.   809
       $\times\,530$

61.   607
       $\times\,460$

62.   800
       $\times\,325$

63.   700
       $\times\,274$

64.   987
       $\times\,349$

65.   688
       $\times\,674$

66.   312
       $\times\,134$

67.   423
       $\times\,427$

68.   379
       $\times\,500$

69.   684
       $\times\,700$

70.   985
       $\times\,408$

71.   758
       $\times\,209$

72.   3407
       $\times\,\ 309$

73.   5207
       $\times\,\ 902$

74.   4258
       $\times\,\ 986$

75.   6327
       $\times\,\ 876$

76. What is 5763 times 45?

77. What is 7349 times 7?

78. Find the product of 2, 19, and 34.

79. Find the product of 6, 73, and 43.

80. What is 376 multiplied by 402?

81. What is 842 multiplied by 309?

82. Find the product of 233,489 and 3005.

83. Find the product of 34,985 and 9007.

Estimate and then use your calculator to multiply.

84. 8745 × 63	**85.** 4732 × 93	**86.** 39,246 × 29	**87.** 64,409 × 67
88. 2937 × 206	**89.** 8941 × 726	**90.** 3097 × 1025	**91.** 6379 × 2936
92. 32,508 × 591	**93.** 62,504 × 923	**94.** 81,405 × 902	**95.** 66,735 × 844

Objective C   *Application Problems*

96. Rob Hill owns a compact car that averages 43 miles on 1 gallon of gas. How many miles could the car travel on 12 gallons of gas?

97. A plane flying from Los Angeles to Boston uses 865 gallons of jet fuel each hour. How many gallons of jet fuel were used on a 6-hour flight?

98. Anthony Davis purchased 225 shares of Public Service of Colorado for $40 per share. The stock has a yearly dividend of $2 a share, paid in 4 quarterly payments. Find the yearly income from the 225 shares of stock.

99. Assume that a machine at the Coca Cola Bottling Company can fill and cap 4200 bottles of Coke in 1 hour. How many bottles of Coke can the machine fill and cap in 40 hours?

100. A computer graphics screen has 640 rows of pixels, and there are 480 pixels per row. Find the total number of pixels on the screen.

101. Jack Murphy Stadium in San Diego has a capacity of 60,836. For the first 11 home games, the average attendance was 30,013. For the first 4 road games, the average attendance was 16,754. Estimate the total attendance for the 11 home games. Find the total attendance for the first 15 games.

A lighting consultant to a bank suggests that the bank lobby contain 43 can lights, 15 high-intensity lights, 20 fire safety lights, and one chandelier. The table at the right gives the costs for each type of light from two companies. Use this table for Exercises 102 and 103.

	Company A	Company B
Can lights	$2 each	$3 each
High-intensity	$6 each	$4 each
Fire safety	$12 each	$11 each
Chandelier	$998 each	$1089 each
	1018	*1107*

102. Which company offers the lights for the lower total price?

103. How much can the lighting designer save by purchasing the lights from the company that offers the lower total price?

The table at the right shows the hourly wages of four different job classifications at a small construction company. Use this table for Exercises 104 to 106.

Type of Work	Wage per Hour
Electrician	$17
Plumber	$15
Clerk	$8
Bookkeeper	$10

104. The owner of this company wants to provide the electrical installation for a new house. Based on the architectural plans for the house, it is estimated that it will require 3 electricians each working 50 hours to complete the job. What is the estimated cost for the electricians' labor?

105. Carlos Vasquez, a plumbing contractor, hires 4 plumbers from this company at the hourly wage given in the table. If each plumber works 23 hours, what are the total wages paid by Carlos?

106. The owner of this company estimates that remodeling a kitchen will require 1 electrician working 30 hours and 1 plumber working 33 hours. This project also requires 3 hours of clerical work and 4 hours of bookkeeping. What is the total cost for these four components of this remodeling?

APPLYING THE CONCEPTS

107. Determine whether each of the following statements is always true, sometimes true, or never true.
  a. A whole number times zero is zero.
  b. A whole number times one is the whole number.
  c. The product of two whole numbers is greater than either one of the whole numbers.

108. According to the National Safety Council, in a recent year a death resulting from an accident occurred at the rate of 1 every 5 minutes. At this rate, how many accidental deaths occurred each hour? Each day? Throughout the year? Explain how you arrived at your answers.

109. In Brazil, 713 acres are deforested each hour. At this rate, how many acres of deforestation occur each day? In a 30-day month? Throughout the year? Explain how you arrived at your answers.

110. Pick your favorite number between 1 and 9. Multiply the number by 3. Multiply that product by 37,037. How is the product related to your favorite number? Explain why this works. (Suggestion: Multiply 3 and 37,037 first.)

111. There are quite a few tricks based on whole numbers. Here's one about birthdays. Write down the month in which you were born. Multiply by 5. Add 7. Multiply by 20. Subtract 100. Add the day of the month on which you were born. Multiply by 4. Subtract 100. Multiply by 25. Add the year you were born. Subtract 3400. The answer is the month/day/year of your birthday.

1.5   Division of Whole Numbers

Objective A   **To divide by a single digit with no remainder in the quotient** ....

Division is used to separate objects into equal groups.

A store manager wants to display 24 new objects equally on 4 shelves. From the diagram, we see that the manager would place 6 objects on each shelf.

The manager's division problem can be written as follows:

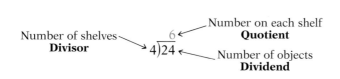

Note that the quotient multiplied by the divisor equals the dividend.

$4\overline{)24}^{\,6}$ because | 6 Quotient | $\times$ | 4 Divisor | $=$ | 24 Dividend |

$9\overline{)54}^{\,6}$ because 6 $\times$ 9 $=$ 54

$8\overline{)40}^{\,5}$ because 5 $\times$ 8 $=$ 40

Here are some important quotients and the properties of zero in division:

Important Quotients

Any whole number, except zero, divided by itself is 1.

$8\overline{)8}^{\,1}$ $14\overline{)14}^{\,1}$ $10\overline{)10}^{\,1}$

Any whole number divided by 1 is the whole number.

$1\overline{)9}^{\,9}$ $1\overline{)27}^{\,27}$ $1\overline{)10}^{\,10}$

Properties of Zero in Division

Zero divided by any other whole number is zero.

$7\overline{)0}^{\,0}$ $13\overline{)0}^{\,0}$ $10\overline{)0}^{\,0}$

Division by zero is not allowed.

$0\overline{)8}^{\,?}$ There is no number whose product with 0 is 8.

When the dividend is a larger whole number, the digits in the quotient are found in steps.

➡ Divide 4)3192 and check.

$$\begin{array}{r} 7 \\ 4)\overline{3192} \\ -28 \\ \hline 39 \end{array}$$

- Think 4)31.
- Subtract 7 × 4.
- Bring down the 9.

$$\begin{array}{r} 79 \\ 4)\overline{3192} \\ -28 \\ \hline 39 \\ -36 \\ \hline 32 \end{array}$$

- Think 4)39.
- Subtract 9 × 4.
- Bring down the 2.

$$\begin{array}{r} 798 \\ 4)\overline{3192} \\ -28 \\ \hline 39 \\ -36 \\ \hline 32 \\ -32 \\ \hline 0 \end{array}$$

- Think 4)32.
- Subtract 8 × 4.

Check:
$$\begin{array}{r} 798 \\ \times \quad 4 \\ \hline 3192 \end{array}$$

The place-value chart can be used to show why this method works.

$$\begin{array}{r} \text{HUNDREDS} \;\; \text{TENS} \;\; \text{ONES} \\ 7 \;\; 9 \;\; 8 \\ 4)\overline{3 \;\; 1 \;\; 9 \;\; 2} \\ -2 \;\; 8 \;\; 0 \;\; 0 \quad \text{7 hundreds} \times 4 \\ \hline 3 \;\; 9 \;\; 2 \\ -3 \;\; 6 \;\; 0 \quad \text{9 tens} \times 4 \\ \hline 3 \;\; 2 \\ -3 \;\; 2 \quad \text{8 ones} \times 4 \\ \hline 0 \end{array}$$

There are other ways of expressing division.

54 divided by 9 equals 6.

54 ÷ 9 equals 6.

$\dfrac{54}{9}$ equals 6.

Example 1   Divide $7\overline{)56}$ and check.

Solution
$$\frac{8}{7\overline{)56}}$$

Check: $8 \times 7 = 56$

You Try It 1   Divide $9\overline{)63}$ and check.

Your solution

Example 2   Divide $2808 \div 8$ and check.

Solution
$$
\begin{array}{r}
351 \\
8\overline{)\ 2808} \\
-24 \\
\hline
40 \\
-40 \\
\hline
08 \\
-\ 8 \\
\hline
0
\end{array}
$$

Check: $351 \times 8 = 2808$

You Try It 2   Divide $4077 \div 9$ and check.

Your solution

Example 3   Divide $7\overline{)2856}$ and check.

Solution
$$
\begin{array}{r}
408 \\
7\overline{)\ 2856} \\
-28 \\
\hline
05 \\
-0 \\
\hline
56 \\
-56 \\
\hline
0
\end{array}
$$

- Think $7\overline{)5}$. Place 0 in quotient.
  Subtract 0×7.
  Bring down the 6.

Check: $408 \times 7 = 2856$

You Try It 3   Divide $9\overline{)6345}$ and check.

Your solution

Solutions on p. S2

Objective B   *To divide by a single digit with a remainder in the quotient* ....

Sometimes it is not possible to separate objects into a whole number of equal groups.

A baker has 14 muffins to pack into 3 boxes. Each box holds 4 muffins. From the diagram, we see that after the baker places 4 muffins in each box, there are 2 left over. The 2 is called the **remainder.**

The clerk's division problem could be written

$$
\begin{array}{r}
4 \quad\text{(Number in each box)} \leftarrow \text{Quotient} \\
3\overline{)\,14} \leftarrow \text{Dividend} \\
-12 \quad\text{(Total number of objects)} \\
\hline
2 \leftarrow \text{Remainder} \\
\text{(Number left over)}
\end{array}
$$

Divisor (Number of boxes) $\longrightarrow$

The answer to a division problem with a remainder is frequently written

$$
\begin{array}{r}
4 \text{ r2} \\
3\overline{)14}
\end{array}
$$

Note that
$$
\boxed{\underset{\text{Quotient}}{4} \times \underset{\text{Divisor}}{3}} + \boxed{\underset{\text{Remainder}}{2}} = \boxed{\underset{\text{Dividend}}{14}}
$$

Example 4 Divide $4\overline{)2522}$ and check.

Solution
$$
\begin{array}{r}
630 \text{ r2} \\
4\overline{)\,2522} \\
-24 \\
\hline
12 \\
-12 \\
\hline
02 \\
-\ 0 \\
\hline
2
\end{array}
$$

• Think $4\overline{)2}$. Place 0 in quotient.
  Subtract 0 × 4.

Check: $(630 \times 4) + 2 =$
$\quad\quad 2520 \ \ + 2 = 2522$

You Try It 4 Divide $6\overline{)5225}$ and check.

Your solution

Example 5 Divide $9\overline{)27,438}$ and check.

Solution
$$
\begin{array}{r}
3,048 \text{ r6} \\
9\overline{)\,27,438} \\
-27 \\
\hline
0\ 4 \\
-\ 0 \\
\hline
43 \\
-36 \\
\hline
78 \\
-72 \\
\hline
6
\end{array}
$$

• Think $9\overline{)4}$.
• Subtract 0 × 9.

Check: $(3048 \times 9) + 6 =$
$\quad\quad 27,432 \ \ + 6 = 27,438$

You Try It 5 Divide $7\overline{)21,409}$ and check.

Your solution

Solutions on p. S2

Objective C   *To divide by larger whole numbers* ···

When the divisor has more than one digit, estimate at each step by using the first digit of the divisor. If that product is too large, lower the guess by 1 and try again.

➡ Divide 34)1598 and check.

$$\begin{array}{r} 5 \\ 34)\overline{1598} \\ -170 \end{array}$$ • Think 3)15.
   • Subtract 5 × 34.

170 is too large. Lower the guess by 1 and try again.

$$\begin{array}{r} 4 \\ 34)\overline{1598} \\ -136 \\ \hline 238 \end{array}$$ • Subtract 4 × 34.

$$\begin{array}{r} 47 \\ 34)\overline{1598} \\ -136 \\ \hline 238 \\ -238 \\ \hline 0 \end{array}$$ • Think 3)23.
   • Subtract 7 × 34.

Check:
$$\begin{array}{r} 47 \\ \times 34 \\ \hline 188 \\ 141 \\ \hline 1598 \end{array}$$

The phrases below are used to indicate the operation of division. An example is shown at the right of each phrase.

the quotient of   the quotient of 9 and 3   9 ÷ 3
divided by   6 divided by 2   6 ÷ 2

Example 6   Find 7077 divided by 34 and check.

You Try It 6   Divide 4578 ÷ 42 and check.

Solution
$$\begin{array}{r} 208 \text{ r}5 \\ 34)\overline{7077} \\ -68 \\ \hline 27 \\ -\ 0 \\ \hline 277 \\ -272 \\ \hline 5 \end{array}$$
   • Think 34)27.
   • Place 0 in the quotient.
   • Subtract 0 × 34.

Your solution

Check: (208 × 34) + 5 =
            7072   + 5 = 7077

Solution on p. S2

Example 7   Find the quotient of 21,312 and 56 and check.

Solution

$$
\begin{array}{r}
380 \text{ r}32 \\
56\overline{)21{,}312} \\
-16\ 8 \\
\hline
4\ 51 \\
-4\ 48 \\
\hline
32 \\
-\ \ 0 \\
\hline
32
\end{array}
$$

• Think $5\overline{)21}$.

4×56 is too large. Try 3.

Check: $(380 \times 56) + 32 =$
$\qquad 21{,}280 \ \ + 32 = 21{,}312$

You Try It 7   Divide $18{,}359 \div 39$ and check.

Your solution

Example 8   Divide $427\overline{)24{,}782}$ and check.

Solution

$$
\begin{array}{r}
58 \text{ r}16 \\
427\overline{)24{,}782} \\
-21\ 35 \\
\hline
3\ 432 \\
-3\ 416 \\
\hline
16
\end{array}
$$

Check: $(58 \times 427) + 16 =$
$\qquad 24{,}766 \ \ + 16 = 24{,}782$

You Try It 8   Divide $534\overline{)33{,}219}$ and check.

Your solution

Example 9   Divide $386\overline{)206{,}149}$ and check.

Solution

$$
\begin{array}{r}
534 \text{ r}25 \\
386\overline{)206{,}149} \\
-193\ 0 \\
\hline
13\ 14 \\
-11\ 58 \\
\hline
1\ 569 \\
-1\ 544 \\
\hline
25
\end{array}
$$

Check: $(534 \times 386) + 25 =$
$\qquad 206{,}124 \ \ + 25 = 206{,}149$

You Try It 9   Divide $515\overline{)216{,}848}$ and check.

Your solution

Solutions on p. S3

ESTIMATION

Estimating the Quotient of Two Whole Numbers

Estimate and then use your calculator to find $36,936 \div 54$.

To estimate a quotient, round each number so that all the digits are zero except the first digit. Then divide.

$$36,936 \div 54 \approx$$
$$40,000 \div 50 = 800$$

The estimated answer is 800.

Now use your calculator to find the exact answer.

36936 ÷ 54 = 684

The exact answer is 684.

Objective D   *To solve application problems* ··············

The *average* of several numbers is the sum of all the numbers divided by the number of numbers.

$$\text{Average test score} = \frac{498}{6} = 83$$

➡ The table at the right shows the number of home dates and the total home attendance of the baseball teams in the National League. Find the average home attendance for the Chicago team. Round to the nearest whole number.

Team	Home Dates	Home Att.
Atlanta	69	3,296,967
Chicago	74	2,446,912
Cincinnati	69	2,189,722
Colorado	67	3,872,511
Florida	67	2,629,117
Houston	74	1,913,944
Los Angeles	71	2,796,973
Montreal	72	1,374,708
New York	70	1,708,606
Philadelphia	74	2,869,808
Pittsburgh	70	1,514,206
St. Louis	72	2,578,292
San Diego	73	1,277,268
San Francisco	73	2,362,524

Strategy

Determine from the table the total attendance and the number of home dates for the Chicago team. To find the average home attendance, divide the total attendance (2,446,912) by the number of home dates (74).

Solution

```
        33,066
   74) 2,446,912
      -2 22
        226
       -222
         49
        - 0
         4 91
        -4 44
           472
          -444
            28
```

- When rounding to the nearest whole number, compare twice the remainder to the divisor. If twice the remainder is less than the divisor, drop the remainder. If twice the remainder is greater than or equal to the divisor, add 1 to the units digit of the quotient.

- Twice the remainder is 2 × 28 = 56. Because 56 < 74, drop the remainder.

The average attendance is 33,066.

Example 10

Ngan Hui, a freight supervisor, shipped 192,600 bushels of wheat in 9 railroad cars. Find the amount of wheat shipped in each car.

Strategy

To find the amount of wheat shipped in each car, divide the number of bushels (192,600) by the number of cars (9).

Solution

$$
\begin{array}{r}
21{,}400 \\
9{\overline{\smash{\big)}\,192{,}600}} \\
-18 \phantom{0{,}000} \\
\hline
12 \\
-9 \\
\hline
36 \\
-36 \\
\hline
0
\end{array}
$$

Each car carried 21,400 bushels of wheat.

You Try It 10

Suppose a Firestone retail outlet can store 270 tires on 15 shelves. How many tires can be stored on each shelf?

Strategy

Your solution

Example 11

The car you are buying costs $11,216. A down payment of $2000 is required. The remaining balance is paid in 48 equal monthly payments. What is the monthly payment?

Strategy

To find the monthly payment:

- Find the remaining balance by subtracting the down payment ($2000) from the total cost of the car ($11,216).
- Divide the remaining balance by the number of equal monthly payments (48).

Solution

$$
\begin{array}{r}
11{,}216 \\
-\;2{,}000 \\
\hline
9{,}216
\end{array}
$$
remaining balance

$$
\begin{array}{r}
192 \\
48{\overline{\smash{\big)}\,9216}} \\
-48 \\
\hline
441 \\
-432 \\
\hline
96 \\
-96 \\
\hline
0
\end{array}
$$

The monthly payment is $192.

You Try It 11

A soft-drink manufacturer produces 12,600 cans of soft drink each hour. Cans are packed 24 to a case. How many cases of soft drink are produced in 8 hours?

Your strategy

Your solution

Solutions on p. S3

1.5 Exercises

· ·

Objective A

Divide.

1. $4\overline{)8}$ **2.** $3\overline{)9}$ **3.** $6\overline{)36}$ **4.** $9\overline{)81}$

5. $7\overline{)49}$ **6.** $5\overline{)80}$ **7.** $6\overline{)96}$ **8.** $6\overline{)480}$

9. $4\overline{)840}$ **10.** $3\overline{)690}$ **11.** $7\overline{)308}$ **12.** $7\overline{)203}$

13. $9\overline{)6327}$ **14.** $4\overline{)2120}$ **15.** $8\overline{)7280}$ **16.** $9\overline{)8118}$

17. $3\overline{)64,680}$ **18.** $4\overline{)50,760}$ **19.** $6\overline{)21,480}$ **20.** $5\overline{)18,050}$

21. Find the quotient of 1446 and 3.   **22.** Find the quotient of 4123 and 7.

23. What is 7525 divided by 7?   **24.** What is 32,364 divided by 4?

Objective B

Divide.

25. $4\overline{)9}$ **26.** $2\overline{)7}$ **27.** $5\overline{)27}$ **28.** $9\overline{)88}$ **29.** $3\overline{)40}$

30. $6\overline{)97}$ **31.** $8\overline{)83}$ **32.** $5\overline{)54}$ **33.** $7\overline{)632}$ **34.** $4\overline{)363}$

35. $4\overline{)921}$ **36.** $7\overline{)845}$ **37.** $8\overline{)1635}$ **38.** $5\overline{)1548}$ **39.** $7\overline{)9432}$

40. $7\overline{)8124}$ **41.** $3\overline{)5162}$ **42.** $5\overline{)3542}$ **43.** $8\overline{)3274}$

44. $4\overline{)15,300}$ **45.** $7\overline{)43,500}$ **46.** $8\overline{)72,354}$ **47.** $5\overline{)43,542}$

48. Find the quotient of 3107 and 8.

49. Find the quotient of 8642 and 8.

50. What is 45,738 divided by 4? Round to the nearest ten.

51. What is 37,896 divided by 9? Round to the nearest hundred.

52. What is 3572 divided by 7? Round to the nearest ten.

53. What is 78,345 divided by 4? Round to the nearest hundred.

Objective C

Divide.

54. $27\overline{)96}$ **55.** $44\overline{)82}$ **56.** $42\overline{)87}$ **57.** $67\overline{)93}$

58. $41\overline{)897}$ **59.** $32\overline{)693}$ **60.** $23\overline{)784}$ **61.** $25\overline{)772}$

62. $74\overline{)600}$ **63.** $92\overline{)500}$ **64.** $70\overline{)329}$ **65.** $50\overline{)467}$

66. $36\overline{)7225}$ **67.** $44\overline{)8821}$ **68.** $19\overline{)3859}$ **69.** $32\overline{)9697}$

70. $88\overline{)3127}$ **71.** $92\overline{)6177}$ **72.** $33\overline{)8943}$ **73.** $27\overline{)4765}$

74. $22\overline{)98,654}$ **75.** $77\overline{)83,629}$ **76.** $64\overline{)38,912}$ **77.** $78\overline{)31,434}$

78. $206\overline{)3097}$ **79.** $504\overline{)6504}$ **80.** $654\overline{)1217}$ **81.** $546\overline{)2344}$

82. Find the quotient of 5432 and 21.

83. Find the quotient of 8507 and 53.

84. What is 37,294 divided by 72?

85. What is 76,788 divided by 46?

86. Find 23,457 divided by 43. Round to the nearest hundred.

87. Find 341,781 divided by 43. Round to the nearest ten.

Estimate and then use your calculator to divide.

88. $76\overline{)389,804}$

89. $53\overline{)117,925}$

90. $29\overline{)637,072}$

91. $67\overline{)738,072}$

92. $38\overline{)934,648}$

93. $34\overline{)906,304}$

94. $309\overline{)876,324}$

95. $642\overline{)323,568}$

96. $209\overline{)632,016}$

97. $614\overline{)332,174}$

98. $179\overline{)5,734,444}$

99. $374\overline{)7,712,254}$

Objective D   *Application Problems*

100. Assume that the American Red Cross, the Boys Club, the Girls Club, and the North County Crisis Center collected $548,000 to promote and provide community services. What amount did each organization receive if the money was divided evenly?

101. An insurance agent drives a car with a 16-gallon gas tank. The agent used 128 gallons of gas in traveling 3456 miles. Find the average number of miles traveled on each gallon of gas.

The five highest paid baseball players for the year 1997 are listed at the right. This is the contract salary and does not include endorsements. The following exercises do not include everything the players are responsible for. However, it is interesting to see the income for each event for the different players.

Name	Annual Income
Albert Belle	$10,000,000
Cecil Fielder	$9,237,000
Barry Bonds	$8,513,000
Roger Clemens	$8,250,000
Jeff Bagwell	$8,015,000

Source: USA TODAY research, USA TODAY, March 4, 1997

102. Assume that Roger Clemens pitched in 40 games. Find the average income per game that Clemens pitched.

103. Albert Belle was signed because of his home run hitting ability. Assume that Belle breaks the record and hits 64 home runs in a season. Find the income per home run that Belle receives.

104. Assume that Cecil Fielder plays in 150 games. Find the average salary that Fielder receives per game.

105. A computer can store 2,211,840 bytes of information on 6 disks. How many bytes of information can be stored on 1 disk?

106. Ken Martinez, a computer analyst, received $5376 for working 168 hours on a computer consulting project. Find the hourly rate that Ken charged.

107. Marie Sarro, a design consultant, made a down payment of $1560 on a car costing $10,536.
   a. What is the remaining balance to be paid?
   b. The balance is to be paid in 48 equal monthly payments. Find the monthly payment.

The table at the right shows the highest paid athletes in four professional sports for the year 1996. Michael Jordan plays professional basketball, Albert Belle plays professional baseball, Mario Lemieux plays professional hockey, and Troy Aikman plays professional football. Use this list for Exercises 108 to 111.

Name	Annual Income
Jordan	$30,140,000
Belle	$10,000,000
Lemieux	$11,320,000
Aikman	$5,370,000

Source: USA TODAY research, USA TODAY, April 3, 1997

108. There are 82 games in a professional basketball season. Assuming that Michael Jordan played in all 82 games, find his average salary per game. Round to the nearest whole number.

109. The average worker in the United States works approximately 2000 hours per year. Assume that Mario Lemieux worked 2000 hours. Find his average hourly wage.

110. Approximately how many times Troy Aikman's annual income was Michael Jordan's annual income? Round to the nearest whole number.

111. There are 162 games in a professional baseball season and 16 games in a professional football season. Find Albert Belle's and Troy Aikman's average salary per game. Approximately how many times Albert Belle's average salary per game was Troy Aikman's average salary per game? Round to the nearest whole number.

APPLYING THE CONCEPTS

112. A palindromic number is a whole number that remains unchanged when its digits are written in reverse order. For instance, 292 is a palindromic number. Find the smallest three-digit palindromic number that is divisible by 4.

113. Find the smallest four-digit palindromic number (see Exercise 112) that is divisible by 8. (Helpful fact: A whole number whose last three digits are divisible by 8 is itself divisible by 8.)

114. The number 10,981 is not divisible by 4. By rearranging the digits, find the largest possible number that is divisible by 4.

115. Determine whether each of the following statements is true or false.
   a. Any whole number divided by zero is zero.   **b.** $\dfrac{0}{0} = 1$
   c. Zero divided by any whole number, except zero, is zero.

116. Explain how the answer to a division problem can be checked.

1.6 Exponential Notation and the Order of Operations Agreement

Objective A *To simplify expressions that contain exponents* ....

Repeated multiplication of the same factor can be written in two ways:

$$3 \cdot 3 \cdot 3 \cdot 3 \cdot 3 \quad \text{or} \quad 3^5 \leftarrow \textbf{exponent}$$

The exponent indicates how many times the factor occurs in the multiplication. The expression 3^5 is in **exponential notation.**

It is important to be able to read numbers written in exponential notation.

$6 = 6^1$ is read "six to the first power" or just "six." Usually the exponent 1 is not written.

$6 \cdot 6 = 6^2$ is read "six squared" or "six to the second power."

$6 \cdot 6 \cdot 6 = 6^3$ is read "six cubed" or "six to the third power."

$6 \cdot 6 \cdot 6 \cdot 6 = 6^4$ is read "six to the fourth power."

$6 \cdot 6 \cdot 6 \cdot 6 \cdot 6 = 6^5$ is read "six to the fifth power."

Each place value in the place-value chart can be expressed as a power of 10.

$$
\begin{aligned}
\text{Ten} &= 10 &=& \quad 10 &=& 10^1 \\
\text{Hundred} &= 100 &=& \quad 10 \cdot 10 &=& 10^2 \\
\text{Thousand} &= 1000 &=& \quad 10 \cdot 10 \cdot 10 &=& 10^3 \\
\text{Ten-Thousand} &= 10{,}000 &=& \quad 10 \cdot 10 \cdot 10 \cdot 10 &=& 10^4 \\
\text{Hundred-Thousand} &= 100{,}000 &=& \quad 10 \cdot 10 \cdot 10 \cdot 10 \cdot 10 &=& 10^5 \\
\text{Million} &= 1{,}000{,}000 &=& \quad 10 \cdot 10 \cdot 10 \cdot 10 \cdot 10 \cdot 10 &=& 10^6
\end{aligned}
$$

To simplify a numerical expression containing exponents, write each factor as many times as indicated by the exponent and carry out the indicated multiplication.

$$4^3 = 4 \cdot 4 \cdot 4 = 64$$
$$2^2 \cdot 3^4 = (2 \cdot 2) \cdot (3 \cdot 3 \cdot 3 \cdot 3) = 4 \cdot 81 = 324$$

Example 1 Write $3 \cdot 3 \cdot 3 \cdot 5 \cdot 5$ in exponential notation.

Solution $3 \cdot 3 \cdot 3 \cdot 5 \cdot 5 = 3^3 \cdot 5^2$

You Try It 1 Write $2 \cdot 2 \cdot 2 \cdot 2 \cdot 3 \cdot 3 \cdot 3$ in exponential notation.

Your solution

Example 2 Write as a power of 10:
$10 \cdot 10 \cdot 10 \cdot 10$

Solution $10 \cdot 10 \cdot 10 \cdot 10 = 10^4$

You Try It 2 Write as a power of 10:
$10 \cdot 10 \cdot 10 \cdot 10 \cdot 10 \cdot 10 \cdot 10$

Your solution

Example 3 Simplify $3^2 \cdot 5^3$.

Solution $3^2 \cdot 5^3 = (3 \cdot 3) \cdot (5 \cdot 5 \cdot 5)$
$= 9 \cdot 125 = 1125$

You Try It 3 Simplify $2^3 \cdot 5^2$.

Your solution

Solutions on p. S3

Objective B*   *To use the Order of Operations Agreement to simplify expressions ....

More than one operation may occur in a numerical expression. The answer may be different, depending on the order in which the operations are performed. For example, consider $3 + 4 \times 5$.

Multiply first, then add.

$$3 + \underbrace{4 \times 5}$$
$$\underbrace{3 + 20}$$
$$23$$

Add first, then multiply.

$$\underbrace{3 + 4} \times 5$$
$$\underbrace{7 \times 5}$$
$$35$$

An Order of Operations Agreement is used so that only one answer is possible.

The Order of Operations Agreement

Step 1   Do all the operations inside parentheses.
Step 2   Simplify any number expressions containing exponents.
Step 3   Do multiplication and division as they occur from left to right.
Step 4   Do addition and subtraction as they occur from left to right.

➡ Simplify $3 \times (2 + 1) - 2^2 + 4 \div 2$ by using the Order of Operations Agreement.

$$3 \times \underbrace{(2 + 1)} - 2^2 + 4 \div 2$$
$$\underbrace{3 \times 3 - \underbrace{2^2} + 4 \div 2}$$
$$\underbrace{3 \times 3} - 4 + 4 \div 2$$
$$9 - 4 + \underbrace{4 \div 2}$$
$$\underbrace{9 - 4} + 2$$
$$\underbrace{5 + 2}$$
$$7$$

1.   Perform operations in parentheses.

2.   Simplify expressions with exponents.

3.   Do multiplications and divisions as they occur from left to right.

4.   Do additions and subtractions as they occur from left to right.

One or more of the above steps may not be needed to simplify an expression. In that case, proceed to the next step in the Order of Operations Agreement.

➡ Simplify $5 + 8 \div 2$.

$$5 + \underbrace{8 \div 2}$$
$$\underbrace{5 + 4}$$
$$9$$

No parentheses or exponents. Proceed to step 3 of the Agreement.

3.   Do multiplication or division.

4.   Do addition or subtraction.

Example 4   Simplify: $64 \div (8 - 4)^2 \cdot 9 - 5^2$

Solution
$$64 \div (8 - 4)^2 \cdot 9 - 5^2$$
$$= 64 \div 4^2 \cdot 9 - 5^2$$
$$= 64 \div 16 \cdot 9 - 25$$
$$= 4 \cdot 9 - 25$$
$$= 36 - 25$$
$$= 11$$

You Try It 4   Simplify: $5 \cdot (8 - 4)^2 \div 4 - 2$

Your solution

Solution on p. S3

1.6 Exercises

Objective A

Write the number in exponential notation.

1. $2 \cdot 2 \cdot 2$

2. $7 \cdot 7 \cdot 7 \cdot 7 \cdot 7$

3. $6 \cdot 6 \cdot 6 \cdot 7 \cdot 7 \cdot 7 \cdot 7$

4. $6 \cdot 6 \cdot 9 \cdot 9 \cdot 9 \cdot 9$

5. $2 \cdot 2 \cdot 2 \cdot 3 \cdot 3 \cdot 3$

6. $3 \cdot 3 \cdot 10 \cdot 10$

7. $5 \cdot 7 \cdot 7 \cdot 7 \cdot 7 \cdot 7$

8. $4 \cdot 4 \cdot 4 \cdot 5 \cdot 5 \cdot 5$

9. $3 \cdot 3 \cdot 3 \cdot 6 \cdot 6 \cdot 6 \cdot 6$

10. $2 \cdot 2 \cdot 5 \cdot 5 \cdot 5 \cdot 8$

11. $3 \cdot 3 \cdot 3 \cdot 5 \cdot 9 \cdot 9 \cdot 9$

12. $2 \cdot 2 \cdot 2 \cdot 4 \cdot 7 \cdot 7 \cdot 7$

Simplify.

13. 2^3

14. 2^6

15. $2^4 \cdot 5^2$

16. $2^6 \cdot 3^2$

17. $3^2 \cdot 10^2$

18. $2^3 \cdot 10^4$

19. $6^2 \cdot 3^3$

20. $4^3 \cdot 5^2$

21. $5 \cdot 2^3 \cdot 3$

22. $6 \cdot 3^2 \cdot 4$

23. $2^2 \cdot 3^2 \cdot 10$

24. $3^2 \cdot 5^2 \cdot 10$

25. $0^2 \cdot 4^3$

26. $6^2 \cdot 0^3$

27. $3^2 \cdot 10^4$

28. $5^3 \cdot 10^3$

29. $2^2 \cdot 3^3 \cdot 5$

30. $5^2 \cdot 7^3 \cdot 2$

31. $2 \cdot 3^4 \cdot 5^2$

32. $6 \cdot 2^6 \cdot 7^2$

33. $5^2 \cdot 3^2 \cdot 7^2$

34. $4^2 \cdot 9^2 \cdot 6^2$

35. $3^4 \cdot 2^6 \cdot 5$

36. $4^3 \cdot 6^3 \cdot 7$

37. $4^2 \cdot 3^3 \cdot 10^4$

Objective B

Simplify by using the Order of Operations Agreement.

38. $4 - 2 + 3$

39. $6 - 3 + 2$

40. $6 \div 3 + 2$

41. $8 \div 4 + 8$

42. $6 \cdot 3 + 5$

43. $5 \cdot 9 + 2$

44. $3^2 - 4$

45. $5^2 - 17$

46. $4 \cdot (5 - 3) + 2$ **47.** $3 + (4 + 2) \div 3$ **48.** $5 + (8 + 4) \div 6$ **49.** $8 - 2^2 + 4$

50. $16 \cdot (3 + 2) \div 10$ **51.** $12 \cdot (1 + 5) \div 12$ **52.** $10 - 2^3 + 4$ **53.** $5 \cdot 3^2 + 8$

54. $16 + 4 \cdot 3^2$ **55.** $12 + 4 \cdot 2^3$ **56.** $16 + (8 - 3) \cdot 2$ **57.** $7 + (9 - 5) \cdot 3$

58. $2^2 + 3 \cdot (6 - 2)^2$ **59.** $3^3 + 5 \cdot (8 - 6)^3$ **60.** $2^2 \cdot 3^2 + 2 \cdot 3$ **61.** $4 \cdot 6 + 3^2 \cdot 4^2$

62. $16 - 2 \cdot 4$ **63.** $12 + 3 \cdot 5$ **64.** $3 \cdot (6 - 2) + 4$

65. $5 \cdot (8 - 4) - 6$ **66.** $8 - (8 - 2) \div 3$ **67.** $12 - (12 - 4) \div 4$

68. $8 + 2 - 3 \cdot 2 \div 3$ **69.** $10 + 1 - 5 \cdot 2 \div 5$ **70.** $3 \cdot (4 + 2) \div 6$

71. $(7 - 3)^2 \div 2 - 4 + 8$ **72.** $20 - 4 \div 2 \cdot (3 - 1)^3$ **73.** $12 \div 3 \cdot 2^2 + (7 - 3)^2$

74. $(4 - 2) \cdot 6 \div 3 + (5 - 2)^2$ **75.** $18 - 2 \cdot 3 + (4 - 1)^3$ **76.** $100 \div (2 + 3)^2 - 8 \div 2$

APPLYING THE CONCEPTS

77. Memory in computers is measured in bytes. One kilobyte (1 K) is 2^{10} bytes. Write this number in standard form.

78. Explain the difference in the order of operations for **a.** $\dfrac{14 - 2}{2} \div 2 \cdot 3$ and **b.** $\dfrac{14 - 2}{2} \div (2 \cdot 3)$. Work the two problems. What is the difference between the larger and the smaller answer?

79. If a number is divisible by 6 and 10, is the number divisible by 30? If so, explain why. If not, give an example.

1.7   Prime Numbers and Factoring

Objective A   To factor numbers ....

Whole-number factors of a number divide that number evenly (there is no remainder).

1, 2, 3, and 6 are whole-number factors of 6 because they divide 6 evenly.

$$\overset{6}{1)6} \quad \overset{3}{2)6} \quad \overset{2}{3)6} \quad \overset{1}{6)6}$$

Note that both the divisor and the quotient are factors of the dividend.

To find the factors of a number, try dividing the number by 1, 2, 3, 4, 5, ... Those numbers that divide the number evenly are its factors. Continue this process until the factors start to repeat.

⇒ Find all the factors of 42.

$42 \div 1 = 42$	1 and 42 are factors.
$42 \div 2 = 21$	2 and 21 are factors.
$42 \div 3 = 14$	3 and 14 are factors.
$42 \div 4$	Will not divide evenly
$42 \div 5$	Will not divide evenly
$42 \div 6 = 7$	6 and 7 are factors. ⎫ Factors are repeating; all the
$42 \div 7 = 6$	7 and 6 are factors. ⎭ factors of 42 have been found.

1, 2, 3, 6, 7, 14, 21, and 42 are factors of 42.

The following rules are helpful in finding the factors of a number.

2 is a factor of a number if the last digit of the number is 0, 2, 4, 6, or 8.

436 ends in 6; therefore, 2 is a factor of 436. ($436 \div 2 = 218$)

3 is a factor of a number if the sum of the digits of the number is divisible by 3.

The sum of the digits of 489 is $4 + 8 + 9 = 21$. 21 is divisible by 3. Therefore, 3 is a factor of 489. ($489 \div 3 = 163$)

5 is a factor of a number if the last digit of the number is 0 or 5.

520 ends in 0; therefore, 5 is a factor of 520. ($520 \div 5 = 104$)

Example 1   Find all the factors of 30.

Solution $30 \div 1 = 30$
$30 \div 2 = 15$
$30 \div 3 = 10$
$30 \div 4$ Will not divide
evenly
$30 \div 5 = 6$
$30 \div 6 = 5$

1 2, 3, 5, 6, 10, 15, and 30 are factors of 30.

You Try It 1   Find all the factors of 40.

Your solution

Solution on p. S3

Objective B   **To find the prime factorization of a number** ·····················

POINT OF INTEREST

Prime numbers are an important part of cryptology, the study of secret codes. To ensure that codes cannot be broken, a cryptologist uses prime numbers that have hundreds of digits.

A number is a **prime number** if its only whole-number factors are 1 and itself. 7 is prime because its only factors are 1 and 7. If a number is not prime, it is called a **composite number.** Because 6 has factors of 2 and 3, 6 is a composite number. The number 1 is not considered a prime number; therefore it is not included in the following list of prime numbers less than 50.

$$2, 3, 5, 7, 11, 13, 17, 19, 23, 29, 31, 37, 41, 43, 47$$

The **prime factorization** of a number is the expression of the number as a product of its prime factors. We use a "T-diagram" to find the prime factors of 60. Begin with the smallest prime number as a trial divisor, and continue with prime numbers as trial divisors until the final quotient is 1.

$$
\begin{array}{c|c}
\multicolumn{2}{c}{60} \\
\hline
2 & 30 \\
2 & 15 \\
3 & 5 \\
5 & 1
\end{array}
\qquad
\begin{aligned}
60 \div 2 &= 30 \\
30 \div 2 &= 15 \\
15 \div 3 &= 5 \\
5 \div 5 &= 1
\end{aligned}
$$

The prime factorization of 60 is $2 \cdot 2 \cdot 3 \cdot 5$.

Finding the prime factorization of larger numbers can be more difficult. Try each prime number as a trial divisor. Stop when the square of the trial divisor is greater than the number being factored.

⇒ Find the prime factorization of 106.

$$
\begin{array}{c|c}
\multicolumn{2}{c}{106} \\
\hline
2 & 53 \\
53 & 1
\end{array}
$$

• **53 cannot be divided evenly by 2, 3, 5, 7, or 11. Prime numbers greater than 11 need not be tested because 11^2 is greater than 53.**

The prime factorization of 106 is $2 \cdot 53$.

Example 2   Find the prime factorization of 315.

Solution

$$
\begin{array}{c|c}
\multicolumn{2}{c}{315} \\
\hline
3 & 105 \\
3 & 35 \\
5 & 7 \\
7 & 1
\end{array}
$$

$$315 = 3 \cdot 3 \cdot 5 \cdot 7$$

You Try It 2   Find the prime factorization of 44.

Your solution

Example 3   Find the prime factorization of 201.

Solution

$$
\begin{array}{c|c}
\multicolumn{2}{c}{201} \\
\hline
3 & 67 \\
67 & 1
\end{array}
$$

• Try only 2, 3, 5, 7, and 11 because $11^2 > 67$.

$$201 = 3 \cdot 67$$

You Try It 3   Find the prime factorization of 177.

Your solution

Solutions on p. S3

1.7 Exercises

· ·

Objective A

Find all the factors of the number.

1. 4

2. 6

3. 10

4. 20

5. 7

6. 12

7. 9

8. 8

9. 13

10. 17

11. 18

12. 24

13. 56

14. 36

15. 45

16. 28

17. 29

18. 33

19. 22

20. 26

21. 52

22. 49

23. 82

24. 37

25. 57

26. 69

27. 48

28. 64

29. 95

30. 46

31. 54

32. 50

33. 66

34. 77

35. 80

36. 100

37. 96

38. 85

39. 90

40. 101

Objective B

Find the prime factorization.

41. 6   **42.** 14   **43.** 17 ~ prime   **44.** 83

45. 24   **46.** 12   **47.** 27 = 3^3 **48.** 9 =

49. 36 = $2^2 \cdot 3^2$ **50.** 40 = $2^3 \cdot 5$ **51.** 19 = prime   **52.** 37 ~ prime

53. 90 = $2 \cdot 5 \cdot 3^2$ **54.** 65 = $5 \cdot 13$ **55.** 115 = $5 \cdot 23$ **56.** 80 = $2^4 \cdot 5$

57. 18 = $2 \cdot 3^2$ **58.** 26 = $2 \cdot 13$ **59.** 28 = $2^2 \cdot 7$ **60.** 49 = $7 \cdot 7$

61. 31   **62.** 42   **63.** 62   **64.** 81

65. 22   **66.** 39   **67.** 101   **68.** 89

69. 66   **70.** 86   **71.** 74   **72.** 95

73. 67   **74.** 78   **75.** 55   **76.** 46

77. 120   **78.** 144   **79.** 160   **80.** 175

81. 216   **82.** 400   **83.** 625   **84.** 225

APPLYING THE CONCEPTS

85. Twin primes are two prime numbers that differ by 2. For instance, 17 and 19 are twin primes. Find three sets of twin primes, not including 17 and 19.

86. In 1742, Christian Goldbach conjectured that every even number greater than 2 could be expressed as the sum of two prime numbers. Show that this conjecture is true for 8, 24, and 72. (*Note*: Mathematicians have not yet been able to determine whether Goldbach's conjecture is true or false.)

87. Explain why 2 is the only even prime number.

88. Explain the method of finding prime numbers using the Sieve of Erathosthenes.

Focus on Problem Solving

You encounter problem-solving situations every day. Some problems are easy to solve, and you may mentally solve these problems without considering the steps you are taking in order to draw a conclusion. Others may be more challenging and require more thought and consideration.

Suppose a friend suggests that you both take a trip over spring break. You'd like to go. What questions go through your mind? You might ask yourself some of the following questions:

How much will the trip cost? What will be the cost for travel, hotel rooms, meals, etc.?

Are some costs going to be shared by both me and my friend?

Can I afford it?

How much money do I have in the bank?

How much more money than I have now do I need?

How much time is there to earn that much money?

How much can I earn in that amount of time?

How much money must I keep in the bank in order to pay the next tuition bill (or some other expense)?

These questions require different mathematical skills. Determining the cost of the trip requires **estimation**; for example, you must use your knowledge of air fares or the cost of gasoline to arrive at an estimate of these costs. If some of the costs are going to be shared, you need to **divide** those costs by 2 in order to determine your share of the expense. The question regarding how much more money you need requires **subtraction**: the amount needed minus the amount currently in the bank. To determine how much money you can earn in the given amount of time requires **multiplication**—for example, the amount you earn per week times the number of weeks to be worked. To determine if the amount you can earn in the given amount of time is sufficient, you need to use your knowledge of **order relations** to compare the amount you can earn with the amount needed.

Facing the problem-solving situation described above may not seem difficult to you. The reason may be that you have faced similar situations before and, therefore, know how to work through this one. You may feel better prepared to deal with a circumstance such as this one because you know what questions to ask. An important aspect of learning to solve problems is learning what questions to ask. As you work through application problems in this text, try to become more conscious of the mental process you are going through. You might begin the process by asking yourself the following questions whenever you are solving an application problem:

1. Have I read the problem enough times to be able to understand the situation being described?

2. Will restating the problem in different words help me to better understand the problem situation?

3. What facts are given? (You might make a list of the information contained in the problem.)

4. What information is being asked for?

5. What relationship exists between the given facts? What relationship exists between the given facts and the solution?

6. What mathematical operations are needed in order to solve the problem?

Try to focus on the problem-solving situation and not the computation or getting the answer quickly. And remember, the more problems you solve, the better able you will be to solve other problems in the future, partly because you are learning what questions to ask.

Projects and Group Activities

Order of Operations

Does your calculator use the Order of Operations Agreement? To find out, try this problem:

$$2 + 4 \cdot 7$$

If your answer is 30, then the calculator uses the Order of Operations Agreement. If your answer is 42, it does not use that agreement.

Even if your calculator does not use the Order of Operations Agreement, you can still correctly evaluate numerical expressions. The parentheses keys, $\boxed{(}$ and $\boxed{)}$, are used for this purpose.

Remember that $2 + 4 \cdot 7$ means $2 + (4 \cdot 7)$ because the multiplication must be completed before the addition. To evaluate this expression, enter the following:

Enter: 2 $\boxed{+}$ $\boxed{(}$ 4 $\boxed{\times}$ 7 $\boxed{)}$ $\boxed{=}$

Display: 2   2 $\boxed{(}$ 4   4   7   28   30

When using your calculator to evaluate numerical expressions, insert parentheses around multiplications or divisions. This has the effect of forcing the calculator to do the operations in the order you want rather than in the order the calculator wants.

Evaluate.

1. $3 \cdot 8 - 5$

2. $6 + 8 \div 2$

3. $3 \cdot (8 - 2)^2$

4. $24 - (4 - 2)^2 \div 4$

5. $3 + (6 \div 2 + 4)^2 - 2$

6. $16 \div 2 + 4 \cdot (8 - 12 \div 4)^2 - 50$

7. $3 \cdot (15 - 2 \cdot 3) - 36 \div 3$

8. $4 \cdot 2^2 - (12 + 24 \div 6) + 5$

9. $16 \div 4 \cdot 3 + (3 \cdot 4 - 5) + 2$

10. $15 \cdot 3 \div 9 + (2 \cdot 6 - 3) + 4$

Patterns in Mathematics

For the circle at the left, use a straight line to connect each dot on the circle with every other dot on the circle. How many different straight lines are there?

Follow the same procedure for each of the circles shown below. How many different straight lines are there in each?

Find a pattern to describe the number of dots on a circle and the corresponding number of different lines drawn. Use the pattern to determine the number of different lines that would be drawn in a circle with 7 dots and in a circle with 8 dots.

You are arranging a tennis tournament with 9 players. Following the pattern of finding the number of lines drawn on a circle, find the number of singles matches that can be played among the 9 players if each player plays each of the other players only once.

Search the World Wide Web

Go to the Internet and find www.census.gov. Click on U.S. population count. On the next screen, click on U.S. and estimate the following to the nearest thousand. Assume that the same rate of increase in population will continue into the future.

1. What is the population of the United States today?

2. Find the increase in population for a 24-hour period.

3. Using the information found in Exercise 2, find the increase in population for a 30-day period. Find the increase in population for one year (365 days).

4. Using the information in Exercise 3, estimate the population in the United States 50 years from now.

Click back and then click on "World Population." Estimate to the nearest million.

5. How much did the population increase in the last month? In the last year?

6. Use the increase in population for the past year from Exercise 5 to estimate the population of the world 10 years from now and 50 years from now.

Chapter Summary

Key Words

The *whole numbers* are 0, 1, 2, 3, 4, 5, 6, 7, 8, 9, 10, ...

The symbol for "*is less than*" is $<$.

The symbol for "*is greater than*" is $>$.

The position of a digit in a number determines the digit's *place value*.

Giving an approximate value for an exact number is called *rounding*.

An expression of the form 4^2 is in *exponential notation*, where 4 is the *base* and 2 is the *exponent*.

A number is *prime* if its only whole-number factors are 1 and itself.

The *prime factorization* of a number is the expression of the number as a product of its prime factors.

Essential Rules

The Addition Property of Zero	Zero added to a number does not change the number. $5 + 0 = 0 + 5 = 5$
The Commutative Property of Addition	Two numbers can be added in either order. $6 + 5 = 5 + 6 = 11$
The Associative Property of Addition	Grouping numbers to be added in any order gives the same result. $(2 + 3) + 5 = 2 + (3 + 5) = 10$
The Multiplication Property of Zero	The product of a number and zero is zero. $0 \times 3 = 3 \times 0 = 0$
The Multiplication Property of One	The product of a number and one is the number. $1 \times 8 = 8 \times 1 = 8$
The Commutative Property of Multiplication	Two numbers can be multiplied in any order. $5 \times 2 = 2 \times 5 = 10$
The Associative Property of Multiplication	Grouping numbers to be multiplied in any order gives the same result. $(3 \times 2) \times 5 = 3 \times (2 \times 5) = 30$
The Properties of Zero in Division	Zero divided by any other number is zero. Division by zero is not allowed.

Order of Operations Agreement

Step 1 Perform operations inside grouping symbols.
Step 2 Simplify expressions with exponents.
Step 3 Do multiplications and divisions as they occur from left to right.
Step 4 Do additions and subtractions as they occur from left to right.

Chapter Review

1. Simplify: $3 \cdot 2^3 \cdot 5^2$

2. Write 10,327 in expanded form.

3. Find all the factors of 18.

4. Find the sum of 5894, 6301, and 298.

5. Subtract: 4926
  $- \ 3177$

6. Divide: $7\overline{)14{,}945}$

7. Place the correct symbol, $<$ or $>$, between the two numbers: 101   87

8. Write $5 \cdot 5 \cdot 7 \cdot 7 \cdot 7 \cdot 7 \cdot 7$ in exponential notation.

9. What is 2019 multiplied by 307?

10. What is 10,134 decreased by 4725?

11. Add: 298
     461
   $+ \ 322$

12. Simplify: $2^3 - 3 \cdot 2$

13. Find the prime factorization of 42.

14. Write 276,057 in words.

15. Find the quotient of 109,763 and 84.

16. Write two million eleven thousand forty-four in standard form.

17. Find all the factors of 30.

18. Simplify: $3^2 + 2^2 \cdot (5 - 3)$

19. Simplify: $8 \cdot (6 - 2)^2 \div 4$

20. Find the prime factorization of 72.

21. Write $2 \cdot 2 \cdot 2 \cdot 2 \cdot 5 \cdot 5 \cdot 5$ in exponential notation.

22. Multiply:
$$\begin{array}{r} 843 \\ \times\ 27 \\ \hline \end{array}$$

23. Vincent Meyers, a sales assistant, earns $240 for working a 40-hour week. Last week Vincent worked an additional 12 hours at $12 an hour. Find Vincent's total pay for last week's work.

24. Louis Reyes, a sales executive, drove a car 351 miles on 13 gallons of gas. Find the number of miles driven per gallon of gasoline.

25. A car is purchased for $8940, with a down payment of $1500. The balance is paid in 48 equal monthly payments. Find the monthly car payment.

26. An insurance account executive received commissions of $723, $544, $812, and $488 during a 4-week period. Find the total income from commissions for the 4 weeks.

27. You had a balance of $516 in your checking account before making deposits of $88 and $213. Find the total amount deposited, and determine your new account balance.

28. You have a car payment of $123 per month. What is the total of the car payments over a 12-month period?

The graph at the right shows the amount that companies from different countries spend on business trips. Use the graph for Exercises 29 to 31.

29. How much more does a U.S. company spend for business travel and entertainment than does a company from Italy?

30. How much more does a U.S. company spend for business travel and entertainment than the combined spending of a company from the U.K. and a company from Italy?

31. Does a company from the United States outspend the combined spending of a company from Germany and a company from the U.K.?

Big (Travel) Spenders

U.S. companies spend more than twice the amount many European companies spend for business travel and entertainment. Spending per employee:

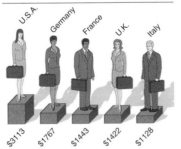

U.S.A. $3113   Germany $1767   France $1443   U.K. $1422   Italy $1128

Chapter Test

1. Simplify: $3^3 \cdot 4^2$

432

2. Write 207,068 in words.

Tw

3. Subtract: 17,495
                  $-$ 8,162

9333

4. Find all the factors of 20.

1 2 4 5 10 20

5. Multiply: 9736
                  $\times$ 704

6. Simplify: $4^2 \cdot (4-2) \div 8 + 5 = 9$

7. Write 906,378 in expanded form.

900,000 + 6,000 + 300 + 70 + 8

8. Round 74,965 to the nearest hundred.

6000

9. Divide: $97)\overline{108,764}$

R27

10. Write $3 \cdot 3 \cdot 3 \cdot 7 \cdot 7$ in exponential form.

$3^3 \cdot 7^2$

11. Find the sum of 89,756, 9094, and 37,065.

12. Find the prime factorization of 84.

2^2, 3 · 7

13. Simplify: $16 \div 4 \cdot 2 - (7-5)^2 = 4$

14. Find the product of 90,763 and 8. =

726,104

15. Write one million two hundred four thousand six in standard form.

1,204,006

16. Divide: $7)\overline{60,972}$

8700, R2

17. Place the correct symbol, < or >, between the two numbers: 21 > 19

18. Find the quotient of 5624 and 8.

$$\begin{array}{r} 703 \\ 8\overline{)5624} \end{array}$$

19. Add: 25,492
           +71,306

20. Find the difference between 29,736 and 9814.

19,922

The table at the right shows the estimated starting salaries of bachelor's degree candidates with engineering degrees. Use this table for Exercises 21 and 22.

Bachelor's Degree	Starting Salary
Chemical engineering	$42,758
Mechanical engineering	$39,852
Electrical engineering	$38,811
Industrial engineering	$37,732

Source: Michigan State University

21. What is the salary difference between the starting salaries of bachelor's degree candidates with degrees in mechanical engineering and industrial engineering?

$12,100

22. Find the average salary of the bachelor's degree candidates with these engineering degrees. Round to the nearest whole number.

39,788

23. A farmer harvested 48,290 pounds of lemons from one grove and 23,710 pounds of lemons from another grove. The lemons were packed in boxes with 24 pounds of lemons in each box. How many boxes were needed to pack the lemons?

3000

24. An investor receives $237 each month from a corporate bond fund. How much will the investor receive over a 12-month period?

244

25. A family drives 425 miles the first day, 187 miles the second day, and 243 miles the third day of their vacation. The odometer read 47,626 miles at the start of the vacation.
  a. How many miles were driven during the 3 days?
  b. What is the odometer reading at the end of the 3 days?

855 m
4 48 m

2

Fractions

Furniture makers can create intricate inlaid-wood patterns in, for example, dining tables or cabinets. Each piece of the pattern is precisely cut to very exact measurements. Measuring the pieces to be cut and ensuring that the pattern will fit the furniture requires that the furniture maker understand fractions and the operations on fractions.

Objectives

Section 2.1
To find the least common multiple (LCM)
To find the greatest common factor (GCF)

Section 2.2
To write a fraction that represents part of a whole
To write an improper fraction as a mixed number or a whole number, and a mixed number as an improper fraction

Section 2.3
To find equivalent fractions by raising to higher terms
To write a fraction in simplest form

Section 2.4
To add fractions with the same denominator
To add fractions with unlike denominators
To add whole numbers, mixed numbers, and fractions
To solve application problems

Section 2.5
To subtract fractions with the same denominator
To subtract fractions with unlike denominators
To subtract whole numbers, mixed numbers, and fractions
To solve application problems

Section 2.6
To multiply fractions
To multiply whole numbers, mixed numbers, and fractions
To solve application problems

Section 2.7
To divide fractions
To divide whole numbers, mixed numbers, and fractions
To solve application problems

Section 2.8
To identify the order relation between two fractions
To simplify expressions containing exponents
To use the Order of Operations Agreement to simplify expressions

Egyptian Fractions

The Rhind papyrus is one of the earliest written accounts of mathematics.[1] In the papyrus, a scribe named Ahmes gives an early account of the concept of fractions. A portion of the Rhind papyrus is rendered here with its hieroglyphic transcription.

The early Egyptians primarily used unit fractions. These are fractions in which the numerator is a 1. To write a fraction, a small oval was placed above a series of lines. The number of lines indicated the denominator. Some examples of these fractions are

$$\frac{\bigcirc}{||||} = \frac{1}{4} \qquad \supset = \frac{1}{2}$$

In the first example, each line represents a 1. Because there are 4 lines, the fraction is $\frac{1}{4}$.

The second example is the special symbol that was used for the fraction $\frac{1}{2}$.

[1] Papyrus comes from the stem of a plant. The stem was dried and then pounded thin. The resulting material served as a primitive type of paper.

2.1 The Least Common Multiple and Greatest Common Factor

Objective A   *To find the least common multiple (LCM)* ....

The **multiples** of a number are the products of that number and the numbers 1, 2, 3, 4, 5, ...

$3 \times 1 = 3$
$3 \times 2 = 6$
$3 \times 3 = 9$
$3 \times 4 = 12$ The multiples of 3 are 3, 6, 9, 12, 15, ...
$3 \times 5 = 15$
.
.
.

A number that is a multiple of two or more numbers is a **common multiple** of those numbers.

The multiples of 4 are 4, 8, 12, 16, 20, 24, 28, 32, 36, ...
The multiples of 6 are 6, 12, 18, 24, 30, 36, 42, ...
Some common multiples of 4 and 6 are 12, 24, and 36.

The **least common multiple** (LCM) is the smallest common multiple of two or more numbers.

The least common multiple of 4 and 6 is 12.

Listing the multiples of each number is one way to find the LCM. Another way to find the LCM uses the prime factorization of each number.

To find the LCM of 450 and 600, find the prime factorization of each number and write the factorization of each number in a table. Circle the largest product in each column. The LCM is the product of the circled numbers.

	2	3	5
450 =	2	(3 · 3)	5 · 5
600 =	(2 · 2 · 2)	3	(5 · 5)

In the column headed by 5, the products are equal. Circle just one product.

The LCM is the product of the circled numbers.
The LCM = 2 · 2 · 2 · 3 · 3 · 5 · 5 = 1800.

Example 1   Find the LCM of 24, 36, and 50.

Solution

	2	3	5
24 =	(2 · 2 · 2)	3	
36 =	2 · 2	(3 · 3)	
50 =	2		(5 · 5)

The LCM =
2 · 2 · 2 · 3 · 3 · 5 · 5 = 1800.

You Try It 1   Find the LCM of 50, 84, and 135.

Your solution

Solution on p. S4

Objective B   *To find the greatest common factor (GCF)* ....

Recall that a number that divides another number evenly is a factor of that number. 64 can be evenly divided by 1, 2, 4, 8, 16, 32, and 64. 1, 2, 4, 8, 16, 32, and 64 are factors of 64.

A number that is a factor of two or more numbers is a **common factor** of those numbers.

The factors of 30 are 1, 2, 3, 5, 6, 10, 15, and 30.
The factors of 105 are 1, 3, 5, 7, 15, 21, 35, and 105.
The common factors of 30 and 105 are 1, 3, 5, and 15.

The **greatest common factor** (GCF) is the largest common factor of two or more numbers.

The greatest common factor of 30 and 105 is 15.

Listing the factors of each number is one way of finding the GCF. Another way to find the GCF uses the prime factorization of each number.

To find the GCF of 126 and 180, find the prime factorization of each number and write the factorization of each number in a table. Circle the smallest product in each column that does not have a blank. The GCF is the product of the circled numbers.

	2	3	5	7
126 =	②	(3 · 3)		7
180 =	2 · 2	3 · 3	5	

In the column headed by 3, the products are equal. Circle just one product.
Columns 5 and 7 have a blank, so 5 and 7 are not common factors of 126 and 180. Do not circle any number in these columns.

The GCF is the product of the circled numbers.
The GCF = 2 · 3 · 3 = 18.

Example 2   Find the GCF of 90, 168, and 420.

Solution

	2	3	5	7
90 =	②	3 · 3	5	
168 =	2 · 2 · 2	③		7
420 =	2 · 2	3	5	7

The GCF = 2 · 3 = 6.

You Try It 2   Find the GCF of 36, 60, and 72.

Your solution

Example 3   Find the GCF of 7, 12, and 20.

Solution

	2	3	5	7
7 =				7
12 =	2 · 2	3		
20 =	2 · 2		5	

Since no numbers are circled, the GCF = 1.

You Try It 3   Find the GCF of 11, 24, and 30.

Your solution

Solutions on p. S4

2.1 Exercises

· ·

Objective A

Find the LCM.

1. 5, 8   **2.** 3, 6   **3.** 3, 8   **4.** 2, 5   **5.** 5, 6

6. 5, 7   **7.** 4, 6   **8.** 6, 8   **9.** 8, 12   **10.** 12, 16

11. 5, 12   **12.** 3, 16   **13.** 8, 14   **14.** 6, 18   **15.** 3, 9

16. 4, 10   **17.** 8, 32   **18.** 7, 21   **19.** 9, 36   **20.** 14, 42

21. 44, 60   **22.** 120, 160   **23.** 102, 184   **24.** 123, 234   **25.** 4, 8, 12

26. 5, 10, 15   **27.** 3, 5, 10   **28.** 2, 5, 8   **29.** 3, 8, 12   **30.** 5, 12, 18

31. 9, 36, 64   **32.** 18, 54, 63   **33.** 16, 30, 84 $=$ 1680   **34.** 9, 12, 15

Objective B

Find the GCF.

35. 3, 5   **36.** 5, 7   **37.** 6, 9   **38.** 18, 24   **39.** 15, 25

40. 14, 49   **41.** 25, 100   **42.** 16, 80   **43.** 32, 51   **44.** 21, 44

45. 12, 80   **46.** 8, 36   **47.** 16, 140   **48.** 12, 76

49. 24, 30   **50.** 48, 144   **51.** 44, 96   **52.** 18, 32

53. 3, 5, 11   **54.** 6, 8, 10   **55.** 7, 14, 49   **56.** 6, 15, 36

57. 10, 15, 20   **58.** 12, 18, 20   **59.** 24, 40, 72   **60.** 3, 17, 51

61. 17, 31, 81   **62.** 14, 42, 84   **63.** 25, 125, 625   **64.** 12, 68, 92

65. 28, 35, 70   **66.** 1, 49, 153   **67.** 32, 56, 72   **68.** 24, 36, 48

APPLYING THE CONCEPTS

69. Define the phrase *relatively prime numbers*. List three pairs of relatively prime numbers.

70. Joe Salvo, a clerk, works three days and then has a day off. A friend works five days and then has a day off. How many days after Joe and his friend have a day off together will they have another day off together?

71. Find the LCM of the following pairs of numbers: 2 and 3, 5 and 7, and 11 and 19. Can you draw a conclusion about the LCM of two prime numbers? Suggest a way of finding the LCM of three prime numbers.

72. Find the GCF of the following pairs of numbers: 3 and 5, 7 and 11, and 29 and 43. Can you draw a conclusion about the GCF of two prime numbers? What is the GCF of three prime numbers?

73. Is the LCM of two numbers always divisible by the GCF of the two numbers? If so, explain why. If not, give an example.

74. Using the pattern for the first two triangles at the right, determine the center number of the last triangle.

75. The ancient Mayans used two calendars, a solar calendar of 365 days and a ritual calendar of 220 days. If a solar year and the ritual year begin on the same day, how many solar years and how many ritual years will pass before this situation occurs again?
(*Mathematics Teacher*, November 1993, page 104)

2.2   Introduction to Fractions

Objective A   *To write a fraction that represents part of a whole* ....

A **fraction** can represent the number of equal parts of a whole.

The shaded portion of the circle is represented by the fraction $\frac{4}{7}$. Four-sevenths of the circle are shaded.

Each part of a fraction has a name.

POINT OF INTEREST

The fraction bar was first used in 1050 by al-Hassar. It is also called a vinculum.

Fraction bar $\rightarrow \dfrac{4 \leftarrow \text{Numerator}}{7 \leftarrow \text{Denominator}}$

A **proper fraction** is a fraction less than 1. The numerator of a proper fraction is smaller than the denominator. The shaded portion of the circle can be represented by the proper fraction $\frac{3}{4}$.

A **mixed number** is a number greater than 1 with a whole-number part and a fractional part. The shaded portion of the circles can be represented by the mixed number $2\frac{1}{4}$.

An **improper fraction** is a fraction greater than or equal to 1. The numerator of an improper fraction is greater than or equal to the denominator. The shaded portion of the circles can be represented by the improper fraction $\frac{9}{4}$. The shaded portion of the square can be represented by $\frac{4}{4}$.

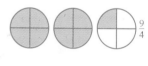

Example 1
Express the shaded portion of the circles as a mixed number.

Solution $3\frac{2}{5}$

Example 2
Express the shaded portion of the circles as an improper fraction.

Solution $\frac{17}{5}$

You Try It 1
Express the shaded portion of the circles as a mixed number.

 $4\frac{1}{4}$

Your solution

You Try It 2
Express the shaded portion of the circles as an improper fraction.

Your solution

Solutions on p. S4

Objective B   **To write an improper fraction as a mixed number or a whole number, and a mixed number as an improper fraction** ....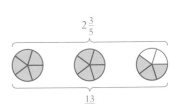

Note from the diagram that the mixed number $2\frac{3}{5}$ and the improper fraction $\frac{13}{5}$ both represent the shaded portion of the circles.

$$2\frac{3}{5} = \frac{13}{5}$$

An improper fraction can be written as a mixed number.

➡ Write $\frac{13}{5}$ as a mixed number.

Divide the numerator by the denominator.	To write the fractional part of the mixed number, write the remainder over the divisor.	Write the answer.

$$\begin{array}{r} 2 \\ 5 \overline{)\ 13} \\ -10 \\ \hline 3 \end{array}$$

$$\begin{array}{r} 2\frac{3}{5} \\ 5 \overline{)\ 13} \\ -10 \\ \hline 3 \end{array}$$

$$\frac{13}{5} = 2\frac{3}{5}$$

To write a mixed number as an improper fraction, multiply the denominator of the fractional part by the whole-number part. The sum of this product and the numerator of the fractional part is the numerator of the improper fraction. The denominator remains the same.

➡ Write $7\frac{3}{8}$ as an improper fraction.

$$7\frac{3}{8} = \frac{(8 \times 7) + 3}{8} = \frac{56 + 3}{8} = \frac{59}{8} \qquad 7\frac{3}{8} = \frac{59}{8}$$

Example 3   Write $\frac{21}{4}$ as a mixed number.

Solution $\begin{array}{r} 5 \\ 4 \overline{)\ 21} \\ -20 \\ \hline 1 \end{array}$ $\frac{21}{4} = 5\frac{1}{4}$

You Try It 3   Write $\frac{22}{5}$ as a mixed number.

Your solution $\frac{22}{5} = 4\frac{2}{5}$ ✓

Example 4   Write $\frac{18}{6}$ as a whole number.

Solution $\begin{array}{r} 3 \\ 6 \overline{)\ 18} \\ -18 \\ \hline 0 \end{array}$ $\frac{18}{6} = 3$

Note: The remainder is zero.

You Try It 4   Write $\frac{28}{7}$ as a whole number.

Your solution $\frac{28}{7} = 4$

Example 5   Write $21\frac{3}{4}$ as an improper fraction.

Solution $21\frac{3}{4} = \frac{84 + 3}{4} = \frac{87}{4}$

You Try It 5   Write $14\frac{5}{8}$ as an improper fraction.

Your solution $\frac{117}{8}$

Solutions on p. S4

2.2 Exercises

Objective A

Express the shaded portion of the circle as a fraction.

1. 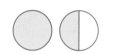 $\frac{3}{4}$

2. $\frac{4}{7}$

3. 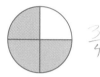 $\frac{7}{8}$

4. 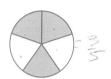 $=\frac{3}{5}$

Express the shaded portion of the circles as a mixed number.

5. $1\frac{1}{2}$

6. $2\frac{2}{3}$

7.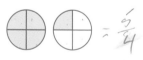

8.

9.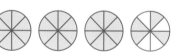

10.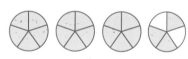

Express the shaded portion of the circles as an improper fraction.

11.  $=\frac{6}{4}$

12.  $=\frac{7}{16}$

13.

14.

15.

16.

17. Shade $\frac{5}{6}$ of

18. Shade $\frac{3}{8}$ of

19. Shade $1\frac{2}{5}$ of

20. Shade $1\frac{3}{4}$ of

21. Shade $\frac{6}{5}$ of

22. Shade $\frac{7}{3}$ of

Objective B

Write the improper fraction as a mixed number or a whole number.

23. $\dfrac{11}{4}$ **24.** $\dfrac{16}{3}$ **25.** $\dfrac{20}{4}$ **26.** $\dfrac{18}{9}$ **27.** $\dfrac{9}{8}$ **28.** $\dfrac{13}{4}$

29. $\dfrac{23}{10}$ **30.** $\dfrac{29}{2}$ **31.** $\dfrac{48}{16}$ **32.** $\dfrac{51}{3}$ **33.** $\dfrac{8}{7}$ **34.** $\dfrac{16}{9}$

35. $\dfrac{7}{3}$ **36.** $\dfrac{9}{5}$ **37.** $\dfrac{16}{1}$ **38.** $\dfrac{23}{1}$ **39.** $\dfrac{17}{8}$ **40.** $\dfrac{31}{16}$

41. $\dfrac{12}{5} = 2\frac{2}{5}$ **42.** $\dfrac{19}{3} = 6\frac{1}{3}$ **43.** $\dfrac{9}{9} = 1$ **44.** $\dfrac{40}{8} = 5$ **45.** $\dfrac{72}{8} = 9$ **46.** $\dfrac{3}{3} = 1$

Write the mixed number as an improper fraction.

47. $2\dfrac{1}{3}$ **48.** $4\dfrac{2}{3}$ **49.** $6\dfrac{1}{2}$ **50.** $8\dfrac{2}{3}$ **51.** $6\dfrac{5}{6}$ **52.** $7\dfrac{3}{8}$

53. $9\dfrac{1}{4}$ **54.** $6\dfrac{1}{4}$ **55.** $10\dfrac{1}{2}$ **56.** $15\dfrac{1}{8}$ **57.** $8\dfrac{1}{9}$ **58.** $3\dfrac{5}{12}$

59. $5\dfrac{3}{11}$ **60.** $3\dfrac{7}{9}$ **61.** $2\dfrac{5}{8}$ **62.** $12\dfrac{2}{3}$ **63.** $1\dfrac{5}{8}$ **64.** $5\dfrac{3}{7}$

65. $11\dfrac{1}{9} = \dfrac{100}{9}$ **66.** $12\dfrac{3}{5} = \dfrac{63}{5}$ **67.** $3\dfrac{3}{8} = \dfrac{27}{8}$ **68.** $4\dfrac{5}{9} = \dfrac{41}{9}$ **69.** $6\dfrac{7}{13} = \dfrac{85}{13}$ **70.** $8\dfrac{5}{14}$

APPLYING THE CONCEPTS

71. What fraction of the states in the United States of America have names that begin with the letter M? What fraction of the states have names that begin and end with a vowel?

72. Find the business section of your local newspaper. Choose a stock and record the fluctuations in the stock price for one week. Explain the part that fractions play in reporting the price and change in price of the stock.

73. Explain in your own words the procedure for rewriting a mixed number as an improper fraction.

2.3 Writing Equivalent Fractions

Objective A   *To find equivalent fractions by raising to higher terms* ....

Equal fractions with different denominators are called **equivalent fractions.**

$\frac{4}{6}$ is equivalent to $\frac{2}{3}$.

Remember that the Multiplication Property of One stated that the product of a number and one is the number. This is true for fractions as well as whole numbers. This property can be used to write equivalent fractions.

$$\frac{2}{3} \times 1 = \frac{2}{3} \times \frac{1}{1} = \frac{2 \cdot 1}{3 \cdot 1} = \frac{2}{3}$$

$$\frac{2}{3} \times 1 = \frac{2}{3} \times \boxed{\frac{2}{2}} = \frac{2 \cdot 2}{3 \cdot 2} = \frac{4}{6} \qquad \frac{4}{6} \text{ is equivalent to } \frac{2}{3}.$$

$$\frac{2}{3} \times 1 = \frac{2}{3} \times \boxed{\frac{4}{4}} = \frac{2 \cdot 4}{3 \cdot 4} = \frac{8}{12} \qquad \frac{8}{12} \text{ is equivalent to } \frac{2}{3}.$$

$\frac{2}{3}$ was rewritten as the equivalent fractions $\frac{4}{6}$ and $\frac{8}{12}$.

➡ Write a fraction that is equivalent to $\frac{5}{8}$ and has a denominator of 32.

$$8\overline{)32} \quad {}^{4}$$

$$\frac{5}{8} = \frac{5 \cdot 4}{8 \cdot 4} = \frac{20}{32}$$

- Divide the larger denominator by the smaller.
- Multiply the numerator and denominator of the given fraction by the quotient (4).

$\frac{20}{32}$ is equivalent to $\frac{5}{8}$.

Example 1   Write $\frac{2}{3}$ as an equivalent fraction that has a denominator of 42.

Solution $3\overline{)42}{}^{14} \qquad \frac{2}{3} = \frac{2 \cdot 14}{3 \cdot 14} = \frac{28}{42}$

$\frac{28}{42}$ is equivalent to $\frac{2}{3}$.

You Try It 1   Write $\frac{3}{5}$ as an equivalent fraction that has a denominator of 45.

Your solution $\frac{27}{45}$ ✓

Example 2   Write 4 as a fraction that has a denominator of 12.

Solution   Write 4 as $\frac{4}{1}$.

$1\overline{)12}{}^{12} \qquad 4 = \frac{4 \cdot 12}{1 \cdot 12} = \frac{48}{12}$

$\frac{48}{12}$ is equivalent to 4.

You Try It 2   Write 6 as a fraction that has a denominator of 18.

Your solution $\frac{6}{1} \times \frac{18}{18} = \frac{108}{18}$ ✓

Solutions on p. S4

Objective B **To write a fraction in simplest form** ··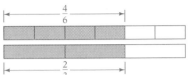

A fraction is in **simplest form** when there are no common factors in the numerator and the denominator.

The fractions $\frac{4}{6}$ and $\frac{2}{3}$ are equivalent fractions.

$\frac{4}{6}$ has been written in simplest form as $\frac{2}{3}$.

The Multiplication Property of One can be used to write fractions in simplest form. Write the numerator and denominator of the given fraction as a product of factors. Write factors common to both the numerator and denominator as an improper fraction equivalent to 1.

$$\frac{4}{6} = \frac{2 \cdot 2}{2 \cdot 3} = \boxed{\frac{2}{2}} \cdot \frac{2}{3} = 1 \cdot \frac{2}{3} = \frac{2}{3}$$

The process of eliminating common factors is displayed with slashes through the common factors as shown at the right.

$$\frac{4}{6} = \frac{\overset{1}{\cancel{2}} \cdot 2}{\underset{1}{\cancel{2}} \cdot 3} = \frac{2}{3}$$

To write a fraction in simplest form, eliminate the common factors.

$$\frac{18}{30} = \frac{\overset{1}{\cancel{2}} \cdot \overset{1}{\cancel{3}} \cdot 3}{\underset{1}{\cancel{2}} \cdot \underset{1}{\cancel{3}} \cdot 5} = \frac{3}{5}$$

An improper fraction can be changed to a mixed number.

$$\frac{22}{6} = \frac{\overset{1}{\cancel{2}} \cdot 11}{\underset{1}{\cancel{2}} \cdot 3} = \frac{11}{3} = 3\frac{2}{3}$$

Example 3 Write $\frac{15}{40}$ in simplest form.

Solution $\dfrac{15}{40} = \dfrac{3 \cdot \overset{1}{\cancel{5}}}{2 \cdot 2 \cdot 2 \cdot \underset{1}{\cancel{5}}} = \dfrac{3}{8}$

You Try It 3 Write $\frac{16}{24}$ in simplest form.

Your solution

Example 4 Write $\frac{6}{42}$ in simplest form.

Solution $\dfrac{6}{42} = \dfrac{\overset{1}{\cancel{2}} \cdot \overset{1}{\cancel{3}}}{\underset{1}{\cancel{2}} \cdot \underset{1}{\cancel{3}} \cdot 7} = \dfrac{1}{7}$

You Try It 4 Write $\frac{8}{56}$ in simplest form.

Your solution

Example 5 Write $\frac{8}{9}$ in simplest form.

Solution $\dfrac{8}{9} = \dfrac{2 \cdot 2 \cdot 2}{3 \cdot 3} = \dfrac{8}{9}$

$\frac{8}{9}$ is already in simplest form because there are no common factors in the numerator and denominator.

You Try It 5 Write $\frac{15}{32}$ in simplest form.

Your solution

Example 6 Write $\frac{30}{12}$ in simplest form.

Solution $\dfrac{30}{12} = \dfrac{\overset{1}{\cancel{2}} \cdot \overset{1}{\cancel{3}} \cdot 5}{\underset{1}{\cancel{2}} \cdot 2 \cdot \underset{1}{\cancel{3}}} = \dfrac{5}{2} = 2\frac{1}{2}$

You Try It 6 Write $\frac{48}{36}$ in simplest form.

Your solution

Solutions on p. S4

2.3 Exercises

Objective A

Write an equivalent fraction with the given denominator.

1. $\dfrac{1}{2} = \dfrac{5}{10}$ 　　 **2.** $\dfrac{1}{4} = \dfrac{4}{16}$ 　　 **3.** $\dfrac{3}{16} = \dfrac{9}{48}$ 　　 **4.** $\dfrac{5}{9} = \dfrac{45}{81}$ 　　 **5.** $\dfrac{3}{8} = \dfrac{12}{32}$

6. $\dfrac{7}{11} = \dfrac{21}{33}$ 　　 **7.** $\dfrac{3}{17} = \dfrac{9}{51}$ 　　 **8.** $\dfrac{7}{10} = \dfrac{63}{90}$ 　　 **9.** $\dfrac{3}{4} = \dfrac{}{16}$ 　　 **10.** $\dfrac{5}{8} = \dfrac{20}{32}$

11. $3 = \dfrac{27}{9}$ 　　 **12.** $5 = \dfrac{125}{25}$ 　　 **13.** $\dfrac{1}{3} = \dfrac{20}{60}$ 　　 **14.** $\dfrac{1}{16} = \dfrac{3}{48}$ 　　 **15.** $\dfrac{11}{15} = \dfrac{44}{60}$

16. $\dfrac{3}{50} = \dfrac{18}{300}$ 　　 **17.** $\dfrac{2}{3} = \dfrac{12}{18}$ 　　 **18.** $\dfrac{5}{9} = \dfrac{20}{36}$ 　　 **19.** $\dfrac{5}{7} = \dfrac{35}{49}$ 　　 **20.** $\dfrac{7}{8} = \dfrac{28}{32}$

21. $\dfrac{5}{9} = \dfrac{10}{18}$ 　　 **22.** $\dfrac{11}{12} = \dfrac{33}{36}$ 　　 **23.** $7 = \dfrac{21}{3}$ 　　 **24.** $9 = \dfrac{36}{4}$ 　　 **25.** $\dfrac{7}{9} = \dfrac{35}{45}$

26. $\dfrac{5}{6} = \dfrac{35}{42}$ 　　 **27.** $\dfrac{15}{16} = \dfrac{60}{64}$ 　　 **28.** $\dfrac{11}{18} = \dfrac{33}{54}$ 　　 **29.** $\dfrac{3}{14} = \dfrac{21}{98}$ 　　 **30.** $\dfrac{5}{6} = \dfrac{120}{144}$

31. $\dfrac{5}{8} = \dfrac{30}{48}$ 　　 **32.** $\dfrac{7}{12} = \dfrac{56}{96}$ 　　 **33.** $\dfrac{5}{14} = \dfrac{15}{42}$ 　　 **34.** $\dfrac{2}{3} = \dfrac{28}{42}$ 　　 **35.** $\dfrac{17}{24} = \dfrac{102}{144}$

36. $\dfrac{5}{13} = \dfrac{65}{169}$ 　　 **37.** $\dfrac{3}{8} = \dfrac{153}{408}$ 　　 **38.** $\dfrac{9}{16} = \dfrac{153}{272}$ 　　 **39.** $\dfrac{17}{40} = \dfrac{340}{800}$ 　　 **40.** $\dfrac{9}{25} = \dfrac{360}{1000}$

Objective B

Write the fraction in simplest form.

41. $\dfrac{4}{12} = \dfrac{1}{3}$ 　　 **42.** $\dfrac{8}{22} = \dfrac{4}{11}$ 　　 **43.** $\dfrac{22}{44} = \dfrac{2}{4} = \dfrac{1}{2}$ 　　 **44.** $\dfrac{2}{14} = \dfrac{1}{7}$ 　　 **45.** $\dfrac{2}{12} = \dfrac{1}{6}$

46. $\dfrac{50}{75}$

47. $\dfrac{40}{36}$

48. $\dfrac{12}{8}$

49. $\dfrac{0}{30}$

50. $\dfrac{10}{10}$

51. $\dfrac{9}{22}$

52. $\dfrac{14}{35}$

53. $\dfrac{75}{25}$

54. $\dfrac{8}{60}$

55. $\dfrac{16}{84}$

56. $\dfrac{20}{44}$

57. $\dfrac{12}{35}$

58. $\dfrac{8}{36}$

59. $\dfrac{28}{44}$

60. $\dfrac{12}{16}$

61. $\dfrac{16}{12}$

62. $\dfrac{24}{18}$

63. $\dfrac{24}{40}$

64. $\dfrac{44}{60}$

65. $\dfrac{8}{88}$

66. $\dfrac{9}{90}$

67. $\dfrac{144}{36}$

68. $\dfrac{140}{297}$

69. $\dfrac{48}{144}$

70. $\dfrac{32}{120}$

71. $\dfrac{60}{100}$

72. $\dfrac{33}{110}$

73. $\dfrac{36}{16}$

74. $\dfrac{80}{45}$

75. $\dfrac{32}{160}$

APPLYING THE CONCEPTS

76. Make a list of five different fractions that are equivalent to $\dfrac{2}{3}$.

77. Make a list of five different fractions that are equivalent to 3.

78. Show that $\dfrac{15}{24} = \dfrac{5}{8}$ by using a diagram.

79. Explain the procedure for finding equivalent fractions.

80. Explain the procedure for reducing fractions.

2.4 Addition of Fractions and Mixed Numbers

Objective A   *To add fractions with the same denominator* ....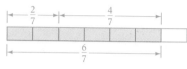

Fractions with the same denominator are added by adding the numerators and placing the sum over the common denominator. After adding, write the sum in simplest form.

➡ Add: $\dfrac{2}{7} + \dfrac{4}{7}$

$$\begin{array}{r} \dfrac{2}{7} \\ +\dfrac{4}{7} \\ \hline \dfrac{6}{7} \end{array}$$

- Add the numerators and place the sum over the common denominator.

$$\dfrac{2}{7} + \dfrac{4}{7} = \dfrac{2+4}{7} = \dfrac{6}{7}$$

Example 1   Add: $\dfrac{5}{12} + \dfrac{11}{12}$

Solution
$$\begin{array}{r} \dfrac{5}{12} \\ +\dfrac{11}{12} \\ \hline \dfrac{16}{12} = \dfrac{4}{3} = 1\dfrac{1}{3} \end{array}$$

You Try It 1   Add: $\dfrac{3}{8} + \dfrac{7}{8}$

Your solution

Solution on p. S4

Objective B   *To add fractions with unlike denominators* ....

To add fractions with unlike denominators, first rewrite the fractions as equivalent fractions with a common denominator. The common denominator is the LCM of the denominators of the fractions.

➡ Find the total of $\dfrac{1}{2}$ and $\dfrac{1}{3}$.

The common denominator is the LCM of 2 and 3. LCM = 6. The LCM of denominators is sometimes called the **least common denominator** (LCD).

Write equivalent fractions using the LCM.
$$\dfrac{1}{2} = \dfrac{3}{6}$$
$$+\dfrac{1}{3} = \dfrac{2}{6}$$

Add the fractions.
$$\begin{array}{r} \dfrac{1}{2} = \dfrac{3}{6} \\ +\dfrac{1}{3} = \dfrac{2}{6} \\ \hline \dfrac{5}{6} \end{array}$$

Example 2 Find $\frac{7}{12}$ more than $\frac{3}{8}$.

Solution
$$\frac{3}{8} = \frac{9}{24}$$
$$+\frac{7}{12} = \frac{14}{24}$$
$$\frac{23}{24}$$

• The LCM of 8 and 12 is 24.

You Try It 2 Find the sum of $\frac{5}{12}$ and $\frac{9}{16}$.

Your solution

Example 3 Add: $\frac{5}{8} + \frac{7}{9}$

Solution
$$\frac{5}{8} = \frac{45}{72}$$
$$+\frac{7}{9} = \frac{56}{72}$$
$$\frac{101}{72} = 1\frac{29}{72}$$

• The LCM of 8 and 9 is 72.

You Try It 3 Add: $\frac{7}{8} + \frac{11}{15}$

Your solution

Example 4 Add: $\frac{2}{3} + \frac{3}{5} + \frac{5}{6}$

Solution
$$\frac{2}{3} = \frac{20}{30}$$
$$\frac{3}{5} = \frac{18}{30}$$
$$+\frac{5}{6} = \frac{25}{30}$$
$$\frac{63}{30} = 2\frac{3}{30} = 2\frac{1}{10}$$

• The LCM of 3, 5, and 6 is 30.

You Try It 4 Add: $\frac{3}{4} + \frac{4}{5} + \frac{5}{8}$

Your solution

Solutions on pp. S4–S5

Objective C *To add whole numbers, mixed numbers, and fractions* ....

The sum of a whole number and a fraction is a mixed number.

➡ Add: $2 + \frac{2}{3}$

$$\boxed{2} + \frac{2}{3} = \boxed{\frac{6}{3}} + \frac{2}{3} = \frac{8}{3} = 2\frac{2}{3}$$

To add a whole number and a mixed number, write the fraction, then add the whole numbers.

➡ Add: $7\frac{2}{5} + 4$

Write the fraction.

$$7\frac{2}{5}$$
$$+ 4$$
$$\overline{\frac{2}{5}}$$

Add the whole numbers.

$$7\frac{2}{5}$$
$$+ 4$$
$$\overline{11\frac{2}{5}}$$

To add two mixed numbers, add the fractional parts and then add the whole numbers. Remember to reduce the sum to simplest form.

⇒ What is $6\frac{14}{15}$ added to $5\frac{4}{9}$?

The LCM of 9 and 15 is 45.

Add the fractional parts.

$$5\frac{4}{9} = 5\frac{20}{45}$$
$$+\ 6\frac{14}{15} = 6\frac{42}{45}$$
$$\overline{\phantom{+\ 6\frac{14}{15} = }\ \frac{62}{45}}$$

Add the whole numbers.

$$5\frac{4}{9} = 5\frac{20}{45}$$
$$+\ 6\frac{14}{15} = 6\frac{42}{45}$$
$$\overline{\phantom{+\ 6\frac{14}{15} = }\ 11\frac{62}{45} = 11 + 1\frac{17}{45} = 12\frac{17}{45}}$$

Example 5   Add: $5 + \frac{3}{8}$

Solution $5 + \frac{3}{8} = 5\frac{3}{8}$

You Try It 5   What is 7 added to $\frac{6}{11}$?

Your solution

Example 6   Find 17 increased by $3\frac{3}{8}$.

Solution
$$17$$
$$+\ 3\frac{3}{8}$$
$$\overline{20\frac{3}{8}}$$

You Try It 6   Find the sum of 29 and $17\frac{5}{12}$.

Your solution

Example 7   Add: $5\frac{2}{3} + 11\frac{5}{6} + 12\frac{7}{9}$

Solution
$$5\frac{2}{3} = 5\frac{12}{18} \quad \bullet \text{ LCM} = 18.$$
$$11\frac{5}{6} = 11\frac{15}{18}$$
$$+\ 12\frac{7}{9} = 12\frac{14}{18}$$
$$\overline{\phantom{+\ 12\frac{7}{9} = }\ 28\frac{41}{18} = 30\frac{5}{18}}$$

You Try It 7   Add: $7\frac{4}{5} + 6\frac{7}{10} + 13\frac{11}{15}$

Your solution

Example 8   Add: $11\frac{5}{8} + 7\frac{5}{9} + 8\frac{7}{15}$

Solution
$$11\frac{5}{8} = 11\frac{225}{360} \quad \bullet \text{ LCM} = 360.$$
$$7\frac{5}{9} = 7\frac{200}{360}$$
$$+\ 8\frac{7}{15} = 8\frac{168}{360}$$
$$\overline{\phantom{+\ 8\frac{7}{15} = }\ 26\frac{593}{360} = 27\frac{233}{360}}$$

You Try It 8   Add: $9\frac{3}{8} + 17\frac{7}{12} + 10\frac{14}{15}$

Your solution

Solutions on p. S5

Objective D   To solve application problems ....

Example 9

A rain gauge collected $2\frac{1}{3}$ inches of rain in October, $5\frac{1}{2}$ inches in November, and $3\frac{3}{8}$ inches in December. Find the total rainfall for the 3 months.

Strategy

To find the total rainfall for the 3 months, add the 3 amounts of rainfall $\left(2\frac{1}{3}, 5\frac{1}{2}, \text{ and } 3\frac{3}{8}\right)$.

Solution

$$2\frac{1}{3} = 2\frac{8}{24}$$
$$5\frac{1}{2} = 5\frac{12}{24}$$
$$+\, 3\frac{3}{8} = 3\frac{9}{24}$$
$$\overline{\qquad\qquad\qquad}$$
$$10\frac{29}{24} = 11\frac{5}{24}$$

The total rainfall for the 3 months was $11\frac{5}{24}$ inches.

You Try It 9

On Monday, you spent $4\frac{1}{2}$ hours in class, $3\frac{3}{4}$ hours studying, and $1\frac{1}{3}$ hours driving. Find the number of hours spent on these three activities.

Your strategy

Your solution

Example 10

Barbara Walsh worked 4 hours, $2\frac{1}{3}$ hours, and $5\frac{2}{3}$ hours this week on a part-time job. Barbara is paid $6 an hour. How much did she earn this week?

Strategy

To find how much Barbara earned:
- Find the total number of hours worked.
- Multiply the total number of hours worked by the hourly wage ($6).

Solution

$$
\begin{array}{ll}
4 & \quad 12 \\
2\frac{1}{3} & \quad \times\ \$6 \\
+\,5\frac{2}{3} & \quad \overline{\ \$72\ } \\
\overline{\qquad\quad} & \\
11\frac{3}{3} = 12 \text{ hours worked} &
\end{array}
$$

Barbara earned $72 this week.

You Try It 10

Jeff Sapone, a carpenter, worked $1\frac{2}{3}$ hours of overtime on Monday, $3\frac{1}{3}$ hours of overtime on Tuesday, and 2 hours of overtime on Wednesday. At an overtime hourly rate of $24, find Jeff's overtime pay for these 3 days.

Your strategy

Your solution

Solutions on p. S5

2.4 Exercises

Objective A

Add.

1. $\dfrac{2}{7} + \dfrac{1}{7}$

2. $\dfrac{3}{11} + \dfrac{5}{11}$

3. $\dfrac{1}{2} + \dfrac{1}{2}$

4. $\dfrac{1}{3} + \dfrac{2}{3}$

5. $\dfrac{8}{11} + \dfrac{7}{11}$

6. $\dfrac{9}{13} + \dfrac{7}{13}$

7. $\dfrac{8}{5} + \dfrac{9}{5}$

8. $\dfrac{5}{3} + \dfrac{7}{3}$

9. $\dfrac{3}{5} + \dfrac{8}{5} + \dfrac{3}{5}$

10. $\dfrac{3}{8} + \dfrac{5}{8} + \dfrac{7}{8}$

11. $\dfrac{3}{4} + \dfrac{1}{4} + \dfrac{5}{4}$

12. $\dfrac{2}{7} + \dfrac{4}{7} + \dfrac{5}{7}$

13. $\dfrac{3}{8} + \dfrac{7}{8} + \dfrac{1}{8}$

14. $\dfrac{5}{12} + \dfrac{7}{12} + \dfrac{1}{12}$

15. $\dfrac{4}{15} + \dfrac{7}{15} + \dfrac{11}{15}$

16. $\dfrac{3}{4} + \dfrac{3}{4} + \dfrac{1}{4}$

17. $\dfrac{3}{16} + \dfrac{5}{16} + \dfrac{7}{16}$

18. $\dfrac{5}{18} + \dfrac{11}{18} + \dfrac{17}{18}$

19. $\dfrac{3}{11} + \dfrac{5}{11} + \dfrac{7}{11}$

20. $\dfrac{5}{7} + \dfrac{4}{7} + \dfrac{5}{7}$

21. Find the sum of $\dfrac{4}{9}$ and $\dfrac{5}{9}$.

22. Find the sum of $\dfrac{5}{12}$, $\dfrac{1}{12}$, and $\dfrac{11}{12}$.

23. Find the total of $\dfrac{5}{8}$, $\dfrac{3}{8}$, and $\dfrac{7}{8}$.

24. Find the total of $\dfrac{4}{13}$, $\dfrac{7}{13}$, and $\dfrac{11}{13}$.

Objective B

Add.

25. $\dfrac{1}{2} + \dfrac{2}{3}$

26. $\dfrac{2}{3} + \dfrac{1}{4}$

27. $\dfrac{3}{14} + \dfrac{5}{7}$

28. $\dfrac{3}{5} + \dfrac{7}{10}$

29. $\dfrac{8}{15} + \dfrac{7}{20}$

30. $\dfrac{1}{6} + \dfrac{7}{9}$

31. $\dfrac{3}{8} + \dfrac{9}{14}$

32. $\dfrac{5}{12} + \dfrac{5}{16}$

33. $\dfrac{3}{20} + \dfrac{7}{30}$

34. $\dfrac{5}{12} + \dfrac{7}{30}$

35. $\dfrac{2}{3} + \dfrac{6}{19}$

36. $\dfrac{1}{2} + \dfrac{3}{29}$

37. $\dfrac{1}{3} + \dfrac{5}{6} + \dfrac{7}{9}$

38. $\dfrac{2}{3} + \dfrac{5}{6} + \dfrac{7}{12}$

39. $\dfrac{5}{6} + \dfrac{1}{12} + \dfrac{5}{16}$

40. $\dfrac{2}{9} + \dfrac{7}{15} + \dfrac{4}{21}$

41. $\dfrac{2}{3} + \dfrac{1}{5} + \dfrac{7}{12}$

42. $\dfrac{3}{4} + \dfrac{4}{5} + \dfrac{7}{12}$

43. $\dfrac{1}{4} + \dfrac{4}{5} + \dfrac{5}{9}$

44. $\dfrac{2}{3} + \dfrac{3}{5} + \dfrac{7}{8}$

45. $\dfrac{5}{16} + \dfrac{11}{18} + \dfrac{17}{24}$

46. $\dfrac{3}{10} + \dfrac{14}{15} + \dfrac{9}{25}$

47. $\dfrac{2}{3} + \dfrac{5}{8} + \dfrac{7}{9}$

48. $\dfrac{1}{3} + \dfrac{2}{9} + \dfrac{7}{8}$

49. What is $\dfrac{3}{8}$ added to $\dfrac{3}{5}$?

50. What is $\dfrac{5}{9}$ added to $\dfrac{7}{12}$?

51. Find the sum of $\dfrac{3}{8}$, $\dfrac{5}{6}$, and $\dfrac{7}{12}$.

52. Find the sum of $\dfrac{11}{12}$, $\dfrac{13}{24}$, and $\dfrac{4}{15}$.

53. Find the total of $\dfrac{1}{2}$, $\dfrac{5}{8}$, and $\dfrac{7}{9}$.

54. Find the total of $\dfrac{5}{14}$, $\dfrac{3}{7}$, and $\dfrac{5}{21}$.

Objective C

Add.

55. $\begin{aligned} & 1\dfrac{1}{2} \\ + & 2\dfrac{1}{6} \\ \hline \end{aligned}$

56. $\begin{aligned} & 2\dfrac{2}{5} \\ + & 3\dfrac{3}{10} \\ \hline \end{aligned}$

57. $\begin{aligned} & 4\dfrac{1}{2} \\ + & 5\dfrac{7}{12} \\ \hline \end{aligned}$

58. $\begin{aligned} & 3\dfrac{3}{8} \\ + & 2\dfrac{5}{16} \\ \hline \end{aligned}$

59. $\begin{aligned} & 4 \\ + & 5\dfrac{2}{7} \\ \hline \end{aligned}$

60. $\begin{aligned} & 6\dfrac{8}{9} \\ + & 12 \\ \hline \end{aligned}$

61. $\begin{aligned} & 3\dfrac{5}{8} \\ + & 2\dfrac{11}{20} \\ \hline \end{aligned}$

62. $\begin{aligned} & 4\dfrac{5}{12} \\ + & 6\dfrac{11}{18} \\ \hline \end{aligned}$

63. $7\dfrac{5}{12} + 2\dfrac{9}{16}$

64. $9\dfrac{1}{2} + 3\dfrac{3}{11}$

65. $6\dfrac{1}{3} + 2\dfrac{3}{13}$

66. $8\dfrac{21}{40} + 6\dfrac{21}{32}$

67. $8\dfrac{29}{30} + 7\dfrac{11}{40}$

68. $17\dfrac{5}{16} + 3\dfrac{11}{24}$

69. $17\dfrac{3}{8} + 7\dfrac{7}{20}$

70. $14\dfrac{7}{12} + 29\dfrac{13}{21}$

71. $5\dfrac{7}{8} + 27\dfrac{5}{12}$

72. $7\dfrac{5}{6} + 3\dfrac{5}{9}$

73. $7\dfrac{5}{9} + 2\dfrac{7}{12}$

74. $3\dfrac{1}{2} + 2\dfrac{3}{4} + 1\dfrac{5}{6}$

75. $2\dfrac{1}{2} + 3\dfrac{2}{3} + 4\dfrac{1}{4}$

76. $3\dfrac{1}{3} + 7\dfrac{1}{5} + 2\dfrac{1}{7}$

77. $3\dfrac{1}{2} + 3\dfrac{1}{5} + 8\dfrac{1}{9}$

78. $6\dfrac{5}{9} + 6\dfrac{5}{12} + 2\dfrac{5}{18}$

79. $2\dfrac{3}{8} + 4\dfrac{7}{12} + 3\dfrac{5}{16}$

80. $2\dfrac{1}{8} + 4\dfrac{2}{9} + 5\dfrac{17}{18}$

81. $6\dfrac{5}{6} + 17\dfrac{2}{9} + 18\dfrac{5}{27}$

82. $4\dfrac{7}{20} + \dfrac{17}{80} + 25\dfrac{23}{60}$

83. Find the sum of $2\dfrac{4}{9}$ and $5\dfrac{7}{12}$.

84. Find $5\dfrac{5}{6}$ more than $3\dfrac{3}{8}$.

85. What is $4\dfrac{3}{4}$ added to $9\dfrac{1}{3}$?

86. What is $4\dfrac{8}{9}$ added to $9\dfrac{1}{6}$?

87. Find the total of $2\dfrac{2}{3}$, $4\dfrac{5}{8}$, and $2\dfrac{2}{9}$.

88. Find the total of $1\dfrac{5}{8}$, $3\dfrac{5}{6}$, and $7\dfrac{7}{24}$.

Objective D *Application Problems*

89. A family with an income of \$38,000 spends $\dfrac{1}{3}$ of its income on housing, $\dfrac{1}{8}$ on transportation, and $\dfrac{1}{4}$ on food. Find the total fractional amount of the family's income that is spent on these three items.

90. A table 30 inches high has a top that is $1\dfrac{1}{8}$ inches thick. Find the total thickness of the table top after a $\dfrac{3}{16}$-inch veneer is applied.

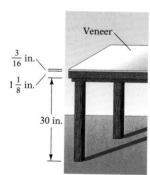

91. On June 24, 1997, the price of one share of BrMySq stock was \$76$\dfrac{3}{8}$. On June 25, 1997, the stock increased in value by \$8$\dfrac{3}{8}$ per share. Find the value of one share of the stock after this increase.

92. Find the length of the shaft.

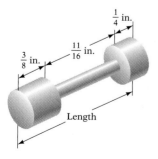

93. Find the length of the shaft.

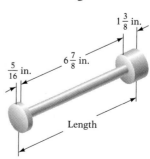

94. You are working a part-time job that pays $7 an hour. You worked 5, $3\frac{3}{4}$, $2\frac{1}{3}$, $1\frac{1}{4}$, and $7\frac{2}{3}$ hours during the last five days.
    a. Find the total number of hours you worked during the last five days.
    b. Find your total wages for the five days.

95. Fred Thomson, a nurse, worked $2\frac{2}{3}$ hours of overtime on Monday, $1\frac{1}{4}$ hours on Wednesday, $1\frac{1}{3}$ hours on Friday, and $6\frac{3}{4}$ hours on Saturday.
    a. Find the total number of overtime hours worked during the week.

    b. At an overtime hourly wage of $22 per hour, how much overtime pay does Fred receive?

96. Mt. Baldy had $5\frac{3}{4}$ inches of snow in December, $15\frac{1}{2}$ inches in January, and $9\frac{5}{8}$ inches in February. Find the total snowfall for the three months.

97. Alan bought 200 shares of a utility stock for $26\frac{3}{16}$ per share. The monthly gains for the next three months were $1\frac{1}{2}$, $\frac{5}{16}$, and $2\frac{5}{8}$ per share. Find the value of the stock at the end of the three months.

APPLYING THE CONCEPTS

98. What is a unit fraction? Find the sum of the three largest unit fractions. Is there a smallest unit fraction? If so, write it down. If not, explain why.

99. Use a model to illustrate and explain the addition of fractions with unlike denominators.

100. A survey was conducted to determine people's favorite color from among blue, green, red, purple, or other. The surveyor claims that $\frac{1}{3}$ of the people responded blue, $\frac{1}{6}$ responded green, $\frac{1}{8}$ responded red, $\frac{1}{12}$ responded purple, and $\frac{2}{5}$ responded some other color. Is this possible? Explain your answer.

101. The following are the average portions of each day that a person spends for each activity: sleeping, $\frac{1}{3}$; working, $\frac{1}{3}$; personal hygiene, $\frac{1}{24}$; eating, $\frac{1}{8}$; rest and relaxation, $\frac{1}{12}$. Do these five activities account for an entire day? Explain your answer.

2.5 Subtraction of Fractions and Mixed Numbers

Objective A *To subtract fractions with the same denominator* ....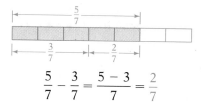

Fractions with the same denominator are subtracted by subtracting the numerators and placing the difference over the common denominator. After subtracting, write the fraction in simplest form.

➡ Subtract: $\dfrac{5}{7} - \dfrac{3}{7}$

$$\begin{array}{r} \dfrac{5}{7} \\ -\dfrac{3}{7} \\ \hline \dfrac{2}{7} \end{array}$$

• Subtract the numerators and place the difference over the common denominator

$$\frac{5}{7} - \frac{3}{7} = \frac{5-3}{7} = \frac{2}{7}$$

Example 1 Find $\dfrac{17}{30}$ less $\dfrac{11}{30}$.

Solution
$$\begin{array}{r} \dfrac{17}{30} \\ -\dfrac{11}{30} \\ \hline \dfrac{6}{30} = \dfrac{1}{5} \end{array}$$

You Try It 1 Subtract: $\dfrac{16}{27} - \dfrac{7}{27}$

Your solution

Solution on p. S5

Objective B *To subtract fractions with unlike denominators* ....

To subtract fractions with unlike denominators, first rewrite the fractions as equivalent fractions with a common denominator. As with adding fractions, the common denominator is the LCM of the denominators of the fractions.

➡ Subtract: $\dfrac{5}{6} - \dfrac{1}{4}$

The common denominator is the LCM of 6 and 4. LCM = 12.

Build equivalent fractions using the LCM.

$$\begin{array}{r} \dfrac{5}{6} = \dfrac{10}{12} \\ -\dfrac{1}{4} = \dfrac{3}{12} \\ \hline \end{array}$$

Subtract the fractions.

$$\begin{array}{r} \dfrac{5}{6} = \dfrac{10}{12} \\ -\dfrac{1}{4} = \dfrac{3}{12} \\ \hline \dfrac{7}{12} \end{array}$$

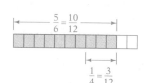

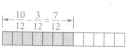

Example 2 Subtract: $\dfrac{11}{16} - \dfrac{5}{12}$

Solution

$$\dfrac{11}{16} = \dfrac{33}{48}$$

• LCM = 48

$$-\dfrac{5}{12} = \dfrac{20}{48}$$
$$\dfrac{13}{48}$$

You Try It 2 Subtract: $\dfrac{13}{18} - \dfrac{7}{24}$

Your solution

Solution on p. S5

Objective C   **To subtract whole numbers, mixed numbers, and fractions** ......

To subtract mixed numbers without borrowing, subtract the fractional parts and then subtract the whole numbers.

➡ Subtract: $5\dfrac{5}{6} - 2\dfrac{3}{4}$

Subtract the fractional parts.

$$5\dfrac{5}{6} = 5\dfrac{10}{12}$$

• The LCM of 6 and 4 is 12.

$$-2\dfrac{3}{4} = 2\dfrac{9}{12}$$
$$\dfrac{1}{12}$$

Subtract the whole numbers.

$$5\dfrac{5}{6} = 5\dfrac{10}{12}$$
$$-2\dfrac{3}{4} = 2\dfrac{9}{12}$$
$$3\dfrac{1}{12}$$

Subtraction of mixed numbers sometimes involves borrowing.

➡ Subtract: $5 - 2\dfrac{5}{8}$

Borrow 1 from 5.

$$5 \;\; = \overset{4}{\cancel{5}}\,1$$
$$-2\dfrac{5}{8} = 2\dfrac{5}{8}$$

Write 1 as a fraction so that the fractions have the same denominators.

$$5 \;\; = 4\dfrac{8}{8}$$
$$-2\dfrac{5}{8} = 2\dfrac{5}{8}$$

Subtract the mixed numbers.

$$5 \;\; = 4\dfrac{8}{8}$$
$$-2\dfrac{5}{8} = 2\dfrac{5}{8}$$
$$2\dfrac{3}{8}$$

➡ Subtract: $7\dfrac{1}{6} - 2\dfrac{5}{8}$

Write equivalent fractions using the LCM.

$$7\dfrac{1}{6} = 7\dfrac{4}{24}$$
$$-2\dfrac{5}{8} = 2\dfrac{15}{24}$$

Borrow 1 from 7. Add the 1 to $\dfrac{4}{24}$. Write $1\dfrac{4}{24}$ as $\dfrac{28}{24}$.

$$7\dfrac{1}{6} = \overset{6}{7}1\dfrac{4}{24} = 6\dfrac{28}{24}$$
$$-2\dfrac{5}{8} = \;\; 2\dfrac{15}{24} = 2\dfrac{15}{24}$$

Subtract the mixed numbers.

$$7\dfrac{1}{6} = 6\dfrac{28}{24}$$
$$-2\dfrac{5}{8} = 2\dfrac{15}{24}$$
$$4\dfrac{13}{24}$$

Example 3   Subtract: $15\frac{7}{8} - 12\frac{2}{3}$

Solution

$$15\frac{7}{8} = 15\frac{21}{24}$$ LCM = 24.

$$-\ 12\frac{2}{3} = 12\frac{16}{24}$$

$$\overline{\qquad\qquad 3\frac{5}{24}}$$

You Try It 3   Subtract: $17\frac{5}{9} - 11\frac{5}{12}$

Your solution

Example 4   Subtract: $9 - 4\frac{3}{11}$

Solution

$$9\ \ = 8\frac{11}{11}$$ LCM = 11.

$$-\ 4\frac{3}{11} = 4\frac{3}{11}$$

$$\overline{\qquad\qquad 4\frac{8}{11}}$$

You Try It 4   Subtract: $8 - 2\frac{4}{13}$

Your solution

Example 5   Find $11\frac{5}{12}$ decreased by $2\frac{11}{16}$.

Solution

$$11\frac{5}{12} = 11\frac{20}{48} = 10\frac{68}{48}$$ LCM = 48.

$$-\ 2\frac{11}{16} =\ \ 2\frac{33}{48} =\ \ 2\frac{33}{48}$$

$$\overline{\qquad\qquad\qquad\qquad 8\frac{35}{48}}$$

You Try It 5   What is $21\frac{7}{9}$ minus $7\frac{11}{12}$?

Your solution

Solutions on p. S5

Objective D   To solve application problems ....

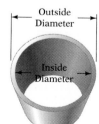

Find the inside diameter of a bushing with an outside diameter of $3\frac{3}{8}$ inches and a wall thickness of $\frac{1}{4}$ inches.

$$\begin{array}{r} \frac{1}{4} \\ +\ \frac{1}{4} \\ \hline \frac{2}{4} = \frac{1}{2} \end{array}$$

• Add $\frac{1}{4}$ to $\frac{1}{4}$ to find the total thickness of the two walls.

$$\begin{array}{r} 3\frac{3}{8} = 3\frac{3}{8} = 2\frac{11}{8} \\ -\ \frac{1}{2} =\ \frac{4}{8} =\ \ \frac{4}{8} \\ \hline 2\frac{7}{8} \end{array}$$

• Subtract the total thickness of the two walls to find the inside diameter.

The inside diameter of the bushing is $2\frac{7}{8}$ inches.

Example 6

A $2\frac{2}{3}$-inch piece is cut from a $6\frac{5}{8}$-inch board. How much of the board is left?

Strategy

To find the length remaining, subtract the length of the piece cut from the total length of the board.

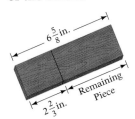

Solution

$$6\frac{5}{8} = 6\frac{15}{24} = 5\frac{39}{24}$$
$$-\,2\frac{2}{3} = 2\frac{16}{24} = 2\frac{16}{24}$$
$$\overline{\phantom{-\,2\frac{2}{3} = 2\frac{16}{24} = 2}\,3\frac{23}{24}}$$

$3\frac{23}{24}$ inches of the board are left.

Example 7

Two painters are staining a house. In 1 day one painter stained $\frac{1}{3}$ of the house, and the other stained $\frac{1}{4}$ of the house. How much of the job remains to be done?

Strategy

To find how much of the job remains:
- Find the total amount of the house already stained $\left(\frac{1}{3} + \frac{1}{4}\right)$.
- Subtract the amount already stained from 1, which represents the complete job.

Solution

$$\frac{1}{3} = \frac{4}{12} \qquad\qquad 1 = \frac{12}{12}$$
$$+\,\frac{1}{4} = \frac{3}{12} \qquad -\,\frac{7}{12} = \frac{7}{12}$$
$$\overline{\phantom{+\,\frac{1}{4} = }\frac{7}{12}} \qquad\qquad \overline{\phantom{-\,\frac{7}{12} = }\frac{5}{12}}$$

$\frac{5}{12}$ of the house remains to be stained.

You Try It 6

A flight from New York to Los Angeles takes $5\frac{1}{2}$ hours. After the plane has been in the air for $2\frac{3}{4}$ hours, how much flight time remains?

Your strategy

Your solution

You Try It 7

A patient is put on a diet to lose 24 pounds in 3 months. The patient lost $7\frac{1}{2}$ pounds the first month and $5\frac{3}{4}$ pounds the second month. How much weight must be lost the third month to achieve the goal?

Your strategy

Your solution

Solutions on p. S6

2.5 Exercises

. . . .

Objective A

Subtract.

1. $\dfrac{9}{17}$
$-\dfrac{7}{17}$

2. $\dfrac{11}{15}$
$-\dfrac{3}{15}$

3. $\dfrac{11}{12}$
$-\dfrac{7}{12}$

4. $\dfrac{13}{15}$
$-\dfrac{4}{15}$

5. $\dfrac{9}{20}$
$-\dfrac{7}{20}$

6. $\dfrac{48}{55}$
$-\dfrac{13}{55}$

7. $\dfrac{42}{65}$
$-\dfrac{17}{65}$

8. $\dfrac{11}{24}$
$-\dfrac{5}{24}$

9. $\dfrac{23}{30}$
$-\dfrac{13}{30}$

10. $\dfrac{17}{42}$
$-\dfrac{5}{42}$

11. What is $\dfrac{5}{14}$ less than $\dfrac{13}{14}$?

12. What is $\dfrac{7}{19}$ less than $\dfrac{17}{19}$?

13. Find the difference between $\dfrac{7}{8}$ and $\dfrac{5}{8}$.

14. Find the difference between $\dfrac{7}{12}$ and $\dfrac{5}{12}$.

15. What is $\dfrac{18}{23}$ minus $\dfrac{9}{23}$?

16. What is $\dfrac{7}{9}$ minus $\dfrac{3}{9}$?

17. Find $\dfrac{17}{24}$ decreased by $\dfrac{11}{24}$.

18. Find $\dfrac{19}{30}$ decreased by $\dfrac{11}{30}$.

Objective B

Subtract.

19. $\dfrac{2}{3}$
$-\dfrac{1}{6}$

20. $\dfrac{7}{8}$
$-\dfrac{5}{16}$

21. $\dfrac{5}{8}$
$-\dfrac{2}{7}$

22. $\dfrac{5}{6}$
$-\dfrac{3}{7}$

23. $\dfrac{5}{7}$
$-\dfrac{3}{14}$

24. $\dfrac{5}{9}$
$-\dfrac{7}{15}$

25. $\dfrac{8}{15}$
$-\dfrac{7}{20}$

26. $\dfrac{7}{9}$
$-\dfrac{1}{6}$

27. $\dfrac{9}{14}$
$-\dfrac{3}{8}$

28. $\dfrac{5}{12}$
$-\dfrac{5}{16}$

Subtract.

29. $\dfrac{46}{51}$
$-\dfrac{3}{17}$

30. $\dfrac{9}{16}$
$-\dfrac{17}{32}$

31. $\dfrac{21}{35}$
$-\dfrac{5}{14}$

32. $\dfrac{19}{40}$
$-\dfrac{3}{16}$

33. $\dfrac{29}{60}$
$-\dfrac{3}{40}$

34. What is $\dfrac{3}{5}$ less than $\dfrac{11}{12}$?

35. What is $\dfrac{5}{9}$ less than $\dfrac{11}{15}$?

36. Find the difference between $\dfrac{11}{24}$ and $\dfrac{7}{18}$.

37. Find the difference between $\dfrac{9}{14}$ and $\dfrac{5}{42}$.

38. Find $\dfrac{11}{12}$ decreased by $\dfrac{11}{15}$.

39. Find $\dfrac{17}{20}$ decreased by $\dfrac{7}{15}$.

40. What is $\dfrac{13}{20}$ minus $\dfrac{1}{6}$?

41. What is $\dfrac{5}{6}$ minus $\dfrac{7}{9}$?

Objective C

Subtract.

42. $5\dfrac{7}{12}$
$-2\dfrac{5}{12}$

43. $16\dfrac{11}{15}$
$-11\dfrac{8}{15}$

44. $72\dfrac{21}{23}$
$-16\dfrac{17}{23}$

45. $19\dfrac{16}{17}$
$-\ 9\dfrac{7}{17}$

46. $6\dfrac{1}{3}$
-2

47. $5\dfrac{7}{8}$
-1

48. 10
$-\ 6\dfrac{1}{3}$

49. 3
$-2\dfrac{5}{21}$

50. $6\dfrac{2}{5}$
$-4\dfrac{4}{5}$

51. $16\dfrac{3}{8}$
$-10\dfrac{7}{8}$

52. $25\dfrac{4}{9}$
$-16\dfrac{7}{9}$

53. $8\dfrac{3}{7}$
$-2\dfrac{6}{7}$

54. $16\dfrac{2}{5}$
$-\ 8\dfrac{4}{9}$

55. $23\dfrac{7}{8}$
$-16\dfrac{2}{3}$

56. 6
$-4\dfrac{3}{5}$

57. $65\dfrac{8}{35}$
$-16\dfrac{11}{14}$

58. $82\dfrac{4}{33}$
$-16\dfrac{5}{22}$

59. $101\dfrac{2}{9}$
$-\ 16$

60. $77\dfrac{5}{18}$
$-\ 61$

61. 17
$-\ 7\dfrac{8}{13}$

62. What is $5\frac{3}{8}$ less than $8\frac{1}{9}$?

63. What is $7\frac{3}{5}$ less than $23\frac{3}{20}$?

64. Find the difference between $9\frac{2}{7}$ and $3\frac{1}{4}$.

65. Find the difference between $12\frac{3}{8}$ and $7\frac{5}{12}$.

66. What is $10\frac{5}{9}$ minus $5\frac{11}{15}$?

67. Find $6\frac{1}{3}$ decreased by $3\frac{3}{5}$.

Objective D *Application Problems*

68. Find the missing dimension.

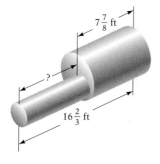

69. Find the missing dimension.

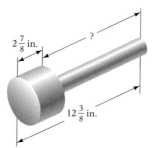

70. The horses in the Kentucky Derby run $1\frac{1}{4}$ miles. In the Belmont Stakes they run $1\frac{1}{2}$ miles, and in the Preakness Stakes they run $1\frac{3}{16}$ miles. How much farther do the horses run in the Kentucky Derby than in the Preakness Stakes? How much farther do they run in the Belmont Stakes than in the Preakness Stakes?

71. In the running high jump in the 1948 Summer Olympic Games, Alice Coachman's distance was $66\frac{1}{8}$ inches. In the same event in the 1972 Summer Olympics, Urika Meyfarth jumped $75\frac{1}{2}$ inches, and in the 1996 Olympic Games, Stefka Kostadinova jumped $80\frac{3}{4}$ inches. Find the difference between Meyfarth's distance and Coachman's distance. Find the difference between Kostadinova's distance and Meyfarth's distance.

72. Two hikers plan a 3-day $27\frac{1}{2}$-mile backpack trip carrying a total of 80 pounds. The hikers plan to travel $7\frac{3}{8}$ miles the first day and $10\frac{1}{3}$ miles the second day.

  a. How many miles do the hikers plan to travel the first two days?

  b. How many miles will be left to travel on the third day?

73. A 12-mile walkathon has three checkpoints. The first is $3\frac{3}{8}$ miles from the starting point. The second checkpoint is $4\frac{1}{3}$ miles from the first.

a. How many miles is it from the starting point to the second checkpoint?

b. How many miles is it from the second checkpoint to the finish line?

74. A patient with high blood pressure who weighs 225 pounds is put on a diet to lose 25 pounds in 3 months. The patient loses $8\frac{3}{4}$ pounds the first month and $11\frac{5}{8}$ pounds the second month. How much weight must be lost the third month for the goal to be achieved?

75. A wrestler is entered in the 172-pound weight class in the conference finals coming up in 3 weeks. The wrestler needs to lose $12\frac{3}{4}$ pounds. The wrestler loses $5\frac{1}{4}$ pounds the first week and $4\frac{1}{4}$ pounds the second week. **a.** Without doing the calculations, can the wrestler reach his weight class by losing less in the third week than was lost in the second week? **b.** How many pounds must be lost in the third week for the desired weight to be reached?

APPLYING THE CONCEPTS

The figure at the right shows a selected portion of the New York Stock Exchange stock prices. The figure shows the closing prices for the stocks on May 25, 1997, the 52-week high, the 52-week low, and the high and low for the day. Use this figure for Exercises 76 to 78.

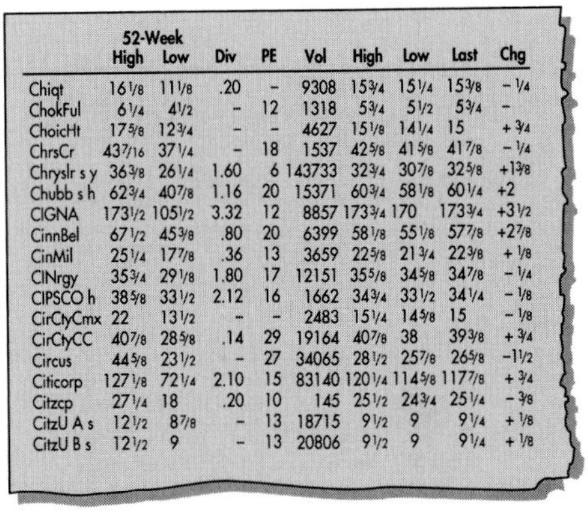

	52-Week High	52-Week Low	Div	PE	Vol	High	Low	Last	Chg
Chiqt	16 1/8	11 1/8	.20	–	9308	15 3/4	15 1/4	15 3/8	– 1/4
ChokFul	6 1/4	4 1/2	–	12	1318	5 3/4	5 1/2	5 3/4	–
ChoicHt	17 5/8	12 3/4	–	–	4627	15 1/8	14 1/4	15	+ 3/4
ChrsCr	43 7/16	37 1/4	–	18	1537	42 5/8	41 5/8	41 7/8	– 1/4
Chryslr s y	36 3/8	26 1/4	1.60	6	143733	32 3/4	30 7/8	32 5/8	+1 3/8
Chubb s h	62 3/4	40 7/8	1.16	20	15371	60 3/4	58 1/8	60 1/4	+2
CIGNA	173 1/2	105 1/2	3.32	12	8857	173 3/4	170	173 3/4	+3 1/2
CinnBel	67 1/2	45 3/8	.80	20	6399	58 1/8	55 1/8	57 7/8	+2 7/8
CinMil	25 1/4	17 7/8	.36	13	3659	22 5/8	21 3/4	22 3/8	+ 1/8
ClNrgy	35 3/4	29 1/8	1.80	17	12151	35 5/8	34 5/8	34 7/8	– 1/4
CIPSCO h	38 5/8	33 1/2	2.12	16	1662	34 3/4	33 1/2	34 1/4	– 1/8
CirCtyCmx	22	13 1/2	–	–	2483	15 1/4	14 5/8	15	– 1/8
CirCtyCC	40 7/8	28 5/8	.14	29	19164	40 7/8	38	39 3/8	+ 3/4
Circus	44 5/8	23 1/2	–	27	34065	28 1/2	25 7/8	26 5/8	–1 1/2
Citicorp	127 1/8	72 1/4	2.10	15	83140	120 1/4	114 5/8	117 7/8	+ 3/4
Citzcp	27 1/4	18	.20	10	145	25 1/2	24 3/4	25 1/4	– 3/8
CitzU A s	12 1/2	8 7/8	–	13	18715	9 1/2	9	9 1/4	+ 1/8
CitzU B s	12 1/2	9	–	13	20806	9 1/2	9	9 1/4	+ 1/8

76. Find the price of one share of Circus at the end of the day, May 25.

77. Find the difference between the price of one share of Citicorp stock at the 52-week low price and the price at the end of the May 25 trading day.

78. Find the 52-week difference in the price of one share of ChrsCr Stock.

79. Fill in the square to produce a true statement: $5\frac{1}{3} - \square = 2\frac{1}{2}$.

80. Fill in the square to produce a true statement: $\square - 4\frac{1}{2} = 1\frac{5}{8}$.

81. Fill in the blank squares at the right so that the sum of the numbers along any row, column, or diagonal is the same. The resulting square is called a magic square.

		$\frac{3}{4}$
	$\frac{5}{8}$	
$\frac{1}{2}$		$\frac{7}{8}$

82. If $\frac{4}{15}$ of an electrician's income is spent for housing, what fraction of the electrician's income is not spent for housing?

2.6 Multiplication of Fractions and Mixed Numbers

Objective A *To multiply fractions* ....

The product of two fractions is the product of the numerators over the product of the denominators.

➡ Multiply: $\dfrac{2}{3} \times \dfrac{4}{5}$

$$\frac{2}{3} \times \frac{4}{5} = \frac{2 \cdot 4}{3 \cdot 5} = \frac{8}{15}$$

- • Multiply the numerators.
- • Multiply the denominators.

The product $\dfrac{2}{3} \times \dfrac{4}{5}$ can be read "$\dfrac{2}{3}$ times $\dfrac{4}{5}$" or "$\dfrac{2}{3}$ of $\dfrac{4}{5}$."

Reading the times sign as "of" is useful in application problems.

$\dfrac{4}{5}$ of the bar is shaded.

Shade $\dfrac{2}{3}$ of the $\dfrac{4}{5}$ already shaded.

$\dfrac{8}{15}$ of the bar is then shaded light yellow.

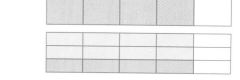

$$\frac{2}{3} \text{ of } \frac{4}{5} = \frac{2}{3} \times \frac{4}{5} = \frac{8}{15}$$

After multiplying two fractions, write the product in simplest form.

➡ Multiply: $\dfrac{3}{4} \times \dfrac{14}{15}$

$$\frac{3}{4} \times \frac{14}{15} = \frac{3 \cdot 14}{4 \cdot 15}$$

- • Multiply the numerators.
- • Multiply the denominators.

$$= \frac{3 \cdot 2 \cdot 7}{2 \cdot 2 \cdot 3 \cdot 5}$$

- • Write the prime factorization of each number.

$$= \frac{\overset{1}{\cancel{3}} \cdot \overset{1}{\cancel{2}} \cdot 7}{\underset{1}{\cancel{2}} \cdot 2 \cdot \underset{1}{\cancel{3}} \cdot 5} = \frac{7}{10}$$

- • Eliminate the common factors. Then multiply the factors of the numerator and denominator.

This example could also be worked by using the GCF.

$$\frac{3}{4} \times \frac{14}{15} = \frac{42}{60}$$

- • Multiply the numerators.
- • Multiply the denominators.

$$= \frac{6 \cdot 7}{6 \cdot 10}$$

- • The GCF of 42 and 60 is 6. Factor 6 from 42 and 60.

$$= \frac{\overset{1}{\cancel{6}} \cdot 7}{\underset{1}{\cancel{6}} \cdot 10} = \frac{7}{10}$$

- • Eliminate the GCF.

Example 1

Multiply $\frac{4}{15}$ and $\frac{5}{28}$.

Solution

$$\frac{4}{15} \times \frac{5}{28} = \frac{4 \cdot 5}{15 \cdot 28} = \frac{\overset{1}{\cancel{2}} \cdot \overset{1}{\cancel{2}} \cdot \overset{1}{\cancel{5}}}{3 \cdot \underset{1}{\cancel{5}} \cdot \underset{1}{\cancel{2}} \cdot \underset{1}{\cancel{2}} \cdot 7} = \frac{1}{21}$$

You Try It 1

Multiply $\frac{4}{21}$ and $\frac{7}{44}$.

Your solution

Example 2

Find the product of $\frac{9}{20}$ and $\frac{33}{35}$.

Solution

$$\frac{9}{20} \times \frac{33}{35} = \frac{9 \cdot 33}{20 \cdot 35} = \frac{3 \cdot 3 \cdot 3 \cdot 11}{2 \cdot 2 \cdot 5 \cdot 5 \cdot 7} = \frac{297}{700}$$

You Try It 2

Find the product of $\frac{2}{21}$ and $\frac{10}{33}$.

Your solution

Example 3

What is $\frac{14}{9}$ times $\frac{12}{7}$?

Solution

$$\frac{14}{9} \times \frac{12}{7} = \frac{14 \cdot 12}{9 \cdot 7} = \frac{2 \cdot \overset{1}{\cancel{7}} \cdot 2 \cdot 2 \cdot \overset{1}{\cancel{3}}}{3 \cdot \underset{1}{\cancel{3}} \cdot \underset{1}{\cancel{7}}} = \frac{8}{3} = 2\frac{2}{3}$$

You Try It 3

What is $\frac{16}{5}$ times $\frac{15}{24}$?

Your solution

Solutions on p. S6

Objective B   *To multiply whole numbers, mixed numbers, and fractions* ....

To multiply a whole number by a fraction or mixed number, first write the whole number as a fraction with a denominator of 1.

➡ Multiply: $4 \times \frac{3}{7}$

$$4 \times \frac{3}{7} = \frac{4}{1} \times \frac{3}{7} = \frac{4 \cdot 3}{1 \cdot 7} = \frac{2 \cdot 2 \cdot 3}{7} = \frac{12}{7} = 1\frac{5}{7}$$

• Write 4 with a denominator of 1; then multiply the fractions.

When one or more of the factors in a product is a mixed number, write the mixed number as an improper fraction before multiplying.

➡ Multiply: $2\frac{1}{3} \times \frac{3}{14}$

$$2\frac{1}{3} \times \frac{3}{14} = \frac{7}{3} \times \frac{3}{14} = \frac{7 \cdot 3}{3 \cdot 14} = \frac{\overset{1}{\cancel{7}} \cdot \overset{1}{\cancel{3}}}{\underset{1}{\cancel{3}} \cdot 2 \cdot \underset{1}{\cancel{7}}} = \frac{1}{2}$$

• Write $2\frac{1}{3}$ as an improper fraction; then multiply the fractions.

Example 4

Multiply: $4\frac{5}{6} \times \frac{12}{13}$

Solution

$$4\frac{5}{6} \times \frac{12}{13} = \frac{29}{6} \times \frac{12}{13} = \frac{29 \cdot 12}{6 \cdot 13}$$

$$= \frac{29 \cdot \overset{1}{2} \cdot 2 \cdot \overset{1}{3}}{\underset{1}{2} \cdot \underset{1}{3} \cdot 13} = \frac{58}{13} = 4\frac{6}{13}$$

You Try It 4

Multiply: $5\frac{2}{5} \times \frac{5}{9}$

Your solution

Example 5

Find $5\frac{2}{3}$ times $4\frac{1}{2}$.

Solution

$$5\frac{2}{3} \times 4\frac{1}{2} = \frac{17}{3} \times \frac{9}{2} = \frac{17 \cdot 9}{3 \cdot 2}$$

$$= \frac{17 \cdot \overset{1}{3} \cdot 3}{\underset{1}{3} \cdot 2} = \frac{51}{2} = 25\frac{1}{2}$$

You Try It 5

Multiply: $3\frac{2}{5} \times 6\frac{1}{4}$

Your solution

Example 6

Multiply: $4\frac{2}{5} \times 7$

Solution

$$4\frac{2}{5} \times 7 = \frac{22}{5} \times \frac{7}{1} = \frac{22 \cdot 7}{5 \cdot 1}$$

$$= \frac{2 \cdot 11 \cdot 7}{5} = \frac{154}{5} = 30\frac{4}{5}$$

You Try It 6

Multiply: $3\frac{2}{7} \times 6$

Your solution

Solutions on p. S6

Objective C   *To solve application problems* ....

Length (ft)	Weight (lb/ft)
$6\frac{1}{2}$	$\frac{3}{8}$
$8\frac{5}{8}$	$1\frac{1}{4}$
$10\frac{3}{4}$	$2\frac{1}{2}$
$12\frac{7}{12}$	$4\frac{1}{3}$

The table at the left lists the length of steel rods and the weight per foot. The weight per foot is measured in pounds for each foot of rod and is abbreviated as lb/ft.

⇒ Find the weight of the steel bar that is $10\frac{3}{4}$ feet long.

Strategy

To find the weight of the steel bar, multiply its length by the weight per foot.

Solution $10\frac{3}{4} \times 2\frac{1}{2} = \frac{43}{4} \times \frac{5}{2} = \frac{43 \cdot 5}{4 \cdot 2} = \frac{215}{8} = 26\frac{7}{8}$

The weight of the $10\frac{3}{4}$-foot rod is $26\frac{7}{8}$ lb.

Example 7

An electrician earns $150 for each day worked. What are the electrician's earnings for working $4\frac{1}{2}$ days?

You Try It 7

Over the last 10 years, a house increased in value by $3\frac{1}{2}$ times. The price of the house 10 years ago was $30,000. What is the value of the house today?

Strategy

To find the electrician's total earnings, multiply the daily earnings ($150) by the number of days worked $\left(4\frac{1}{2}\right)$.

Your strategy

Solution $150 \times 4\frac{1}{2} = \frac{150}{1} \times \frac{9}{2}$

$$= \frac{150 \cdot 9}{1 \cdot 2}$$

$$= 675$$

The electrician's earnings are $675.

Your solution

Example 8

The value of a small office building and the land on which it is built is $90,000. The value of the land is $\frac{1}{4}$ the total value. What is the value of the building (in dollars)?

You Try It 8

A paint company bought a drying chamber and an air compressor for spray painting. The total cost of the two items was $60,000. The drying chamber's cost was $\frac{4}{5}$ of the total cost. What was the cost of the air compressor?

Strategy

To find the value of the building:

- Find the value of the land $\left(\frac{1}{4} \times 90,000\right)$.
- Subtract the value of the land from the total value.

Your strategy

Solution $\frac{1}{4} \times 90,000 = \frac{90,000}{4}$

$$= 22,500 \quad \text{value of the land}$$

$$\begin{array}{r} 90,000 \\ - 22,500 \\ \hline 67,500 \end{array}$$

The value of the building is $67,500.

Your solution

Solutions on p. S6

2.6 Exercises

. . . .

Objective A

Multiply.

1. $\dfrac{2}{3} \times \dfrac{7}{8}$ 2. $\dfrac{1}{2} \times \dfrac{2}{3}$ 3. $\dfrac{5}{16} \times \dfrac{7}{15}$ 4. $\dfrac{3}{8} \times \dfrac{6}{7}$

5. $\dfrac{1}{6} \times \dfrac{1}{8}$ 6. $\dfrac{2}{5} \times \dfrac{5}{6}$ 7. $\dfrac{11}{12} \times \dfrac{6}{7}$ 8. $\dfrac{11}{12} \times \dfrac{3}{5}$

9. $\dfrac{1}{6} \times \dfrac{6}{7}$ 10. $\dfrac{3}{5} \times \dfrac{10}{11}$ 11. $\dfrac{1}{5} \times \dfrac{5}{8}$ 12. $\dfrac{6}{7} \times \dfrac{14}{15}$

13. $\dfrac{8}{9} \times \dfrac{27}{4}$ 14. $\dfrac{3}{5} \times \dfrac{3}{10}$ 15. $\dfrac{5}{6} \times \dfrac{1}{2}$ 16. $\dfrac{3}{8} \times \dfrac{5}{12}$

17. $\dfrac{16}{9} \times \dfrac{27}{8}$ 18. $\dfrac{5}{8} \times \dfrac{16}{15}$ 19. $\dfrac{3}{2} \times \dfrac{4}{9}$ 20. $\dfrac{5}{3} \times \dfrac{3}{7}$

21. $\dfrac{7}{8} \times \dfrac{3}{14}$ 22. $\dfrac{2}{9} \times \dfrac{1}{5}$ 23. $\dfrac{1}{10} \times \dfrac{3}{8}$ 24. $\dfrac{5}{12} \times \dfrac{6}{7}$

25. $\dfrac{15}{8} \times \dfrac{16}{3}$ 26. $\dfrac{5}{6} \times \dfrac{4}{15}$ 27. $\dfrac{1}{2} \times \dfrac{2}{15}$ 28. $\dfrac{3}{8} \times \dfrac{5}{16}$

29. $\dfrac{5}{7} \times \dfrac{14}{15}$ 30. $\dfrac{3}{8} \times \dfrac{15}{41}$ 31. $\dfrac{5}{12} \times \dfrac{42}{65}$ 32. $\dfrac{16}{33} \times \dfrac{55}{72}$

33. $\dfrac{12}{5} \times \dfrac{5}{3}$ 34. $\dfrac{17}{9} \times \dfrac{81}{17}$ 35. $\dfrac{16}{85} \times \dfrac{125}{84}$ 36. $\dfrac{19}{64} \times \dfrac{48}{95}$

37. Multiply $\frac{7}{12}$ and $\frac{15}{42}$.

38. Multiply $\frac{32}{9}$ and $\frac{3}{8}$.

39. Find the product of $\frac{5}{9}$ and $\frac{3}{20}$.

40. Find the product of $\frac{7}{3}$ and $\frac{15}{14}$.

41. What is $\frac{1}{2}$ times $\frac{8}{15}$?

42. What is $\frac{3}{8}$ times $\frac{12}{17}$?

Objective B

Multiply.

43. $4 \times \frac{3}{8}$

44. $14 \times \frac{5}{7}$

45. $\frac{2}{3} \times 6$

46. $\frac{5}{12} \times 40$

47. $\frac{1}{3} \times 1\frac{1}{3}$

48. $\frac{2}{5} \times 2\frac{1}{2}$

49. $1\frac{7}{8} \times \frac{4}{15}$

50. $2\frac{1}{5} \times \frac{5}{22}$

51. $55 \times \frac{3}{10}$

52. $\frac{5}{14} \times 49$

53. $4 \times 2\frac{1}{2}$

54. $9 \times 3\frac{1}{3}$

55. $2\frac{1}{7} \times 3$

56. $5\frac{1}{4} \times 8$

57. $3\frac{2}{3} \times 5$

58. $4\frac{2}{9} \times 3$

59. $\frac{1}{2} \times 3\frac{3}{7}$

60. $\frac{3}{8} \times 4\frac{4}{5}$

61. $6\frac{1}{8} \times \frac{4}{7}$

62. $5\frac{1}{3} \times \frac{5}{16}$

63. $5\frac{1}{8} \times 5$

64. $6\frac{1}{9} \times 2$

65. $\frac{3}{8} \times 4\frac{1}{2}$

66. $\frac{5}{7} \times 2\frac{1}{3}$

67. $6 \times 2\frac{2}{3}$

68. $6\frac{1}{8} \times 0$

69. $1\frac{1}{3} \times 2\frac{1}{4}$

70. $2\frac{5}{8} \times \frac{3}{23}$

71. $2\frac{5}{8} \times 3\frac{2}{5}$

72. $5\frac{3}{16} \times 5\frac{1}{3}$

73. $3\frac{1}{7} \times 2\frac{1}{8}$

74. $16\frac{5}{8} \times 1\frac{1}{16}$

75. $2\dfrac{2}{5} \times 3\dfrac{1}{12}$ **76.** $2\dfrac{2}{3} \times \dfrac{3}{20}$ **77.** $5\dfrac{1}{5} \times 3\dfrac{1}{13}$ **78.** $3\dfrac{3}{4} \times 2\dfrac{3}{20}$

79. $10\dfrac{1}{4} \times 3\dfrac{1}{5}$ **80.** $12\dfrac{3}{5} \times 1\dfrac{3}{7}$ **81.** $5\dfrac{3}{7} \times 5\dfrac{1}{4}$ **82.** $6\dfrac{1}{2} \times 1\dfrac{3}{13}$

83. Multiply $2\dfrac{1}{2}$ and $3\dfrac{3}{5}$.   **84.** Multiply $4\dfrac{3}{8}$ and $3\dfrac{3}{5}$.

85. Find the product of $2\dfrac{1}{8}$ and $\dfrac{5}{17}$.   **86.** Find the product of $12\dfrac{2}{5}$ and $3\dfrac{7}{31}$.

87. What is $1\dfrac{3}{8}$ times $2\dfrac{1}{5}$?   **88.** What is $3\dfrac{1}{8}$ times $2\dfrac{4}{7}$?

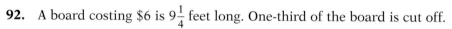

Objective C   *Application Problems*

89. Salmon costs $8 per pound. Find the cost of $2\dfrac{3}{4}$ pounds of salmon.

90. Maria Rivera can walk $3\dfrac{1}{2}$ miles in 1 hour. At this rate, how far can Maria walk in $\dfrac{1}{3}$ hour?

91. A Honda Civic travels 38 miles on each gallon of gasoline. How many miles can the car travel on $9\dfrac{1}{2}$ gallons of gasoline?

$3\dfrac{1}{2}$ Miles

1 Hour

?

$\dfrac{1}{3}$ Hour

92. A board costing $6 is $9\dfrac{1}{4}$ feet long. One-third of the board is cut off.
  a. Without doing the calculation, is the piece being cut off at least 4 feet long?
  b. What is the length of the piece cut off?

93. The F-1 engine in the first stage of the Saturn 5 rocket burns 214,000 gallons of propellant in 1 minute. The first stage burns $2\dfrac{1}{2}$ minutes before burnout. How much propellant is used before burnout?

94. A family budgets $\dfrac{2}{5}$ of its monthly income of $3200 per month for housing and utilities.
  a. What amount is budgeted for housing and utilities?
  b. What amount remains for purposes other than housing and utilities?

95. $\dfrac{5}{6}$ of a chemistry class of 36 has passing grades. $\dfrac{1}{5}$ of the students with passing grades received an A.
  a. How many students passed the chemistry course?
  b. How many students received A grades?

96. The parents of the Newton Junior High School Choir members are making robes for the choir. Each robe requires $2\dfrac{5}{8}$ yards of material at a cost of $8 per yard. Find the total cost of 24 choir robes.

97. A college spends $\frac{5}{8}$ of its monthly income on employee salaries. During one month the college had an income of $712,000. How much of the monthly income remained after the employees' salaries were paid?

The table at the right shows the length of steel rods and their weight per foot. Use this table for Exercises 98 to 100.

Length (ft)	Weight (lb/ft)
$6\frac{1}{2}$	$\frac{3}{8}$
$8\frac{5}{8}$	$1\frac{1}{4}$
$10\frac{3}{4}$	$2\frac{1}{2}$
$12\frac{7}{12}$	$4\frac{1}{3}$

98. Find the weight of $6\frac{1}{2}$ feet of steel rod.

99. Find the weight of $12\frac{7}{12}$ feet of steel rod.

100. Find the total weight of $8\frac{5}{8}$ feet and $10\frac{3}{4}$ feet of steel rod.

101. A state park has reserved $\frac{4}{5}$ of its total acreage for a wildlife preserve. Three-fourths of the wildlife preserve is heavily wooded. What fraction of the state park is heavily wooded?

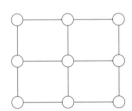

State Park

102. The manager of a mutual fund has one-half of the portfolio invested in bonds. Of the amount invested in bonds, $\frac{3}{8}$ is invested in corporate bonds. What fraction of the total portfolio is invested in corporate bonds?

APPLYING THE CONCEPTS

103. The product of 1 and a number is $\frac{1}{2}$. Find the number.

104. Our calendar is based on the solar year, which is $365\frac{1}{4}$ days. Use this fact to explain leap years.

105. If two positive fractions, each less than 1, are multiplied, is the product less than 1?

106. Is the product of two positive fractions always greater than either one of the two numbers? If so, explain why. If not, give an example.

107. Which of the labeled points on the number line at the right could be the graph of the product of B and C?

108. Fill in the circles on the square at the right with the fractions $\frac{1}{6}$, $\frac{5}{18}$, $\frac{4}{9}$, $\frac{5}{9}$, $\frac{2}{3}$, $\frac{3}{4}$, $1\frac{1}{9}$, $1\frac{1}{2}$, and $2\frac{1}{4}$ so that the product of any row is equal to $\frac{5}{18}$. (*Note:* There is more than one answer.)

2.7 Division of Fractions and Mixed Numbers

Objective A *To divide fractions*

The **reciprocal** of a fraction is the fraction with the numerator and denominator interchanged. For instance, the reciprocal of $\frac{2}{3}$ is $\frac{3}{2}$. The process of interchanging the numerator and denominator of a fraction is called **inverting** the fraction.

To find the reciprocal of a whole number, first write the whole number as a fraction with a denominator of 1; then find the reciprocal of that fraction.

The reciprocal of 5 is $\frac{1}{5}$. $\left(\text{Think } 5 = \frac{5}{1}\right)$

Reciprocals are used to rewrite division problems as related multiplication problems. Look at the following two problems:

$$8 \div 2 = 4 \qquad\qquad 8 \times \frac{1}{2} = 4$$

8 divided by 2 is **4**.   8 times the reciprocal of 2 is **4**.

"Divided by" means the same as "times the reciprocal of." Thus "$\div\ 2$" can be replaced with "$\times \frac{1}{2}$," and the answer will be the same. Fractions are divided by making this replacement.

➡ Divide: $\dfrac{2}{3} \div \dfrac{3}{4}$ $\dfrac{2}{3} \div \dfrac{3}{4} = \dfrac{2}{3} \times \dfrac{4}{3} = \dfrac{2 \cdot 4}{3 \cdot 3} = \dfrac{2 \cdot 2 \cdot 2}{3 \cdot 3} = \dfrac{8}{9}$

Example 1   Divide: $\dfrac{5}{8} \div \dfrac{4}{9}$

Solution $\dfrac{5}{8} \div \dfrac{4}{9} = \dfrac{5}{8} \times \dfrac{9}{4} = \dfrac{5 \cdot 9}{8 \cdot 4}$

$\qquad = \dfrac{5 \cdot 3 \cdot 3}{2 \cdot 2 \cdot 2 \cdot 2 \cdot 2} = \dfrac{45}{32} = 1\dfrac{13}{32}$

You Try It 1   Divide: $\dfrac{3}{7} \div \dfrac{2}{3}$

Your solution

Example 2   Find the quotient of $\dfrac{3}{5}$ and $\dfrac{12}{25}$.

Solution $\dfrac{3}{5} \div \dfrac{12}{25} = \dfrac{3}{5} \times \dfrac{25}{12} = \dfrac{3 \cdot 25}{5 \cdot 12}$

$\qquad = \dfrac{\overset{1}{\cancel{3}} \cdot \overset{1}{\cancel{5}} \cdot 5}{\underset{1}{\cancel{5}} \cdot 2 \cdot 2 \cdot \underset{1}{\cancel{3}}} = \dfrac{5}{4} = 1\dfrac{1}{4}$

You Try It 2   Divide: $\dfrac{3}{4} \div \dfrac{9}{10}$

Your solution

Solutions on p. S7

Objective B *To divide whole numbers, mixed numbers, and fractions*

To divide a fraction and a whole number, first write the whole number as a fraction with a denominator of 1.

➡ Divide: $\dfrac{3}{7} \div 5$

$\dfrac{3}{7} \div \boxed{5} = \dfrac{3}{7} \div \boxed{\dfrac{5}{1}} = \dfrac{3}{7} \times \dfrac{1}{5} = \dfrac{3 \cdot 1}{7 \cdot 5} = \dfrac{3}{35}$ • Write 5 with a denominator of 1; then divide the fractions.

When one of the numbers in a quotient is a mixed number, write the mixed number as an improper fraction before dividing.

➡ Divide: $4\frac{2}{3} \div \frac{8}{15}$

Write $4\frac{2}{3}$ as an improper fraction; then divide the fractions.

$$4\frac{2}{3} \div \frac{8}{15} = \frac{14}{3} \div \frac{8}{15} = \frac{14}{3} \times \frac{15}{8} = \frac{14 \cdot 15}{3 \cdot 8} = \frac{\overset{1}{2} \cdot 7 \cdot \overset{1}{3} \cdot 5}{\underset{1}{3} \cdot 2 \cdot \underset{1}{2} \cdot 2} = \frac{35}{4} = 8\frac{3}{4}$$

➡ Divide: $1\frac{13}{15} \div 4\frac{4}{5}$

Write the mixed numbers as improper fractions. Then divide the fractions.

$$1\frac{13}{15} \div 4\frac{4}{5} = \frac{28}{15} \div \frac{24}{5} = \frac{28}{15} \times \frac{5}{24} = \frac{28 \cdot 5}{15 \cdot 24} = \frac{\overset{1}{2} \cdot \overset{1}{2} \cdot 7 \cdot \overset{1}{5}}{3 \cdot \underset{1}{5} \cdot \underset{1}{2} \cdot 2 \cdot 2 \cdot 3} = \frac{7}{18}$$

Example 3   Divide $\frac{4}{9}$ by 5.

Solution

$$\frac{4}{9} \div 5 = \frac{4}{9} \div \frac{5}{1} = \frac{4}{9} \times \frac{1}{5}$$

$$= \frac{4 \cdot 1}{9 \cdot 5} = \frac{2 \cdot 2}{3 \cdot 3 \cdot 5} = \frac{4}{45}$$

You Try It 3   Divide $\frac{5}{7}$ by 6.

Your solution

Example 4

Find the quotient of $\frac{3}{8}$ and $2\frac{1}{10}$.

Solution

$$\frac{3}{8} \div 2\frac{1}{10} = \frac{3}{8} \div \frac{21}{10} = \frac{3}{8} \times \frac{10}{21}$$

$$= \frac{3 \cdot 10}{8 \cdot 21} = \frac{\overset{1}{3} \cdot \overset{1}{2} \cdot 5}{2 \cdot 2 \cdot 2 \cdot \underset{1}{3} \cdot 7} = \frac{5}{28}$$

You Try It 4

Find the quotient of $12\frac{3}{5}$ and 7.

Your solution

Example 5   Divide: $2\frac{3}{4} \div 1\frac{5}{7}$

Solution

$$2\frac{3}{4} \div 1\frac{5}{7} = \frac{11}{4} \div \frac{12}{7} = \frac{11}{4} \times \frac{7}{12} = \frac{11 \cdot 7}{4 \cdot 12}$$

$$= \frac{11 \cdot 7}{2 \cdot 2 \cdot 2 \cdot 2 \cdot 3} = \frac{77}{48} = 1\frac{29}{48}$$

You Try It 5   Divide: $3\frac{2}{3} \div 2\frac{2}{5}$

Your solution

Solutions on p. S7

Example 6 Divide: $1\frac{13}{15} \div 4\frac{1}{5}$

You Try It 6 Divide: $2\frac{5}{6} \div 8\frac{1}{2}$

Solution

$$1\frac{13}{15} \div 4\frac{1}{5} = \frac{28}{15} \div \frac{21}{5} = \frac{28}{15} \times \frac{5}{21} = \frac{28 \cdot 5}{15 \cdot 21}$$

$$= \frac{2 \cdot 2 \cdot \overset{1}{\cancel{7}} \cdot \overset{1}{\cancel{5}}}{3 \cdot \underset{1}{\cancel{5}} \cdot 3 \cdot \underset{1}{\cancel{7}}} = \frac{4}{9}$$

Your solution

Example 7 Divide: $4\frac{3}{8} \div 7$

You Try It 7 Divide: $6\frac{2}{5} \div 4$

Solution

$$4\frac{3}{8} \div 7 = \frac{35}{8} \div \frac{7}{1} = \frac{35}{8} \times \frac{1}{7}$$

$$= \frac{35 \cdot 1}{8 \cdot 7} = \frac{5 \cdot \overset{1}{\cancel{7}}}{2 \cdot 2 \cdot 2 \cdot \underset{1}{\cancel{7}}} = \frac{5}{8}$$

Your solution

Solutions on p. S7

Objective C *To solve application problems*

Example 8

A car used $15\frac{1}{2}$ gallons of gasoline on a 310-mile trip. How many miles can this car travel on 1 gallon of gasoline?

Strategy
To find the number of miles, divide the number of miles traveled by the number of gallons of gasoline used.

Solution

$$310 \div 15\frac{1}{2} = \frac{310}{1} \div \frac{31}{2}$$

$$= \frac{310}{1} \times \frac{2}{31}$$

$$= \frac{310 \cdot 2}{1 \cdot 31}$$

$$= 20$$

The car travels 20 miles on 1 gallon of gasoline.

You Try It 8

Leon Dern purchased a $\frac{1}{2}$- ounce gold coin for $195. What would the price of a 1-ounce coin be?

Your strategy

Your solution

Solution on p. S7

Example 9

A 12-foot board is cut into pieces $2\frac{1}{4}$ feet long for use as bookshelves. What is the length of the remaining piece after as many shelves as possible are cut?

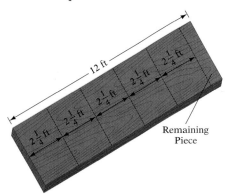

Strategy

To find the length of the remaining piece:

- Divide the total length by the length of each shelf $\left(2\frac{1}{4}\right)$. This will give you the number of shelves cut, with a certain fraction of a shelf left over.
- Multiply the fraction left over by the length of one shelf to determine the length of the remaining piece.

Solution

$$12 \div 2\frac{1}{4} = \frac{12}{1} \div \frac{9}{4} = \frac{12}{1} \times \frac{4}{9}$$

$$= \frac{12 \cdot 4}{1 \cdot 9} = \frac{16}{3} = 5\frac{1}{3}$$

5 pieces $2\frac{1}{4}$ feet long

1 piece $\frac{1}{3}$ of $2\frac{1}{4}$ feet long

$$\frac{1}{3} \times 2\frac{1}{4} = \frac{1}{3} \times \frac{9}{4} = \frac{1 \cdot 9}{3 \cdot 4} = \frac{3}{4}$$

The length of the piece remaining is $\frac{3}{4}$ foot.

You Try It 9

A 16-foot board is cut into pieces $3\frac{1}{3}$ feet long for shelves for a bookcase. What is the length of the remaining piece after as many shelves as possible are cut?

Your strategy

Your solution

Solution on p. S7

2.7 Exercises

Objective A

Divide.

1. $\dfrac{1}{3} \div \dfrac{2}{5}$

2. $\dfrac{3}{7} \div \dfrac{3}{2}$

3. $\dfrac{3}{7} \div \dfrac{3}{7}$

4. $0 \div \dfrac{1}{2}$

5. $0 \div \dfrac{3}{4}$

6. $\dfrac{16}{33} \div \dfrac{4}{11}$

7. $\dfrac{5}{24} \div \dfrac{15}{36}$

8. $\dfrac{11}{15} \div \dfrac{1}{12}$

9. $\dfrac{15}{16} \div \dfrac{16}{39}$

10. $\dfrac{2}{15} \div \dfrac{3}{5}$

11. $\dfrac{8}{9} \div \dfrac{4}{5}$

12. $\dfrac{11}{15} \div \dfrac{5}{22}$

13. $\dfrac{1}{9} \div \dfrac{2}{3}$

14. $\dfrac{10}{21} \div \dfrac{5}{7}$

15. $\dfrac{2}{5} \div \dfrac{4}{7}$

16. $\dfrac{3}{8} \div \dfrac{5}{12}$

17. $\dfrac{1}{2} \div \dfrac{1}{4}$

18. $\dfrac{1}{3} \div \dfrac{1}{9}$

19. $\dfrac{1}{5} \div \dfrac{1}{10}$

20. $\dfrac{4}{15} \div \dfrac{2}{5}$

21. $\dfrac{7}{15} \div \dfrac{14}{5}$

22. $\dfrac{5}{8} \div \dfrac{15}{2}$

23. $\dfrac{14}{3} \div \dfrac{7}{9}$

24. $\dfrac{7}{4} \div \dfrac{9}{2}$

25. $\dfrac{5}{9} \div \dfrac{25}{3}$

26. $\dfrac{5}{16} \div \dfrac{3}{8}$

27. $\dfrac{2}{3} \div \dfrac{1}{3}$

28. $\dfrac{4}{9} \div \dfrac{1}{9}$

29. $\dfrac{5}{7} \div \dfrac{2}{7}$

30. $\dfrac{5}{6} \div \dfrac{1}{9}$

31. $\dfrac{2}{3} \div \dfrac{2}{9}$

32. $\dfrac{5}{12} \div \dfrac{5}{6}$

33. $4 \div \dfrac{2}{3}$

34. $\dfrac{2}{3} \div 4$

35. $\dfrac{3}{2} \div 3$

36. $3 \div \dfrac{3}{2}$

37. Divide $\frac{7}{8}$ by $\frac{3}{4}$.

38. Divide $\frac{7}{12}$ by $\frac{3}{4}$.

39. Find the quotient of $\frac{5}{7}$ and $\frac{3}{14}$.

40. Find the quotient of $\frac{6}{11}$ and $\frac{9}{32}$.

Objective B

Divide.

41. $\frac{5}{6} \div 25$

42. $22 \div \frac{3}{11}$

43. $6 \div 3\frac{1}{3}$

44. $5\frac{1}{2} \div 11$

45. $6\frac{1}{2} \div \frac{1}{2}$

46. $\frac{3}{8} \div 2\frac{1}{4}$

47. $\frac{5}{12} \div 4\frac{4}{5}$

48. $1\frac{1}{2} \div 1\frac{3}{8}$

49. $8\frac{1}{4} \div 2\frac{3}{4}$

50. $3\frac{5}{9} \div 32$

51. $4\frac{1}{5} \div 21$

52. $6\frac{8}{9} \div \frac{31}{36}$

53. $\frac{11}{12} \div 2\frac{1}{3}$

54. $\frac{7}{8} \div 3\frac{1}{4}$

55. $\frac{5}{16} \div 5\frac{3}{8}$

56. $\frac{9}{14} \div 3\frac{1}{7}$

57. $35 \div \frac{7}{24}$

58. $\frac{3}{8} \div 2\frac{3}{4}$

59. $\frac{11}{18} \div 2\frac{2}{9}$

60. $\frac{21}{40} \div 3\frac{3}{10}$

61. $2\frac{1}{16} \div 2\frac{1}{2}$

62. $7\frac{3}{5} \div 1\frac{7}{12}$

63. $1\frac{2}{3} \div \frac{3}{8}$

64. $16 \div \frac{2}{3}$

65. $1\frac{5}{8} \div 4$

66. $13\frac{3}{8} \div \frac{1}{4}$

67. $16 \div 1\frac{1}{2}$

68. $9 \div \frac{7}{8}$

69. $16\frac{5}{8} \div 1\frac{2}{3}$

70. $24\frac{4}{5} \div 2\frac{3}{5}$

71. $1\frac{1}{3} \div 5\frac{8}{9}$

72. $13\frac{2}{3} \div 0$

73. $82\dfrac{3}{5} \div 19\dfrac{1}{10}$ **74.** $45\dfrac{3}{5} \div 15$ **75.** $102 \div 1\dfrac{1}{2}$

76. $0 \div 3\dfrac{1}{2}$ **77.** $8\dfrac{2}{7} \div 1$ **78.** $6\dfrac{9}{16} \div 1\dfrac{3}{32}$

79. $8\dfrac{8}{9} \div 2\dfrac{13}{18}$ **80.** $10\dfrac{1}{5} \div 1\dfrac{7}{10}$ **81.** $7\dfrac{3}{8} \div 1\dfrac{27}{32}$

82. Divide $7\dfrac{7}{9}$ by $5\dfrac{5}{6}$.   **83.** Divide $2\dfrac{3}{4}$ by $1\dfrac{23}{32}$.

84. Find the quotient of $8\dfrac{1}{4}$ and $1\dfrac{5}{11}$.   **85.** Find the quotient of $\dfrac{14}{17}$ and $3\dfrac{1}{9}$.

Objective C   *Application Problems*

86. Individual cereal boxes contain $\dfrac{3}{4}$ ounce of cereal. How many boxes can be filled with 600 ounces of cereal?

87. A box of Post's Great Grains cereal costing $4 contains 16 ounces of cereal. How many $1\dfrac{1}{3}$-ounce portions can be served from this box?

88. A $\dfrac{5}{8}$-carat diamond was purchased for $1200. What would a similar diamond weighing 1 carat cost?

89. The Inverness Investor Group bought $8\dfrac{1}{3}$ acres of land for $200,000. What was the cost of each acre?

90. KU Energy stock is offered for $31\dfrac{5}{8}$ per share. How many shares can you buy for $1265?

91. A nut moves $\dfrac{5}{32}$ inch for each turn. Find the number of turns it will take for the nut to move $1\dfrac{7}{8}$ inches.

92. The Hammond Company purchased $9\dfrac{3}{4}$ acres for a housing project. One and one-half acres were set aside for a park.

  a. How many acres are available for housing?

  b. How many $\dfrac{1}{4}$-acre parcels of land can be sold after the land for the park is set aside?

93. A chef purchased a roast that weighed $10\frac{3}{4}$ pounds. After the fat was trimmed and the bone removed, the roast weighed $9\frac{1}{3}$ pounds.

   a. What was the total weight of the fat and bone?

   b. How many $\frac{1}{3}$-pound servings can be cut from the roast?

94. A 15-foot board is cut into pieces $3\frac{1}{2}$ feet long for a bookcase. What is the length of the piece remaining after as many shelves as possible have been cut?

95. A scale of $\frac{1}{2}$ inch to 1 foot is used to draw the plans for a house. The scale measurements for three walls are given in the table at the right. Complete the table to determine the actual wall lengths for the three walls a, b, and c.

Wall	Scale	Actual Wall Length
a	$6\frac{1}{4}$ in.	?
b	9 in.	?
c	$7\frac{7}{8}$ in.	?

APPLYING THE CONCEPTS

96. On a map, two cities are $4\frac{5}{8}$ inches apart. If $\frac{3}{8}$ inch on the map represents 60 miles, what is the number of miles between the two cities?

97. Is the quotient always less than the dividend in a division problem? Explain.

98. Fill in the box to make a true statement.

   a. $\frac{3}{4} \cdot \boxed{} = \frac{1}{2}$
   b. $\frac{2}{3} \cdot \boxed{} = 1\frac{3}{4}$

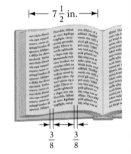

$\longleftarrow 7\frac{1}{2}$ in. $\longrightarrow$

99. A page of type in a certain textbook is $7\frac{1}{2}$ inches wide. If the page is divided into three equal columns, with $\frac{3}{8}$ inch between columns, how wide is each column?

$\frac{3}{8} \qquad \frac{3}{8}$

100. A whole number is both multiplied and divided by the same proper fraction. Which is greater, the product or the quotient?

101. Fractions are multiplied by multiplying the numerators and multiplying the denominators. Consider dividing fractions in a similar manner. Divide the numerators and divide the denominators.

$$\frac{4}{15} \div \frac{2}{5} = \frac{4 \div 2}{15 \div 5} = \frac{2}{3}$$

This gives the same answer as the traditional method.

$$\frac{4}{15} \div \frac{2}{5} = \frac{4}{15} \cdot \frac{5}{2} = \frac{20}{30} = \frac{2}{3}$$

Try this method for the following division problems.

   a. $\frac{5}{6} \div \frac{1}{3}$
   b. $\frac{4}{21} \div \frac{2}{7}$
   c. $\frac{5}{9} \div \frac{5}{3}$
   d. $\frac{15}{16} \div \frac{3}{8}$

102. Does the method of dividing fractions shown above always work? Give an example of when the traditional method would be a better choice.

2.8 Order, Exponents, and the Order of Operations Agreement

Objective A   *To identify the order relation between two fractions* ....

Recall that whole numbers can be graphed as points on the number line. Fractions can also be graphed as points on the number line.

The graph of $\dfrac{3}{4}$ on the number line

The number line can be used to determine the order relation between two fractions. A fraction that appears to the left of a given fraction is less than the given fraction. A fraction that appears to the right of a given fraction is greater than the given fraction.

$\dfrac{1}{8} < \dfrac{3}{8} \qquad \dfrac{6}{8} > \dfrac{3}{8}$

To find the order relation between two fractions with the same denominator, compare numerators. The fraction that has the smaller numerator is the smaller fraction. When the denominators are different, begin by writing equivalent fractions with a common denominator; then compare numerators.

➡ Find the order relation between $\dfrac{11}{18}$ and $\dfrac{5}{8}$.

The LCM of 18 and 8 is 72.

$\dfrac{11}{18} = \dfrac{44}{72}$ ← Smaller numerator $\dfrac{11}{18} < \dfrac{5}{8}$ or $\dfrac{5}{8} > \dfrac{11}{18}$

$\dfrac{5}{8} = \dfrac{45}{72}$ ← Larger numerator

Example 1   Place the correct symbol, < or >, between the two numbers.

$\dfrac{5}{12} \qquad \dfrac{7}{18}$

Solution $\dfrac{5}{12} = \dfrac{15}{36} \qquad \dfrac{7}{18} = \dfrac{14}{36}$

$\dfrac{5}{12} > \dfrac{7}{18}$

You Try It 1   Place the correct symbol, < or >, between the two numbers.

$\dfrac{9}{14} \qquad \dfrac{13}{21}$

Your solution

Solution on p. S7

Objective B   *To simplify expressions containing exponents* ....

Repeated multiplication of the same fraction can be written in two ways:

$$\dfrac{1}{2} \cdot \dfrac{1}{2} \cdot \dfrac{1}{2} \cdot \dfrac{1}{2} \qquad \text{or} \qquad \left(\dfrac{1}{2}\right)^4 \leftarrow \text{Exponent}$$

The exponent indicates how many times the fraction occurs as a factor in the multiplication. The expression $\left(\dfrac{1}{2}\right)^4$ is in exponential notation.

Example 2   Simplify: $\left(\frac{5}{6}\right)^3 \cdot \left(\frac{3}{5}\right)^2$

Solution $\left(\frac{5}{6}\right)^3 \cdot \left(\frac{3}{5}\right)^2 = \left(\frac{5}{6} \cdot \frac{5}{6} \cdot \frac{5}{6}\right) \cdot \left(\frac{3}{5} \cdot \frac{3}{5}\right)$

$= \dfrac{\overset{1}{\cancel{5}} \cdot \overset{1}{\cancel{5}} \cdot 5 \cdot \overset{1}{\cancel{3}} \cdot \overset{1}{\cancel{3}}}{2 \cdot \underset{1}{\cancel{3}} \cdot 2 \cdot \underset{1}{\cancel{3}} \cdot 2 \cdot 3 \cdot \underset{1}{\cancel{5}} \cdot \underset{1}{\cancel{5}}} = \dfrac{5}{24}$

You Try It 2   Simplify: $\left(\frac{7}{11}\right)^2 \cdot \left(\frac{2}{7}\right)$

Your solution

Solution on p. S7

Objective C   *To use the Order of Operations Agreement to simplify expressions* ....

The Order of Operations Agreement is used for fractions as well as whole numbers.

> **Step 1**   Do all operations inside parentheses.
> **Step 2**   Simplify any number expressions containing exponents.
> **Step 3**   Do multiplications and divisions as they occur from left to right.
> **Step 4**   Do additions and subtractions as they occur from left to right.

➡ Simplify $\frac{14}{15} - \left(\frac{1}{2}\right)^2 \times \left(\frac{2}{3} + \frac{4}{5}\right)$ by using the Order of Operations Agreement.

$\frac{14}{15} - \left(\frac{1}{2}\right)^2 \times \left(\frac{2}{3} + \frac{4}{5}\right)$ **1.** Perform operations in parentheses.

$\frac{14}{15} - \left(\frac{1}{2}\right)^2 \times \frac{22}{15}$ **2.** Simplify expressions with exponents.

$\frac{14}{15} - \frac{1}{4} \times \frac{22}{15}$ **3.** Do multiplications and divisions as they occur from left to right.

$\frac{14}{15} - \frac{11}{30}$ **4.** Do additions and subtractions as they occur from left to right.

$\frac{17}{30}$

One or more of the above steps may not be needed to simplify an expression. In that case, proceed to the next step in the Order of Operations Agreement.

Example 3   Simplify: $\left(\frac{3}{4}\right)^2 \div \left(\frac{3}{8} - \frac{1}{12}\right)$

Solution $\left(\frac{3}{4}\right)^2 \div \left(\frac{3}{8} - \frac{1}{12}\right)$

$= \left(\frac{3}{4}\right)^2 \div \left(\frac{7}{24}\right) = \frac{9}{16} \div \frac{7}{24}$

$= \frac{9}{16} \cdot \frac{24}{7} = \frac{27}{14} = 1\frac{13}{14}$

You Try It 3   Simplify:

$\left(\frac{1}{13}\right)^2 \cdot \left(\frac{1}{4} + \frac{1}{6}\right) \div \frac{5}{13}$

Your solution

Solution on p. S8

2.8 Exercises

· ·

Objective A

Place the correct symbol, $<$ or $>$, between the two numbers.

1. $\dfrac{11}{40}$ $\quad$ $\dfrac{19}{40}$

2. $\dfrac{92}{103}$ $\quad$ $\dfrac{19}{103}$

3. $\dfrac{2}{3}$ $\quad$ $\dfrac{5}{7}$

4. $\dfrac{2}{5}$ $\quad$ $\dfrac{3}{8}$

5. $\dfrac{5}{8}$ $\quad$ $\dfrac{7}{12}$

6. $\dfrac{11}{16}$ $\quad$ $\dfrac{17}{24}$

7. $\dfrac{7}{9}$ $\quad$ $\dfrac{11}{12}$

8. $\dfrac{5}{12}$ $\quad$ $\dfrac{7}{15}$

9. $\dfrac{13}{14}$ $\quad$ $\dfrac{19}{21}$

10. $\dfrac{13}{18}$ $\quad$ $\dfrac{7}{12}$

11. $\dfrac{7}{24}$ $\quad$ $\dfrac{11}{30}$

12. $\dfrac{13}{36}$ $\quad$ $\dfrac{19}{48}$

Objective B

Simplify.

13. $\left(\dfrac{3}{8}\right)^2$

14. $\left(\dfrac{5}{12}\right)^2$

15. $\left(\dfrac{2}{9}\right)^3$

16. $\left(\dfrac{1}{2}\right)\cdot\left(\dfrac{2}{3}\right)^2$

17. $\left(\dfrac{2}{3}\right)\cdot\left(\dfrac{1}{2}\right)^4$

18. $\left(\dfrac{1}{3}\right)^2\cdot\left(\dfrac{3}{5}\right)^3$

19. $\left(\dfrac{2}{5}\right)^3\cdot\left(\dfrac{5}{7}\right)^2$

20. $\left(\dfrac{5}{9}\right)^3\cdot\left(\dfrac{18}{25}\right)^2$

21. $\left(\dfrac{1}{3}\right)^4\cdot\left(\dfrac{9}{11}\right)^2$

22. $\left(\dfrac{1}{2}\right)^6\cdot\left(\dfrac{32}{35}\right)^2$

23. $\left(\dfrac{2}{3}\right)^4\cdot\left(\dfrac{81}{100}\right)^2$

24. $\left(\dfrac{1}{6}\right)\cdot\left(\dfrac{6}{7}\right)^2\cdot\left(\dfrac{2}{3}\right)$

25. $\left(\dfrac{2}{7}\right)\cdot\left(\dfrac{7}{8}\right)^2\cdot\left(\dfrac{8}{9}\right)$

26. $3\cdot\left(\dfrac{3}{5}\right)^3\cdot\left(\dfrac{1}{3}\right)^2$

27. $4\cdot\left(\dfrac{3}{4}\right)^3\cdot\left(\dfrac{4}{7}\right)^2$

28. $11\cdot\left(\dfrac{3}{8}\right)^3\cdot\left(\dfrac{8}{11}\right)^2$

29. $5\cdot\left(\dfrac{3}{5}\right)^3\cdot\left(\dfrac{2}{3}\right)^4$

30. $\left(\dfrac{2}{7}\right)^2\cdot\left(\dfrac{7}{9}\right)^2\cdot\left(\dfrac{9}{11}\right)^2$

Objective C

Simplify using the Order of Operations Agreement.

31. $\dfrac{1}{2} - \dfrac{1}{3} + \dfrac{2}{3}$

32. $\dfrac{2}{5} + \dfrac{3}{10} - \dfrac{2}{3}$

33. $\dfrac{1}{3} \div \dfrac{1}{2} + \dfrac{3}{4}$

34. $\dfrac{3}{5} \div \dfrac{6}{7} + \dfrac{4}{5}$

35. $\dfrac{4}{5} + \dfrac{3}{7} \cdot \dfrac{14}{15}$

36. $\dfrac{2}{3} + \dfrac{5}{8} \cdot \dfrac{16}{35}$

37. $\left(\dfrac{3}{4}\right)^2 - \dfrac{5}{12}$

38. $\left(\dfrac{3}{5}\right)^3 - \dfrac{3}{25}$

39. $\dfrac{5}{6} \cdot \left(\dfrac{2}{3} - \dfrac{1}{6}\right) + \dfrac{7}{18}$

40. $\dfrac{3}{4} \cdot \left(\dfrac{11}{12} - \dfrac{7}{8}\right) + \dfrac{5}{16}$

41. $\dfrac{7}{12} - \left(\dfrac{2}{3}\right)^2 + \dfrac{5}{8}$

42. $\dfrac{11}{16} - \left(\dfrac{3}{4}\right)^2 + \dfrac{7}{12}$

43. $\dfrac{3}{4} \cdot \left(\dfrac{4}{9}\right)^2 + \dfrac{1}{2}$

44. $\dfrac{9}{10} \cdot \left(\dfrac{2}{3}\right)^3 + \dfrac{2}{3}$

45. $\left(\dfrac{1}{2} + \dfrac{3}{4}\right) \div \dfrac{5}{8}$

46. $\left(\dfrac{2}{3} + \dfrac{5}{6}\right) \div \dfrac{5}{9}$

47. $\dfrac{3}{8} \div \left(\dfrac{5}{12} + \dfrac{3}{8}\right)$

48. $\dfrac{7}{12} \div \left(\dfrac{2}{3} + \dfrac{5}{9}\right)$

49. $\left(\dfrac{3}{8}\right)^2 \div \left(\dfrac{3}{7} + \dfrac{3}{14}\right)$

50. $\left(\dfrac{5}{6}\right)^2 \div \left(\dfrac{5}{12} + \dfrac{2}{3}\right)$

51. $\dfrac{2}{5} \div \dfrac{3}{8} \cdot \dfrac{4}{5}$

APPLYING THE CONCEPTS

52. $\dfrac{2}{3} < \dfrac{3}{4}$. Is $\dfrac{2+3}{3+4}$ less than $\dfrac{2}{3}$, greater than $\dfrac{2}{3}$, or between $\dfrac{2}{3}$ and $\dfrac{3}{4}$?

53. A farmer died and left 17 horses to be divided among 3 children. The first child was to receive $\dfrac{1}{2}$ of the horses, the second child $\dfrac{1}{3}$ of the horses, and the third child $\dfrac{1}{9}$ of the horses. The executor for the family's estate realized that 17 horses could not be divided by halves, thirds, or ninths and so added a neighbor's horse to the farmer's. With 18 horses, the executor gave 9 horses to the first child, 6 horses to the second child, and 2 horses to the third child. This accounted for the 17 horses, so the executor returned the borrowed horse to the neighbor. Explain why this worked.

Focus on Problem Solving

An application problem may not provide all the information that is needed to solve the problem. Sometimes, however, the necessary information is common knowledge.

You are traveling by bus from Boston to New York. The trip is 4 hours long. If the bus leaves Boston at 10 A.M., what time should you arrive in New York?

What other information do you need to solve this problem?

You need to know that, using a 12-hour clock, the hours run

10 A.M.
11 A.M.
12 P.M.
1 P.M.
2 P.M.

Four hours after 10 A.M. is 2 P.M.

You should arrive in New York at 2 P.M.

You purchase a 32¢ stamp at the post office and hand the clerk a one-dollar bill. How much change do you receive?

What information do you need to solve this problem?

You need to know that there are 100¢ in one dollar.

Your change is 100¢ − 32¢.

$$100 - 32 = 68$$

You receive 68¢ in change.

What information do you need to know to solve each of the following problems?

1. You sell a dozen tickets to a fundraiser. Each ticket costs $10. How much money do you collect?

2. The weekly lab period for your science course is one hour and twenty minutes long. Find the length of the science lab period in minutes.

3. An employee's monthly salary is $1750. Find the employee's annual salary.

4. A survey revealed that eighth graders spend an average of 3 hours each day watching television. Find the total time an eighth grader spends watching TV each week.

5. You want to buy a carpet for a room that is 15 feet wide and 18 feet long. Find the amount of carpet that you need.

Projects and Group Activities

Music In musical notation, notes are printed on a staff, which is a set of five horizontal lines and the spaces between them. The notes of a musical composition are grouped into measures, or bars. Vertical lines separate measures on a staff. The shape of a note indicates how long it should be held. The whole note has the longest time value of any note. Each time value is divided by 2 in order to find the next smallest note value.

Notes

Whole $\frac{1}{2}$ $\frac{1}{4}$ $\frac{1}{8}$ $\frac{1}{16}$ $\frac{1}{32}$ $\frac{1}{64}$

The time signature is a fraction that appears at the beginning of a piece of music. The numerator of the fraction indicates the number of beats in a measure. The denominator indicates what kind of note receives one beat. For example, music written in $\frac{2}{4}$ time has 2 beats to a measure, and a quarter note receives one beat. One measure in $\frac{2}{4}$ time may have 1 half note, 2 quarter notes, 4 eighth notes, or any other combination of notes totaling 2 beats. Other common time signatures include $\frac{4}{4}$, $\frac{3}{4}$, and $\frac{6}{8}$.

1. Explain the meaning of the 6 and the 8 in the time signature $\frac{6}{8}$. Give some possible combinations of notes in one measure of a piece written in $\frac{4}{4}$ time.

2. What does a dot at the right of a note indicate? What is the effect of a dot at the right of a half note? A quarter note? An eighth note?

3. Symbols called rests are used to indicate periods of silence in a piece of music. What symbols are used to indicate the different time values of rests?

4. Find some examples of musical compositions written in different time signatures. Use a few measures from each to show that the sum of the time values of the notes and rests in each measure equals the numerator of the time signature.

Construction

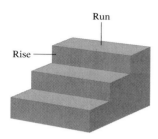

Suppose you are involved in building your own home. Design a stairway from the first floor of the house to the second floor. Some of the questions you will need to answer follow.

What is the distance from the floor of the first story to the floor of the second story?

Typically, what is the number of steps in a stairway?

What is a reasonable length for the run of each step?

What width wood is being used to build the staircase?

In designing the stairway, remember that each riser should be the same height and each run should be the same length. And the width of the wood used for the steps will have to be incorporated in the calculation.

Search the World Wide Web

There are many addresses on the Web where you can find investment information. Some of these addresses are:

http://www.streeteye.com/
http://www.brill.com/fundlink
http://www.thegroup.net:80/invest
http://stocks.com/

Below is a printout for MCN Energy Group Inc. for June 9, 1997, from http://www.streeteye.com/.

Last Sale	29 1/4	52 Week High	32 5/8
Tick	Down	52 Week Low	22 3/4
Net Change	+ 1/8	Volatility	20.06
Percent Change	+ 0.43	Ex-Dividend Date	08/06/97
Exchange	New York	Dividend Amount	0.243
Time of Last Sale	14:03	Dividend Frequency	Quarterly
Size of Last Sale	300	Earnings per Share	1.71
Open	29 1/8	P/E Ratio	17.10
High	29 3/8	Yield	3.32
Low	29	Shares Outstanding	67197
Volume	28200		
Previous Close	29 1/8		

Search these Web sites until you become familiar with the information that can be found on each site. Assume that you have $10,000 to invest. Make up some rules, such as that you cannot own more than 5 stocks at one time and you cannot make more than two trades a week. Assume that there are no commission fees. Keep a weekly record of your stocks and see if you can beat the professional investors.

Chapter Summary

Key Words

The *least common multiple* (LCM) is the smallest common multiple of two or more numbers.

The *greatest common factor* (GCF) is the largest common factor of two or more numbers.

A *fraction* can represent the number of equal parts of a whole.

A *proper fraction* is a fraction less than 1.

A *mixed number* is a number greater than 1 with a whole-number part and a fractional part.

An *improper fraction* is a fraction greater than or equal to 1.

Equal fractions with different denominators are called *equivalent fractions.*

A fraction is in *simplest form* when there are no common factors in the numerator and the denominator.

The *reciprocal* of a fraction is the fraction with the numerator and denominator interchanged.

Inverting is the process of finding the reciprocal of a fraction.

Essential Rules

Addition of Fractions with Like Denominators
To add fractions with like denominators, add the numerators and place the sum over the common denominator.

Addition of Fractions with Unlike Denominators
To add fractions with unlike denominators, first rewrite the fractions as equivalent fractions with the same denominator. Then add the numerators and place the sum over the common denominator.

Subtraction of Fractions with Like Denominators
To subtract fractions with like denominators, subtract the numerators and place the difference over the common denominator.

Subtraction of Fractions with Unlike Denominators
To subtract fractions with unlike denominators, rewrite the fractions as equivalent fractions with the same denominator. Then subtract the numerators and place the difference over the common denominator.

Multiplication of Fractions
To multiply two fractions, multiply the numerators and place the product over the product of the denominators.

Division of Fractions
To divide two fractions, multiply by the reciprocal of the divisor.

Chapter Review

1. Write $\frac{30}{45}$ in simplest form.

2. Simplify: $\left(\frac{3}{4}\right)^3 \cdot \frac{20}{27}$

3. Express the shaded portion of the circles as an improper fraction.

4. Find the total of $\frac{2}{3}$, $\frac{5}{6}$, and $\frac{2}{9}$.

5. Place the correct symbol, $<$ or $>$, between the two numbers.

$\frac{11}{18} \qquad \frac{17}{24}$

6. Subtract: $\begin{aligned} 18\tfrac{1}{6} \\ -\ 3\tfrac{5}{7} \\ \hline \end{aligned}$

7. Simplify: $\frac{2}{7}\left(\frac{5}{8} - \frac{1}{3}\right) \div \frac{3}{5}$

8. Multiply: $2\frac{1}{3} \times 3\frac{7}{8}$

9. Divide: $1\frac{1}{3} \div \frac{2}{3}$

10. Find $\frac{17}{24}$ decreased by $\frac{3}{16}$.

11. Divide: $8\frac{2}{3} \div 2\frac{3}{5}$

12. Find the GCF of 20 and 48.

13. Write an equivalent fraction with the given denominator.

$\frac{2}{3} = \frac{}{36}$

14. What is $\frac{15}{28}$ divided by $\frac{5}{7}$?

15. Write an equivalent fraction with the given denominator.

$\frac{8}{11} = \frac{}{44}$

16. Multiply: $2\frac{1}{4} \times 7\frac{1}{3}$

17. Find the LCM of 18 and 12.

18. Write $\frac{16}{44}$ in simplest form.

19. Add: $\frac{3}{8} + \frac{5}{8} + \frac{1}{8}$

20. Subtract: 16
  $-\ 5\frac{7}{8}$
  _____

21. Add: $4\frac{4}{9} + 2\frac{1}{6} + 11\frac{17}{27}$

22. Find the GCF of 15 and 25.

23. Write $\frac{17}{5}$ as a mixed number.

24. Simplify: $\left(\frac{4}{5} - \frac{2}{3}\right)^2 \div \frac{4}{15}$

25. Add: $\frac{3}{8} + 1\frac{2}{3} + 3\frac{5}{6}$

26. Find the LCM of 18 and 27.

27. Subtract: $\frac{11}{18} - \frac{5}{18}$

28. Write $2\frac{5}{7}$ as an improper fraction.

29. Divide: $\frac{5}{6} \div \frac{5}{12}$

30. Multiply: $\frac{5}{12} \times \frac{4}{25}$

31. What is $\frac{11}{50}$ multiplied by $\frac{25}{44}$?

32. Express the shaded portion of the circles as a mixed number.

33. During three months of the rainy season, $5\frac{7}{8}$, $6\frac{2}{3}$, and $8\frac{3}{4}$ inches of rain fell. Find the total rainfall for the three months.

34. A home building contractor bought $4\frac{2}{3}$ acres for $168,000. What was the cost of each acre?

35. A 15-mile race has three checkpoints. The first checkpoint is $4\frac{1}{2}$ miles from the starting point. The second checkpoint is $5\frac{3}{4}$ miles from the first checkpoint. How many miles is the second checkpoint from the finish line?

36. A compact car gets 36 miles on each gallon of gasoline. How many miles can the car travel on $6\frac{3}{4}$ gallons of gasoline?

Chapter Test

1. Multiply: $\dfrac{9}{11} \times \dfrac{44}{81}$

2. Find the GCF of 24 and 80.

3. Divide: $\dfrac{5}{9} \div \dfrac{7}{18}$

4. Simplify: $\left(\dfrac{3}{4}\right)^2 \div \left(\dfrac{2}{3} + \dfrac{5}{6}\right) - \dfrac{1}{12}$

5. Write $9\dfrac{4}{5}$ as an improper fraction.

6. What is $5\dfrac{2}{3}$ multiplied by $1\dfrac{7}{17}$?

7. Write $\dfrac{40}{64}$ in simplest form.

8. Place the correct symbol, $<$ or $>$, between the two numbers.
$$\dfrac{3}{8} \quad \dfrac{5}{12}$$

9. Simplify: $\left(\dfrac{1}{4}\right)^3 \div \left(\dfrac{1}{8}\right)^2 - \dfrac{1}{6}$

10. Find the LCM of 24 and 40.

11. Subtract: $\dfrac{17}{24} - \dfrac{11}{24}$

12. Write $\dfrac{18}{5}$ as a mixed number.

13. Find the quotient of $6\dfrac{2}{3}$ and $3\dfrac{1}{6}$.

14. Write an equivalent fraction with the given denominator.
$$\dfrac{5}{8} = \dfrac{}{72}$$

15. Add: $\dfrac{5}{6}$

$\dfrac{7}{9}$

$+\dfrac{1}{15}$

_____

16. Subtract: $23\dfrac{1}{8}$

$-\ 9\dfrac{9}{44}$

_____

17. What is $\dfrac{9}{16}$ minus $\dfrac{5}{12}$?

18. Simplify: $\left(\dfrac{2}{3}\right)^4 \cdot \dfrac{27}{32}$

19. Add: $\dfrac{7}{12} + \dfrac{11}{12} + \dfrac{5}{12}$

20. What is $12\dfrac{5}{12}$ more than $9\dfrac{17}{20}$?

21. Express the shaded portion of the circles as an improper fraction.

22. An electrician earns \$120 for each day worked. What is the total of the electrician's earnings for working $3\dfrac{1}{2}$ days?

23. Grant Miura bought $7\dfrac{1}{4}$ acres of land for a housing project. One and three-fourths acres were set aside for a park, and the remaining land was developed into $\dfrac{1}{2}$-acre lots. How many lots were available for sale?

24. Chris Aguilar bought 100 shares of a utility stock at \$24$\dfrac{1}{2}$ per share. The stock gained \$5$\dfrac{5}{8}$ during the first month of ownership and lost \$2$\dfrac{1}{4}$ during the second month. Find the value of 1 share of the utility stock at the end of the second month.

25. The rainfall for a 3-month period was $11\dfrac{1}{2}$ inches, $7\dfrac{5}{8}$ inches, and $2\dfrac{1}{3}$ inches. Find the total rainfall for the 3 months.

Cumulative Review

1. Round 290,496 to the nearest thousand.

$$290,000.$$

2. Subtract: $\begin{array}{r} 390,047 \\ -\ 98,769 \\ \hline 291,278 \end{array}$

3. Find the product of 926 and 79.

$$73154$$

4. Divide: $57\overline{)30,792}$ $540.\ R12$

5. Simplify: $4 \cdot (6 - 3) \div 6 - 1$

$$4 \cdot 3 \div 6 - 1$$
$$12 \qquad 2 - 1$$
$$= 1$$

6. Find the prime factorization of 44.

$$2 \cdot 2 \cdot 11$$

7. Find the LCM of 30 and 42.

$$210$$

8. Find the GCF of 60 and 80.

$$20$$

9. Write $7\frac{2}{3}$ as an improper fraction.

$$\frac{23}{3}$$

10. Write $\frac{25}{4}$ as a mixed number.

$$\frac{25}{4} = 5\frac{5}{4} = 6\frac{1}{4}$$

11. Write an equivalent fraction with the given denominator.
$$\frac{5}{16} = \frac{40}{48} \quad 15$$

12. Write $\frac{24}{60}$ in simplest form.

$$\frac{24}{60} = \frac{3}{10}$$

13. What is $\frac{9}{16}$ more than $\frac{7}{12}$?

$$\frac{9}{16} > \frac{7}{12} \quad \frac{1}{1} \quad 1\frac{7}{48}$$

14. Add: $\begin{array}{r} 3\frac{7}{8} \\ 7\frac{5}{12} \\ +\ 2\frac{15}{16} \end{array}$

15. Find $\frac{3}{8}$ less than $\frac{11}{12}$.

$$\frac{13}{24}$$

16. Subtract: $\begin{array}{r} 5\frac{1}{6} \\ -\ 3\frac{7}{18} \\ \hline 1\frac{7}{9} \end{array}$

17. Multiply: $\dfrac{3}{8} \times \dfrac{14}{15}$

$\dfrac{7}{20}$

18. Multiply: $3\dfrac{1}{8} \times 2\dfrac{2}{5}$

$7\dfrac{1}{2}$

19. Divide: $\dfrac{7}{16} \div \dfrac{5}{12}$

$1\dfrac{1}{20}$

20. Find the quotient of $6\dfrac{1}{8}$ and $2\dfrac{1}{3}$.

$2\dfrac{5}{8}$

21. Simplify: $\left(\dfrac{1}{2}\right)^3 \cdot \dfrac{8}{9}$

$\dfrac{1}{9}$

22. Simplify: $\left(\dfrac{1}{2} + \dfrac{1}{3}\right) \div \left(\dfrac{2}{5}\right)^2$

$\dfrac{5}{24}$

23. Molly O'Brien had $1359 in a checking account. During the week, Molly wrote checks of $128, $54, and $315. Find the amount in the checking account at the end of the week.

$862

24. The tickets for a movie were $5 for an adult and $2 for a student. Find the total income from the sale of 87 adult tickets and 135 student tickets.

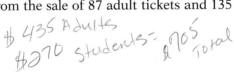

$435 Adults
$270 Students = $705 Total

25. Find the total weight of three packages that weigh $1\dfrac{1}{2}$ pounds, $7\dfrac{7}{8}$ pounds, and $2\dfrac{2}{3}$ pounds.

$12\dfrac{1}{24}$

26. A board $2\dfrac{5}{8}$ feet long is cut from a board $7\dfrac{1}{3}$ feet long. What is the length of the remaining piece?

$4\dfrac{17}{24}$

27. A car travels 27 miles on each gallon of gasoline. How many miles can the car travel on $8\dfrac{1}{3}$ gallons of gasoline?

225

28. Jimmy Santos purchased $10\dfrac{1}{3}$ acres of land to build a housing development. Jimmy donated 2 acres for a park. How many $\dfrac{1}{3}$-acre parcels can be sold from the remaining land?

25

3

Decimals

Bookkeepers record the transactions of a business. This requires excellent skills in adding, subtracting, multiplying, and dividing decimal numbers, which are the numbers we use to represent amounts of money.

Objectives

Decimal Fractions

How would you like to add $\frac{37,544}{23,465} + \frac{5184}{3456}$? These two fractions are very cumbersome, and it would take even a mathematician some time to get the answer.

Well, around 1550, help with such problems arrived with the publication of a book called *La Disme* (*The Tenth*), which urged the use of decimal fractions. A decimal fraction is one in which the denominator is 10, 100, 1000, 10,000, and so on.

This book suggested that all whole numbers were "units" and when written would end with the symbol ⓪. For example, the number 294⓪ would be the number two hundred ninety-four. This is very much like the way numbers are currently written (except for the ⓪).

For a fraction between 0 and 1, a unit was broken down into parts called "primes." The fraction three-tenths would be written

$$\frac{3}{10} = 3①$$ The ① was used to mean the end of the primes, or what are now called tenths.

Each prime was further broken down into "seconds," and each second was broken down into "thirds," and so on. The primes ended with ①, the seconds ended with ②, and the thirds ended with ③.

Examples of these numbers in our modern fraction notation and the old notation are shown below.

$$\frac{37}{100} = 3①7②$$ $$\frac{257}{1000} = 2①5②7③$$

After completing this chapter, you might come back to the problem in the first line. Use decimals instead of fractions to find the answer. The answer is 3.1.

3.1 Introduction to Decimals

Objective A   *To write decimals in standard form and in words* ....

The smallest human bone is found in the middle ear and measures 0.135 inch in length. The number 0.135 is in **decimal notation.**

Note the relationship between fractions and numbers written in decimal notation.

Three-tenths	Three-hundredths	Three-thousandths
$\dfrac{3}{10} = 0.\underline{3}$	$\dfrac{3}{100} = 0.\underline{03}$	$\dfrac{3}{1000} = 0.\underline{003}$
1 zero 1 decimal place	2 zeros 2 decimal places	3 zeros 3 decimal places

A number written in decimal notation has three parts.

351	.	7089
Whole-number part	**Decimal point**	**Decimal part**

A number written in decimal notation is often called simply a **decimal.** The position of a digit in a decimal determines the digit's place value.

In the decimal 351.7089, the position of the digit 9 determines that its place value is ten-thousandths.

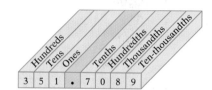

When writing a decimal in words, write the decimal part as if it were a whole number; then name the place value of the last digit.

0.6481   Six thousand four hundred eighty-one ten-thousandths
549.238   Five hundred forty-nine and two hundred thirty-eight thousandths
          (The decimal point is read as "and.")

To write a decimal in standard form, zeros may have to be inserted after the decimal point so that the last digit is in the given place-value position.

Five and thirty-eight <u>hundredths</u>

  8 is in the hundredths' place.   5.3<u>8</u>

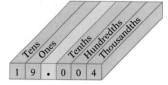

Nineteen and four <u>thousandths</u>

  4 is in the thousandths' place.   19.00<u>4</u>
  Insert two zeros so that 4 is in
  the thousandths' place.

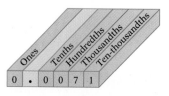

Seventy-one <u>ten-thousandths</u>

  1 is in the ten-thousandths'   0.007<u>1</u>
  place. Insert two zeros so that
  1 is in the ten-thousandths' place.

Example 1	Write 307.4027 in words.	**You Try It 1**	Write 209.05838 in words.
Solution	Three hundred seven and four thousand twenty-seven ten-thousandths	**Your solution**	
Example 2	Write six hundred seven and seven hundred eight hundred-thousandths in standard form.	**You Try It 2**	Write forty-two thousand and two hundred seven millionths in standard form.
Solution	607.00708	**Your solution**	

Solutions on p. S8

Objective B *To round a decimal to a given place value* ....

Rounding decimals is similar to rounding whole numbers except that the digits to the right of the given place value are dropped instead of being replaced by zeros.

If the digit to the right of the given place value is less than 5, drop that digit and all digits to the right. If the digit to the right of the given place value is greater than or equal to 5, increase the number in the given place value by 1 and drop all digits to its right.

➡ Round 26.3799 to the nearest hundredth.

┌─ Given place value
26.3799
└─ 9 > 5 Increase 7 by 1 and drop all digits to the right of 7.

26.3799 rounded to the nearest hundredth is 26.38.

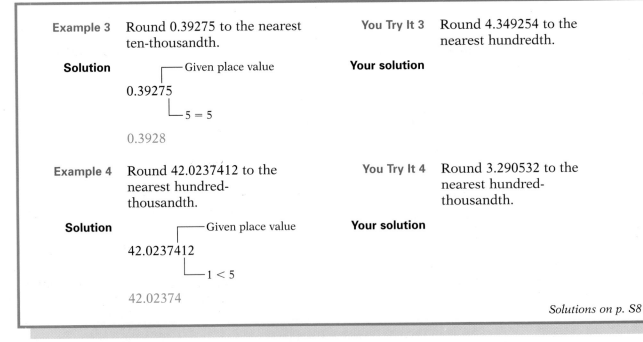

Example 3	Round 0.39275 to the nearest ten-thousandth.	**You Try It 3**	Round 4.349254 to the nearest hundredth.
Solution	┌─ Given place value 0.39275 └─ 5 = 5 0.3928	**Your solution**	
Example 4	Round 42.0237412 to the nearest hundred-thousandth.	**You Try It 4**	Round 3.290532 to the nearest hundred-thousandth.
Solution	┌─ Given place value 42.0237412 └─ 1 < 5 42.02374	**Your solution**	

Solutions on p. S8

3.1 Exercises

Objective A

Write each decimal in words.

1. 0.27

2. 0.92

3. 1.005

4. 3.067

5. 36.4

6. 59.7

7. 0.00035

8. 0.00092

9. 10.007

10. 20.009

11. 52.00095

12. 64.00037

13. 0.0293

14. 0.0717

15. 6.324

16. 8.916

17. 276.3297

18. 418.3115

19. 216.0729

20. 976.0317

21. 4625.0379

22. 2986.0925

23. 1.00001

24. 3.00003

Write each decimal in standard form.

25. Seven hundred sixty-two thousandths

26. Two hundred ninety-five thousandths

27. Sixty-two millionths

28. Forty-one millionths

29. Eight and three hundred four ten-thousandths

30. Four and nine hundred seven ten-thousandths

31. Three hundred four and seven hundredths

32. Eight hundred ninety-six and four hundred seven thousandths

Write each decimal in standard form.

33. Three hundred sixty-two and forty-eight thousandths

34. Seven hundred eighty-four and eighty-four thousandths

35. Three thousand forty-eight and two thousand two ten-thousandths

36. Seven thousand sixty-one and nine thousand one ten-thousandths

---

Objective B

Round each decimal to the given place value.

37. 7.359 Tenths

38. 6.405 Tenths

39. 23.009 Tenths

40. 89.19204 Tenths

41. 22.68259 Hundredths

42. 16.30963 Hundredths

43. 7.072854 Thousandths

44. 1946.3745 Thousandths

45. 62.009435 Thousandths

46. 0.029876 Ten-thousandths

47. 0.012346 Ten-thousandths

48. 1.702596 Nearest whole number

49. 2.079239 Hundred-thousandths

50. 0.0102903 Millionths

51. 0.1009754 Millionths

APPLYING THE CONCEPTS

52. To what decimal place value are timed events in the Olympics recorded? Provide some specific examples of events and the winning times in each.

53. Provide an example of a situation in which a decimal is always rounded up, even if the digit to the right is less than 5. Provide an example of a situation in which a decimal is always rounded down, even if the digit to the right is 5 or greater than 5. (*Hint*: Think about situations in which money changes hands.)

54. Indicate which zeros of the number, if any, need not be entered on a calculator.
 a. 23.500   **b.** 0.000235   **c.** 300.0005   **d.** 0.004050

55. **a.** A decimal number was rounded to 6. Between what two numbers, to the nearest tenth, was the number?
 b. A decimal number was rounded to 10.2. Between what two numbers, to the nearest hundredth, was the number?

3.2 Addition of Decimals

Objective A   *To add decimals* ....

To add decimals, write the numbers so that the decimal points are on a vertical line. Add as for whole numbers, and write the decimal point in the sum directly below the decimal points in the addends.

➡ Add: 0.237 + 4.9 + 27.32

Note that by placing the decimal points on a vertical line, we make sure that digits of the same place value are added.

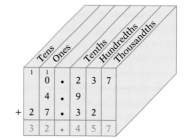

Example 1   Find the sum of 42.3, 162.903, and 65.0729.

Solution

$$
\begin{array}{r}
\overset{1\,1\,1}{42.3} \\
162.903 \\
+\ \ 65.0729 \\
\hline
270.2759
\end{array}
$$

You Try It 1   Add: 4.62 + 27.9 + 0.62054

Your solution

Example 2   Add: 0.83 + 7.942 + 15

Solution

$$
\begin{array}{r}
\overset{1\,1}{0.83} \\
7.942 \\
+\ 15. \\
\hline
23.772
\end{array}
$$

You Try It 2   Add: 6.05 + 12 + 0.374

Your solution

Solutions on p. S8

ESTIMATION

Estimating the Sum of Two or More Decimals

Estimate and then use your calculator to find 23.037 + 16.7892.

To estimate the sum of two or more numbers, round each number to the same place value. In this case, we will round to the nearest whole number. Then add. The estimated answer is 40.

$$
\begin{array}{r}
23.037 \approx\ \ \ 23 \\
+\ 16.7892 \approx +\ 17 \\
\hline
40
\end{array}
$$

Now use your calculator to find the exact result. The exact answer is 39.8262.

23.037 ⊞ 16.7892 ⊟ 39.8262

Objective B   To solve application problems .... 5 6 CT

The 1997 catalog from the West Shore Acres Display Garden has the accompanying list of prices for different numbers and kinds of tulip bulbs. Use this price list for Example 3 and You Try It 3.

		10	20	30
Single Early		$5.80	$11.10	$16.40

One of the first to bloom. 14"-18"; Late March-Early April
CAT.#

050	**APRICOT BEAUTY** Soft salmon rose. Long lasting. 18".
051	**BESTSELLER** Rich golden orange, 14".
052	**CHRISTMAS DREAM** Warm rosy pink. 14".
053	**CHRISTMAS MARVEL** Glowing fuchsia pink, Eleanor's favorite. 14".
054	**GENERAL DEWET** Orange, hint of yellow. Fragrant. 14".
055	**MERRY CHRISTMAS** Cheery "Holiday" red. 14".
056	**PRINCESS IRENE** Salmon orange, purple flame. 14".

Source: 1997 catalog, West Shores Acres Display Garden Catalog, 956 Downey Road, Mount Vernon, WA 98273

Example 3
Find the cost of the following order:

10   Apricot Beauty
30   General Dewet
10   Princess Irene

Strategy
To find the total cost of the order, add the cost of each kind and number of tulips ($5.80, $16.40, $5.80).

Solution
$5.80 + $16.40 + $5.80 = $28.00

The cost of the tulips was $28.00.

You Try It 3
Find the cost of the following order:

30   Christmas Dream
10   Christmas Marvel
30   Merry Christmas

Your strategy

Your solution

Example 4
Dan Burhoe earned a salary of $138.50 for working 5 days this week as a food server. He also received $22.92, $15.80, $19.65, $39.20, and $27.70 in tips during the 5 days. Find his total income for the week.

Strategy
To find the total income, add the tips ($22.92, $15.80, $19.65, $39.20, and $27.70) to the salary ($138.50).

Solution
```
   $138.50
     22.92
     15.80
     19.65
     39.20
 +   27.70
   $263.77
```

Dan's total income for the week was $263.77.

You Try It 4
Anita Khavari, an insurance executive, earns a salary of $425 every four weeks. During the past 4-week period, she received commissions of $485.60, $599.46, $326.75, and $725.42. Find her total income for the past 4-week period.

Your strategy

Your solution

Solutions on p. S8

3.2 Exercises

· ·

Objective A

Add.

1. 16.008 + 2.0385 + 132.06

2. 17.32 + 1.0579 + 16.5

3. 1.792 + 67 + 27.0526

4. 8.772 + 1.09 + 26.5027

5. 3.02 + 62.7 + 3.924

6. 9.06 + 4.976 + 59.6

7. 82.006 + 9.95 + 0.927

8. 0.826 + 8.76 + 79.005

9. 4.307 + 99.82 + 9.078

10.
```
   0.3
+ 0.07
```

11.
```
  0.29
+ 0.4
```

12.
```
 1.007
+ 2.1
```

13.
```
   7.3
+ 9.005
```

14.
```
   4.9257
  27.05
+  9.0063
```

15.
```
   8.72
  99.073
+  2.9736
```

16.
```
   62.4
    9.827
+ 692.44
```

17.
```
   8
  89.43
+  7.0659
```

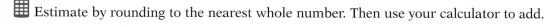 Estimate by rounding to the nearest whole number. Then use your calculator to add.

18.
```
  342.42
   89.625
+ 176.2
```

19.
```
  219.9
    0.872
+  13.42
```

20.
```
  823.9
   82.65
+  46.923
```

21.
```
  678.92
   97.6
+   5.423
```

Objective B   *Application Problems*

22. A family has a mortgage of $814.72, a Visa bill of $216.40, and an electric bill of $87.32. Estimate by rounding the numbers to the nearest hundred dollars, and then calculate the exact amount of the three payments.

23. Find the length of the shaft.

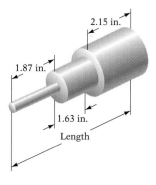

24. Find the length of the shaft.

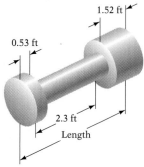

25. Commuting, Mae Chan used 12.4 gallons of gas the first week, 9.8 gallons the second week, 15.2 gallons the third week, and 10.4 gallons the fourth week. Find the total amount of gas she used during the 4 weeks.

26. The odometer on a family's car reads 24,835.9 miles. The car was driven 8.2 miles on Friday, 82.6 miles on Saturday, and 133.6 miles on Sunday.
a. How many miles was the car driven during the three days?
b. Find the odometer reading at the end of the three days.

27. You have $2143.57 in your checking account. You make deposits of $210.98, $45.32, $1236.34, and $27.99. Find the amount in your checking account after you have made the deposits if no money has been withdrawn.

The figure at the right shows the number of viewers who watch television each night of the week. Use this figure for Exercises 28 to 30.

28. Find the total number of television viewers for Friday, Saturday, and Sunday nights.

29. Find the total number of television viewers for Monday, Tuesday, Wednesday, and Thursday nights.

How Many People Tune In Prime-Time TV

	Viewers (Millions)
Mon	91.9
Tues	89.8
Wed	90.6
Thu	93.9
Fri	78.0
Sat	77.1
Sun	87.7

30. Find the total number of television viewers for the week.

APPLYING THE CONCEPTS

The table at the right gives the prices for selected products in a grocery store. Use this table for Exercises 31 and 32.

31. Does a customer with $10 have enough money to purchase raisin bran, bread, milk, lunch meat, and butter?

32. Name three items that would cost more than $6 but less than $7. (There is more than one answer.)

Product	Cost
Raisin bran	3.45
Butter	2.69
Bread	1.23
Popcorn	.89
Potatoes	1.09
Cola (6-pack)	.98
Mayonnaise	2.25
Lunch meat	3.31
Milk	2.18
Toothpaste	2.45

33. Can a piece of rope 4 feet long be wrapped around the box shown at the right?

1.4 ft 1.4 ft 1.4 ft

3.3 Subtraction of Decimals

Objective A *To subtract decimals* ....

To subtract decimals, write the numbers so that the decimal points are on a vertical line. Subtract as for whole numbers, and write the decimal point in the difference directly below the decimal point in the subtrahend.

➡ Subtract 21.532 − 9.875 and check.

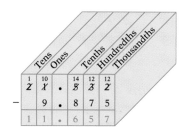

Placing the decimal points on a vertical line ensures that digits of the same place value are subtracted.

$$
\begin{array}{rl}
\textit{Check:} & \quad \text{Subtrahend} \quad\quad \overset{1\;1\;\;11}{9.875} \\
& + \text{Difference} \quad + 11.657 \\ \hline
& = \text{Minuend} \quad\;\; 21.532
\end{array}
$$

➡ Subtract 4.3 − 1.7942 and check.

$$
\begin{array}{r}
\overset{3\quad 12\;9\;9\;10}{\cancel{4}.\cancel{3}\cancel{0}\cancel{0}\cancel{0}} \\
- 1.7942 \\ \hline
2.5058
\end{array}
$$

If necessary, insert zeros in the minuend before subtracting.

$$
\textit{Check:} \quad
\begin{array}{r}
\overset{1\;\;111}{1.7942} \\
+ 2.5058 \\ \hline
4.3000
\end{array}
$$

Example 1 Subtract 39.047 − 7.96 and check.

Solution
$$
\begin{array}{r}
\overset{8\;\;9\;14}{3\cancel{9}.\cancel{0}\cancel{4}7} \\
- \;\; 7.96 \\ \hline
31.087
\end{array}
\qquad
\textit{Check:} \;
\begin{array}{r}
\overset{1\;\;1}{7.96} \\
+ 31.087 \\ \hline
39.047
\end{array}
$$

You Try It 1 Subtract 72.039 − 8.47 and check.

Your solution

Example 2 Find 9.23 less than 29 and check.

Solution
$$
\begin{array}{r}
\overset{1\;18\;\;9\;10}{\cancel{2}\cancel{9}.\cancel{0}\cancel{0}} \\
- \;\; 9.23 \\ \hline
19.77
\end{array}
\qquad
\textit{Check:} \;
\begin{array}{r}
\overset{1\;1\;1}{9.23} \\
+ 19.77 \\ \hline
29.00
\end{array}
$$

You Try It 2 Subtract 35 − 9.67 and check.

Your solution

Example 3 Subtract 1.2 − 0.8235 and check.

Solution
$$
\begin{array}{r}
\overset{0\;\;11\;9\;9\;10}{\cancel{1}.\cancel{2}\cancel{0}\cancel{0}\cancel{0}} \\
- 0.8235 \\ \hline
0.3765
\end{array}
\qquad
\textit{Check:} \;
\begin{array}{r}
\overset{1\;111}{0.8235} \\
+ 0.3765 \\ \hline
1.2000
\end{array}
$$

You Try It 3 Subtract 3.7 − 1.9715 and check.

Your solution

Solutions on p. S8

ESTIMATION

Estimating the Difference Between Two Decimals

Estimate and then use your calculator to find 820.2306 − 475.74815.

To estimate the difference between two numbers, round each number to the same place value. In this case we will round to the nearest ten. Then subtract. The estimated answer is 340.

$$
\begin{array}{r}
820.2306 \approx 820 \\
- \ 475.74815 \approx - \ 480 \\
\hline
340
\end{array}
$$

Now use your calculator to find the exact result. The exact answer is 344.48245.

820.2306 ⊟ 475.74815 🟰 344.48245

Objective B *To solve application problems* ·············   CT

Example 4
You bought a book for $15.87. How much change did you receive from a $20.00 bill?

Strategy
To find the amount of change, subtract the cost of the book ($15.87) from $20.00.

Solution
$$
\begin{array}{r}
\$20.00 \\
- \ 15.87 \\
\hline
\$ \ 4.13
\end{array}
$$

You received $4.13 in change.

You Try It 4
Your breakfast cost $3.85. How much change did you receive from a $5.00 bill?

Your strategy

Your solution

Example 5
You had a balance of $62.41 in your checking account. You then bought a cassette for $8.95, film for $3.17, and a skateboard for $39.77. After paying for these items with a check, how much do you have left in your checking account?

Strategy
To find the new balance:
- Find the total cost of the three items ($8.95 + $3.17 + $39.77).
- Subtract the total cost from the old balance ($62.41).

Solution
$$
\begin{array}{r}
\$ \ 8.95 \\
3.17 \\
+ \ 39.77 \\
\hline
\$51.89 \ \text{total cost}
\end{array}
\qquad
\begin{array}{r}
\$62.41 \\
- \ 51.89 \\
\hline
\$10.52
\end{array}
$$

The new balance is $10.52.

You Try It 5
You had a balance of $2472.69 in your checking account. You then wrote checks for $1025.60, $79.85, and $162.47. Find the new balance in your checking account.

Your strategy

Your solution

Solutions on pp. S8–S9

3.3 Exercises

· ·

Objective A

Subtract and check.

1. 24.037 − 18.41   **2.** 26.029 − 19.31   **3.** 123.07 − 9.4273   **4.** 214 − 7.143

5. 16.5 − 9.7902   **6.** 13.2 − 8.6205   **7.** 235.79 − 20.093   **8.** 463.27 − 40.095

9. 63.005 − 9.1274   **10.** 23.004 − 7.2175   **11.** 92 − 19.2909   **12.** 41.2405 − 25.2709

13. 7.01 − 2.325   **14.** 8.07 − 5.392   **15.** 19.0035 − 8.967

16. 0.32
    − 0.0058

17. 0.78
    − 0.0073

18. 3.005
    − 1.982

19. 6.007
    − 2.734

20. 352.16
    − 90.994

21. 872
    − 80.753

22. 724.32
    − 69

23. 625.46
    − 77.509

24. 362.394
    − 19.4672

25. 421.385
    − 17.5293

26. 19
    − 10.372

27. 23.4
    − 0.921

 Estimate by rounding to the nearest ten. Then use your calculator to subtract.

28. 620.59
    − 132.79

29. 835.07
    − 244.82

30. 67.3
    − 19.793

31. 84.1
    − 48.906

Estimate by rounding to the nearest whole number (nearest one). Then use your calculator to subtract.

32. 93.079256
    − 66.09249

33. 3.7529
    − 1.00784

34. 76.53902
    − 45.73005

35. 9.07325
    − 1.924

Objective B *Application Problems*

36. The manager of the Edgewater Cafe takes a reading of the cash register tape each hour. At 1:00 P.M. the tape read $967.54; at 2:00 P.M. the tape read $1437.15. Find the amount of sales between 1:00 P.M. and 2:00 P.M.

37. Find the missing dimension.

38. Find the missing dimension.

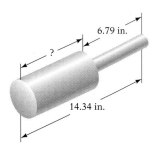

39. You had a balance of $1029.74 in your checking account. You then wrote checks for $67.92, $43.10, and $496.34.
a. Find the total amount of the checks written.
b. Find the new balance in your checking account.

40. The price of gasoline is $1.22 per gallon after the price rose $.07 one month and $.12 the next month. Find the price of gasoline before these increases in price.

41. Rainfall for the last 3 months of the year was 1.42 inches, 5.39 inches, and 3.55 inches. The normal rainfall for the last 3 months of the year is 11.22 inches. How many inches below normal was the rainfall?

42. Grace Herrera owned 357.448 shares of a mutual fund on January 1, 1998. On December 31, 1998, she had 439.917 shares. What was the increase in the number of shares for the year?

43. In 1990, Arie Luyendyk set the Indianapolis 500 average speed record of 185.981 mph. Luyendyk won the race again in 1997 with an average speed of 145.857 mph. Find the difference in average speed for those two races.

The table at the right shows the amount that an investor would pay to buy stocks from various companies. Use the table for Exercises 44 and 45.

44. How much would be saved from buying 200 shares at $25 dollars a share from Quick & Reilly instead of from Schwab?

45. How much would be saved from buying 500 shares at $18 per share from Waterhouse Securities instead of from Merrill Lynch?

Retail Broker	200 sh. @ $25	300 sh. @ $20	500 sh. @ $18
Merrill Lynch	$129.50	$164.85	$225.23
Schwab	$89.00	$95.60	$106.60
Fidelity	$88.50	$95.10	$106.10
Quick & Reilly	$60.50	$65.00	$81.50
Waterhouse Securities	$35.00	$40.82	$57.62

Source: Kiplinger Magazine, March 1997, page 100

APPLYING THE CONCEPTS

46. Find the largest amount by which the estimate of the sum of two decimals with tenths, hundredths, and thousandths places could differ from the exact sum.

3.4 Multiplication of Decimals

Objective A   *To multiply decimals* ....

Decimals are multiplied as if they were whole numbers; then the decimal point is placed in the product. Writing the decimals as fractions shows where to write the decimal point in the product.

$$0.\underline{3} \times 5 = \frac{3}{10} \times \frac{5}{1} = \frac{15}{10} = 1.\underline{5}$$

1 decimal place — 1 decimal place

$$0.\underline{3} \times 0.\underline{5} = \frac{3}{10} \times \frac{5}{10} = \frac{15}{100} = 0.\underline{15}$$

1 decimal place   1 decimal place — 2 decimal places

$$0.\underline{3} \times 0.\underline{05} = \frac{3}{10} \times \frac{5}{100} = \frac{15}{1000} = 0.\underline{015}$$

1 decimal place   2 decimal places — 3 decimal places

To multiply decimals, multiply the numbers as in whole numbers. Write the decimal point in the product so that the number of decimal places in the product is the sum of the decimal places in the factors.

➡ Multiply: 21.4×0.36

$$
\begin{array}{r}
21.4 \\
\times\ 0.36 \\
\hline
1284 \\
642\ \ \ \\
\hline
7.704
\end{array}
$$

21.4 — 1 decimal place
× 0.36 — 2 decimal places
7.704 — 3 decimal places

➡ Multiply: 0.037×0.08

$$
\begin{array}{r}
0.037 \\
\times\ \ 0.08 \\
\hline
0.00296
\end{array}
$$

0.037 — 3 decimal places
× 0.08 — 2 decimal places
0.00296 — 5 decimal places

• Two zeros must be inserted between the 2 and the decimal point so that there are 5 decimal places in the product.

To multiply a decimal by a power of 10 (10, 100, 1000, . . .), move the decimal point to the right the same number of places as there are zeros in the power of 10.

$3.8925 \times 1\underline{0}$ $= 38.925$
 1 zero   1 decimal place

$3.8925 \times 1\underline{00}$ $= 389.25$
 2 zeros   2 decimal places

$3.8925 \times 1\underline{000}$ $= 3892.5$
 3 zeros   3 decimal places

$3.8925 \times 1\underline{0,000}$ $= 38,925.$
 4 zeros   4 decimal places

$3.8925 \times 1\underline{00,000} = 389,250.$
 5 zeros   5 decimal places

Note that a zero must be inserted before the decimal point.

Note that if the power of 10 is written in exponential notation, the exponent indicates how many places to move the decimal point.

$$3.8925 \times 10^1 = 38.925$$
1 decimal place

$$3.8925 \times 10^2 = 389.25$$
2 decimal places

$$3.8925 \times 10^3 = 3892.5$$
3 decimal places

$$3.8925 \times 10^4 = 38,925.$$
4 decimal places

$$3.8925 \times 10^5 = 389,250.$$
5 decimal places

Example 1   Multiply: 920×3.7

Solution
$$
\begin{array}{r}
920 \\
\times \quad 3.7 \\
\hline
644\,0 \\
2760 \\
\hline
3404.0
\end{array}
$$

You Try It 1   Multiply: 870×4.6

Your solution

Example 2   Find 0.00079 multiplied by 0.025.

Solution
$$
\begin{array}{r}
0.00079 \\
\times \quad 0.025 \\
\hline
395 \\
158 \\
\hline
0.00001975
\end{array}
$$

You Try It 2   Find 0.000086 multiplied by 0.057.

Your solution

Example 3   Find the product of 3.69 and 2.07.

Solution
$$
\begin{array}{r}
3.69 \\
\times\, 2.07 \\
\hline
2583 \\
7380 \\
\hline
7.6383
\end{array}
$$

You Try It 3   Find the product of 4.68 and 6.03.

Your solution

Example 4   Multiply: $42.07 \times 10,000$

Solution $42.07 \times 10,000 = 420,700$

You Try It 4   Multiply: 6.9×1000

Your solution

Example 5   Find 3.01 times 10^3.

Solution $3.01 \times 10^3 = 3010$

You Try It 5   Find 4.0273 times 10^2.

Your solution

Solutions on p. S9

ESTIMATION

Estimating the Product of Two Decimals

Estimate and then use your calculator to find 28.259×0.029.

To estimate a product, round each number so that there is one nonzero digit. Then multiply.

$$
\begin{array}{r}
28.259 \approx 30 \\
\times\ 0.029 \approx \times\ 0.03 \\
\hline
0.90
\end{array}
$$

The estimated answer is 0.90.

Now use your calculator to find the exact answer.

$$28.259 \boxed{\times} 0.029 \boxed{=} 0.819511$$

The exact answer is 0.819511.

Objective B   *To solve application problems* ....

The tables below list water rates and meter fees for a city. These tables are used for Example 6 and You Try It 6.

Water Charges			*Meter Charges*	
Commercial	$1.39/1000 gal		*Meter*	*Meter Fee*
Comm Restaurant	$1.39/1000 gal		5/8" & 3/4"	$13.50
Industrial	$1.39/1000 gal		1"	$21.80
Institutional	$1.39/1000 gal		1-1/2"	$42.50
Res—No Sewer			2"	$67.20
Residential—SF			3"	$133.70
>0 <200 gal. per day	$1.15/1000 gal		4"	$208.20
>200 <1500 gal. per day	$1.39/1000 gal		6"	$415.10
>1500 gal. per day	$1.54/1000 gal		8"	$663.70

Example 6

Find the total bill for an industrial water user with a 6-inch meter that uses 152,000 gallons of water for July and August.

Strategy

To find the total cost of water:

- Find the cost of water by multiplying the cost per 1000 gallons ($1.39) by the number of 1000-gallon units used.
- Add the cost of the water to the meter fee ($415.10).

Solution

$$\text{Cost of water} = \frac{152,000}{1000} \cdot 1.39 = 211.28$$

$$\text{Total cost} = 211.28 + 415.10 = 626.38$$

The total cost is $626.38.

You Try It 6

Find the total bill for a commercial user that used 5000 gallons of water per day for July and August. The user has a 3-inch meter.

Your strategy

Your solution

Solution on p. S9

Example 7

It costs $.036 an hour to operate an electric motor. How much does it cost to operate the motor for 120 hours?

Strategy

To find the cost of running the motor for 120 hours, multiply the hourly cost ($.036) by the number of hours the motor is run (120).

Solution

$$
\begin{array}{r}
\$.036 \\
\times \quad 120 \\
\hline
720 \\
36 \quad \\
\hline
\$4.320
\end{array}
$$

The cost of running the motor for 120 hours is $4.32.

You Try It 7

The cost of electricity to run a freezer for 1 hour is $.035. This month the freezer has run for 210 hours. Find the total cost of running the freezer this month.

Your strategy

Your solution

Example 8

Jason Ng earns a salary of $280 for a 40-hour work week. This week he worked 12 hours of overtime at a rate of $10.50 for each hour of overtime worked. Find his total income for the week.

Strategy

To find Jason's total income for the week:

- Find the overtime pay by multiplying the hourly overtime rate ($10.50) by the number of hours of overtime worked (12).
- Add the overtime pay to the weekly salary ($280).

Solution

$$
\begin{array}{r}
\$10.50 \\
\times \quad 12 \\
\hline
21\ 00 \\
105\ 0 \quad \\
\hline
\$126.00 \text{ overtime pay}
\end{array}
\qquad
\begin{array}{r}
\$280.00 \\
+ \quad 126.00 \\
\hline
\$406.00
\end{array}
$$

Jason's total income for this week is $406.00.

You Try It 8

You make a down payment of $175 on a stereo and agree to make payments of $37.18 a month for the next 18 months to repay the remaining balance. Find the total cost of the stereo.

Your strategy

Your solution

Solutions on p. S9

3.4 Exercises

. . . .

Objective A

Multiply.

1.   0.9
$\times$ 0.4

2.   0.7
$\times$ 0.9

3.   0.5
$\times$ 0.6

4.   0.3
$\times$ 0.7

5.   0.5
$\times$ 0.5

6.   0.7
$\times$ 0.7

7.   0.9
$\times$ 0.5

8.   0.2
$\times$ 0.6

9.   7.7
$\times$ 0.9

10.   3.4
$\times$ 0.4

11.   9.2
$\times$ 0.2

12.   2.6
$\times$ 0.7

13.   7.2
$\times$ 0.6

14.   6.8
$\times$ 0.4

15.   7.4
$\times$ 0.1

16.   3.8
$\times$ 0.1

17.   7.9
$\times$ 5

18.   9.3
$\times$ 7

19.   0.68
$\times$ 4

20.   0.83
$\times$ 9

21.   0.67
$\times$ 0.9

22.   0.84
$\times$ 0.3

23.   0.16
$\times$ 0.6

24.   0.47
$\times$ 0.8

25.   2.5
$\times$ 5.4

26.   3.9
$\times$ 1.9

27.   8.4
$\times$ 9.5

28.   7.6
$\times$ 5.8

29.   0.83
$\times$ 5.2

30.   0.24
$\times$ 2.7

31.   0.46
$\times$ 3.9

32.   0.78
$\times$ 6.8

33.   0.2
$\times$ 0.3

34.   0.3
$\times$ 0.3

35.   0.24
$\times$ 0.3

36.   0.17
$\times$ 0.5

37.   1.47
$\times$ .09

38.   6.37
$\times$ 0.05

39.   8.92
$\times$ 0.004

40.   6.75
$\times$ 0.007

Multiply.

41. 0.49
       × 0.16

42. 0.38
       × 0.21

43. 7.6
       × 0.01

44. 5.1
       × 0.01

45. 8.62
       ×   4

46. 5.83
       ×   7

47. 64.5
       ×   9

48. 37.8
       ×   8

49. 2.19
       × 9.2

50. 1.25
       × 5.6

51. 1.85
       × 0.023

52. 37.8
       × 0.052

53. 0.478
       × 0.37

54. 0.526
       ×   0.22

55. 48.3
       × 0.0041

56. 67.2
       × 0.0086

57. 2.437
       ×   6.1

58. 4.237
       × 0.54

59. 0.413
       × 0.0016

60. 0.517
       × 0.0029

61. 94.73
       × 0.57

62. 89.23
       × 0.62

63. 8.005
       × 0.067

64. 9.032
       × 0.019

65. 4.29×0.1

66. 6.78×0.1

67. 5.29×0.4

68. 6.78×0.5

69. 0.68×0.7

70. 0.56×0.9

71. 1.4×0.73

72. 6.3×0.37

73. 5.2×7.3

74. 7.4×2.9

75. 3.8×0.61

76. 7.2×0.72

77. 0.32×10

78. 6.93×10

79. 0.065×100

80. 0.039×100

81. 6.2856×1000

Multiply.

82. 3.2954×1000 **83.** 3.2×1000 **84.** $0.006 \times 10{,}000$ **85.** $3.57 \times 10{,}000$

86. 8.52×10^1 **87.** 0.63×10^1 **88.** 82.9×10^2

89. 0.039×10^2 **90.** 6.8×10^3 **91.** 4.9×10^4

92. 6.83×10^4 **93.** 0.067×10^2 **94.** 0.052×10^2

95. Find the product of 0.0035 and 3.45.   **96.** Find the product of 237 and 0.34.

97. Multiply 3.005 by 0.00392.   **98.** Multiply 20.34 by 1.008.

99. Multiply 1.348 by 0.23.   **100.** Multiply 0.000358 by 3.56.

101. Find the product of 23.67 and 0.0035.   **102.** Find the product of 0.00346 and 23.1.

103. Find the product of 5, 0.45, and 2.3.   **104.** Find the product of 0.03, 23, and 9.45.

Estimate and then use your calculator to multiply.

105.
$$\begin{array}{r} 28.5 \\ \times\ 3.2 \\ \hline \end{array}$$

106.
$$\begin{array}{r} 86.3 \\ \times\ 4.4 \\ \hline \end{array}$$

107.
$$\begin{array}{r} 2.38 \\ \times\ 0.44 \\ \hline \end{array}$$

108.
$$\begin{array}{r} 9.82 \\ \times\ 0.77 \\ \hline \end{array}$$

109.
$$\begin{array}{r} 0.866 \\ \times\ 4.5 \\ \hline \end{array}$$

110.
$$\begin{array}{r} 0.239 \\ \times\ 8.2 \\ \hline \end{array}$$

111.
$$\begin{array}{r} 4.34 \\ \times\ 2.59 \\ \hline \end{array}$$

112.
$$\begin{array}{r} 6.87 \\ \times\ 9.98 \\ \hline \end{array}$$

113.
$$\begin{array}{r} 8.434 \\ \times\ 0.044 \\ \hline \end{array}$$

114.
$$\begin{array}{r} 7.037 \\ \times\ 0.094 \\ \hline \end{array}$$

115.
$$\begin{array}{r} 28.44 \\ \times\ 1.12 \\ \hline \end{array}$$

116.
$$\begin{array}{r} 86.57 \\ \times\ 7.33 \\ \hline \end{array}$$

117.
$$\begin{array}{r} 49.6854 \\ \times\ 39.0672 \\ \hline \end{array}$$

118.
$$\begin{array}{r} 2.00547 \\ \times\ 9.672 \\ \hline \end{array}$$

119.
$$\begin{array}{r} 0.00456 \\ \times\ 0.009542 \\ \hline \end{array}$$

120.
$$\begin{array}{r} 7.00637 \\ \times\ 0.0128 \\ \hline \end{array}$$

Objective B   *Application Problems*

121. It costs $8 a day and $.28 per mile to rent a car. Find the cost to rent a car for five days if the car is driven 530 miles.

122. An electric motor costing $315.45 has an operating cost of $.027 for 1 hour of operation. Find the cost to run the motor for 56 hours. Round to the nearest cent.

123. Four hundred empty soft drink cans weigh 18.75 pounds. A recycling center pays $.75 per pound for the cans. Find the amount received for the 400 cans. Round to the nearest cent.

124. A recycling center pays $.045 per pound for newspapers. Estimate the payment for recycling 520 pounds of newspapers. Find the actual amount received from recycling the newspapers.

125. A broker's fee for buying stock is 0.045 times the price of the stock. An investor bought 100 shares of stock at $38.50 per share. Find the broker's fee.

126. A broker's fee for buying a stock is 0.028 times the price of the stock. An investor bought 100 shares of stock at $54.25 per share. Estimate the broker's fee. Calculate the actual broker's fee.

127. You bought a car for $2000 down and made payments of $127.50 each month for 36 months.
   a. Find the amount of the payments over the 36 months.
   b. Find the total cost of the car.

128. As a nurse, Rob Martinez earns a salary of $344 for a 40-hour work week. This week he worked 15 hours of overtime at a rate of $12.90 for each hour of overtime worked.
   a. Find the amount of overtime pay.
   b. Find Rob's total income for the week.

129. Bay Area Rental Cars charges $12 a day and $.12 per mile for renting a car. You rented a car for 3 days and drove 235 miles. Find the total cost of renting the car.

130. A taxi costs $1.50 and $.20 for each $\frac{1}{8}$ mile driven. Find the cost of hiring a taxi to get from the airport to the hotel—a distance of 5.5 miles.

The table at the right lists three pieces of steel required for a repair project. Use this table for Exercises 131 and 132.

Grade of Steel	Weight (Pounds per Foot)	Required Number of Feet	Cost per Pound
1	2.2	8	$1.20
2	3.4	6.5	1.35
3	6.75	15.4	1.94

131. Find the total cost of each of the grades of steel.

132. Find the total cost of the three pieces of steel.

A confectioner ships holiday packs of candy and nuts anywhere in the United States. At the right is a price list for nuts and candy, and below is a table of shipping charges to zones in the United States. For any fraction of a pound, use the next higher weight. Use these tables for Exercise 133. (16 oz = 1 lb)

Code	Description	Price
112	Almonds 16 oz	4.75
116	Cashews 8 oz	2.90
117	Cashews 16 oz	5.50
130	Macadamias 7 oz	5.25
131	Macadamias 16 oz	9.95
149	Pecan halves 8 oz	6.25
155	Mixed nuts 10 oz	4.80
160	Cashew brittle 8 oz	1.95
182	Pecan roll 8 oz	3.70
199	Chocolate peanuts 8 oz	1.90

Pounds	Zone 1	Zone 2	Zone 3	Zone 4
1–3	6.55	6.85	7.25	7.75
4–6	7.10	7.40	7.80	8.30
7–9	7.50	7.80	8.20	8.70
10–12	7.90	8.20	8.60	9.10

133. Find the cost of sending the following orders to the given mail zone.

a. Code	Quantity		b. Code	Quantity		c. Code	Quantity
116	2		112	1		117	3
130	1		117	4		131	1
149	3		131	2		155	2
182	4		160	3		160	4
Mail to zone 4.			182	5		182	1
			Mail to zone 3.			199	3
						Mail to zone 2.	

APPLYING THE CONCEPTS

134. An emissions test for cars requires that of the total engine exhaust, less than 1 part per thousand $\left(\dfrac{1}{1000} = 0.001\right)$ be hydrocarbon emissions. Using this figure, determine which of the cars in the table below would fail the emissions test.

Car	Total Engine Exhaust	Hydrocarbon Emission
1	367,921	36
2	401,346	42
3	298,773	21
4	330,045	32
5	432,989	45

Chris works at B & W Garage as an auto mechanic and has just completed an engine overhaul for a customer. To determine the cost of the repair job, Chris keeps a list of times worked and parts used. A parts list and a list of the times worked are shown below. Use these tables for Exercises 135 to 138.

Parts Used		Time Spent		Price List		
Item	Quantity	Day	Hours	Item Number	Description	Unit Price
Gasket set	1	Monday	7.0	27345	Valve spring	$1.85
Ring set	1	Tuesday	7.5	41257	Main bearing	3.40
Valves	8	Wednesday	6.5	54678	Valve	4.79
Wrist pins	8	Thursday	8.5	29753	Ring set	33.98
Valve springs	16	Friday	9.0	45837	Gasket set	48.99
Rod bearings	8			23751	Timing chain	42.95
Main bearings	5			23765	Fuel pump	77.59
Valve seals	16			28632	Wrist pin	2.71
Timing chain	1			34922	Rod bearing	2.67
				2871	Valve seal	0.42

135. Organize a table of data showing the parts used, the unit price for each, and the price of the quantity used. *Hint:* Use the following headings for the table.

Quantity   *Item Number*   *Description*   *Unit Price*   *Total*

136. Add up the numbers in the "Total" column to find the total cost of the parts.

137. If the charge for labor is $26.75 per hour, compute the cost of labor.

138. What is the total cost for parts and labor?

139. Explain how the decimal point is placed when a number is multiplied by 10, 100, 1000, 10,000, etc.

140. Explain how the decimal point is placed in the product of two decimals.

141. Show how the decimal is placed in the product of 1.3×2.31 by first writing each number as a fraction and then multiplying. Now change back to decimal notation.

3.5   Division of Decimals

Objective A   *To divide decimals* ....

To divide decimals, move the decimal point in the divisor to the right to make the divisor a whole number. Move the decimal point in the dividend the same number of places to the right. Place the decimal point in the quotient directly over the decimal point in the dividend, and then divide as in whole numbers.

⟹ Divide: $3.25\overline{)15.275}$

$$3.25.\overline{)15.27.5}$$

Move the decimal point 2 places to the right in the divisor and then in the dividend. Place the decimal point in the quotient.

$$
\begin{array}{r}
4.7 \\
325.\overline{)\,1527.5} \\
-1300 \\
\hline
227\ 5 \\
-227\ 5 \\
\hline
0
\end{array}
$$

Moving the decimal point the same number of decimal places in the divisor and dividend does not change the value of the quotient, because this process is the same as multiplying the numerator and denominator of a fraction by the same number. In the example above,

$$3.25\overline{)15.275} = \frac{15.275}{3.25} = \frac{15.275 \times 100}{3.25 \times 100} = \frac{1527.5}{325} = 325\overline{)1527.5}$$

When dividing decimals, we usually round the quotient off to a specified place value, rather than writing the quotient with a remainder.

⟹ Divide: $0.3\overline{)0.56}$
    Round to the nearest hundredth.

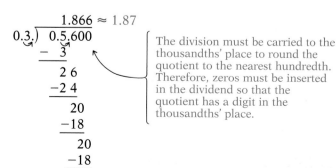

The division must be carried to the thousandths' place to round the quotient to the nearest hundredth. Therefore, zeros must be inserted in the dividend so that the quotient has a digit in the thousandths' place.

➡ Divide: 57.93 ÷ 3.24
Round to the nearest thousandth.

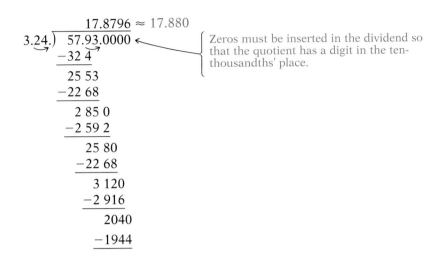

$$17.8796 \approx 17.880$$

$$3.24.\overline{)\ 57.93.0000} \quad\longleftarrow$$

Zeros must be inserted in the dividend so that the quotient has a digit in the ten-thousandths' place.

$$\begin{array}{r}
-32\ 4 \\ \hline
25\ 53 \\
-22\ 68 \\ \hline
2\ 85\ 0 \\
-2\ 59\ 2 \\ \hline
25\ 80 \\
-22\ 68 \\ \hline
3\ 120 \\
-2\ 916 \\ \hline
2040 \\
-1944 \\ \hline
\end{array}$$

To divide a decimal by a power of 10 (10, 100, 1000, . . .), move the decimal point to the left the same number of places as there are zeros in the power of 10.

34.65 ÷ 1<u>0</u>   = 3.465
      1 zero   1 decimal place

34.65 ÷ 1<u>00</u>   = 0.3465
      2 zeros   2 decimal places

34.65 ÷ 1<u>000</u>   = 0.03465

Note that a zero must be inserted between the 3 and the decimal point.

      3 zeros   3 decimal places

34.65 ÷ 1<u>0,000</u> = 0.003465

Note that two zeros must be inserted between the 3 and the decimal point.

      4 zeros   4 decimal places

If the power of 10 is written in exponential notation, the exponent indicates how many places to move the decimal point.

$34.65 \div 10^1 = 3.465$ 1 decimal place

$34.65 \div 10^2 = 0.3465$ 2 decimal places

$34.65 \div 10^3 = 0.03465$ 3 decimal places

$34.65 \div 10^4 = 0.003465$ 4 decimal places

Example 1   Divide: 0.1344 ÷ 0.032

Solution

$$0.032.\overline{)0.134.4} \\
\begin{array}{r}
4.2 \\
-128 \\ \hline
6\ 4 \\
-6\ 4 \\ \hline
0
\end{array}$$

You Try It 1   Divide: 0.1404 ÷ 0.052

Your solution

Solution on p. S9

Example 2 Divide: $58.092 \div 82$
Round to the nearest
thousandth.

Solution

$$
\begin{array}{r}
0.7084 \approx 0.708 \\
82)\overline{58.0920} \\
-57\ 4 \\
\hline
69 \\
-\ \ 0 \\
\hline
692 \\
-656 \\
\hline
360 \\
-328 \\
\hline
\end{array}
$$

You Try It 2 Divide: $37.042 \div 76$
Round to the nearest
thousandth.

Your solution

Example 3 Divide: $420.9 \div 7.06$
Round to the nearest tenth.

Solution

$$
\begin{array}{r}
59.61 \approx 59.6 \\
7.06.)\overline{420.90.00} \\
-353\ 0 \\
\hline
67\ 90 \\
-63\ 54 \\
\hline
4\ 36\ 0 \\
-4\ 23\ 6 \\
\hline
12\ 40 \\
-\ \ 7\ 06 \\
\hline
\end{array}
$$

You Try It 3 Divide: $370.2 \div 5.09$
Round to the nearest tenth.

Your solution

Example 4 Divide: $402.75 \div 1000$

Solution $402.75 \div 1000 = 0.40275$

You Try It 4 Divide: $309.21 \div 10,000$

Your solution

Example 5 What is 0.625 divided by 10^2?

Solution $0.625 \div 10^2 = 0.00625$

You Try It 5 What is 42.93 divided by 10^4?

Your solution

Solutions on pp. S9–S10

ESTIMATION

Estimating the Quotient of Two Decimals

Estimate and then use your calculator to find $282.18 \div 0.48$.

To estimate a quotient, round each number so
that there is one nonzero digit. Then divide.

$$282.18 \div 0.48 \approx$$
$$300 \div 0.5 = 600$$

The estimated answer is 600.

Now use your calculator to find the
exact answer.

$282.18 \boxed{\div} 0.48 \boxed{=} 587.875$

The exact answer is 587.875.

Objective B   To solve application problems ···

Gasoline Taxes in Dollars per Gallon

State	Taxes
Arkansas	$.185
Georgia	$.875
Nebraska	$.264
Wisconsin	$.237

The table at the right shows the total amount of gasoline tax paid per gallon of gas in selected states in 1997. Use this table for Example 6 and You Try It 6.

Example 6
Eddie Lopez's car gets 28 miles per gallon of gas. In 1997, he drove 12,110 miles in Arkansas. How much did he pay, to the nearest dollar, in gasoline taxes?

Strategy
To find the amount he paid in gasoline taxes:

- Find the total number of gallons of gas he used by dividing his total miles traveled (12,110) by the number of miles traveled per gallon (28).
- Multiply the state tax ($.185) by the total number of gallons of gasoline used.

Solution
$12{,}110 \div 28 = 432.5$
$0.185 \times 432.5 = 80.0125$

Eddie paid approximately $80 for gasoline taxes.

You Try It 6
In 1997, Susan Beckman drove her car 9675 miles in Georgia. If her car gets 22.5 miles per gallon, how much did she pay in gasoline taxes?

Your strategy

Your solution

Example 7
In 1996, AFLAG had earnings before income taxes of $650,001,000. AFLAG paid total income taxes of $255,638,000. Find the net earnings per share. AFLAG had issued 144,512,000 shares of stock. Round to the nearest cent.

Strategy
To find the net earnings per share:

- Find the net income by subtracting $255,638,000 from $650,001,000.
- Divide the difference by the number of shares (144,512,000).

Solution
$650{,}001{,}000 - 255{,}638{,}000 = 394{,}363{,}000$
$394{,}363{,}000 \div 144{,}512{,}000 \approx 2.728929$

Net earnings per share are approximately $2.73.

You Try It 7
A Nielsen survey of the number of people (in millions) who watch television during the week is given in the table below.

Mon.	Tues.	Wed.	Thu.	Fri.	Sat.	Sun.
91.9	89.8	90.6	93.9	78.0	77.1	87.7

Find the average number of people watching television per day.

Your strategy

Your solution

Solutions on p. S10

3.5 Exercises

· ·

Objective A

Divide.

1. $3\overline{)2.46}$

2. $7\overline{)3.71}$

3. $0.8\overline{)3.84}$

4. $0.9\overline{)6.93}$

5. $0.7\overline{)62.3}$

6. $0.4\overline{)52.8}$

7. $0.4\overline{)24}$

8. $0.5\overline{)65}$

9. $0.7\overline{)59.01}$

10. $0.9\overline{)8.721}$

11. $0.5\overline{)16.15}$

12. $0.8\overline{)77.6}$

13. $0.7\overline{)3.542}$

14. $0.6\overline{)2.436}$

15. $6.3\overline{)8.19}$

16. $3.2\overline{)7.04}$

17. $3.6\overline{)0.396}$

18. $2.7\overline{)0.648}$

19. $6.9\overline{)26.22}$

20. $1.7\overline{)84.66}$

Divide. Round to the nearest tenth.

21. $55.62 \div 8.8$

22. $25.43 \div 5.4$

23. $5.427 \div 9.5$

24. $1.837 \div 1.4$

25. $18.4 \div 7.3$

26. $52.9 \div 8.1$

27. $0.183 \div 0.17$

28. $0.381 \div 0.47$

29. $6.924 \div 0.053$

Divide. Round to the nearest hundredth.

30. $4.817 \div 16$

31. $6.467 \div 8$

32. $0.0418 \div 0.53$

33. $19.08 \div 0.45$

34. $21.792 \div 0.96$

35. $38.665 \div 0.95$

36. $13.97 \div 25.4$

37. $27.738 \div 60.3$

38. $3.171 \div 45.3$

Divide. Round to the nearest thousandth.

39. $1.028 \div 54$

40. $6.729 \div 27$

41. $0.0437 \div 0.5$

42. $75.469 \div 77.8$

43. $34.31 \div 95.3$

44. $0.2695 \div 2.67$

45. $0.4871 \div 4.72$

46. $0.1142 \div 17.2$

47. $0.2307 \div 26.7$

Divide. Round to the nearest whole number.

48. $16.5 \div 4$

49. $89.76 \div 90$

50. $1.94 \div 0.3$

51. $1.0478 \div 0.413$

52. $2.148 \div 0.519$

53. $0.79 \div 0.778$

54. $3.092 \div 0.075$

55. $392 \div 6.9$

56. $8.729 \div 0.075$

Divide.

57. $4.07 \div 10$

58. $0.039 \div 10$

59. $42.67 \div 10$

60. $389.7 \div 100$

61. $1.037 \div 100$

62. $237.835 \div 100$

63. $8.295 \div 1000$

64. $82,547 \div 1000$

65. $825.37 \div 1000$

66. $8.35 \div 10$

67. $0.32 \div 10$

68. $87.65 \div 10$

69. $23.627 \div 10^2$

70. $2.954 \div 10^2$

71. $0.0053 \div 10^2$

72. $289.32 \div 10^3$

73. $1.8932 \div 10^3$

74. $0.139 \div 10^3$

75. Divide 44.208 by 2.4.

76. Divide 0.04664 by 0.44.

77. Find the quotient of 723.15 and 45.

78. Find the quotient of 3.3463 and 3.07.

79. Divide 13.5 by 10^3.

80. Divide 0.045 by 10^5.

81. Find the quotient of 23.678 and 1000.

82. Find the quotient of 7.005 and 10,000.

83. What is 0.0056 divided by 0.05?

84. What is 123.8 divided by 0.02?

Estimate and then use your calculator to divide. Round your calculated answer to the nearest ten-thousandth.

85. 42.42 ÷ 3.8

86. 69.8 ÷ 7.2

87. 389 ÷ 0.44

88. 642 ÷ 0.83

89. 6.394 ÷ 3.5

90. 8.429 ÷ 4.2

91. 1.235 ÷ 0.021

92. 7.456 ÷ 0.072

93. 95.443 ÷ 1.32

94. 423.0925 ÷ 4.0927

95. 1.000523 ÷ 429.07

96. 0.03629 ÷ 0.00054

Objective B   *Application Problems*

97. Ramon, a high school football player, gained 162 yards on 26 carries in a high school football game. Find the average number of yards gained per carry. Round to the nearest hundredth.

98. Ross Lapointe earns $39,440.64 for 12 months' work as a park ranger. How much does he earn in 1 month?

99. A car with an odometer reading of 17,814.2 is filled with 9.4 gallons of gas. At an odometer reading of 18,130.4, the tank is empty and the car is filled with 12.4 gallons of gas. How many miles does the car travel on 1 gallon of gasoline?

100. A case of diet cola costs $6.79. If there are 24 cans in a case, find the cost per can. Round to the nearest cent.

101. Anne is building bookcases that are 3.4 feet long. How many complete shelves can be cut from a 12-foot board?

102. Earl is 52 years old and is buying $70,000 of life insurance for an annual premium of $703.80. If he pays each annual premium in 12 equal installments, how much is each monthly payment?

103. An oil company has issued 3,541,221,500 shares of stock. The company paid $6,090,990,120 in dividends. Find the dividend for each share of stock. Round to the nearest cent.

104. The total budget for the United States in 1996 was $1.63 trillion. If each person in the United States were to pay the same amount of taxes, how much would each person pay to raise that amount of money? Assume that there are 267 million people in the United States. Round to the nearest dollar.

105. You buy a home entertainment center for $1242.58. The down payment is $400, and the balance is to be paid in 18 equal monthly payments.
   a. Find the amount to be paid in monthly payments.
   b. Find the amount of each monthly payment.

APPLYING THE CONCEPTS

106. Explain how the decimal point is moved when dividing a number by 10, 100, 1,000, 10,000, etc.

107. A ball point pen priced at 50¢ was not selling. When the price was reduced to a different whole number of cents, the entire stock sold for $31.95. How many cents were charged per pen when the price was reduced? (*Hint*: There is more than one possible answer.)

108. Explain how baseball batting averages are determined. Then find Tony Gwynn's batting average with 175 hits out of 489 at bats. Round to the nearest thousandth.

109. Explain how the decimal point is placed in the quotient when dividing by a decimal.

For each of the problems below, insert a $+$, $-$, $\times$, or $\div$ into the square so that the statement is true.

110. $3.45 \,\square\, 0.5 = 6.9$ **111.** $3.46 \,\square\, 0.24 = 0.8304$ **112.** $6.009 \,\square\, 4.68 = 1.329$

113. $0.064 \,\square\, 1.6 = 0.1024$ **114.** $9.876 \,\square\, 23.12 = 32.996$ **115.** $3.0381 \,\square\, 1.23 = 2.47$

Fill in the square to make a true statement.

116. $6.47 - \square = 1.253$ **117.** $6.47 + \square = 9$ **118.** $0.009 \div \square = 0.36$

3.6 Comparing and Converting Fractions and Decimals

Objective A   *To convert fractions to decimals* ....

Every fraction can be written as a decimal. To write a fraction as a decimal, divide the numerator of the fraction by the denominator. The quotient can be rounded to the desired place value.

➡ Convert $\frac{3}{7}$ to a decimal.

$$\begin{array}{r} 0.42857 \\ 7\overline{)3.00000} \end{array}$$ $\frac{3}{7}$ rounded to the nearest hundredth is 0.43.

$\frac{3}{7}$ rounded to the nearest thousandth is 0.429.

$\frac{3}{7}$ rounded to the nearest ten-thousandth is 0.4286.

➡ Convert $3\frac{2}{9}$ to a decimal. Round to the nearest thousandth.

$$3\frac{2}{9} = \frac{29}{9} \qquad \begin{array}{r} 3.2222 \\ 9\overline{)29.0000} \end{array}$$ $3\frac{2}{9}$ rounded to the nearest thousandth is 3.222.

Example 1   Convert $\frac{3}{8}$ to a decimal. Round to the nearest hundredth.

Solution $\begin{array}{r} 0.375 \\ 8\overline{)3.000} \end{array} \approx 0.38$

You Try It 1   Convert $\frac{9}{16}$ to a decimal. Round to the nearest tenth.

Your solution

Example 2   Convert $2\frac{3}{4}$ to a decimal. Round to the nearest tenth.

Solution $2\frac{3}{4} = \frac{11}{4} \qquad \begin{array}{r} 2.75 \\ 4\overline{)11.00} \end{array} \approx 2.8$

You Try It 2   Convert $4\frac{1}{6}$ to a decimal. Round to the nearest hundredth.

Your solution

Solutions on p. S10

Objective B   *To convert decimals to fractions* ....

To convert a decimal to a fraction, remove the decimal point and place the decimal part over a denominator equal to the place value of the last digit in the decimal.

$$0.47 \overset{\text{hundredths}}{=} \frac{47}{100} \qquad\qquad 7.45 \overset{\text{hundredths}}{=} 7\frac{45}{100} = 7\frac{9}{20}$$

$$0.275 \overset{\text{thousandths}}{=} \frac{275}{1000} = \frac{11}{40} \qquad 0.16\frac{2}{3} \overset{\text{hundredths}}{=} \frac{16\frac{2}{3}}{100} = 16\frac{2}{3} \div 100 = \frac{50}{3} \times \frac{1}{100} = \frac{1}{6}$$

Example 3   Convert 0.82 and 4.75 to fractions.

Solution $0.82 = \dfrac{82}{100} = \dfrac{41}{50}$

$4.75 = 4\dfrac{75}{100} = 4\dfrac{3}{4}$

You Try It 3   Convert 0.56 and 5.35 to fractions.

Your solution

Example 4   Convert $0.15\dfrac{2}{3}$ to a fraction.

Solution $0.15\dfrac{2}{3} = \dfrac{15\frac{2}{3}}{100} = 15\dfrac{2}{3} \div 100$

$= \dfrac{47}{3} \times \dfrac{1}{100} = \dfrac{47}{300}$

You Try It 4   Convert $0.12\dfrac{7}{8}$ to a fraction.

Your solution

Solutions on p. S10

Objective C   *To identify the order relation between two decimals or between a decimal and a fraction* ....

Decimals, like whole numbers and fractions, can be graphed as points on the number line. The number line can be used to show the order of decimals. A decimal that appears to the right of a given number is greater than the given number. A decimal that appears to the left of a given number is less than the given number.

3.00 3.05 3.10 3.15 3.20 3.25 3.30 3.35 3.40

Note that 3, 3.0, and 3.00 represent the same number.

➡ Find the order relation between $\dfrac{3}{8}$ and 0.38.

$\dfrac{3}{8} = 0.375$ $0.38 = 0.380$

$0.375 < 0.380$

$\dfrac{3}{8} < 0.38$

Example 5   Place the correct symbol, < or >, between the numbers.

$\dfrac{5}{16}$ 0.32

Solution $\dfrac{5}{16} \approx 0.313$

$0.313 < 0.32$

$\dfrac{5}{16} < 0.32$

You Try It 5   Place the correct symbol, < or >, between the numbers.

0.63 $\dfrac{5}{8}$

Your solution

Solution on p. S10

3.6 Exercises

. . . .

Objective A

Convert the fraction to a decimal. Round to the nearest thousandth.

1. $\dfrac{5}{8}$ **2.** $\dfrac{7}{12}$ **3.** $\dfrac{2}{3}$ **4.** $\dfrac{5}{6}$ **5.** $\dfrac{1}{6}$ **6.** $\dfrac{7}{8}$

7. $\dfrac{5}{12}$ **8.** $\dfrac{9}{16}$ **9.** $\dfrac{7}{4}$ **10.** $\dfrac{5}{3}$ **11.** $1\dfrac{1}{2}$ **12.** $2\dfrac{1}{3}$

13. $\dfrac{16}{4}$ **14.** $\dfrac{36}{9}$ **15.** $\dfrac{3}{1000}$ **16.** $\dfrac{5}{10}$ **17.** $7\dfrac{2}{25}$ **18.** $16\dfrac{7}{9}$

19. $37\dfrac{1}{2}$ **20.** $87\dfrac{1}{2}$ **21.** $\dfrac{3}{8}$ **22.** $\dfrac{11}{16}$ **23.** $\dfrac{5}{24}$ **24.** $\dfrac{4}{25}$

25. $3\dfrac{1}{3}$ **26.** $8\dfrac{2}{5}$ **27.** $5\dfrac{4}{9}$ **28.** $3\dfrac{1}{12}$ **29.** $\dfrac{5}{16}$ **30.** $\dfrac{11}{12}$

Objective B

Convert the decimal to a fraction.

31. 0.8   **32.** 0.4   **33.** 0.32   **34.** 0.48   **35.** 0.125

36. 0.485   **37.** 1.25   **38.** 3.75   **39.** 16.9   **40.** 17.5

41. 8.4   **42.** 10.7   **43.** 8.437   **44.** 9.279   **45.** 2.25

46. 7.75   **47.** $0.15\dfrac{1}{3}$ **48.** $0.17\dfrac{2}{3}$ **49.** $0.87\dfrac{7}{8}$ **50.** $0.12\dfrac{5}{9}$

Convert the decimal to a fraction.

51. 1.68   **52.** 7.38   **53.** 0.045   **54.** 0.085   **55.** 16.72

56. 82.32   **57.** 0.33   **58.** 0.57   **59.** $0.33\frac{1}{3}$ **60.** $0.66\frac{2}{3}$

Objective C

Place the correct symbol, $<$ or $>$, between the numbers.

61. 0.15   0.5   **62.** 0.6   0.45   **63.** 6.65   6.56   **64.** 3.89   3.98

65. 2.504   2.054   **66.** 0.025   0.105   **67.** $\frac{3}{8}$ 0.365   **68.** $\frac{4}{5}$ 0.802

69. $\frac{2}{3}$ 0.65   **70.** 0.85 $\frac{7}{8}$ **71.** $\frac{5}{9}$ 0.55   **72.** $\frac{7}{12}$ 0.58

73. 0.62 $\frac{7}{15}$ **74.** $\frac{11}{12}$ 0.92   **75.** 0.161 $\frac{1}{7}$ **76.** 0.623   0.6023

77. 0.86   0.855   **78.** 0.87   0.087   **79.** 1.005   0.5   **80.** 0.033   0.3

APPLYING THE CONCEPTS

81. Which of the following is true?
  a. $\frac{137}{300} = 0.456666667$ **b.** $\frac{137}{300} < 0.45666666$ **c.** $\frac{137}{300} > 0.45666666$

82. Is $\frac{7}{13}$ in decimal form a repeating decimal? Why or why not?

83. If a number is rounded to the nearest thousandth, is it always greater than if it was rounded to the nearest hundredth? Give examples to support your answer.

84. Convert $\frac{1}{9}, \frac{2}{9}, \frac{3}{9}$, and $\frac{4}{9}$ to decimals. Describe the pattern. Use the pattern to convert $\frac{5}{9}, \frac{7}{9}$, and $\frac{8}{9}$ to decimals.

85. Explain the difference between terminating, repeating, and nonrepeating decimals. Give an example of each kind of decimal.

Focus on Problem Solving

Problems in mathematics or real life involve a question or a need and information or circumstances about that need. Solving problems in the sciences usually involves a question, observation, and measurements of some kind.

One of the challenges of problem solving in the sciences is to separate the relevant information about a problem from other information. Following is an example from the physical sciences in which some relevant information was omitted.

Hooke's Law states that the distance that a weight will stretch a spring is directly proportional to the weight on the spring. That is, $d = kF$, where d is the distance the spring is stretched and F is the force. In an experiment to verify this law, some physics students were continually getting inconsistent results. Finally, the instructor discovered that the heat produced when the lights were turned on was affecting the experiment. In this case, relevant information was omitted, namely that the temperature of the spring can affect the distance it will stretch.

A lawyer drove 8 miles to the train station. After a 35-minute ride of 18 miles, the lawyer walked 10 minutes to the office. Find the total time it took the lawyer to get to work.

From this situation, answer the following before reading on.

a. What is asked for?

b. Is there enough information to answer the question?

c. Is information given that is not necessary?

Here are the answers.

a. We want the total time for the lawyer to get to work.

b. No. We do not know the time it takes the lawyer to get to the train station.

c. Yes. The distance to the train station and the distance of the train ride are not necessary to answer the question.

In the following problems,

a. What is asked for?

b. Is there enough information to answer the question?

c. Is some information not needed?

1. A customer bought 6 boxes of strawberries and paid with a $20 bill. What was the change?

2. A board is cut into two pieces. One piece is 3 feet longer than the other piece. What is the length of the original board?

3. A family rented a car for their vacation and drove 680 miles. The cost of the rental car was $21 per day with 150 free miles per day and $.15 for each mile driven above the number of free miles allowed. How many miles did the family drive per day?

4. An investor bought 8 acres of land for $80,000. One and one-half acres were set aside for a park, and the remainder was developed into one-half-acre lots. How many lots were available for sale?

5. You wrote checks of $43.67, $122.88, and $432.22 after making a deposit of $768.55. How much do you have left in your checking account?

Projects and Group Activities

Topographical Maps   Carpenters use fractions to measure the wood that is used to frame a house. For instance, a door entry may measure $42\frac{1}{2}$ inches. However, the grading contractor (the person who levels the lot on which the house is built) measures the height of the lot by using decimals. For instance, a certain place may be at a height of 554.2 feet. (The height is measured above sea level; so 554.2 means 554.2 feet above sea level.)

A surveyor provides the grading contractor with a grading plan that shows the elevation of each point of the lot. These plans are drawn so that the house can be sited in such a way that water will drain away from it. The diagram below is a **topographical map** for a lot. Along each closed curve, called a **contour curve,** the lot is at the same height above sea level. For instance, every point on the curve in red is 556.5 feet above sea level.

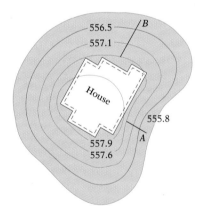

Using the map above, answer the following questions.

1. What is the elevation of the highest point on the lot?

2. What is the elevation of the lowest point on the lot?

3. What is the difference in elevation between the highest and lowest points on the lot?

4. Assuming that this map is drawn to scale, describe the significance of how steep the slope is along line *A* compared to that along line *B*.

5. Acquire a forest service contour map of a portion of a national forest and plan a cross-country hike, choosing a trail that avoids the steepest ascent.

Search the World Wide Web

Go to the Internet and find http://globe3.gsfc.nasa.gov/cgi-bin/show.cgi/&page= help-contour-productn.ht. This explains the basics of contour maps, and shows how to produce a simple contour map from scattered data points as shown below. This contour map is different from the one above in that in this exercise, the contour line connects data values of equal temperature. Complete the contour map that is shown on the Web site and discuss the meaning of (a) contour line, (b) data point, and (c) interpolation.

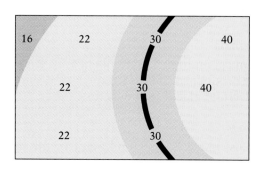

The data points that show 30 degrees are connected by a dotted line in the diagram at the left. To the right of the dotted line the temperature is warmer, and to the left of the dotted line the temperature is colder.

The Internet also provides a great deal of information on booking airline flights, car rentals, ocean cruises, and hotel reservations. Information can also be found on renting recreational vehicles, campground costs, and Amtrak vacation packages.

Go to the Internet and find http://www.cruiseweb.com/. Here you can find information on many cruises to all parts of the world. Plan a cruise of your choice and calculate the cost, including the airfare. Airfare cost can be found at http://www.airfare.com.

Go to the Internet and find http://www.amtrak.com. This address provides the history of Amtrak and vacation packages. Plan a vacation, include the route, with stopovers at two different hotels. Hotel information can be found at http://www.webscope.com/travel/chains.html.

If you like camping, the cost of renting recreational vehicles can be found at http://www.rvlink.com. If seeing Europe by rail is interesting, you can check out the cost on the Internet. The Internet address is http://www.starnetinc.com/eurorail/railindx.htm.

Chapter Summary

Key Words

A number written in *decimal notation* has three parts: a whole-number part, a decimal point, and a decimal part.

The position of a digit in a *decimal* determines the digit's *place value*.

Essential Rules

To Write a Decimal in Words

To write a decimal in words, write the decimal part as if it were a whole number. Then name the place value of the last digit.

To Add Decimals

To add decimals, write the numbers so that the decimal points are on a vertical line. Add as in whole numbers, and place the decimal point in the sum directly below the decimal point in the addends.

To Subtract Decimals

To subtract decimals, place the numbers so that the decimal points are on a vertical line. Subtract as for whole numbers, and write the decimal point in the difference directly below the decimal point in the subtrahend.

To Multiply Decimals

To multiply decimals, multiply the numbers as in whole numbers. Place the decimal point in the product so that the number of decimal places in the product is the sum of the decimal places in the factors.

To Divide Decimals

To divide decimals, move the decimal point in the divisor to make it a whole number. Move the decimal point in the dividend the same number of places to the right. Place the decimal point in the quotient directly over the decimal point in the dividend. Then divide as in whole numbers.

To Write a Fraction as a Decimal

To write a fraction as a decimal, divide the numerator of the fraction by the denominator. Round the quotient to the desired number of places.

To Convert a Decimal to a Fraction

To convert a decimal to a fraction, remove the decimal point and place the decimal part over a denominator equal to the place value of the last digit in the decimal.

Chapter Review

1. Find the quotient of 3.6515 and 0.067.

2. Find the sum of 369.41, 88.3, 9.774, and 366.474.

3.. Place the correct symbol, $<$ or $>$, between the two numbers.
    0.055   0.1

4. Write 22.0092 in words.

5. Round 0.05678235 to the nearest hundred-thousandth.

6. Convert $2\frac{1}{3}$ to a decimal. Round to the nearest hundredth.

7. Convert 0.375 to a fraction.

8. Add: $3.42 + 0.794 + 32.5$

9. Write thirty-four and twenty-five thousandths in standard form.

10. Place the correct symbol, $<$ or $>$, between the two numbers.
    $\frac{5}{8}$ 0.62

11. Convert $\frac{7}{9}$ to a decimal. Round to the nearest thousandth.

12. Convert $0.66\frac{2}{3}$ to a fraction.

13. Subtract: $27.31 - 4.4465$

14. Round 7.93704 to the nearest hundredth.

15. Find the product of 3.08 and 2.9.

16. Write 342.37 in words.

17. Write three and six thousand seven hundred fifty-three hundred-thousandths in standard form.

18. Multiply: 34.79
           $\times$ 0.74

19. Divide: $0.053\overline{)0.349482}$

20. What is 7.796 decreased by 2.9175?

21. You had a balance of $895.68 in your checking account. You then wrote checks of $145.72 and $88.45. Find the new balance in your checking account.

22. The state income tax on the business you own is $560 plus 0.08 times your profit. You made a profit of $63,000 last year. Find the amount of income tax you paid last year.

23. A car costing $5944.20 is bought with a down payment of $1500 and 36 equal monthly payments. Find the amount of each monthly payment.

24. You have $237.44 in your checking account. You make deposits of $56.88, $127.40, and $56.30. Find the amount in your checking account after you make the deposits.

Chapter Test

1. Place the correct symbol, < or >, between the two numbers.

0.66   0.666

2. Subtract: 13.027
− 8.94

3. Write 45.0302 in words.

4. Convert $\frac{9}{13}$ to a decimal. Round to the nearest thousandth. .00923

5. Convert 0.825 to a fraction.

6. Round 0.07395 to the nearest ten-thousandth.

7. Find 0.0569 divided by 0.037. Round to the nearest thousandth.

8. Find 9.23674 less than 37.003.

9. Round 7.0954625 to the nearest thousandth.

10. Divide: 0.006)‾1.392‾

11. Add: 270.93
97.
1.976
+ 88.675

12. Find the missing dimension.

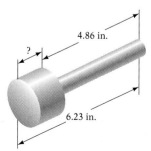
4.86 in.
?
6.23 in.

13. Multiply: 1.37
                $\times\,0.004$

14. What is the total of 62.3, 4.007, and 189.65?

15. Write two hundred nine and seven thousand eighty-six hundred-thousandths in standard form.

16. A car was bought for $6392.60, with a down payment of $1250. The balance was paid in 36 monthly payments. Find the amount of each monthly payment.

17. You received a salary of $363.75, a commission of $954.82, and a bonus of $225. Find your total income.

18. A long-distance telephone call costs $.85 for the first 3 minutes and $.42 for each additional minute. Find the cost of a 12-minute long-distance telephone call.

The table at the right shows the postal rates for selected weights for single-piece and presorted mail. Use this table for Exercises 19 and 20.

Weight (not over)	Single piece	Presorted
1 ounce	$.32	$.295
2 ounces	.55	.525
3 ounces	.78	.709
4 ounces	1.01	.939
5 ounces	1.24	1.69

19. Find the total cost of mailing the following:
3 single pieces weighing 2.3 ounces each
2 single pieces weighing 3.4 ounces each
50 presorted pieces weighing 0.3 ounce each

20. Find the total cost of mailing the following:
7 single pieces weighing 0.4 ounce each
30 presorted pieces weighing 0.7 ounce each
75 presorted pieces weighing 1.4 ounces each
Round to the nearest cent.

Cumulative Review

1. Divide: $89\overline{)20{,}932}$

2. Simplify: $2^3 \cdot 4^2$

3. Simplify: $2^2 - (7 - 3) \div 2 + 1$

4. Find the LCM of 9, 12, and 24.

5. Write $\frac{22}{5}$ as a mixed number.

6. Write $4\frac{5}{8}$ as an improper fraction.

7. Build an equivalent fraction with the given denominator.
$$\frac{5}{12} = \frac{}{60}$$

8. Add: $\frac{3}{8} + \frac{5}{12} + \frac{9}{16}$

9. What is $5\frac{7}{12}$ increased by $3\frac{7}{18}$?

10. Subtract: $9\frac{5}{9} - 3\frac{11}{12}$

11. Multiply: $\frac{9}{16} \times \frac{4}{27}$

12. Find the product of $2\frac{1}{8}$ and $4\frac{5}{17}$.

13. Divide: $\frac{11}{12} \div \frac{3}{4}$

14. What is $2\frac{3}{8}$ divided by $2\frac{1}{2}$?

15. Simplify: $\left(\frac{2}{3}\right)^2 \cdot \left(\frac{3}{4}\right)^3$

16. Simplify: $\left(\frac{2}{3}\right)^2 - \left(\frac{2}{3} - \frac{1}{2}\right) + 2$

17. Write 65.0309 in words.

18. Add: 379.006
27.523
9.8707
+ 88.2994

19. What is 29.005 decreased by 7.9286?

20. Multiply: 9.074
                   × 6.09

21. Divide: $8.09\overline{)17.42963}$. Round to the nearest thousandth.

22. Convert $\frac{11}{15}$ to a decimal. Round to the nearest thousandth.

23. Convert $0.16\frac{2}{3}$ to a fraction.

24. Place the correct symbol, < or >, between the two numbers.

$\frac{8}{9}$ 0.98

25. An airplane had 204 passengers aboard. During a stop, 97 passengers got off the plane and 127 passengers got on the plane. How many passengers were on the continuing flight?

26. An investor purchased stock at $32\frac{1}{8}$ per share. During the first 2 months of ownership, the stock lost $\frac{3}{4}$ and then gained $1\frac{1}{2}$. Find the value of each share of stock at the end of the 2 months.

27. You have a checking account balance of $814.35. You then write checks for $42.98, $16.43, and $137.56. Find your checking account balance after you write the checks.

28. A machine lathe takes 0.017 inch from a brass bushing that is 1.412 inches thick. Find the resulting thickness of the bushing.

29. The state income tax on your business is $820 plus 0.08 times your profit. You made a profit of $64,860 last year. Find the amount of income tax you paid last year.

30. You bought a camera costing $210.96. The down payment is $20, and the balance is to be paid in 8 equal monthly payments. Find the monthly payment.

4

Ratio and Proportion

Special-effects artists use scale models to create dinosaurs, exploding spaceships, and aliens that inhabit the spaceships. A scale model of a dinosaur is produced by using ratios and proportions to determine each dimension of the scale model.

Objectives

Section 4.1
To write the ratio of two quantities in simplest form
To solve application problems

Section 4.2
To write rates
To write unit rates
To solve application problems

Section 4.3
To determine whether a proportion is true
To solve proportions
To solve application problems

Musical Scales

When a metal wire is stretched tight and then plucked, a sound is heard. Guitars, banjos, and violins are examples of instruments that use this principle to produce music. A piano is another example of this principle, but the sound is produced by the string's being struck by a small, hammerlike object.

After the string is plucked or struck, the string begins to vibrate. The number of times the string vibrates in 1 second is called the frequency of the vibration, or the pitch. Normally humans can hear vibrations as low as 16 cps (cycles per second) and as high as 20,000 cps. The longer the string, the lower the pitch of the sound; the shorter the string, the higher the pitch of the sound. In fact, a string half as long as another string vibrates twice as fast.

Vibrating String

Most music that is heard today is based on what is called the chromatic or twelve-tone scale. For this scale, a vibration of 261 cps is called middle C. A string half as long as the string for middle C vibrates twice as fast and produces a musical note one octave higher.

To produce the notes between the two C's, strings of different lengths that produce the desired pitches are chosen. Recall that as the string gets shorter, the pitch increases. A top view of a grand piano illustrates how the strings vary in length.

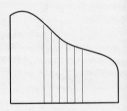

A well-tempered chromatic scale is one in which the string lengths are chosen so that the ratios of the frequencies of adjacent notes are the same.

$$\frac{C}{C\#} = \frac{C\#}{D} = \frac{D}{D\#} = \frac{D\#}{E} = \frac{E}{F} = \frac{F}{F\#} = \frac{F\#}{G} = \frac{G}{G\#} = \frac{G\#}{A} =$$

$$\frac{A}{A\#} = \frac{A\#}{B} = \frac{B}{C}$$

The common ratio for the chromatic scale is approximately $\frac{1}{1.0595}$.

4.1 Ratio

Objective A   **To write the ratio of two quantities in simplest form** ....

Quantities such as 3 feet, 12 cents, and 9 cars are number quantities written with **units**.

3 feet
12 cents   These are only some examples of units. Shirts, dollars, trees,
9 cars   miles, and gallons are further examples.
↑
units

A **ratio** is a comparison of two quantities that have the *same* units. This comparison can be written three different ways:

1. As a fraction
2. As two numbers separated by a colon (:)
3. As two numbers separated by the word *to*

The ratio of the lengths of two boards, one 8 feet long and the other 10 feet long, can be written as

1. $\dfrac{8 \text{ feet}}{10 \text{ feet}} = \dfrac{8}{10} = \dfrac{4}{5}$
2. 8 feet : 10 feet = 8 : 10 = 4 : 5
3. 8 feet to 10 feet = 8 to 10 = 4 to 5

A ratio is in **simplest form** when the two numbers do not have a common factor. Note that in a ratio, the units are not written.

This ratio means that the smaller board is $\dfrac{4}{5}$ the length of the longer board.

Example 1
Write the comparison $6 to $8 as a ratio in simplest form using a fraction, a colon, and the word *to*.

Solution $\dfrac{\$6}{\$8} = \dfrac{6}{8} = \dfrac{3}{4}$
$6 : $8 = 6 : 8 = 3 : 4
$6 to $8 = 6 to 8 = 3 to 4

You Try It 1
Write the comparison 20 pounds to 24 pounds as a ratio in simplest form using a fraction, a colon, and the word *to*.

Your solution

Example 2
Write the comparison 18 quarts to 6 quarts as a ratio in simplest form using a fraction, a colon, and the word *to*.

Solution $\dfrac{18 \text{ quarts}}{6 \text{ quarts}} = \dfrac{18}{6} = \dfrac{3}{1}$
18 quarts : 6 quarts =
18 : 6 = 3 : 1
18 quarts to 6 quarts =
18 to 6 = 3 to 1

You Try It 2
Write the comparison 64 miles to 8 miles as a ratio in simplest form using a fraction, a colon, and the word *to*.

Your solution

Solutions on p. S10

Objective B **To solve application problems** .... ⟨ 7 ⟩ CT

Use the table below for Example 3 and You Try It 3.

Board Feet of Wood at a Lumber Store

Pine	Ash	Oak	Cedar
20,000	18,000	10,000	12,000

Example 3

Find, as a fraction in simplest form, the ratio of the number of board feet of pine to the number of board feet of oak.

Strategy

To find the ratio, write the ratio of board feet of pine (20,000) to board feet of oak (10,000) in simplest form.

Solution

$$\frac{20,000}{10,000} = \frac{2}{1}$$

The ratio is $\frac{2}{1}$.

You Try It 3

Find, as a fraction in simplest form, the ratio of the number of board feet of cedar to board feet of ash.

Your strategy

Your solution

Example 4

The cost of building a patio cover was $250 for labor and $350 for materials. What, as a fraction in simplest form, is the ratio of the cost of materials to the total cost for labor and materials?

Strategy

To find the ratio, write the ratio of the cost of materials ($350) to the total cost ($250 + $350) in simplest form.

Solution

$$\frac{\$350}{\$250 + \$350} = \frac{350}{600} = \frac{7}{12}$$

The ratio is $\frac{7}{12}$.

You Try It 4

A company spends $20,000 a month for television advertising and $15,000 a month for radio advertising. What, as a fraction in simplest form, is the ratio of the cost of radio advertising to the total cost of radio and television advertising?

Your strategy

Your solution

Solutions on p. S10

4.1 Exercises

. . . .

Objective A

Write the comparison as a ratio in simplest form using a fraction, a colon (:), and the word *to*.

1. 3 pints to 15 pints

2. 6 pounds to 8 pounds

3. $40 to $20

4. 10 feet to 2 feet

5. 3 miles to 8 miles

6. 2 hours to 3 hours

7. 37 hours to 24 hours

8. 29 inches to 12 inches

9. 6 minutes to 6 minutes

10. 8 days to 12 days

11. 35 cents to 50 cents

12. 28 inches to 36 inches

13. 30 minutes to 60 minutes

14. 25 cents to 100 cents

15. 32 ounces to 16 ounces

16. 12 quarts to 4 quarts

17. 3 cups to 4 cups

18. 6 years to 7 years

19. $5 to $3

20. 30 yards to 12 yards

21. 12 quarts to 18 quarts

22. $20 to $28

23. 14 days to 7 days

24. 9 feet to 3 feet

Objective B   *Application Problems*

Write ratios in simplest form using a fraction.

			Family Budget				
Housing	*Food*	*Transportation*	*Taxes*	*Utilities*	*Miscellaneous*		*Total*
$800	$400	$300	$350	$150	$400		$2400

25. Use the table to find the ratio of housing cost to total expenses.

26. Use the table to find the ratio of food cost to total expenses.

27. Use the table to find the ratio of utilities cost to food cost.

28. Use the table to find the ratio of transportation cost to housing cost.

29. National Collegiate Athletic Association (NCAA) statistics show that for every 154,000 high school seniors playing basketball, only 4000 will play college basketball as first-year students. Write the ratio of the number of first-year students playing college basketball to the number of high school seniors playing basketball.

30. NCAA statistics show that for every 2800 college seniors playing college basketball, only 50 will play as rookies in the National Basketball Association. Write the ratio of the number of National Basketball Association rookies to the number of college seniors playing basketball.

31. A transformer has 40 turns in the primary coil and 480 turns in the secondary coil. State the ratio of the number of turns in the primary coil to the number of turns in the secondary coil.

32. Rita Sterling bought a computer system for $2400. Five years later she sold the computer for $900. Find the ratio of the amount she received for the computer to the cost of the computer.

33. A house with an original value of $90,000 increased in value to $110,000 in 5 years.
    a. Find the increase in the value of the house.
    b. What is the ratio of the increase in value to the original value of the house?

34. A decorator bought a box of ceramic floor tile for $21 and a box of wood tile for $33.
    a. What was the total cost of the box of ceramic tile and the box of wood tile?
    b. What is the ratio of the cost of the box of wood tile to the total cost?

35. The price of gasoline jumped from $.96 to $1.26 in 1 year. What is the ratio of the increase in price to the original price?

APPLYING THE CONCEPTS

A bank uses the ratio of a borrower's total monthly debts to the borrower's total monthly income to determine the maximum monthly payment for a potential homeowner. This ratio is called the debt–income ratio. Use the homeowner's income–debt table at the right for Exercises 36 and 37.

Income	Debts
$3500	$900
250	170
140	160
	95

36. Compute the debt–income ratio for the potential homeowner.

37. If Central Trust Bank will make a loan to a customer whose debt–income ratio is less than $\frac{1}{3}$, will the potential homeowner qualify? Explain your answer.

38. To make a home loan, First National Bank requires a debt–income ratio that is less than $\frac{2}{5}$. Would the homeowner whose income–debt table is given at the right qualify for a loan using these standards?

Income		Debts	
Salary	3400	Mortgage	1800
Interest	83	Property tax	104
Rent	650	Insurance	35
Dividends	34	Liabilities	120
		Credit card	234
		Car loan	197

39. Is the value of a ratio always less than 1? Explain.

4.2   Rates

Objective A   *To write rates* ....

A **rate** is a comparison of two quantities that have *different* units. A rate is written as a fraction.

A distance runner ran 26 miles in 4 hours. The distance-to-time rate is written

$$\frac{26 \text{ miles}}{4 \text{ hours}} = \frac{13 \text{ miles}}{2 \text{ hours}}$$

A rate is in **simplest form** when the numbers that form the rate have no common factors. Note that the units are written as part of the rate.

Example 1   Write "6 roof supports for every 9 feet" as a rate in simplest form.

Solution $\dfrac{6 \text{ supports}}{9 \text{ feet}} = \dfrac{2 \text{ supports}}{3 \text{ feet}}$

You Try It 1   Write "15 pounds of fertilizer for 12 trees" as a rate in simplest form.

Your solution

Solution on p. S11

Objective B   *To write unit rates* ....

A **unit rate** is a rate in which the number in the denominator is 1.

$\dfrac{\$3.25}{1 \text{ pound}}$ or \$3.25/pound is read "\$3.25 per pound."

To find unit rates, divide the number in the numerator of the rate by the number in the denominator of the rate.

A car traveled 344 miles on 16 gallons of gasoline. To find the miles per gallon (unit rate), divide the numerator of the rate by the denominator of the rate.

$\dfrac{344 \text{ miles}}{16 \text{ gallons}}$ is the rate.

$16)\overline{344.0}^{\,21.5}$ 21.5 miles/gallon is the unit rate.

Example 2   Write "300 feet in 8 seconds" as a unit rate.

Solution $\dfrac{300 \text{ feet}}{8 \text{ seconds}}$ $8)\overline{300.0}^{\,37.5}$

37.5 feet/second

You Try It 2   Write "260 miles in 8 hours" as a unit rate.

Your solution

Solution on p. S11

Objective C   **To solve application problems** ·· (7) [CT]

The table at the right shows typical air fare costs for long routes.

Long Routes	Miles	Fare
New York–Los Angeles	2475	$683
San Francisco–Dallas	1464	$536
Denver–Pittsburgh	1302	$525
Minneapolis–Hartford	1050	$483

⇒ Find the cost per mile for the four routes. Which route is the most expensive, and which is the least expensive, for each mile flown?

Strategy
To find the cost per mile, divide the fare for each route by the miles flown. Compare the costs per mile to determine the most expensive and least expensive routes per mile.

Solution   New York–Los Angeles $\frac{683}{2475} \approx 0.28$

San Francisco–Dallas $\frac{536}{1464} \approx 0.37$

Denver–Pittsburgh $\frac{525}{1302} \approx 0.40$

Minneapolis–Hartford $\frac{483}{1050} = 0.46$

The Minneapolis–Hartford route is the most expensive per mile, and the New York–Los Angeles route is the least expensive per mile.

Example 3
As an investor, Jung Ho purchased 100 shares of stock for $1500. One year later, Jung sold the 100 shares for $1800. What was his profit per share?

Strategy
To find Jung's profit per share:
• Find the total profit by subtracting the original cost ($1500) from the selling price ($1800).
• Find the profit per share (unit rate) by dividing the total profit by the number of shares of stock (100).

Solution

$$
\begin{array}{r}
\$1800 \\
-\ 1500 \\
\hline
\$300
\end{array}
\quad \text{total profit}
$$

$$
\begin{array}{r}
\$3 \\
100\overline{)\$300}
\end{array}
$$

Jung Ho's profit per share was $3.

You Try It 3
Erik Peltier, a jeweler, purchased 5 ounces of gold for $1625. Later, he sold the 5 ounces for $1720. What was Erik's profit per ounce?

Your strategy

Your solution

Solution on p. S11

4.2 Exercises

· ·

Objective A

Write as a rate in simplest form.

1. 3 pounds of meat for 4 people

2. 30 ounces in 24 glasses

3. $80 for 12 boards

4. 84 cents for 6 bars of soap

5. 300 miles on 15 gallons

6. 88 feet in 8 seconds

7. 20 children in 8 families

8. 48 leaves on 9 plants

9. 16 gallons in 2 hours

10. 25 ounces in 5 minutes

Objective B

Write as a unit rate.

11. 10 feet in 4 seconds

12. 816 miles in 6 days

13. $1300 earned in 4 weeks

14. $27,000 earned in 12 months

15. 1100 trees planted on 10 acres

16. 3750 words on 15 pages

17. $32.97 earned in 7 hours

18. $315.70 earned in 22 hours

19. 628.8 miles in 12 hours

20. 388.8 miles in 8 hours

21. 344.4 miles on 12.3 gallons of gasoline

22. 409.4 miles on 11.5 gallons of gasoline

23. $349.80 for 212 pounds

24. $11.05 for 3.4 pounds

Objective C   *Application Problems*

25. An automobile was driven 326.6 miles on 11.5 gallons of gas. Find the number of miles driven per gallon of gas.

26. You drive 246.6 miles in 4.5 hours. Find the number of miles driven per hour.

27. The Saturn-5 rocket uses 534,000 gallons of fuel in 2.5 minutes. How much fuel does the rocket use per minute?

28. An investor paid $116.75 a share for 500 shares of Citicorp and receives $1050 in yearly dividends. Find the dividend per share.

29. An investor purchased 280 shares of GTE for $11,830.
   a. Estimate the cost per share.
   b. Find the actual cost per share.

30. Enova investors have bought 116,572,000 shares of the corporation. In 1996 Enova paid $181,852,000 in dividends. Find the dividend per share paid by the corporation. Round to the nearest cent.

31. Assume that Apple Computer produced 5000 compact disks for $26,536.32. Of the disks made, 122 did not meet company standards.
   a. How many compact disks did meet company standards?
   b. What was the cost per disk for those disks that met company standards?

32. The Pierre family purchased a 250-pound side of beef for $365.75 and had it packaged. During the packaging, 75 pounds of beef were discarded as waste.
   a. How many pounds of beef were packaged?
   b. What was the cost per pound for the packaged beef?

33. The Bear Valley Fruit Stand purchased 250 boxes of strawberries for $162.50. All the strawberries were sold for $312.50. What was the profit per box of strawberries?

34. The table at the right shows the population and the area of four countries. Find the population density (people per square mile) for each country. Round to the nearest tenth.

Country	Population	Area (square miles)
Australia	18,322,000	2,968,000
Cambodia	10,561,000	70,000
India	936,546,000	1,269,000
United States	267,000,000	3,619,000

APPLYING THE CONCEPTS

35. You have a choice of receiving a wage of $34,000 per year, $2840 per month, $650 per week, or $18 per hour. Which pay choice would you take? Assume a 40-hour week with 52 weeks per year.

36. The price–earnings ratio of a company's stock is one measure used by stock market analysts to assess the financial well-being of the company. Explain the meaning of the price–earnings ratio.

4.3 Proportions

Objective A *To determine whether a proportion is true* ....

POINT OF INTEREST

Proportions were studied by the earliest mathematicians. Clay tablets uncovered by archeologists show evidence of proportions in Egyptian and Babylonian cultures dating from 1800 B.C.

A **proportion** is an expression of the equality of two ratios or rates.

$$\frac{50 \text{ miles}}{4 \text{ gallons}} = \frac{25 \text{ miles}}{2 \text{ gallons}}$$

Note that the units of the numerators are the same and the units of the denominators are the same.

$$\frac{3}{6} = \frac{1}{2}$$

This is the equality of two ratios.

A proportion is **true** if the fractions are equal when written in lowest terms.

In any true proportion, the "cross products" are equal.

➡ Is $\frac{2}{3} = \frac{8}{12}$ a true proportion?

$$\frac{2}{3} \diagup\!\!\!\!\diagdown \frac{8}{12} \begin{array}{l} \rightarrow 3 \times 8 = 24 \\ \rightarrow 2 \times 12 = 24 \end{array}$$

The cross products *are* equal.
$\frac{2}{3} = \frac{8}{12}$ is a true proportion.

A proportion is **not true** if the fractions are not equal when reduced to lowest terms.

If the cross products are not equal, then the proportion is not true.

➡ Is $\frac{4}{5} = \frac{8}{9}$ a true proportion?

$$\frac{4}{5} \diagup\!\!\!\!\diagdown \frac{8}{9} \begin{array}{l} \rightarrow 5 \times 8 = 40 \\ \rightarrow 4 \times 9 = 36 \end{array}$$

The cross products *are not* equal.
$\frac{4}{5} = \frac{8}{9}$ is not a true proportion.

Example 1
Use cross products to determine whether $\frac{5}{8} = \frac{10}{16}$ is a true proportion.

Solution

$$\frac{5}{8} \diagup\!\!\!\!\diagdown \frac{10}{16} \begin{array}{l} \rightarrow 8 \times 10 = 80 \\ \rightarrow 5 \times 16 = 80 \end{array}$$

The proportion is true.

You Try It 1
Use cross products to determine whether $\frac{6}{10} = \frac{9}{15}$ is a true proportion.

Your solution

Example 2
Use cross products to determine whether $\frac{62 \text{ miles}}{4 \text{ gallons}} = \frac{33 \text{ miles}}{2 \text{ gallons}}$ is a true proportion.

Solution

$$\frac{62}{4} \diagup\!\!\!\!\diagdown \frac{33}{2} \begin{array}{l} \rightarrow 4 \times 33 = 132 \\ \rightarrow 62 \times 2 = 124 \end{array}$$

The proportion is not true.

You Try It 2
Use cross products to determine whether $\frac{\$32}{6 \text{ hours}} = \frac{\$90}{8 \text{ hours}}$ is a true proportion.

Your solution

Solutions on p. S11

Objective B *To solve proportions* ··

Sometimes one of the numbers in a proportion is unknown. In this case, it is necessary to *solve* the proportion.

To **solve** a proportion, find a number to replace the unknown so that the proportion is true.

➡ Solve: $\dfrac{9}{6} = \dfrac{3}{n}$

$$\dfrac{9}{6} = \dfrac{3}{n}$$

$9 \times n = 6 \times 3$ • Find the cross products.

$9 \times n = 18$

$n = 18 \div 9$ • Think of $9 \times n = 18$ as $9)\overline{18}$.

$n = 2$

Check:

$$\dfrac{9}{6} \quad\times\quad \dfrac{3}{2} \quad \begin{array}{l} 6 \times 3 = 18 \\ 9 \times 2 = 18 \end{array}$$

Example 3

Solve $\dfrac{n}{12} = \dfrac{25}{60}$ and check.

Solution

$n \times 60 = 12 \times 25$

$n \times 60 = 300$

$n = 300 \div 60$

$n = 5$

Check:

$$\dfrac{5}{12} \quad\times\quad \dfrac{25}{60} \quad \begin{array}{l} 12 \times 25 = 300 \\ 5 \times 60 = 300 \end{array}$$

Example 4

Solve $\dfrac{4}{9} = \dfrac{n}{16}$. Write the answer to the nearest tenth.

Solution

$4 \times 16 = 9 \times n$

$64 = 9 \times n$

$64 \div 9 = n$

$7.1 \approx n$

Note: A rounded answer is an approximation. Therefore, the answer to a check will not be exact.

You Try It 3

Solve $\dfrac{n}{14} = \dfrac{3}{7}$ and check.

Your solution

You Try It 4

Solve $\dfrac{5}{8} = \dfrac{n}{20}$.

Your solution

Solutions on p. S11

Example 5

Solve $\frac{28}{52} = \frac{7}{n}$ and check.

Solution

$28 \times n = 52 \times 7$
$28 \times n = 364$
$\quad\quad n = 364 \div 28$
$\quad\quad n = 13$

Check:

$$\frac{28}{52} \;\substack{\diagdown\\\diagup}\; \frac{7}{13} \quad\longrightarrow\quad \begin{array}{l} 52 \times 7 = 364 \\ 28 \times 13 = 364 \end{array}$$

Example 6

Solve $\frac{15}{n} = \frac{8}{3}$. Write the answer to the nearest hundredth.

Solution

$15 \times 3 = n \times 8$
$\quad\quad 45 = n \times 8$
$45 \div 8 = n$
$\quad 5.63 \approx n$

Example 7

Solve $\frac{n}{9} = \frac{3}{1}$ and check.

Solution

$n \times 1 = 9 \times 3$
$n \times 1 = 27$
$\quad\quad n = 27 \div 1$
$\quad\quad n = 27$

Check:

$$\frac{27}{9} \;\substack{\diagdown\\\diagup}\; \frac{3}{1} \quad\longrightarrow\quad \begin{array}{l} 9 \times 3 = 27 \\ 27 \times 1 = 27 \end{array}$$

Example 8

Solve $\frac{5}{9} = \frac{15}{n}$ and check.

Solution

$5 \times n = 9 \times 15$
$5 \times n = 135$
$\quad\quad n = 135 \div 5$
$\quad\quad n = 27$

Check:

$$\frac{5}{9} \;\substack{\diagdown\\\diagup}\; \frac{15}{27} \quad\longrightarrow\quad \begin{array}{l} 9 \times 15 = 135 \\ 5 \times 27 = 135 \end{array}$$

You Try It 5

Solve $\frac{15}{20} = \frac{12}{n}$ and check.

Your solution

You Try It 6

Solve $\frac{12}{n} = \frac{7}{4}$. Write the answer to the nearest hundredth.

Your solution

You Try It 7

Solve $\frac{n}{12} = \frac{4}{1}$ and check.

Your solution

You Try It 8

Solve $\frac{3}{8} = \frac{12}{n}$ and check.

Your solution

Solutions on p. S11

Objective C   To solve application problems ·······································

Example 9

A mason determines that 9 cement blocks are required for a retaining wall 2 feet long. At this rate, how many cement blocks are required for a retaining wall that is 24 feet long?

Strategy

To find the number of cement blocks for a retaining wall 24 feet long, write and solve a proportion, using n to represent the number of blocks required.

Solution

$$\frac{9 \text{ cement blocks}}{2 \text{ feet}} = \frac{n \text{ cement blocks}}{24 \text{ feet}}$$

$$9 \times 24 = 2 \times n$$
$$216 = 2 \times n$$
$$216 \div 2 = n$$
$$108 = n$$

108 cement blocks are required for a 24-foot retaining wall.

You Try It 9

Twenty-four jars can be packed in 6 identical boxes. At this rate, how many jars can be packed in 15 boxes?

Your strategy

Your solution

Example 10

The dosage of a certain medication is 2 ounces for every 50 pounds of body weight. How many ounces of this medication are required for a person who weighs 175 pounds?

Strategy

To find the number of ounces of medication for a person weighing 175 pounds, write and solve a proportion, using n to represent the number of ounces of medication for a 175-pound person.

Solution

$$\frac{2 \text{ ounces}}{50 \text{ pounds}} = \frac{n \text{ ounces}}{175 \text{ pounds}}$$

$$2 \times 175 = 50 \times n$$
$$350 = 50 \times n$$
$$350 \div 50 = n$$
$$7 = n$$

7 ounces of medication are required for a 175-pound person.

You Try It 10

Three tablespoons of a liquid plant fertilizer are to be added to every 4 gallons of water. How many tablespoons of fertilizer are required for 10 gallons of water?

Your strategy

Your solution

Solutions on p. S11

4.3 Exercises

· ·

Objective A

Determine whether the proportion is true or not true.

1. $\dfrac{4}{8} = \dfrac{10}{20}$ **2.** $\dfrac{39}{48} = \dfrac{13}{16}$ **3.** $\dfrac{7}{8} = \dfrac{11}{12}$ **4.** $\dfrac{15}{7} = \dfrac{17}{8}$

5. $\dfrac{27}{8} = \dfrac{9}{4}$ **6.** $\dfrac{3}{18} = \dfrac{4}{19}$ **7.** $\dfrac{45}{135} = \dfrac{3}{9}$ **8.** $\dfrac{3}{4} = \dfrac{54}{72}$

9. $\dfrac{16}{3} = \dfrac{48}{9}$ **10.** $\dfrac{15}{5} = \dfrac{3}{1}$ **11.** $\dfrac{7}{40} = \dfrac{7}{8}$ **12.** $\dfrac{9}{7} = \dfrac{6}{5}$

13. $\dfrac{50 \text{ miles}}{2 \text{ gallons}} = \dfrac{25 \text{ miles}}{1 \text{ gallon}}$ **14.** $\dfrac{16 \text{ feet}}{10 \text{ seconds}} = \dfrac{24 \text{ feet}}{15 \text{ seconds}}$

15. $\dfrac{6 \text{ minutes}}{5 \text{ cents}} = \dfrac{30 \text{ minutes}}{25 \text{ cents}}$ **16.** $\dfrac{16 \text{ pounds}}{12 \text{ days}} = \dfrac{20 \text{ pounds}}{14 \text{ days}}$

17. $\dfrac{\$15}{4 \text{ pounds}} = \dfrac{\$45}{12 \text{ pounds}}$ **18.** $\dfrac{270 \text{ trees}}{6 \text{ acres}} = \dfrac{90 \text{ trees}}{2 \text{ acres}}$

19. $\dfrac{300 \text{ feet}}{4 \text{ rolls}} = \dfrac{450 \text{ feet}}{7 \text{ rolls}}$ **20.** $\dfrac{1 \text{ gallon}}{4 \text{ quarts}} = \dfrac{7 \text{ gallons}}{28 \text{ quarts}}$

21. $\dfrac{\$65}{5 \text{ days}} = \dfrac{\$26}{2 \text{ days}}$ **22.** $\dfrac{80 \text{ miles}}{2 \text{ hours}} = \dfrac{110 \text{ miles}}{3 \text{ hours}}$

23. $\dfrac{7 \text{ tiles}}{4 \text{ feet}} = \dfrac{42 \text{ tiles}}{20 \text{ feet}}$ **24.** $\dfrac{15 \text{ feet}}{3 \text{ yards}} = \dfrac{90 \text{ feet}}{18 \text{ yards}}$

Objective B

Solve. Round to the nearest hundredth.

25. $\dfrac{n}{4} = \dfrac{6}{8}$

26. $\dfrac{n}{7} = \dfrac{9}{21}$

27. $\dfrac{12}{18} = \dfrac{n}{9}$

28. $\dfrac{7}{21} = \dfrac{35}{n}$

29. $\dfrac{6}{n} = \dfrac{24}{36}$

30. $\dfrac{3}{n} = \dfrac{15}{10}$

31. $\dfrac{n}{45} = \dfrac{17}{135}$

32. $\dfrac{9}{4} = \dfrac{18}{n}$

33. $\dfrac{n}{6} = \dfrac{2}{3}$

34. $\dfrac{5}{12} = \dfrac{n}{144}$

35. $\dfrac{n}{5} = \dfrac{7}{8}$

36. $\dfrac{4}{n} = \dfrac{9}{5}$

37. $\dfrac{n}{11} = \dfrac{32}{4}$

38. $\dfrac{3}{4} = \dfrac{8}{n}$

39. $\dfrac{5}{12} = \dfrac{n}{8}$

40. $\dfrac{36}{20} = \dfrac{12}{n}$

41. $\dfrac{n}{15} = \dfrac{21}{12}$

42. $\dfrac{40}{n} = \dfrac{15}{8}$

43. $\dfrac{32}{n} = \dfrac{1}{3}$

44. $\dfrac{5}{8} = \dfrac{42}{n}$

45. $\dfrac{18}{11} = \dfrac{16}{n}$

46. $\dfrac{25}{4} = \dfrac{n}{12}$

47. $\dfrac{28}{8} = \dfrac{12}{n}$

48. $\dfrac{n}{30} = \dfrac{65}{120}$

49. $\dfrac{0.3}{5.6} = \dfrac{n}{25}$

50. $\dfrac{1.3}{16} = \dfrac{n}{30}$

51. $\dfrac{0.7}{9.8} = \dfrac{3.6}{n}$

52. $\dfrac{1.9}{7} = \dfrac{13}{n}$

Objective C   Application Problems

Solve. Round to the nearest hundredth.

53. A 6-ounce package of Puffed Wheat contains 600 calories. How many calories are in a 0.5-ounce serving of the cereal?

54. A car travels 70.5 miles on 3 gallons of gas. Find the distance that the car can travel on 14 gallons of gas.

55. Ron Stokes uses 2 pounds of fertilizer for every 100 square feet of lawn for landscape maintenance. At this rate, how many pounds of fertilizer did he use on a lawn that measures 2500 square feet?

Solve. Round to the nearest hundredth.

56. A nursery provides a liquid plant food by adding 1 gallon of water for each 2 ounces of plant food. At this rate, how many ounces of plant food are required for 25 gallons of water?

57. A manufacturer of baseball equipment makes 4 aluminum bats for every 15 bats made from wood. On a day when 100 aluminum bats are made, how many wooden bats are produced?

58. A brick wall 20 feet in length contains 1040 bricks. At the same rate, how many bricks would it take to build a wall 48 feet in length?

59. The scale on the map at the right is 1.25 inches equals 10 miles. Find the distance between Carlsbad and Del Mar, which are 2 inches apart on the map.

60. The scale on the plans for a new house is 1 inch equals 3 feet. Find the length and width of a room that measures 5 inches by 8 inches on the drawing.

61. The dosage for a medication is $\frac{1}{3}$ ounce for every 40 pounds of body weight. At this rate, how many ounces of medication should a physician prescribe for a patient who weighs 150 pounds?

62. A bank requires a monthly payment of $33.45 on a $2500 loan. At the same rate, find the monthly payment on a $10,000 loan.

63. A pre-election survey showed that 2 out of every 3 eligible voters would cast ballots in the county election. At this rate, how many people in a county of 240,000 eligible voters would vote in the election?

64. A paint manufacturer suggests using 1 gallon of paint for every 400 square feet of a wall. At this rate, how many gallons of paint would be required for a room that has 1400 square feet of wall?

65. A 60-year-old male can obtain $10,000 of life insurance for $35.35 per month. At this rate, what is the monthly cost of $50,000 of life insurance?

66. Suppose a computer chip manufacturer knows from experience that in an average production run of 2000 circuit boards, 60 will be defective. What number of defective circuit boards can be expected from a run of 25,000 circuit boards?

67. You own 240 shares of a computer stock. The company declares a stock split of 5 shares for every 3 owned. How many shares of stock will you own after the stock split?

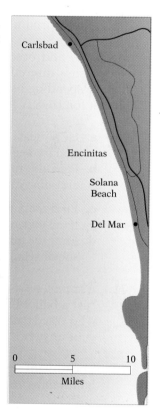

Solve. Round to the nearest hundredth.

68. Carlos Capasso owns 50 shares of Texas Utilities that pay dividends of $153. At this rate, what dividend would Carlos receive after buying 300 additional shares of Texas Utilities?

69. The director of data processing at a college estimates that the ratio of student time to administrative time on a certain computer is $3:2$. During a month in which the computer was used 200 hours for administration, how many hours was it used by students?

APPLYING THE CONCEPTS

The table at the right shows how each dollar of projected spending by the federal government for 1998 is distributed. Social security, interest payments, Medicare, Medicaid, and other entitlements are fixed expenditures. Nondefense discretionary and defense are the only discretionary spending by the federal government. The projected budget for 1998 is $1,687.5 billion.

How Your Federal Tax Dollar Is Spent	
Social Security	23 cents
Interest payments	15 cents
Medicare	12 cents
Medicaid	6 cents
Other entitlements	12 cents
Non-defense discretionary	17 cents
Defense	15 cents

Source: Office of Management and Budget

70. **a.** Is at least one-half of federal spending discretionary spending?
   b. Find the ratio of the fixed expenditures to the discretionary spending.

   c. Find the amount of the 1998 budget to be spent on fixed expenditures.
   d. Find the amount of the 1998 budget to be spent on social security.

71. A survey of voters in a city claimed that 2 people of every 5 who voted cast a ballot in favor of city amendment A and that 3 people of every 4 who voted cast a ballot against amendment A. Is this possible? Explain your answer.

72. The ratio of weight on the moon to weight on Earth is $1:6$. If a bowling ball weighs 16 pounds on Earth, what would it weigh on the moon?

73. When engineers design a new car, they first build a model of the car. The ratio of the size of a part on the model to the actual size of the part is $2:5$. If a door is 1.3 feet long on the model, what is the length of the door on the car?

74. Write a word problem that requires solving a proportion to find the answer.

75. Choose a local pizza restaurant and a particular type of pizza. Determine the size and cost of a medium pizza and of a large pizza. (Use regular prices and no special discounts.) Is $\frac{\text{cost of medium}}{\text{size of medium}}$ approximately equal to $\frac{\text{cost of large}}{\text{size of large}}$? Explain your answer.

Focus on Problem Solving

A very useful problem-solving strategy is looking for a pattern.

Problem   A legend says that a peasant invented the game of chess and gave it to a very rich king as a present. The king so enjoyed the game that he gave the peasant the choice of anything in the kingdom. The peasant's request was simple: "Place one grain of wheat on the first square, 2 grains on the second square, 4 grains on the third square, 8 on the fourth square, and continue doubling the number of grains until the last square of the chessboard is reached." How many grains of wheat must the king give the peasant?

Solution   A chessboard consists of 64 squares. To find the total number of grains of wheat on the 64 squares, we begin by looking at the amount of wheat on the first few squares.

Square 1	Square 2	Square 3	Square 4	Square 5	Square 6	Square 7	Square 8
1	2	4	8	16	32	64	128
1	3	7	15	31	63	127	255

The bottom row of numbers represents the sum of the number of grains of wheat up to and including that square. For instance, the number of grains of wheat on the first 7 squares is $1 + 2 + 4 + 8 + 16 + 32 + 64 = 127$.

One pattern to observe is that the number of grains of wheat on a square can be expressed as a power of 2.

The number of grains on square $n = 2^{n-1}$.

For example, the number of grains on square $7 = 2^{7-1} = 2^6 = 64$.

A second pattern of interest is that the number *below* a square (the total number of grains up to and including that square) is one less than the number of grains of wheat *on* the next square. For example, the number *below* square 7 is one less than the number *on* square 8 ($128 - 1 = 127$). From this observation, the number of grains of wheat on the first 8 squares is the number on square 8 (128) plus one less than the number on square 8 (127): The total number of grains of wheat on the first 8 squares is $128 + 127 = 255$.

From this observation,

$$\text{Number of grains of wheat on the chessboard} = \text{number of grains on square 64} + \text{one less than the number of grains on square 64}$$

$$= 2^{64-1} + (2^{64-1} - 1)$$

$$= 2^{63} + 2^{63} - 1 \approx 18{,}000{,}000{,}000{,}000{,}000{,}000$$

To give you an idea of the magnitude of this number, this is more wheat than has been produced in the world since chess was invented.

The same king decided to have a banquet in the long banquet room of the palace to celebrate the invention of chess. The king had 50 square tables, and each table could seat only one person on each side. The king pushed the tables together to form one long banquet table. How many people can sit at this table? *Hint:* Try constructing a pattern by using 2 tables, 3 tables, and 4 tables.

Projects and Group Activities

The Golden Ratio   There are certain designs that have been repeated over and over in both art and architecture. One of these involves the **golden rectangle.**

A golden rectangle is drawn at the right. Begin with a square that measures, say, 2 inches on a side. Now measure the distance from *A* to *B*. Place this length along the bottom of the square, starting at *A*. The resulting rectangle is a golden rectangle.

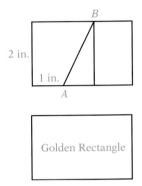

The **golden ratio** is the ratio of the length of the golden rectangle to its width. If you have drawn the rectangle following the procedure above, you will find that the golden ratio is approximately 1.6.

The golden ratio appears in many different situations. Some historians claim that some of the great pyramids of Egypt are based on the golden ratio. The drawing at the right shows the Pyramid of Gizeh, which dates from approximately 2600 B.C. The ratio of the height to a side of the base is approximately 1.6.

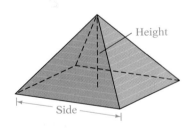

1. The canvas of the Mona Lisa painted by Leonardo da Vinci is a golden rectangle. However, there are other instances of the golden rectangle in the painting itself. Do some research on this painting and write a few paragraphs summarizing your findings.

2. What do 3 × 5 and 5 × 8 index cards have to do with the golden rectangle?

3. When was the United Nations building in New York built? What does the front of that building have to do with a golden rectangle?

4. When was the Parthenon in Athens, Greece, built? What does the front of that building have to do with a golden rectangle?

Drawing the Floor Plans for a Building

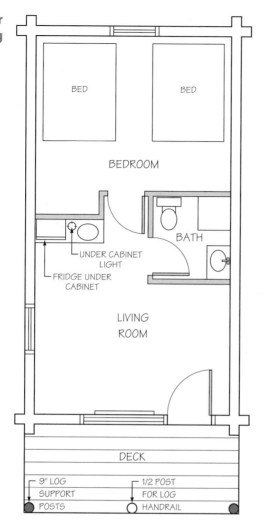

The drawing at the left is a sketch of the floor plan for a cabin at a resort in the mountains of Utah. The measurements are missing. Assume that you are the architect and will finish the drawing. You will have to decide the size of the rooms and put in the measurements to scale.

Design a cabin that you would like to own. Select a scale and draw all the rooms to scale.

If you are interested in architecture, visit an architect who is using CAD (computer-aided design). Computer technology has revolutionized the field of architectural design.

Small Business and Gross Income

Do some research on your local newspaper. What is the newspaper's circulation? How often is an edition of the newspaper published? What is the cost per issue?

Is there a special rate for subscribers to the newspaper? What is the cost of a subscription? What is the length of time for which a subscription is paid? How many of the newspaper's readers are subscribers? Use this figure and the newspaper's total circulation to determine the number of copies sold at newsstands.

Use the figures you have gathered in answering the questions above to determine the total annual income, or **gross income,** derived from sales of the newspaper.

Search the World Wide Web

The framers of the Constitution decided to use a ratio to determine the number of representatives from each state. It was determined that each state would have one representative for every 30,000 citizens, with a minimum of one representative. Congress has changed this ratio over the years, so that we now have 435 representatives.

Find the number of representatives from your state. Determine the ratio of citizens to representatives. Also do this for the most populous state and for the least populous state.

The following Web sites will give you information on the number of representatives for each state and the population of each state.

For representatives: http://clerkweb.house.gov/mbrcmtee/members/mbrsstate/ UnOfLMbr.htm

For population: http://wwwnt.state.id.us/dfm/pop9601.txt

Chapter Summary

Key Words

Quantities such as 8 feet and 60 miles are number quantities written with *units*.

A *ratio* is a comparison of two quantities that have the same units.

A ratio is in *simplest form* when the two numbers that form the ratio have no common factors.

A *rate* is a comparison of two quantities that have different units.

A rate is in *simplest form* when the numbers that form the rate have no common factors.

A *unit rate* is a rate in which the number in the denominator is 1.

A *proportion* is an expression of the equality of two ratios or rates.

Essential Rules

To Find Unit Rates
To find unit rates, divide the number in the numerator of the rate by the number in the denominator of the rate.

To Solve a Proportion
One of the numbers in a proportion may be unknown. To solve a proportion, find a number to replace the unknown so that the proportion is true.

Ways to Express a Ratio
A ratio can be written three different ways:

1. As a fraction
2. As two numbers separated by a colon (:)
3. As two numbers separated by the word *to*

Chapter Review

1. Determine whether the proportion is true or not true. *True*

$$\frac{2}{9} = \frac{10}{45}$$

2. Write the comparison 32 dollars to 80 dollars as a ratio in simplest form using a fraction, a colon (:), and the word *to*.

32 : 80

3. Write "250 miles in 4 hours" as a unit rate.

4. Determine whether the proportion is true or not true.

$$\frac{8}{15} = \frac{32}{60}$$

5. Solve the proportion.

$$\frac{16}{n} = \frac{4}{17} \quad n = 68$$

6. Write "$300 earned in 40 hours" as a unit rate. 7.50

7. Write "$8.75 for 5 pounds" as a unit rate.

1.75 lb

8. Write the comparison 8 feet to 28 feet as a ratio in simplest form using a fraction, a colon (:), and the word *to*.

8 : 28

9. Solve the proportion.

$$\frac{n}{8} = \frac{9}{2} \quad = n = 36$$

10. Solve the proportion. Round to hundredths.

$$\frac{18}{35} = \frac{10}{n} \quad 9.44$$

11. Write the comparison 6 inches to 15 inches as a ratio in simplest form using a fraction, a colon (:), and the word *to*.

6 : 15

12. Determine whether the proportion is true or not true. *not true*

$$\frac{3}{8} = \frac{10}{24}$$

13. Write "$15 in 4 hours" as a rate in simplest form.

$$\frac{15}{4}$$

14. Write "326.4 miles on 12 gallons" as a unit rate. 27.3/10

15. Write the comparison 12 days to 12 days as a ratio in simplest form using a fraction, a colon (:), and the word *to*.

 12/12 = 1/1

16. Determine whether the proportion is true or not true. *true*

$$\frac{5}{7} = \frac{25}{35}$$

17. Solve the proportion. Round to hundredths.
$$\frac{24}{11} = \frac{n}{30}$$
65.415

18. Write "100 miles in 3 hours" as a rate in simplest form.

$$\frac{100}{3}$$

19. In 5 years, the price of a calculator went from $40 to $24. What is the ratio of the decrease in price to the original price?

$$\frac{40-24}{40} = \frac{16}{40} = \frac{2}{5}$$

20. The property tax on a $45,000 home is $900. At the same rate, what is the property tax on a home valued at $120,000?

$$\frac{45000}{900} = \frac{120,000}{2,400}$$

21. The high temperature during a 24-hour period was 84 degrees, and the low temperature was 42 degrees. Write the ratio of the high temperature to the low temperature for the 24-hour period.

$$\frac{84}{42} = \frac{2}{1}$$

22. The total cost of manufacturing 1000 radios was $36,600. Of the radios made, 24 did not pass inspection. Find the cost per radio of the radios that did pass inspection.

$1000 - 24 = 976$

$$\frac{36,600}{976} = 37.50$$

23. A brick wall 40 feet in length contains 448 concrete blocks. At the same rate, how many blocks would it take to build a wall that is 120 feet in length?

$$\frac{40}{120} = \frac{40}{1344}$$

24. A retail computer store spends $30,000 a year on TV advertising and $12,000 on newspaper advertising. Find the ratio of TV advertising to newspaper advertising.

$$\frac{30}{12} = \frac{5}{2}$$

25. A 15-pound turkey costs $10.20. What is the cost per pound? $.68.$

26. Mahesh drove 198.8 miles in 3.5 hours. Find the average number of miles he drove per hour. 56.8

27. An insurance policy costs $3.87 for every $1000 of insurance. At this rate, what is the cost of $50,000 of insurance? 193.50

28. Pascal Hollis purchased 80 shares of stock for $3580. What is the cost per share? 44.75

29. Monique used 1.5 pounds of fertilizer for every 200 square feet of lawn. How many pounds of fertilizer will she have to use on a lawn that measures 3000 square feet?

30. A house had an original value of $80,000 but increased in value to $120,000 in 2 years. Find the ratio of the increase to the original value. $\frac{1}{2}$

$$\frac{120}{80} = \frac{40,000}{80,000} = \frac{1}{2}$$

Chapter Test

1. Write "$22,036.80 earned in 12 months" as a unit rate.

2. Write the comparison 40 miles to 240 miles as a ratio in simplest form using a fraction, a colon (:), and the word *to*.

3. Write "18 supports for every 8 feet" as a rate in simplest form.

4. Determine whether the proportion is true or not true.
$$\frac{40}{125} = \frac{5}{25}$$

5. Write the comparison 12 days to 8 days as a ratio in simplest form using a fraction, a colon (:), and the word *to*.

6. Solve the proportion.
$$\frac{5}{12} = \frac{60}{n}$$

7. Write "256.2 miles on 8.4 gallons of gas" as a unit rate.

8. Write the comparison 27 dollars to 81 dollars as a ratio in simplest form using a fraction, a colon (:), and the word *to*.

9. Determine whether the proportion is true or not true.
$$\frac{5}{14} = \frac{25}{70}$$

10. Solve the proportion.
$$\frac{n}{18} = \frac{9}{4}$$

11. Write "$81 for 12 boards" as a rate in simplest form.

12. Write the comparison 18 feet to 30 feet as a ratio in simplest form using a fraction, a colon (:), and the word *to*.

13. Fifty shares of a utility stock pay a dividend of $62.50. At the same rate, find the dividend paid on 500 shares of the utility stock.

14. The average summer temperature in a California desert is 112 degrees. In a city 100 miles away, the average temperature is 86 degrees. Write the ratio of the average city temperature to the average desert temperature.

15. A plane travels 2421 miles in 4.5 hours. Find the plane's speed in miles per hour.

16. A research scientist estimates that the human body contains 88 pounds of water for every 100 pounds of body weight. At this rate, estimate the number of pounds of water in a college student who weighs 150 pounds.

17. If 40 feet of lumber costs $69.20, what is the per-foot cost of the lumber?

18. The dosage of a medicine is $\frac{1}{4}$ ounce for every 50 pounds of body weight. How many ounces of this medication are required for a person who weighs 175 pounds?

19. An automobile sales company spends $25,000 each month for television advertising and $40,000 each month for radio advertising. Find, as a fraction in simplest form, the ratio of the cost of radio advertising to the total cost of advertising.

20. The property tax on a house valued at $175,000 is $1500. At the same rate, find the property tax on a house valued at $140,000.

Cumulative Review

1. Subtract: 20,095
                 $-$ 10,937

2. Write $2 \cdot 2 \cdot 2 \cdot 2 \cdot 3 \cdot 3 \cdot 3$ in exponential notation.

3. Simplify: $4 - (5 - 2)^2 \div 3 + 2$

4. Find the prime factorization of 160.

5. Find the LCM of 9, 12, and 18.

6. Find the GCF of 28 and 42.

7. Reduce $\frac{40}{64}$ to simplest form.

8. Find $4\frac{7}{15}$ more than $3\frac{5}{6}$.

9. What is $4\frac{5}{9}$ less than $10\frac{1}{6}$?

10. Multiply: $\frac{11}{12} \times 3\frac{1}{11}$

11. Find the quotient of $3\frac{1}{3}$ and $\frac{5}{7}$.

12. Simplify: $\left(\frac{2}{5} + \frac{3}{4}\right) \div \frac{3}{2}$

13. Write 4.0709 in words.

14. Round 2.09762 to the nearest hundredth.

15. Divide: $8.09\overline{)16.0976}$
    Round to the nearest thousandth.

16. Convert $0.06\frac{2}{3}$ to a fraction.

17. Write the comparison 25 miles to 200 miles as a ratio in simplest form.

18. Write "87 cents for 6 bars of soap" as a rate in simplest form.

19. Write "250.5 miles on 7.5 gallons of gas" as a unit rate.

20. Solve $\dfrac{40}{n} = \dfrac{160}{17}$. Round to the nearest hundredth.

21. A car traveled 457.6 miles in 8 hours. Find the car's speed in miles per hour.

22. Solve the proportion.
$$\frac{12}{5} = \frac{n}{15}$$

23. You had $1024 in your checking account. You then wrote checks for $192 and $88. What is your new checking account balance?

24. Malek Khatri buys a tractor for $22,760. A down payment of $5000 is required. The balance remaining is paid in 48 equal monthly installments. What is the monthly payment?

25. Yuko is assigned to read a book containing 175 pages. She reads $\dfrac{2}{5}$ of the book during Thanksgiving vacation. How many pages of the assignment remain to be read?

26. A building contractor bought $2\dfrac{1}{3}$ acres of land for $84,000. What was the cost of each acre?

27. Benjamin Eli bought a shirt for $21.79 and a tie for $8.59. He used a $50 bill to pay for the purchases. Find the amount of change.

28. A college baseball player had 42 hits in 155 at-bats. Find the baseball player's batting average. Round to the nearest thousandth.

29. A soil conservationist estimates that a river bank is eroding at the rate of 3 inches every 6 months. At this rate, how many inches will be eroded in 50 months?

30. The dosage of a medicine is $\dfrac{1}{2}$ ounce for every 50 pounds of body weight. How many ounces of this medication are required for a person who weighs 160 pounds?

5

Percents

A water treatment technologist monitors and controls the quality of a city's drinking water. To ensure the quality of the water, the technicians must measure the percent of various quantities, including chlorine, bacteria, and sediment.

Objectives

Section 5.1
To write a percent as a fraction or a decimal
To write a fraction or a decimal as a percent

Section 5.2
To find the amount when the percent and the base are given
To solve application problems

Section 5.3
To find the percent when the base and amount are given
To solve application problems

Section 5.4
To find the base when the percent and amount are given
To solve application problems

Section 5.5
To solve percent problems using proportions
To solve application problems

Percent Symbol

The idea of using percent dates back many hundreds of years. Percents are used in business for all types of consumer and business loans, in chemistry to measure the percent concentration of an acid, in economics to measure the increases or decreases in the consumer price index (CPI), and in many other areas that affect our daily lives.

The word *percent* comes from the Latin phrase *per centum*, which means "by the hundred." The symbol that is used today for percent is %, but this was not always the symbol.

The present symbol apparently is a result of abbreviations for the word "percent."

One abbreviation was p. cent; later, p. 100 and p. $\overset{o}{c}$ were used. From p. $\overset{o}{c}$, the abbreviation changed to p$\frac{o}{o}$ around the 17th century. This probably was a result of continual writing of p. $\overset{o}{c}$ and the eventual closing of the "c" to make an "o." By the 19th century, the "p" in front of the symbol p$\frac{o}{o}$ was no longer written. The bar that separated the o's became a slash, and the modern symbol % became widely used.

5.1 Introduction to Percents

Objective A *To write a percent as a fraction or a decimal* ....

Percent means "parts of 100." In the figure at the right, there are 100 parts. Because 13 of the 100 parts are shaded, 13% of the figure is shaded.

In most applied problems involving percents, it is necessary either to rewrite a percent as a fraction or a decimal or to rewrite a fraction or a decimal as a percent.

To write a percent as a fraction, remove the percent sign and multiply by $\frac{1}{100}$.

$$13\% = 13 \times \frac{1}{100} = \frac{13}{100}.$$

To rewrite a percent as a decimal, remove the percent sign and multiply by 0.01.

$$13\% = 13 \times 0.01 = 0.13$$

> Move the decimal point two places to the left. Then remove the percent sign.

Example 1 Write 120% as a fraction and as a decimal.

Solution $120\% = 120 \times \dfrac{1}{100} = \dfrac{120}{100}$

$$= 1\frac{1}{5}$$

$120\% = 120 \times 0.01 = 1.2$

Note that percents larger than 100 are greater than 1.

You Try It 1 Write 125% as a fraction and as a decimal.

Your solution

Example 2 Write $16\frac{2}{3}\%$ as a fraction.

Solution $16\dfrac{2}{3}\% = 16\dfrac{2}{3} \times \dfrac{1}{100}$

$$= \frac{50}{3} \times \frac{1}{100} = \frac{50}{300} = \frac{1}{6}$$

You Try It 2 Write $33\frac{1}{3}\%$ as a fraction.

Your solution

Example 3 Write 0.5% as a decimal.

Solution $0.5\% = 0.5 \times 0.01 = 0.005$

You Try It 3 Write 0.25% as a decimal.

Your solution

Solutions on p. S12

Objective B *To write a fraction or a decimal as a percent* ....

A fraction or a decimal can be written as a percent by multiplying by 100%.

⇒ Write $\frac{3}{8}$ as a percent.

$$\frac{3}{8} = \frac{3}{8} \times 100\% = \frac{3}{8} \times \frac{100}{1}\% = \frac{300}{8}\% = 37\frac{1}{2}\% \text{ or } 37.5\%$$

⇒ Write 0.37 as a percent.

$$0.37 \quad = \quad 0.37 \times 100\% \quad = \quad 37\%$$

Move the decimal point two places to the right. Then write the percent sign.

Example 4 Write 0.015 as a percent.

Solution $0.015 = 0.015 \times 100\%$
$= 1.5\%$

You Try It 4 Write 0.048 as a percent.

Your solution

Example 5 Write 2.15 as a percent.

Solution $2.15 = 2.15 \times 100\% = 215\%$

You Try It 5 Write 3.67 as a percent.

Your solution

Example 6 Write $0.33\frac{1}{3}$ as a percent.

Solution $0.33\frac{1}{3} = 0.33\frac{1}{3} \times 100\%$

$= 33\frac{1}{3}\%$

You Try It 6 Write $0.62\frac{1}{2}$ as a percent.

Your solution

Example 7 Write $\frac{2}{3}$ as a percent.
Write the remainder in fractional form.

Solution $\frac{2}{3} = \frac{2}{3} \times 100\% = \frac{200}{3}\%$

$= 66\frac{2}{3}\%$

You Try It 7 Write $\frac{5}{6}$ as a percent.
Write the remainder in fractional form.

Your solution

Example 8 Write $2\frac{2}{7}$ as a percent.
Round to the nearest tenth.

Solution $2\frac{2}{7} = \frac{16}{7} = \frac{16}{7} \times 100\%$

$= \frac{1600}{7}\% \approx 228.6\%$

You Try It 8 Write $1\frac{4}{9}$ as a percent.
Round to the nearest tenth.

Your solution

Solutions on p. S12

5.1 Exercises

Objective A

Write as a fraction and as a decimal.

1. 25%   **2.** 40%   **3.** 130%   **4.** 150%

5. 100%   **6.** 87%   **7.** 73%   **8.** 45%

9. 383%   **10.** 425%   **11.** 70%   **12.** 55%

13. 88%   **14.** 64%   **15.** 32%   **16.** 18%

Write as a fraction.

17. $66\frac{2}{3}\%$ **18.** $12\frac{1}{2}\%$ **19.** $83\frac{1}{3}\%$ **20.** $3\frac{1}{8}\%$ **21.** $11\frac{1}{9}\%$ **22.** $\frac{3}{8}\%$

23. $45\frac{5}{11}\%$ **24.** $15\frac{3}{8}\%$ **25.** $4\frac{2}{7}\%$ **26.** $5\frac{3}{4}\%$ **27.** $6\frac{2}{3}\%$ **28.** $8\frac{2}{3}\%$

Write as a decimal.

29. 6.5%   **30.** 12.3%   **31.** 0.55%   **32.** 2%

33. 8.25%   **34.** 5.05%   **35.** 6.75%   **36.** 3.08%

37. 0.45%   **38.** 6.4%   **39.** 80.4%   **40.** 16.7%

Objective B

Write as a percent.

41. 0.16   **42.** 0.73   **43.** 0.05   **44.** 0.13   **45.** 0.01   **46.** 0.95

47. 0.70   **48.** 1.07   **49.** 1.24   **50.** 2.07   **51.** 0.004   **52.** 0.37

53. 0.006   **54.** 1.012   **55.** 3.106   **56.** 0.12

Write as a percent. Round to the nearest tenth.

57. $\frac{27}{50}$ **58.** $\frac{37}{100}$ **59.** $\frac{1}{3}$ **60.** $\frac{2}{5}$

61. $\dfrac{5}{8}$ **62.** $\dfrac{1}{8}$ **63.** $\dfrac{1}{6}$ **64.** $1\dfrac{1}{2}$

65. $\dfrac{7}{40}$ **66.** $1\dfrac{2}{3}$ **67.** $1\dfrac{7}{9}$ **68.** $\dfrac{7}{8}$

Write as a percent. Write the remainder in fractional form.

69. $\dfrac{15}{50}$ **70.** $\dfrac{12}{25}$ **71.** $\dfrac{7}{30}$ **72.** $\dfrac{1}{3}$

73. $2\dfrac{3}{8}$ **74.** $1\dfrac{2}{3}$ **75.** $2\dfrac{1}{6}$ **76.** $\dfrac{7}{8}$

APPLYING THE CONCEPTS

77. Determine whether the statement is true or false. If the statement is false, give an example to show that the statement is false.
  a. Multiplying a number by a percent always decreases the number.
  b. Dividing by a percent always increases the number.
  c. The word *percent* means "per hundred."
  d. A percent is always less than one.

78. Write the part of the square that is shaded as a fraction, as a decimal, and as a percent. Write the part of the square that is not shaded as a fraction, as a decimal, and as a percent.

79. Explain in your own words how to change a percent to a decimal and a decimal to a percent.

80. A sale on computers advertised $\dfrac{1}{3}$ off the regular price. What percent of the regular price does this represent?

81. A suit was priced at 50% off the regular price. What fraction of the regular price does this represent?

82. If $\dfrac{2}{5}$ of the population voted in an election, what percent of the population did not vote?

83. Is $\dfrac{1}{2}\%$ the same as 0.5? If not, what is the difference between 0.5 and the decimal equivalent of $\dfrac{1}{2}\%$?

84. Is 9.4% the same as $9\dfrac{2}{5}\%$? If not, what is the difference between the decimal equivalent of 9.4% and $9\dfrac{2}{5}\%$?

85. How can you recognize a fraction that represents a number that is less than 1%?

5.2   Percent Equations: Part I

Objective A   *To find the amount when the percent and the base are given* ···

A real estate broker receives a payment that is 4% of an $85,000 sale. To find the amount the broker receives requires answering the question "4% of $85,000 is what?"

This sentence can be written using mathematical symbols and then solved for the unknown number.

$$4\% \quad \text{of} \quad \$85{,}000 \quad \text{is} \quad \text{what?}$$
$$\downarrow \qquad \downarrow \qquad \downarrow \qquad \downarrow \qquad \downarrow$$

$$\boxed{\begin{array}{c}\text{percent}\\4\%\end{array}} \times \boxed{\begin{array}{c}\text{base}\\\$85{,}000\end{array}} = \boxed{\begin{array}{c}\text{amount}\\n\end{array}}$$

of   is written as × (times)
is   is written as = (equals)
what is written as n (the unknown number)

$$0.04 \quad \times \quad \$85{,}000 \quad = \quad n$$
$$\$3400 \quad = \quad n$$

Note that the percent is written as a decimal.

The broker receives a payment of $3400.

The solution was found by solving the basic percent equation for amount.

The Basic Percent Equation

$$\boxed{\text{Percent}} \times \boxed{\text{base}} = \boxed{\text{amount}}$$

In most cases, the percent is written as a decimal before the basic percent equation is solved. However, some percents are more easily written as a fraction than as a decimal. For example,

$$33\tfrac{1}{3}\% = \frac{1}{3} \qquad\qquad 66\tfrac{2}{3}\% = \frac{2}{3} \qquad\qquad 16\tfrac{2}{3}\% = \frac{1}{6} \qquad\qquad 83\tfrac{1}{3}\% = \frac{5}{6}$$

Example 1   Find 5.7% of 160.

Solution $n = 0.057 \times 160$
$n = 9.12$

Note that the words "what is" are missing from the problem but are implied by the word "Find."

You Try It 1   Find 6.3% of 150.

Your solution

Example 2   What is $33\tfrac{1}{3}\%$ of 90?

Solution $n = \dfrac{1}{3} \times 90$
$n = 30$

You Try It 2   What is $16\tfrac{2}{3}\%$ of 66?

Your solution

Solutions on p. S12

Objective B   *To solve application problems* ....

Solving percent problems requires identifying the three elements of the basic percent equation. Recall that these three parts are *percent, base,* and *amount.* Usually the base follows the phrase "percent of."

The table at the right shows the approximate value of various cars in 1997. According to *Money* magazine (March 1997), in 5 years, the value of the Firebird will decrease from its 1997 value by 45%, the value of the Camaro will decrease by 43% of its 1997 value, and the value of the Mustang will decrease by 40% of its 1997 value.

Car	1997 Retail Value
Pontiac Firebird	$22,884
Chevrolet Camaro	$23,170
Ford Mustang	$23,985

➡ Using the estimates from *Money* magazine, find the resale value of the Ford Mustang in 5 years.

Strategy   To find the resale value in 5 years,

- Write and solve the basic percent equation to find the amount of the decrease. The percent is 40%; the base is $23,985.
- Subtract the decrease in value from the 1997 retail value.

Solution   Percent × base = amount

$$40\% \times 23,985 = n$$
$$0.40 \times 23,985 = n$$
$$9594 = n \qquad \bullet \text{ **Amount of decrease**}$$
$$23,985 - 9594 = 14,391$$

The value of the Mustang in 5 years will be $14,391.

Example 3
A quality control inspector found that 1.2% of 2500 telephones inspected were defective. How many telephones inspected were not defective?

Strategy
To find the number of nondefective phones:

- Find the number of defective phones. Write and solve a basic percent equation, using n to represent the number of defective phones (amount). The percent is 1.2% and the base is 2500.
- Subtract the number of defective phones from the number of phones inspected (2500).

Solution
$$1.2\% \times 2500 = n$$
$$0.012 \times 2500 = n$$
$$30 = n \text{ defective phones}$$
$$2500 - 30 = 2470$$

2470 telephones were not defective.

You Try It 3
An electrician's hourly wage was $13.50 before an 8% raise. What is the new hourly wage?

Your strategy

Your solution

Solution on p. S12

5.2 Exercises

Objective A

Solve.

1. 8% of 100 is what? 8

2. 16% of 50 is what? 8

3. 27% of 40 is what? 10.8

4. 52% of 95 is what? 49.4

5. 0.05% of 150 is what? .075

6. 0.075% of 625 is what? .46.875

7. 125% of 64 is what? 80

8. 210% of 12 is what? 25.2

9. Find 10.7% of 485. 51.895

10. Find 12.8% of 625. 80

11. What is 0.25% of 3000? 7.5

12. What is 0.06% of 250? .15

13. 80% of 16.25 is what? 13

14. 26% of 19.5 is what? 5.07

15. What is $1\frac{1}{2}$% of 250? 3.75

16. What is $5\frac{3}{4}$% of 65? 3.7375

17. $16\frac{2}{3}$% of 120 is what? 20

18. $83\frac{1}{3}$% of 246 is what? 205

19. What is $33\frac{1}{3}$% of 630? 210

20. What is $66\frac{2}{3}$% of 891? 594

21. Which is larger: 5% of 95, or 75% of 6?

22. Which is larger: 112% of 5, or 0.45% of 800?

23. Which is smaller: 79% of 16, or 20% of 65?

24. Which is smaller: 15% of 80, or 95% of 15?

25. Which is smaller: 2% of 1500, or 72% of 40?

26. Which is larger: 22% of 120, or 84% of 32?

27. Find 31.294% of 82,460. 25805.0324

28. Find 123.94% of 275,976.

342044.65

Objective B   Application Problems

29. A car dealer's sticker price for a Ford Ranger V-6 is $17,820. The dealer's invoice cost for this truck is 94% of the sticker price. Find the dealer's invoice cost for this truck. 16,750.80

30. Natasha Gomez receives a salary of $2240 per month. Of this amount, 18% is deducted for income tax. Find the amount deducted for income tax. 403.20

31. In 1987, the average number of worker hours required to build a car was 36. In 1997, the average number of worker hours required to build a car was approximately 70% of the average number of worker hours required in 1987. What was the average number of worker hours required to build a car in 1997? *25.2*

32. In one year, Blockbuster Video customers rented 24% of the approximately 3,700,000,000 videos rented that year. How many videos did Blockbuster Video rent that year? *888,000,000,00*

33. A General Motors buyers' incentive program offered a 3.5% rebate on the sale price of a new car. What rebate would a customer receive who purchased a $23,500 car under this program? *822.50*

34. A farmer is given an income tax credit of 10% of the cost of farm machinery. What tax credit would the farmer receive on farm equipment that cost $85,000? *8500*

35. A sales tax of 6% of the cost of a car was added to the purchase price of $9500.
   a. How much was the sales tax? *570*
   b. What is the total cost of the car including sales tax? *10,070*

36. During the packaging process for oranges, spoiled oranges are discarded by an inspector. In one day an inspector found that 4.8% of the 20,000 pounds of oranges inspected were spoiled.
   a. How many pounds of oranges were spoiled? *960*
   b. How many pounds of oranges were not spoiled? *19,040*

37. Funtimes Amusement Park has 550 employees and must hire an additional 22% for the vacation season. What is the total number of employees needed for the vacation season? *671*

38. Between two model years, Chrysler Corporation increased the average price of its new models by 2.6%. If the average price of a car was $7856, what was the amount of the increase? *204.26*

APPLYING THE CONCEPTS

The two circle graphs at the right show how surveyed employees actually spend their time and the way they would prefer to spend their time. (WSJ Supplement, Work & Family 3/31/97; from *Families and Work Institute*.) Assuming that employees have 112 hours a week of time that is not spent sleeping, answer Exercises 39 to 42. Round to the nearest tenth of an hour.

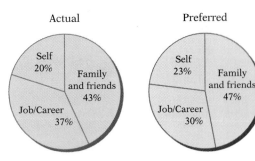

Actual

Self 20%
Family and friends 43%
Job/Career 37%

Preferred

Self 23%
Family and friends 47%
Job/Career 30%

39. What is the actual number of hours per week that employees spend with family and friends?

40. What is the number of hours per week that employees would prefer to spend on job/career?

41. What is the difference between the number of hours an employee preferred to spend on self and the actual amount of time the employee spent on self?

42. What is the difference between the number of hours an employee preferred to spend on family and friends and the actual amount of time the employee spent on family and friends?

5.3   Percent Equations: Part II

Objective A   *To find the percent when the base and amount are given* ....

A recent promotional game at a grocery store listed the probability of winning a prize as "1 chance in 2." A percent can be used to describe the chance of winning. This requires answering the question "What percent of 2 is 1?"

The chance of winning can be found by solving the basic percent equation for *percent*.

What percent of   2   is   1?
    ↓   ↓   ↓   ↓   ↓

$$\boxed{\begin{array}{c}\text{percent}\\ n\end{array}} \times \boxed{\begin{array}{c}\text{base}\\ 2\end{array}} = \boxed{\begin{array}{c}\text{amount}\\ 1\end{array}}$$

$$
\begin{aligned}
n \times 2 &= 1 \\
n &= 1 \div 2 \\
n &= 0.5 \\
n &= 50\%
\end{aligned}
$$

• The solution must be written as a percent to answer the question.

There is a 50% chance of winning a prize.

Example 1   What percent of 40 is 30?

Solution $n \times 40 = 30$
$n = 30 \div 40$
$n = 0.75$
$n = 75\%$

You Try It 1   What percent of 32 is 16?

Your solution   *50*

Example 2   What percent of 12 is 27?

Solution $n \times 12 = 27$
$n = 27 \div 12$
$n = 2.25$
$n = 225\%$

You Try It 2   What percent of 15 is 48?

Your solution   *320%*

Example 3   25 is what percent of 75?

Solution $25 = n \times 75$
$25 \div 75 = n$
$\dfrac{1}{3} = n$
$33\dfrac{1}{3}\% = n$

You Try It 3   30 is what percent of 45?

Your solution

Solutions on p. S12

Objective B **To solve application problems** ....

To solve percent problems, remember that it is necessary to identify the percent, base, and amount. Usually the base follows the phrase "percent of."

Example 4

The monthly house payment for the Kaminski family is $787.50. What percent of the Kaminskis' monthly income of $3750 is the house payment?

Strategy

To find what percent of the income the house payment is, write and solve the basic percent equation, using n to represent the percent. The base is $3750 and the amount is $787.50.

Solution

$n \times \$3750 = \$787.50$

$n = \$787.50 \div \$3750$

$n = 0.21 = 21\%$

The house payment is 21% of the monthly income.

You Try It 4

Tomo Nagata had an income of $33,500 and paid $5025 in income tax. What percent of the income is the income tax?

Your strategy

Your solution

Example 5

On one Thursday night, 33.4 million of the approximately 64.5 million people watching television on the four major networks were not watching *Seinfeld*. What percent of these viewers were watching *Seinfeld*? Round the answer to the nearest percent.

Strategy

To find the percent of viewers watching *Seinfeld*:

- Subtract to find the number of people who were watching *Seinfeld* (64.5 million − 33.4 million).
- Write and solve the basic percent equation, using n to represent the percent. The base is 64.5 and the amount is the number of people watching *Seinfeld*.

Solution

64.5 million − 33.4 million = 31.1 million people were watching *Seinfeld*.

$n \times 64.5 = 31.1$

$n = 31.1 \div 64.5$

$n \approx 0.482$

Approximately 48% of the viewers were watching *Seinfeld*.

You Try It 5

Of the approximately 1,300,000 enlisted women and men in the U.S. military, 416,000 are over the age of 30. What percent of the enlisted people are under the age of 30?

Your strategy

Your solution

Solutions on pp. S12–S13

5.3 Exercises

· ·

Objective A

Solve.

1. What percent of 75 is 24?   *32*

2. What percent of 80 is 20?   *25%*

3. 15 is what percent of 90?   *16.6*

4. 24 is what percent of 60?

5. What percent of 12 is 24?

6. What percent of 6 is 9?

7. What percent of 16 is 6?

8. What percent of 24 is 18?

9. 18 is what percent of 100?

10. 54 is what percent of 100?

11. 5 is what percent of 2000?

12. 8 is what percent of 2500?

13. What percent of 6 is 1.2?

14. What percent of 2.4 is 0.6?

15. 16.4 is what percent of 4.1?

16. 5.3 is what percent of 50?

17. 1 is what percent of 40?

18. 0.3 is what percent of 20?

19. What percent of 48 is 18?

20. What percent of 11 is 88?

21. What percent of 2800 is 7?

22. What percent of 400 is 12?

23. 4.2 is what percent of 175?

24. 41.79 is what percent of 99.5?

25. What percent of 86.5 is 8.304?

26. What percent of 1282.5 is 2.565?

Objective B   *Application Problems*

27. In 1997, total revenues for all U.S. software companies were approximately $18 billion. Of this amount, Microsoft Corporation accounted for approximately $9.5 billion. What percent of total revenues were Microsoft's revenues? Round to the nearest tenth of a percent.

28. Of the approximately 27 million personal and portable computers sold in 1997, Compaq Corporation sold an estimated 3.5 million. What percent of the total did Compaq sell? Round to the nearest tenth of a percent.

29. According to the U.S. Department of Agriculture, of the 63 billion pounds of vegetables produced in the United States in one year, 16 billion pounds were wasted. What percent of vegetables produced were wasted? Round to the nearest tenth of a percent.

30. ◗ In 1997, a Porsche 911 Carrera Targa sold for approximately $70,500. According to *Money* magazine (March 1997), the estimated value of the car 5 years later will be approximately $42,300. What percent of the 1997 selling price is the value 5 years later?

31. ◗ The total number of people in the United States Army is approximately 570,000 (*USA Today*, 3/11/97), of whom 78,000 are women and 492,000 are men. What percent of the total number of people in the Army are women? Round to the nearest tenth of a percent.

32. ◗ Of $2,100,000,000 in revenues that major league baseball anticipates for the 162 games of the 1997 season, $1,200,000,000 will go to the players.
a. How much will go to the owners?
b. What percent of the total revenues will go to the owners? Round to the nearest tenth of a percent.

33. The speed of a PowerPC computer chip in one year was 225 megahertz. Two years later, the speed of the chip increased to 300 megahertz.
a. Find the increase in speed.
b. What percent of the 225-megahertz speed is the increase?

34. To receive a license to sell insurance, an insurance account executive must answer correctly 70% of the 250 questions on a test. Nicholas Mosley answered 177 questions correctly. Did he pass the test?

35. In a test of the breaking strength of concrete slabs for freeway construction, 3 of the 200 slabs tested did not meet safety requirements. What percent of the slabs did meet safety requirements?

APPLYING THE CONCEPTS

The graph at the right shows several categories of average lifetime costs of dog ownership. Use this graph for Exercises 36 and 37. Round answers to the nearest tenth of a percent.

36. What percent of the total amount is spent on food?

37. What percent of the total is spent on veterinary care?

38. Public utility companies will provide consumers with an analysis of their energy bills. For one customer, it was determined that $76 of a total bill of $134 was spent for home heating. What percent (to the nearest tenth) of the total bill was for home heating?

39. The original cost of the Statue of Liberty was approximately $24,000. The cost to refurbish the statue today is approximately $780,000. What percent of the original cost is the cost to refurbish the Statue of Liberty?

40. Write a paragraph on some of the uses of percent that you find in newspapers or magazines.

41. The Fun in the Sun organization claims to have taken a survey of 350 people, asking them to give their favorite outdoor temperature for hiking. The results are given in the table at the right. Explain why these results are not possible.

$1200 Training
$1400 Other
$1100 Flea and tick treatment
$4000 Food
$3900 Veterinary
$3000 Grooming, toys, house

Favorite Temperature	Percent
Greater than 90	5%
80–89	28%
70–79	35%
60–69	32%
Below 60	13%

5.4 Percent Equations: Part III

Objective A **To find the base when the percent and amount are given** ....

In 1997, the average salary of a major league baseball player was $1,320,000. This was 60% of the average salary of a professional basketball player in the NBA. To find the average salary of a NBA basketball player, you must answer the question "60% of what salary is $1,320,000?"

The average salary of a NBA basketball player can be found by solving the basic percent equation for the base.

$$60\% \quad \text{of} \quad \text{what} \quad \text{is} \quad 1,320,000?$$
$$\downarrow \qquad \downarrow \qquad \downarrow \qquad \downarrow \qquad \downarrow$$

| percent 60% | × | base n | = | amount 1,320,000 |

$$0.60 \quad \times \quad n \quad = 1,320,000$$
$$n \quad = 1,320,000 \div 0.60$$
$$n \quad = 2,200,000$$

The average salary of a NBA basketball player was $2,200,000.

Example 1 18% of what is 900?

Solution $0.18 \times n = 900$
$n = 900 \div 0.18$
$n = 5000$

You Try It 1 86% of what is 215?

Your solution

Example 2 30 is 1.5% of what?

Solution $0.015 \times n = 30$
$n = 30 \div 0.015$
$n = 2000$

You Try It 2 15 is 2.5% of what?

Your solution

Example 3 $33\frac{1}{3}\%$ of what is 7?

Solution $\frac{1}{3} \times n = 7$

$n = 7 \div \frac{1}{3}$

$n = 21$

• Note that the percent is written as a fraction.

You Try It 3 $16\frac{2}{3}\%$ of what is 5?

Your solution

Solutions on p. S13

Objective B **To solve application problems** ....

To solve percent problems, it is necessary to identify the percent, base, and amount. Usually the base follows the phrase "percent of."

Example 4
A business office bought a used copy machine for $450, which was 75% of the original cost. What was the original cost of the copier?

Strategy
To find the original cost of the copier, write and solve the basic percent equation, using n to represent the original cost (base). The percent is 75% and the amount is $450.

Solution
$75\% \times n = \$450$
$0.75 \times n = \$450$
$\qquad n = \$450 \div 0.75$
$\qquad n = \$600$

The original cost of the copier was $600.

You Try It 4
A used car has a value of $5229, which is 42% of the car's original value. What was the car's original value?

Your strategy

Your solution

Example 5
A carpenter's wage this year is $19.80 per hour, which is 110% of last year's wage. What was the increase in the hourly wage over last year?

Strategy
To find the increase in the hourly wage over last year:

- Find last year's wage. Write and solve the basic percent equation, using n to represent last year's wage (base). The percent is 110% and the amount is $19.80.
- Subtract last year's wage from this year's wage ($19.80).

Solution
$110\% \times n = \$19.80$
$\quad 1.10 \times n = \$19.80$
$\qquad n = \$19.80 \div 1.10$
$\qquad n = \$18.00$ • **Last year's wage**
$\$19.80 - \$18.00 = \$1.80$

The increase in the hourly wage was $1.80.

You Try It 5
Chang's Sporting Goods has a tennis racket on sale for $44.80, which is 80% of the original price. What is the difference between the original price and the sale price?

Your strategy

Your solution

Solutions on p. S13

5.4 Exercises

Objective A

Solve. Round to the nearest hundredth.

1. 12% of what is 9?

2. 38% of what is 171?

3. 8 is 16% of what?

4. 54 is 90% of what?

5. 10 is 10% of what?

6. 37 is 37% of what?

7. 30% of what is 25.5?

8. 25% of what is 21.5?

9. 2.5% of what is 30?

10. 10.4% of what is 52?

11. 125% of what is 24?

12. 180% of what is 21.6?

13. 18 is 240% of what?

14. 24 is 320% of what?

15. 4.8 is 15% of what?

16. 87.5 is 50% of what?

17. 25.6 is 12.8% of what?

18. 45.014 is 63.4% of what?

19. 0.7% of what is 0.56?

20. 0.25% of what is 1?

21. 30% of what is 2.7?

22. 78% of what is 3.9?

23. 84 is $16\frac{2}{3}$% of what?

24. 120 is $33\frac{1}{3}$% of what?

25. $66\frac{2}{3}$% of what is 72?

26. $83\frac{1}{3}$% of what is 13.5?

27. 6.59% of what is 469.35?

28. 182.3% of what is 46,253?

Objective B   Application Problems

29. The average size of a house in 1997 was 2100 square feet. This is approximately 125% of the average size of a house in 1977. What was the average size of a house in 1977?

30. A used Chevrolet Blazer was purchased for $22,400. This was 70% of the cost of the Blazer when new. What was the cost of the Blazer when it was new?

31. A salesperson received a commission of $820 for selling a car. This was 5% of the selling price of the car. What was the selling price of the car?

32. The per capita personal income in the United States for 1997 was approximately $25,289. This was 104.5% of the per capita personal income in 1996. What was the per capita income in 1996?

33. According to John Dvorak of *PC Magazine* (July 1997), the amount of money spent on Internet products in 1996 was approximately $19,000,000,000. This is approximately 20.6% of the projected amount that will be spent in the year 2000. What amount, to the nearest billion, is expected to be spent in 2000?

34. The Internal Revenue Service says that the average deduction for medical expenses for taxpayers in the $40,000–$50,000 bracket is $4500. This is 26% of the medical expenses claimed by taxpayers in the over $200,000 bracket. How much is the average deduction for medical expense claimed by taxpayers in the over $200,000 bracket? Round to the nearest $1000.

35. During a quality control test, Micronics found that 24 computer boards were defective. This amount was 0.8% of the computer boards tested.
a. How many computer boards were tested?
b. How many computer boards tested were not defective?

36. Of the calls a directory assistance operator received, 441 were requests for telephone numbers listed in the current directory. This accounted for 98% of the calls for assistance that the operator received.
a. How many calls did the operator receive?
b. How many telephone numbers requested were not listed in the current directory?

APPLYING THE CONCEPTS

The table at the right contains nutrition information about a breakfast cereal. Solve Exercises 37 and 38 using information from this table.

37. The recommended daily amount of thiamin for an adult is 1.5 milligrams. Find the amount of thiamin in one serving of cereal with skim milk.

38. The recommended daily amount of copper for an adult is 2 milligrams. Find the amount of copper in one serving of cereal with skim milk.

39. Increase a number by 10%. Now decrease the number by 10%. Is the result the original number? Explain.

40. When a company goes bankrupt, another company may offer to purchase the assets of the company for "25 cents on the dollar." What percent of the value of the company is the buyer paying?

NUTRITION INFORMATION

SERVING SIZE: 1.4 OZ WHEAT FLAKES WITH 0.4 OZ. RAISINS: 39.4 g. ABOUT 1/2 CUP

SERVINGS PER PACKAGE: 14

	CEREAL & RAISINS	WITH 1/2 CUP VITAMINS A & D SKIM MILK

PERCENTAGE OF U.S. RECOMMENDED DAILY ALLOWANCES (U.S. RDA)

	CEREAL & RAISINS	WITH 1/2 CUP SKIM MILK
PROTEIN	4	15
VITAMIN A	15	20
VITAMIN C	**	2
THIAMIN	25	30
RIBOFLAVIN	25	35
NIACIN	25	35
CALCIUM	**	15
IRON	100	100
VITAMIN D	10	25
VITAMIN B₆	25	25
FOLIC ACID...............	25	25
VITAMIN B₁₂...............	25	30
PHOSPHOROUS.........	10	15
MAGNESIUM	10	20
ZINC	25	30
COPPER...................	2	4

* 2% MILK SUPPLIES AN ADDITIONAL 20 CALORIES. 2 g FAT, AND 10 mg CHOLESTEROL.

** CONTAINS LESS THAN 2% OF THE U.S. RDA OF THIS NUTRIENT

5.5 Percent Problems: Proportion Method

Objective A   *To solve percent problems using proportions* ....

Problems that can be solved using the basic percent equation can also be solved using proportions.

The proportion method is based on writing two ratios. One ratio is the percent ratio, written as $\frac{percent}{100}$. The second ratio is the amount-to-base ratio, written as $\frac{amount}{base}$. These two ratios form the proportion:

$$\frac{\textbf{percent}}{\textbf{100}} = \frac{\textbf{amount}}{\textbf{base}}$$

To use the proportion method, first identify the percent, the amount, and the base (the base usually follows the phrase "percent of").

What is 23% of 45?	What percent of 25 is 4?	12 is 60% of what number?
$\frac{23}{100} = \frac{n}{45}$	$\frac{n}{100} = \frac{4}{25}$	$\frac{60}{100} = \frac{12}{n}$
$23 \times 45 = 100 \times n$	$n \times 25 = 100 \times 4$	$60 \times n = 100 \times 12$
$1035 = 100 \times n$	$n \times 25 = 400$	$60 \times n = 1200$
$1035 \div 100 = n$	$n = 400 \div 25$	$n = 1200 \div 60$
$10.35 = n$	$n = 16\%$	$n = 20$

Example 1   15% of what is 7? Round to the nearest hundredth.

Solution
$$\frac{15}{100} = \frac{7}{n}$$
$15 \times n = 100 \times 7$
$15 \times n = 700$
$n = 700 \div 15$
$n \approx 46.67$

You Try It 1   26% of what is 22? Round to the nearest hundredth.

Your solution

Example 2   30% of 63 is what?

Solution
$$\frac{30}{100} = \frac{n}{63}$$
$30 \times 63 = n \times 100$
$1890 = n \times 100$
$1890 \div 100 = n$
$18.90 = n$

You Try It 2   16% of 132 is what?

Your solution

Solutions on p. S13

Objective B *To solve application problems* ················

Example 3
An antiques dealer found that 86% of the 250 items that were sold during one month sold for under $1000. How many items sold for under $1000?

Strategy
To find the number of items that sold for under $1000, write and solve a proportion, using *n* to represent the number of items sold (amount) for less than $1000. The percent is 86% and the base is 250.

Solution

$$\frac{86}{100} = \frac{n}{250}$$
$$86 \times 250 = 100 \times n$$
$$21{,}500 = 100 \times n$$
$$21{,}500 \div 100 = n$$
$$215 = n$$

215 items sold for under $1000.

You Try It 3
Last year it snowed 64% of the 150 days of the ski season at a resort. How many days did it snow?

Your strategy

Your solution

Example 4
In a test of the strength of nylon rope, 5 pieces of the 25 pieces tested did not meet the test standards. What percent of the nylon ropes tested did meet the standards?

Strategy
To find the percent of ropes tested that met the standards:

• Find the number of ropes that met the test standards (25 − 5).
• Write and solve a proportion, using *n* to represent the percent of ropes that met the test standards. The base is 25. The amount is the number of ropes that met the standards.

Solution
25 − 5 = 20 ropes met test
standards

$$\frac{n}{100} = \frac{20}{25}$$
$$n \times 25 = 100 \times 20$$
$$n \times 25 = 2000$$
$$n = 2000 \div 25$$
$$n = 80\%$$

80% of the ropes tested did meet the test standards.

You Try It 4
Five ballpoint pens in a box of 200 were found to be defective. What percent of the pens were not defective?

Your strategy

Your solution

Solutions on pp. S13–S14

5.5 Exercises

Objective A

Solve.

1. 26% of 250 is what?

2. What is 18% of 150?

3. 37 is what percent of 148?

4. What percent of 150 is 33?

5. 68% of what is 51?

6. 126 is 84% of what?

7. What percent of 344 is 43?

8. 750 is what percent of 50?

9. 82 is 20.5% of what?

10. 2.4% of what is 21?

11. What is 6.5% of 300?

12. 96% of 75 is what?

13. 7.4 is what percent of 50? 14.8

14. What percent of 1500 is 693? 36.2%

15. 50.5% of 124 is what? 62.62

16. What is 87.4% of 255? 222.87

17. 120% of what is 6? 5

18. 14 is 175% of what? 8

19. What is 250% of 18? 45

20. 325% of 4.4 is what? 14 3

21. 33 is 220% of what? 15

22. 160% of what is 40? 25

Objective B   Application Problems

23. A charity organization spent $2940 for administrative expenses. This amount is 12% of the money it collected. What is the total amount of money that the club collected?

24. A manufacturer of an anti-inflammatory drug claims that the drug will be effective for 6 hours. An independent testing service determined that the drug was effective for only 80% of the length of time claimed by the manufacturer. Find the length of time the drug will be effective as determined by the testing service.

25. A calculator can be purchased for $28.50. This amount is 40% of the cost of the calculator 8 years ago. What was the cost of the calculator 8 years ago?

26. The Rincon Fire Department received 24 false alarms out of a total of 200 alarms received. What percent of the alarms received were false alarms?

27. 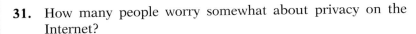 In 1997, Nancy Lopez of the LPGA had an average golf score of 70.71 strokes per round. This was 96.5% of her average golf score per round in 1977, when she joined the LPGA. What was her average golf score per round in 1977? Round to the nearest hundredth.

28. 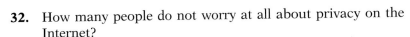 There were approximately 23,000 traffic fatalities related to alcohol in 1987 and 17,000 in 1997. What percent of the 1987 figure is in the 1997 figure? Round to the nearest tenth of a percent.

29. The suggested retail price of Corel WordPerfect 3.5 was $249. However, some mail order catalogs offered the program for $169.95. What percent of the retail price was the mail order price? Round to the nearest tenth of a percent.

30. During one year, approximately 2,240,000 ounces of gold went into the manufacturing of electronic equipment in the United States. This is 16% of all the gold mined in the United States that year. How many ounces of gold were mined in the United States that year?

APPLYING THE CONCEPTS

The figure at the right shows the results of a survey of 1500 people who were asked how much they worry about privacy on the Internet. Use this graph for Exercises 31 and 32.

31. How many people worry somewhat about privacy on the Internet?

32. How many people do not worry at all about privacy on the Internet?

The table below shows (in thousands) the projected increase in demand for teachers by the year 2000. Use this table for Exercises 33 and 34.

33. What percent of the current demand for elementary school teachers is the projected increase? Round to the nearest tenth of a percent.

34. For which level is the projected percent increase from current demand the greatest?

Level	Current Demand (in thousands)	Projected Increase (in thousands)
Elementary	1,597	52
Secondary	1,242	59
Post-secondary	934	58

35. The land area of North America is approximately 9,400,000 square miles. This represents approximately 16% of the total land area of the world. What is the approximate total land area of the world?

36. A certain solution of iodine is used to study the function of the thyroid gland. Approximately every 8 days, the potency of the solution is reduced by 50% of the amount present at that time. By what percent has the potency decreased after 24 days?

37. A certain solution of iron is used to study the formation of blood cells. Approximately every 15 hours, the potency of the solution is reduced by 50% of the amount present at that time. By what percent has the potency decreased after 60 hours?

Focus on Problem Solving

Using a Calculator as a Problem-Solving Tool

A calculator is an important tool for problem solving. Here are a few problems to solve with a calculator. You may need to research some of the questions to find information you do not know.

1. Choose any single-digit positive number. Multiply the number by 1507 and 7373. What is the answer? Choose another positive single-digit number and again multiply by 1507 and 7373. What is the answer? What pattern do you see? Why does this work?

2. The gross domestic product in 1997 was $7,200,000,000,000. Is this more or less than the amount of money that would be placed on the last square of a standard checkerboard if 1 cent is placed on the first square, 2 cents is placed on the second square, 4 cents is placed on the third square, 8 cents is placed on the fourth square, and so on until the 64th square is reached?

3. Which of the reciprocals of the first 16 natural numbers have a terminating decimal representation and which have a repeating decimal representation?

4. What is the largest natural number n for which $4^n > 1 \cdot 2 \cdot 3 \cdot 4 \cdot 5 \cdot \cdots \cdot n$?

5. If $1000 bills are stacked one on top of another, is the height of $1 billion less than or more than the height of the Washington Monument?

6. What is the value of $1 + \cfrac{1}{1 + \cfrac{1}{1 + \cfrac{1}{1 + \cfrac{1}{1 + 1}}}}$?

7. Calculate 15^2, 35^2, 65^2, and 85^2. Study the results. Make a conjecture about a relationship between a number ending in 5 and its square. Use your conjecture to find 75^2 and 95^2. Does your conjecture work for 125^2?

8. Find the sum of the first 1000 natural numbers. (*Hint:* You could just start adding $1 + 2 + 3 + \cdots$, but even if you performed one operation every 3 seconds, it would take you an hour to find the sum. Instead, try pairing the numbers and then adding the number of pairs. Pair 1 and 1000, 2 and 999, 3 and 998, and so on. What is the sum of each pair? How many pairs are there? Use this information to answer the original question.)

9. To qualify for a home loan, a bank requires that the monthly mortgage payment be less than 25% of a borrower's monthly take-home income. A laboratory technician has deductions for taxes, insurance, and retirement that amount to 25% of the technician's monthly gross income. What minimum monthly income must this technician earn to receive a bank loan that has a $1200 per month mortgage payment?

Projects and Group Activities

Consumer Price Index   The Consumer Price Index (CPI) is a percent that is written without the percent sign. For instance, a CPI of 160.1 means 160.1%. This number means that an item that cost $100 between 1982 and 1984 (the base years) would cost $160.10 today. Determining the cost is an application of the basic percent equation.

$$\text{Percent} \times \text{base} = \text{amount}$$
$$\text{CPI} \times \text{cost in base year} = \text{cost today}$$
$$1.601 \times 100 = 160.1 \qquad \bullet \; 160.1\% = 1.601$$

The table below gives the CPI for various products in July of 1997. If you have Internet access, you can obtain current data for the items below plus other items not on this list. Visit http://stats.bls.gov.

Product	CPI
All items	160.1
Food	156.6
Housing	155.8
Clothes	136.1
New cars	145.2
Used cars	154.3
Medical care	233.8
Tobacco	243.2
School books	235.8
Entertainment	162.2

1. Of the items listed, are there any items that in 1997 cost more than twice as much as they cost during the base year? If so, which ones?

2. Of the items listed, are there any items that in 1997 cost more than one-and-one-half times as much as they cost during the base years but less than twice as much as they cost during the base years? If so, which ones?

3. If the cost for textbooks for one semester was $120 in the base years, how much did similar textbooks cost in 1997?

4. If a new car cost $16,000 in 1997, what would a comparable new car have cost during the base years?

5. If a movie ticket cost $7.50 in 1997, what would a comparable movie ticket have cost during the base years?

6. The base year for the CPI was 1967 before the change to 1982–1984. If 1967 were still used as the base year, the CPI for all items (not just those listed above) would be 479.7.
   a. Using the base year of 1967, explain the meaning of a CPI of 479.7.
   b. Using the base year of 1967 and a CPI of 479.7, if textbooks cost $75 for one semester in 1967, how much did similar textbooks cost in 1997?
   c. Using the base year of 1967 and a CPI of 479.7, if a new car cost $16,000 in 1997, what would a comparable new car have cost in 1967?

Economic Inflation A government report that indicates that the *inflation* rate last year was 4% means that the CPI for all items has *increased* by 4% from the previous year. That is, on average, all the items you are buying today (food, clothes, gas, rent, movie tickets, detergent, insurance, etc.) cost 4% more than they cost last year.

This does not mean that the inflation rate is the same for all items. For instance, from 1996 to 1997, the inflation rate for food and beverages was 2.2%. However, gasoline *decreased* in price by 7%. The *deflation* rate for gasoline was 7%.

The amount of inflation (increase in price) or deflation (decrease in price) can be calculated by using the basic percent equation.

$$\text{Percent} \times \text{base} = \text{amount}$$
$$\text{Inflation rate} \times \text{cost last year} = \text{increase over last year's cost}$$
$$\text{Deflation rate} \times \text{cost last year} = \text{decrease over last year's cost}$$

For instance, the inflation rate for clothing was 4.4% and the cost of a pair of jeans last year was $33. To calculate the increase over last year's cost, use the basic percent equation.

$$\text{Inflation rate} \times \text{cost last year} = \text{increase over last year's cost}$$
$$0.044 \times 33 = 1.452$$

The increase over last year's cost was $1.45. Since this amount is the *increase* over last year and last year's cost was $33, *add* this amount to the cost last year to obtain the cost this year.

$$\text{Cost last year} + \text{increase in cost} = \text{cost this year}$$
$$33 + 1.45 = 34.45$$

The cost of the jeans this year is $34.45.

Here is an example of what happens to a commodity that experiences deflation. Suppose the cost of a gallon of gas last year was $1.31 and the deflation rate for gasoline was 7.7%. To calculate the decrease over last year's cost, use the basic percent equation.

$$\text{Deflation rate} \times \text{cost last year} = \text{decrease over last year's cost}$$
$$0.077 \times 1.31 = 0.10087$$

The decrease over last year's cost was $.10. Since this amount is the *decrease* over last year and last year's cost was $1.31, *subtract* this amount from the cost last year to obtain the cost this year.

$$\text{Cost last year} - \text{decrease in cost} = \text{cost this year}$$
$$1.31 - 0.10 = 1.21$$

The cost of one gallon of gas this year is $1.21.

The inflation rate and deflation rate are also calculated by using the basic percent equation.

Suppose that a set of four steel-belted radial tires cost $220 last year, and this year those same tires cost $235. Since the price has *increased*, we will calculate an *inflation* rate by letting n represent the unknown inflation rate.

1. Calculate the increase in cost.

$$\text{Cost this year} - \text{cost last year} = \text{increase in cost}$$
$$235 - 220 = 15$$

2. Calculate the inflation rate.

$$\text{Inflation rate} \times \text{cost last year} = \text{increase in cost}$$
$$n \times 220 = 15$$
$$n = 15 \div 220 \cong 0.068$$

The inflation rate was 6.8%.

The deflation rate is calculated in a similar manner.

Suppose that during the last year the price of the average pair of running shoes decreased from $53 to $49. Since the price has decreased, we will calculate the *deflation* rate by letting *n* represent the unknown deflation rate.

1. Calculate the decrease in cost.

Cost last year − cost this year = decrease in cost
$$53 - 49 = 4$$

2. Calculate the deflation rate.

Deflation rate × cost last year = decrease in cost
$$n \times 53 = 4$$
$$n = 4 \div 53 \cong 0.075$$

The deflation rate was 7.5%.

1. The inflation rate for meats, poultry, fish, and eggs was 4.6% between 1996 and 1997. If a dozen eggs cost $.89 in 1996, how much did the cost of a dozen eggs increase in 1997? Round to the nearest cent.

2. The deflation rate for energy products was 6.2% between 1996 and 1997. If a gallon of heating oil cost $.74 in 1996, how much did the cost of a gallon of heating oil decrease in 1997? Round to the nearest cent.

3. The deflation rate for the typical used car was 2.3% between 1996 and 1997. If a typical used car cost $4500 in 1996, what is the cost of a comparable used car in 1997? Round to the nearest cent.

4. The inflation rate for tobacco products was 4.6% between 1996 and 1997. If a typical pack of cigarettes cost $2.30 in 1996, what is the cost of a typical pack of cigarettes in 1997? Round to the nearest cent.

5. Suppose the inflation rate for airline tickets was 4% between 1996 and 1997 and 3% between 1997 and 1998. What is the cost at the end of 1998 of an airline ticket that cost $250 at the beginning of 1996?

Chapter Summary

Key Words   *Percent* means "parts of 100."

Essential Rules   *To Write a Percent as a Fraction*
To write a percent as a fraction, remove the percent sign and multiply by $\frac{1}{100}$.

To Write a Percent as a Decimal
To write a percent as a decimal, remove the percent sign and multiply by 0.01.

To Write a Decimal as a Percent
To write a decimal as a percent, multiply by 100%.

To Write a Fraction as a Percent
To write a fraction as a percent, multiply by 100%.

Basic Percent Equation   Percent × base = amount

Proportion Method to Solve Percent Equations $\dfrac{\text{Percent}}{100} = \dfrac{\text{amount}}{\text{base}}$

Chapter Review

1. What is 30% of 200?

2. 16 is what percent of 80?

3. Write $1\frac{3}{4}$ as a percent.

4. 20% of what is 15?

5. Write 12% as a fraction.

6. Find 22% of 88.

7. What percent of 20 is 30?

8. $16\frac{2}{3}\%$ of what is 84?

9. Write 42% as a decimal.

10. What is 7.5% of 72?

11. $66\frac{2}{3}\%$ of what is 105?

12. Write 7.6% as a decimal.

13. Find 125% of 62.

14. Write $16\frac{2}{3}\%$ as a fraction.

15. Use the proportion method to find what percent of 25 is 40.

16. 20% of what number is 15? Use the proportion method.

17. Write 0.38 as a percent.

18. 78% of what is 8.5? Round to the nearest tenth.

19. What percent of 30 is 2.2? Round to the nearest tenth of a percent.

20. What percent of 15 is 92? Round to the nearest tenth of a percent.

21. Trent missed 9 out of 60 questions on a history exam. What percent of the questions did he answer correctly? Use the proportion method.

22. A company used 7.5% of its $60,000 advertising budget for TV advertising. How much of the advertising budget was spent for TV advertising?

23. In a two-year period, the population of Houston, Texas, increased from 1,600,000 to 1,700,000. What percent increase does this represent?

24. Joshua purchased a video camera for $980 and paid a sales tax of 6.25% of the cost. What was the total cost of the video camera?

25. In a survey of 350 women and 420 men, 275 of the women and 300 of the men reported that they wore sunscreen often. To the nearest tenth of a percent, what percent of the women wore sunscreen often?

26. It is estimated that the world's population will be 6,100,000,000 by the year 2000. This is 105% of the population in 1997. What was the world's population in 1997? Round to the nearest hundred million.

27. A computer system can be purchased for $1800. This is 60% of what the computer cost 4 years ago. What was the cost of the computer 4 years ago? Use the proportion method.

28. In a recent basketball game, Michael Jordan scored 33 points. This was 30% of all the points scored by the team. How many points were scored by the team?

Chapter Test

1. Write 97.3% as a decimal.

2. Write $83\frac{1}{3}\%$ as a fraction.

3. Write 0.3 as a percent.

4. Write 1.63 as a percent.

5. Write $\frac{3}{2}$ as a percent.

6. Write $\frac{2}{3}$ as a percent.

7. What is 77% of 65?

8. 47.2% of 130 is what?

9. Which is larger:
7% of 120, or 76% of 13?

10. Which is smaller:
13% of 200, or 212% of 12?

11. A fast-food company uses 6% of its $75,000 budget for advertising. What amount of the budget is spent on advertising?

12. During the packaging process for vegetables, spoiled vegetables are discarded by an inspector. In one day an inspector found that 6.4% of the 1250 pounds of vegetables were spoiled. How many pounds of vegetables were not spoiled?

The table at the right contains nutrition information about a breakfast cereal. Solve Exercises 13 and 14 with information taken from this table.

13. The recommended amount of potassium per day for an adult is 3000 milligrams (mg). What percent, to the nearest tenth of a percent, of the daily recommended amount of potassium is provided by one serving of cereal with skim milk?

14. The daily recommended number of calories for a 190-pound man is 2200 calories. What percent, to the nearest tenth of a percent, of the daily recommended number of calories is provided by one serving of cereal with 2% milk?

NUTRITION INFORMATION

SERVING SIZE: 1.4 OZ WHEAT FLAKES WITH
0.4 OZ. RAISINS: 39.4 g. ABOUT 1/2 CUP
SERVINGS PER PACKAGE: 14

	CEREAL & RAISINS	WITH 1/2 CUP VITAMINS A & D SKIM MILK
CALORIES	120	180
PROTEIN, g	3	7
CARBOHYDRATE, g	28	34
FAT, TOTAL, g	1	1*
UNSATURATED, g	1	
SATURATED, g	0	
CHOLESTEROL, mg	0	0*
SODIUM, mg	125	190
POTASSIUM, mg	240	440

* 2% MILK SUPPLIES AN ADDITIONAL 20 CALORIES.
2 g FAT, AND 10 mg CHOLESTEROL.
** CONTAINS LESS THAN 2% OF THE U.S. RDA OF
THIS NUTRIENT

15. The Urban Center Department Store has 125 permanent employees and must hire an additional 20 temporary employees for the holiday season. What percent of the permanent employees is the number hired as temporary employees for the holiday season?

16. Conchita missed 7 out of 80 questions on a math exam. What percent of the questions did she answer correctly? (Round to the nearest tenth of a percent.)

17. 12 is 15% of what?

18. 42.5 is 150% of what? Round to the nearest tenth.

19. A manufacturer of transistors found 384 defective transistors during a quality control study. This amount was 1.2% of the transistors tested. Find the number of transistors tested.

20. A new house was bought for $95,000; 5 years later the house sold for $152,000. The increase was what percent of the original price?

21. 123 is 86% of what number? Round to the nearest tenth.

22. What percent of 12 is 120?

23. A secretary receives a wage of $9.52 per hour. This amount is 112% of last year's salary. What is the dollar increase in the hourly wage over last year?

24. A city has a population of 71,500; 10 years ago the population was 32,500. The population now is what percent of what the population was 10 years ago?

25. The annual license fee on a car is 1.4% of the value of the car. If the license fee during a year was $91.00, what is the value of the car?

Cumulative Review

1. Simplify $18 \div (7 - 4)^2 + 2.$ = 4

2. Find the LCM of 16, 24, and 30.

   240

3. Find the sum of $2\frac{1}{3}$, $3\frac{1}{2}$, and $4\frac{5}{8}$.

   $10\frac{1}{34}$

4. Subtract: $27\frac{5}{12} - 14\frac{9}{16}$

   12.4148

5. Multiply: $7\frac{1}{3} \times 1\frac{5}{7}$

   $17\frac{4}{4}$

6. What is $\frac{14}{27}$ divided by $1\frac{7}{9}$?

    $\frac{7}{34}$

7. Simplify: $\left(\frac{3}{4}\right)^3 \cdot \left(\frac{8}{9}\right)^2$

   $\frac{1}{3}$

8. Simplify: $\left(\frac{2}{3}\right)^2 - \left(\frac{3}{8} - \frac{1}{3}\right) \div \frac{1}{2}$ $\frac{13}{36}$

9. Round 3.07973 to the nearest hundredth.

   3.08

10. Subtract: 3.0902
                 − 1.9706

    1.1196

11. Divide: $0.032\overline{)1.097}$
    Round to the nearest ten-thousandth.

    34.2813

12. Convert $3\frac{5}{8}$ to a decimal.

    3.625

13. Convert 1.75 to a fraction.

    $1\frac{3}{4}$

14. Place the correct symbol, < or >, between the two numbers.

    $\frac{3}{8}$ < 0.87

15. Solve the proportion $\frac{3}{8} = \frac{20}{n}$. Round to the nearest tenth.

    53.3

16. Write "$76.80 earned in 8 hours" as a unit rate.

    9.60

17. Write $18\frac{1}{3}\%$ as a fraction.

$\frac{11}{60}$

18. Write $\frac{5}{6}$ as a percent.

$83 \cdot \frac{1}{3}\%$

19. 16.3% of 120 is what? Round to the nearest hundredth.

19.56

20. 24 is what percent of 18?

$133 \cdot \frac{1}{3}\%$

21. 12.4 is 125% of what?

9.92

22. What percent of 35 is 120? Round to the nearest tenth.

$342\frac{8}{10}\%$

23. Sergio has an income of $740 per week. One-fifth of his income is deducted for income tax payments. Find his take-home pay.

592.00

24. Eunice bought a car for $4321, with a down payment of $1000. The balance was paid in 36 equal monthly payments. Find the monthly payment.

92.25

25. The gasoline tax is $.19 a gallon. Find the number of gallons of gasoline used during a month in which $79.80 was paid in gasoline taxes.

420

26. The real estate tax on a $72,000 home is $1440. At the same rate, find the real estate tax on a home valued at $150,000.

3,000

27. Ken purchased a stereo set for $490 and paid $29.40 in sales tax. What percent of the purchase price was the sales tax?

6%

28. A survey of 300 people showed that 165 people favored a certain candidate for mayor. What percent of the people surveyed did not favor this candidate?

45%

29. The value of a home in the northern part of the United States was $62,000 in 1985. The same home in 1990 had a value of $155,000. What percent of the 1985 value is the 1990 value?

250%

30. The Environmental Protection Agency found that 990 out of 5500 children tested had levels of lead in their blood exceeding federal guidelines. What percent of the children tested had levels of lead in the blood that exceeded federal standards?

18%

6

Applications for Business and Consumers

Buyers are employed by department stores to purchase the various items that are sold in the stores. Sometimes buyers are very specialized and buy only, for instance, clothes. Once the clothes have been purchased, the buyer must determine a price at which to sell the clothes so that the store will make a profit. Markup, one of the topics of this chapter, is the amount that must be added to the cost of the clothes so that the department store makes a profit.

Objectives

A Penny a Day

A fictitious job offer in a newspaper claimed that the salary would be 1¢ on the first of the month and 2¢ on the second of the month. Next month, the salary would be 4¢ on the first and 8¢ on the second of the month. The next month and each succeeding month for 12 months, the procedure of doubling the previous payment would be continued the same way. Do you think you would want the job under these conditions?

This problem is an example of compounding interest, which is similar to the type of interest that is earned on bank or savings deposits. The big difference is that banks and savings and loans do not compound the interest as quickly as in the given example.

The table below shows the amount of salary you would earn for each month and then gives the total annual salary.

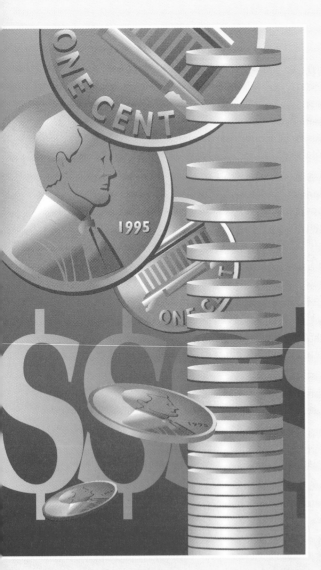

Month	Salary
January	$.01 + $.02 = $.03
February	$.04 + $.08 = $.12
March	$.16 + $.32 = $.48
April	$.64 + $1.28 = $1.92
May	$2.56 + $5.12 = $7.68
June	$10.24 + $20.48 = $30.72
July	$40.96 + $81.92 = $122.88
August	$163.84 + $327.68 = $491.52
September	$655.36 + $1310.72 = $1966.08
October	$2621.44 + $5242.88 = $7864.32
November	$10,485.76 + $20,971.52 = $31,457.28
December	$41,943.04 + $83,886.08 = $125,829.12

Total Annual Salary = $167,772.15

Not a bad annual salary!

6.1 Applications to Purchasing

Objective A *To find unit cost* ....

Frequently stores advertise items for purchase as, say, 2 Red Baron Deep Dish Pizzas for $5.50 or 5 cans of StarKist tuna for $4.25.

The **unit cost** is the cost of one Red Baron Deep Dish Pizza or for one can of StarKist tuna. To find the unit cost, divide the total cost by the number of units.

2 pizzas for $5.50
5.50 ÷ 2 = 2.75
$2.75 is the cost of one pizza.
Unit cost: $2.75 per pizza

5 cans for $4.25
4.25 ÷ 5 = 0.85
$.85 is the cost of one can.
Unit cost: $.85 per can

Example 1
Find the unit cost. Round to the nearest tenth of a cent.
a. 3 gallons of mint chip ice cream for $10
b. 4 ounces of Crest toothpaste for $3.29

Strategy
To find the unit cost, divide the total cost by the number of units.

Solution
a. 10 ÷ 3 ≈ 3.3333
   $3.333 per gallon
b. 3.29 ÷ 4 = 0.8225
   $.823 per ounce

You Try It 1
Find the unit cost. Round to the nearest tenth of a cent.
a. 8 size AA Energizer batteries for $5.59
b. 15 ounces of Revlon shampoo for $1.89

Your strategy

Your solution

Solution on p. S14

Objective B *To find the most economical purchase* ....

Comparison shoppers often find the most economical buy by comparing unit costs.

One store is selling 6 twelve-ounce cans of ginger ale for $1.79, and a second store is selling 24 twelve-ounce cans of ginger ale for $7.47. To find the better buy, compare the unit costs.

1.79 ÷ 6 ≈ 0.298   7.47 ÷ 24 ≈ 0.311
Unit cost: $.298 per can   Unit cost: $.311 per can

Because $.298 < $.311, the better buy is 6 cans for $1.79.

Example 2
Find the more economical purchase:
5 pounds of nails for $3.25, or 4 pounds of nails for $2.58.

Strategy
To find the more economical purchase, compare the unit costs.

Solution
$3.25 \div 5 = 0.65$
$2.58 \div 4 = 0.645$
$\$.645 < \$.65$

The more economical purchase is 4 pounds for $2.58.

You Try It 2
Find the more economical purchase:
6 cans of fruit for $2.52, or 4 cans of fruit for $1.66.

Your strategy

Your solution

Solution on p. S14

Objective C **To find total cost**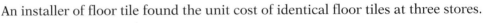

An installer of floor tile found the unit cost of identical floor tiles at three stores.

Store 1	Store 2	Store 3
$1.22 per tile	$1.18 per tile	$1.28 per tile

By comparing the unit costs, the installer determined that store 2 would provide the most economical purchase.

The installer also uses the unit cost to find the total cost of purchasing 300 floor tiles at store 2. The **total cost** is found by multiplying the unit cost by the number of units purchased.

Unit cost	×	number of units	=	total cost
1.18	×	300	=	354

The total cost is $354.

Example 3
Clear redwood lumber costs $2.43 per foot. How much would 25 feet of clear redwood cost?

Strategy
To find the total cost, multiply the unit cost ($2.43) by the number of units (25).

Solution

Unit cost	×	number of units	=	total cost
2.43	×	25	=	60.75

The total cost is $60.75.

You Try It 3
Pine saplings cost $4.96 each. How much would 7 pine saplings cost?

Your strategy

Your solution

Solution on p. S14

6.1 Exercises

· ·

Objective A *Application Problems*

Find the unit cost. Round to the nearest tenth of a cent.

1. Chris & Pitts Bar·B·Q sauce, 23 ounces for $1.69

2. Birds-eye maple, 6 feet for $18.75

3. Diamond walnuts, $2.99 for 8 ounces

4. A&W root beer, 6 cans for $1.69

5. Ibuprofen, 50 tablets for $1.99

6. Visine eye drops, 0.5 ounce for $2.69

7. Adjustable wood clamps, 2 for $9.95

8. Corn, 6 ears for $1.25

9. Cheerios cereal, 15 ounces for $2.29

10. Doritos tortilla chips, 14.5 ounces for $3.79

11. Sheet metal screws, 8 for $.95

12. MJB coffee, 39 ounces for $9.99

Objective B *Application Problems*

Suppose your local supermarket offers the following products at the given prices. Find the more economical purchase.

13. Sutter Home pasta sauce, 25.5 ounces for $3.29, or Muir Glen Organic pasta sauce, 26 ounces for $3.79

14. Kraft mayonnaise, 40 ounces for $2.98, or Springfield mayonnaise, 32 ounces for $2.39

15. Ortega salsa, 20 ounces for $2.59, or La Victoria salsa, 16 ounces for $1.98

16. L'Oreal shampoo, 13 ounces for $3.99, or Cortexx shampoo, 12 ounces for $3.69

17. Golden Sun vitamin E, 200 tablets for $7.39 or 400 tablets for $12.99

18. Ultra Mr. Clean, 20 ounces for $2.67, or Ultra Spic and Span, 14 ounces for $2.19

19. 16 ounces Kraft cheddar cheese, $4.37, or 9 ounces of Land to Lake cheddar cheese, $2.29

20. Bertolli olive oil, 34 ounces for $9.49, or Pompeian olive oil, 8 ounces for $2.39

21. Maxwell House coffee, 7 ounces for $5.59, or Sanka coffee, 2 ounces for $2.37

22. Wagner's vanilla extract, $3.29 for 1.5 ounces, or Durkee vanilla extract, 1 ounce for $2.74

23. Purina Cat Chow, $4.19 for 56 ounces, or Friskies Chef's Blend, $3.37 for 50.4 ounces

24. Kleenex tissues, $1.73 for 250 tissues or Puffs tissues, $1.23 for 175 tissues

---

Objective C   Application Problems

25. If Hormel sliced bacon costs $2.59 per pound, find the total cost of 3 pounds.

26. Used red brick costs $.98 per brick. Find the total cost of 75 bricks.

27. Kiwi fruit cost $.23 each. Find the total cost of 8 kiwi.

28. Boneless chicken filets cost $4.69 per pound. Find the cost of 3.6 pounds. Round to the nearest cent.

29. Herbal tea costs $.98 per ounce. Find the total cost of 6.5 ounces.

30. If Stella Swiss Lorraine cheese costs $5.99 per pound, find the total cost of 0.65 pound. Round to the nearest cent.

31. Red Delicious apples cost $.59 per pound. Find the total cost of 2.1 pounds. Round to the nearest cent.

32. Choice rib eye steak costs $4.49 per pound. Find the total cost of 2.8 pounds. Round to the nearest cent.

33. If Godiva chocolate costs $7.95 per pound, find the total cost of $\frac{3}{4}$ pound. Round to the nearest cent.

34. Color photocopying costs $.11 per page. Find the total cost for photocopying 120 pages.

APPLYING THE CONCEPTS

35. Explain in your own words the meaning of unit pricing.

36. What is the UPC (Universal Product Code) and how is it used?

6.2 Percent Increase and Percent Decrease

Objective A *To find percent increase* ....

Percent increase is used to show how much a quantity has increased over its original value. The statements "food prices increased by 2.3% last year" and "city council members received a 4% pay increase" are examples of percent increase.

➡ According to the Energy Information Administration, the number of alternative-fuel vehicles will increase from 251,000 to 386,000 in 5 years. Find the percent increase in alternative-fuel vehicles.

$$\boxed{\text{New value}} - \boxed{\text{original value}} = \boxed{\text{amount of increase}}$$

$$386{,}000 - 251{,}000 = 135{,}000$$

Now solve the basic percent equation for percent.

$$\text{Percent} \times \text{base} = \text{amount}$$

$$\boxed{\text{Percent increase}} \times \boxed{\text{original value}} = \boxed{\text{amount of increase}}$$

$$n \times 251{,}000 = 135{,}000$$
$$n = 135{,}000 \div 251{,}000$$
$$n \approx 0.5378$$

The number of alternative-fuel vehicles will increase by approximately 54%.

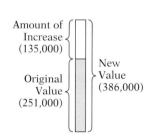

POINT OF INTEREST

According to the U.S. Census Bureau, the number of persons aged 85 and over in the United States will increase to 8.1 million by 2030, a 103% increase from 1995.

Example 1

The average wholesale price of coffee increased from $2 per pound to $3 per pound in one year. What was the percent increase in the price of one pound of coffee?

Strategy

To find the percent increase:

• Find the amount of the increase.
• Solve the basic percent equation for *amount*.

Solution

$$\boxed{\text{New value}} - \boxed{\text{original value}} = \boxed{\text{amount of increase}}$$

$$3 - 2 = 1$$

$$\text{Percent} \times \text{base} = \text{amount}$$
$$n \times 2 = 1$$
$$n = 1 \div 2$$
$$n = 0.50 = 50\%$$

The percent increase was 50%.

You Try It 1

According to the U.S. Geological Society, the number of earthquakes measuring 6.0 to 6.9 on the Richter scale increased from 80 to 150 over a 7-year period. What percent increase in the number of these earthquakes does this represent?

Your strategy

Your solution

Solution on p. S14

Example 2
Chris Carley was earning $6.50 an hour as a nursing assistant before receiving a 10% increase in pay. What is Chris's new hourly pay?

Strategy
To find the new hourly wage:

- Solve the basic percent equation for *amount*.
- Add the amount of the increase to the original wage.

Solution
Percent × base = amount
0.10   × 6.50 =   *n*
          0.65 = *n*

The amount of the increase was $.65.

6.50 + 0.65 = 7.15

The new hourly wage is $7.15.

You Try It 2
Yolanda Liyama was making a wage of $8.50 an hour as a baker before receiving a 14% increase in hourly pay. What is Yolanda's new hourly wage?

Your strategy

Your solution

Solution on p. S14

Objective B   To apply percent increase to business—markup ....

Some of the expenses involved in operating a business are salaries, rent, equipment, and utilities. To pay these expenses and earn a profit, a business must sell a product at a higher price than it paid for the product.

Cost is the price a business pays for a product, and **selling price** is the price at which a business sells a product to a customer. The difference between selling price and cost is called **markup**.

| Selling price | − | cost | = | markup |

or

| Cost | + | markup | = | selling price |

Markup is frequently expressed as a percent of a product's cost. This percent is called the **markup rate.**

| Markup rate | × | cost | = | markup |

➡ Suppose Bicycles Galore purchases an AMP Research B4 bicycle for $2119.20 and sells it for $2649. What markup rate does Bicycles Galore use?

| Selling price | − | cost | = | markup |

2649.00   − 2119.20 =   529.80   • First find the markup.

Percent   ×   base   =   amount   • Then solve the basic
| Markup rate | × | cost | = | markup | percent equation for
   n   × 2119.20 =   529.80   *percent.*
                    n = 529.80 ÷ 2119.20 = 0.25

The markup rate is 25%.

Example 3

The manager of a sporting goods store determines that a markup rate of 36% is necessary to make a profit. What is the markup on a pair of Olin skis that costs the store $225?

Strategy

To find the markup, solve the basic percent equation for *amount*.

Solution

Percent   ×   base   =   amount

| Markup rate | × | cost | = | markup |

$$0.36 \quad × \quad 225 \quad = \quad n$$
$$81 \quad = n$$

The markup is $81.

You Try It 3

A bookstore manager determines that a markup rate of 20% is necessary to make a profit. What is the markup on a book that costs the bookstore $8?

Your strategy

Your solution

Example 4

A plant nursery bought a citrus tree for $4.50 and used a markup rate of 46%. What is the selling price?

Strategy

To find the selling price:

- Find the markup by solving the basic percent equation for *amount*.
- Add the markup to the cost.

Solution

Percent   ×   base   =   amount

| Markup rate | × | cost | = | markup |

$$0.46 \quad × \quad 4.50 \quad = \quad n$$
$$2.07 = n$$

| Cost | + | markup | = | selling price |

$$4.50 \quad + \quad 2.07 \quad = \quad 6.57$$

The selling price is $6.57.

You Try It 4

A clothing store bought a suit for $72 and used a markup rate of 55%. What is the selling price?

Your strategy

Your solution

Solutions on p. S14

Objective C   **To find percent decrease** ....

Percent decrease is used to show how much a quantity has decreased over its original value. The statements "the number of family farms decreased by 2% last year" and "there has been a 50% decrease in the cost of a Pentium chip" are examples of percent decrease.

➡ Between 1996 and 1997, the average cost of gasoline in Washington, D.C., decreased from $1.34 per gallon to $1.20 per gallon. Find the percent decrease in the cost of gasoline for Washington, D.C.

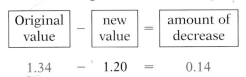

$$\boxed{\text{Original value}} - \boxed{\text{new value}} = \boxed{\text{amount of decrease}}$$

$$1.34 \quad - \quad 1.20 \quad = \quad 0.14$$

Now solve the basic percent equation for percent.

$$\text{Percent} \quad \times \quad \text{base} \quad = \quad \text{amount}$$

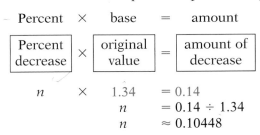

$$\boxed{\text{Percent decrease}} \times \boxed{\text{original value}} = \boxed{\text{amount of decrease}}$$

$$n \quad \times \quad 1.34 \quad = 0.14$$
$$n = 0.14 \div 1.34$$
$$n \approx 0.10448$$

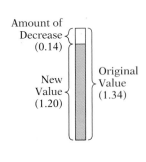

The price of one gallon of gasoline decreased by approximately 10.4%.

Example 5

Arms control treaties between the United States and Russia specify that the United States will decrease the number of its strategic nuclear weapons from 7150 to 3500 by the end of 2003. Find the percent decrease in strategic nuclear weapons for the U.S. Round to the nearest percent.

Strategy

To find the percent decrease:

- Find the amount of the decrease.
- Solve the basic percent equation for *percent*.

Solution

$$\boxed{\text{Original value}} - \boxed{\text{new value}} = \boxed{\text{amount of decrease}}$$

$$7150 \quad - \quad 3500 \quad = \quad 3650$$

$$\text{Percent} \times \text{base} = \text{amount}$$
$$n \quad \times 7150 = \quad 3650$$
$$n = 3650 \div 7150$$
$$n \approx 0.51049$$

The percent decrease is approximately 51%.

You Try It 5

Arms control treaties between the United States and Russia specify that Russia will decrease the number of its strategic nuclear weapons from 6670 to 3100 by the end of 2003. Find the percent decrease in strategic nuclear weapons for Russia. Round to the nearest percent.

Your strategy

Your solution

Solution on p. S14

Example 6

The total sales for December for a stationery store were $16,000. For January, total sales showed an 8% decrease from December's sales. What were the total sales for January?

Strategy

To find the total sales for January:

- Find the amount of decrease by solving the basic percent equation for *amount*.
- Subtract the amount of decrease from the December sales.

Solution

Percent × base = amount

$0.08 \times 16{,}000 = n$

$1280 = n$

The decrease in sales was $1280.

$16{,}000 - 1280 = 14{,}720$

The total sales for January were $14,720.

You Try It 6

Fog decreased the normal 5-mile visibility at an airport by 40%. What was the visibility in the fog?

Your strategy

Your solution

Solution on p. S15

Objective D   **To apply percent decrease to business—discount** ....

To promote sales, a store may reduce the regular price of some of its products temporarily. The reduced price is called the **sale price.** The difference between the regular price and the sale price is called the **discount**.

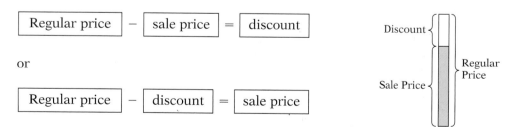

| Regular price | − | sale price | = | discount |

or

| Regular price | − | discount | = | sale price |

Discount is frequently stated as a percent of a product's regular price. This percent is called the **discount rate.**

| Discount rate | × | regular price | = | discount |

Example 7

A GE 25-inch stereo television that regularly sells for $299 is on sale for $250. Find the discount rate. Round to the nearest tenth of a percent.

Strategy

To find the discount rate:

- Find the discount.
- Solve the basic percent equation for *percent*.

Solution

Regular price	−	sale price	=	discount
299	−	250	=	49

Percent	×	base	=	amount
Discount rate	×	regular price	=	discount
n	×	299	=	49

$$n = 49 \div 299$$
$$n \approx 0.1639$$

The discount rate is 16.4%.

Example 8

A Scotts 6-horsepower lawn mower is on sale for 25% off the regular price of $325. Find the sale price.

Strategy

To find the sale price:

- Find the discount by solving the basic percent equation for *amount*.
- Subtract to find the sale price.

Solution

Percent	×	base	=	amount
Discount rate	×	regular price	=	discount
0.25	×	325	=	n

$$81.25 = n$$

Regular price	−	discount	=	sale price
325	−	81.25	=	243.75

The sale price is $243.75.

You Try It 7

A star jasmine shrub that regularly sells for $4.25 is on sale for $3.75. Find the discount rate. Round to the nearest tenth of a percent.

Your strategy

Your solution

You Try It 8

A hardware store is selling a Newport security door for 15% off the regular price of $110. Find the sale price.

Your strategy

Your solution

Solutions on p. S15

6.2 Exercises

●   *Objective A*   *Application Problems*

1. Porsche Cars Canada, Ltd. increased its sales from 310 cars in one year to 372 cars the next year. What percent increase does this represent?

2. Wolfgang Lutz of the International Institute for Applied Systems Analysis estimates that the world's population will increase from approximately 5,800,000,000 in 1997 to 10,600,000,000 in 2077. What percent increase does this represent? Round to the nearest tenth of a percent.

3. The number of students donating $1000 or more to presidential campaigns increased from 1078 in 1992 to 1746 in the 1996 presidential election. What percent increase does this represent? Round to the nearest tenth of a percent.

4. In 1991, there were 13.6 million new cars sold in the United States. From 1991 to 1997, there was approximately a 17% increase in the number of new car sales. How many new cars were sold in the United States in 1997? Round to the nearest hundred thousand.

5. On average, only 25 of every 1000 people worldwide owned a computer in 1991. Four years later, 45 of every 1000 people owned a computer. What percent increase does this represent?

6. The average size of airplanes in the world fleet is estimated to grow from 197 seats in 1996 to 219 seats by 2016. What percent increase does this represent? Round to the nearest tenth of a percent.

7. During one year, the number of people subscribing to direct broadcast satellite systems increased from 2.3 million to 4.3 million. What percent increase does this represent? Round to the nearest tenth of a percent.

8. In 1996 IBM was issued 1876 patents. This was approximately a 35% increase from the previous year. How many patents were issued to IBM in the previous year? Round to the nearest whole number.

9. The National Hockey League increased its spending on newspaper, magazine, television, and billboard advertising from $42,000 to $2,500,000 in 3 years. What percent increase does this represent? Round to the nearest percent.

10. The Nike shoe company employed approximately 14,200 people in 1995. By the end of 1996, it had increased the number of employees by 21%. How many employees did Nike have at the end of 1996?

Objective B   *Application Problems*

11. A window air conditioner cost AirRite Air Conditioning Systems $285. Find the markup on the air conditioner if the markup rate is 25% of the cost.

12. The owner of Kerr Electronics purchased 300 Craig portable CD players at a cost of $85 each. If the owner uses a markup rate of 42%, what is the markup on each of the Craig CD players?

13. A ski and tennis store uses a markup rate of 30% on tennis rackets and 40% on skis. What is the markup on a Prince tennis racket that cost $80?

14. The manager of Brass Antiques has determined that a markup rate of 38% is necessary for a profit to be made. What is the markup on a brass doorknob that costs $45?

15. Computer Inc. uses a markup of $975 on an AMD K6 computer system that costs $3250. What is the markup rate on this system?

16. Saizon Pen & Office Supply uses a markup of $12 on a calculator that costs $20. What markup rate does this amount represent?

17. Giant Photo Service uses a markup rate of 48% on its Model ZA cameras, which cost the shop $162.
    a. What is the markup?
    b. What is the selling price?

18. The Circle R golf pro shop uses a markup rate of 45% on a set of Tour Pro golf clubs that costs the shop $210.
    a. What is the markup?
    b. What is the selling price?

19. According to *Managing a Small Business* from Liraz Publishing Co., goods in a store are often marked up 50 to 100% of the cost. This allows a business to make a profit of 5% to 10%. Suppose a store purchases a pair of jeans for $32 and uses a markup rate of 80% of the cost.
    a. What is the markup?
    b. What is the selling price?

20. Harvest Time Produce Inc. uses a 55% markup rate and pays $.60 for a box of strawberries.
    a. What is the markup?
    b. What is the selling price of a box of strawberries?

21. Resner Builders' Hardware uses a markup rate of 42% for a table saw that costs $160. What is the selling price of the table saw?

22. Brad Burt's Magic Shop uses a markup rate of 48%. What is the selling price of a telescoping sword that costs $50?

Objective C   *Application Problems*

23. A new bridge reduced the normal 45-minute travel time between two cities by 18 minutes. What percent decrease does this represent?

24. According to *Popular Mechanics* (7/97), the Honda EV Plus electric weighs approximately 3600 pounds. The General Motors EV1 weighs 630 pounds less. What percent decrease in weight does this represent?

25. By installing energy-saving equipment, the Pala Rey Youth Camp reduced its normal $800-per-month utility bill by $320. What percent decrease does this amount represent?

26. During the last 40 years, the consumption of eggs in the United States has dropped from 400 eggs per person per year to 260 eggs per person per year. What percent decrease does this amount represent?

27. It is estimated that the value of a new car is reduced 30% after 1 year of ownership. Using this estimate, find how much value a $11,200 new car loses after 1 year.

28. A department store employs 1200 people during the holiday. At the end of the holiday season, the store reduces the number of employees by 45%. What is the decrease in the number of employees?

29. Because of a decrease in demand for super-8 video cameras, Kit's Cameras reduced the orders for these models from 20 per month to 8 per month.
  a. What is the amount of the decrease?
  b. What percent decrease does this amount represent?

30. A new computer system reduced the time for printing the payroll from 52 minutes to 39 minutes.
  a. What is the amount of the decrease?
  b. What percent decrease does this amount represent?

31. Juanita's average expense for gasoline was $76. After joining a car pool, she was able to reduce the expense by 20%.
  a. What was the amount of the decrease?
  b. What is the average monthly gasoline bill now?

32. An oil company paid a dividend of $1.60 per share. After a reorganization, the company reduced the dividend by 37.5%.
  a. What was the amount of the decrease?
  b. What is the new dividend?

33. Because of an improved traffic pattern at a sports stadium, the average amount of time a fan waits to park decreased from 3.5 minutes to 2.8 minutes. What percent decrease does this amount represent?

Objective D   *Application Problems*

34. The Austin College Bookstore is giving a discount of $8 on calculators that normally sell for $24. What is the discount rate?

35. A discount clothing store is selling a $72 sport jacket for $24 off the regular price. What is the discount rate?

36. A disk player that regularly sells for $340 is selling for 20% off the regular price. What is the discount?

37. Dacor Appliances is selling its $450 washing machine for 15% off the regular price. What is the discount?

38. An electric grill that regularly sells for $140 is selling for $42 off the regular price. What is the discount rate?

39. You bought a computer system for $350 off the regular price of $1400. What is the discount rate?

40. Quick Service Gas Station has its regularly priced $45 tune-up on sale for 16% off the regular price.
  a. What is the discount?
  b. What is the sale price?

41. Turkey that regularly sells for $.85 per pound is on sale for 20% off the regular price.
  a. What is the discount?
  b. What is the sale price?

42. An outdoor supply store has regularly priced $160 sleeping bags on sale for $120.
   a. What is the discount?
   b. What is the discount rate?

43. Standard Brands paint that regularly sells for $16 per gallon is on sale for $12 per gallon.
   a. What is the discount?
   b. What is the discount rate?

APPLYING THE CONCEPTS

44. In many instances, there are three numbers that a consumer might expect to see or hear at a new car dealership: sticker price, invoice cost, and selling price. According to CarBargains, a not-for-profit new-car shopping service, the selling price of a car for a consumer may be more or less than the dealer's invoice cost, but rarely is the sticker price. Here are some CarBargains estimates for 1997 full-size trucks.

Model	Best price	Amount to add or subtract from dealer's invoice	Dealer's invoice cost	Sticker price
Ford F-150 XL Styleside	$21,751	Subtract $100	$21,851	$25,060
GMC 1500 Sierra Wideside	$21,180	Add $300	$20,880	$23,821
Chevy C/K 1500 Fleetside	$21,427	Add $500	$20,927	$23,868
Dodge Ram BR1500 Sweptline	$22,011	Add $500	$21,511	$24,535

   a. For the GMC, what is the discount rate from the sticker price to the dealer's invoice cost?
   b. For the Ford F-150, what is the percent decrease from the dealer's invoice cost to the best price?
   c. For which of the trucks listed is the percent increase from the dealer's invoice cost to the best price the greatest?

45. A welder earning $12 per hour is given a 10% raise. To find the new wage, we can multiply $12 by 0.10 and add the product to $12. Can the new wage be found by multiplying $12 by 1.10? Try both methods and compare your answers.

46. Grocers, florists, bakers, and other businesses must consider spoilage when deciding the markup of a product. For instance, suppose a florist purchased 200 roses at a cost of $.86 per rose. The florist wants a markup rate of 50% of the total cost of all the roses and expects 7% of the roses to wilt and therefore not be salable. Find the selling price per rose by answering each of the following questions.
   a. What is the florist's total cost for the 200 roses?
   b. Find the total selling price without spoilage.
   c. Find the number of roses the florist expects to sell. *Hint:* The number of roses the florist expects to sell is:
        % of salable roses × number of roses purchased
   d. To find the selling price per rose, divide the total selling price without spoilage by the number of roses the florist expects to sell. Round to the nearest cent.

47. A promotional sale at a department store offers 25% off the sale price. The sale price is 25% off the regular price. Is this the same as a sale that offers 50% off the regular price? If not, which sale gives the better price? Explain your answer.

48. In your own words, explain how to find a percent increase or a percent decrease.

6.3 Interest

Objective A   *To calculate simple interest* ··

When money is deposited in a bank account, the bank pays the depositor for the privilege of using that money. The amount paid to the depositor is called **interest.** When money is borrowed from a bank, the borrower pays for the privilege of using that money. The amount paid to the bank is also called interest.

The original amount deposited or borrowed is called the **principal.** The amount of interest is a percent of the principal. The percent used to determine the amount of interest is the **interest rate.** Interest rates are given for specific periods of time, usually months or years.

Interest computed on the original principal is called **simple interest.** To calculate simple interest, multiply the principal by the interest rate per period by the number of time periods.

⇒ Calculate the simple interest on $1500 deposited for 2 years at an annual interest rate of 7.5%.

Principal × annual interest rate × time (in years) = interest
1500   ×   0.075   ×   2   =   225

The interest earned is $225.

Example 1
Kamal borrowed $500 from a savings and loan association for 6 months at an annual interest rate of 7%. What is the simple interest due on the loan?

Strategy
To find the simple interest, multiply:

Principal × annual interest rate × time (in years)

Solution   500 × 0.07 × 0.5 = 17.5

The interest due is $17.50.

You Try It 1
A company borrowed $15,000 from a bank for 18 months at an annual interest rate of 8%. What is the simple interest due on the loan?

Your strategy

Your solution

Example 2
A credit card company charges a customer 1.5% per month on the unpaid balance of charges on the credit card. What is the interest due in a month when the customer has an unpaid balance of $54?

Strategy
To find the interest due, multiply the principal by the monthly interest rate by the time (in months).

Solution   54 × 0.015 × 1 = 0.81

The interest charge is $.81.

You Try It 2
A bank offers short-term loans at a simple interest rate of 1.2% per month. What is the interest due on a short-term loan of $400 for 2 months?

Your strategy

Your solution

Solutions on p. S15

Objective B **To calculate compound interest** ··

Usually the interest paid on money deposited or borrowed is compound interest. **Compound interest** is computed not only on the original principal but also on interest already earned. Compound interest is usually compounded annually (once a year), semiannually (twice a year), quarterly (four times a year), or daily.

$100 is invested for 3 years at an annual interest rate of 9% compounded annually. The interest earned over the 3 years is calculated by first finding the interest earned each year.

1st year	Interest earned:	$0.09 \times \$100.00 = \$9.00$
	New principal:	$\$100.00 + \$9.00 = \underline{\$109.00}$
2nd year	Interest earned:	$0.09 \times \$109.00 = \$9.81$
	New principal:	$\$109.00 + \$9.81 = \underline{\$118.81}$
3rd year	Interest earned:	$0.09 \times \$118.81 \approx \$10.69$
	New principal:	$\$118.81 + \$10.69 = \$129.50$

To find the interest earned, subtract the original principal from the new principal.

New principal	−	original principal	=	interest earned
129.50	−	100	=	29.5

The interest earned is $29.50.

Note that the compound interest earned is $29.50. The simple interest earned on the investment would have been only $100 \times 0.09 \times 3 = \$27$.

Calculating compound interest can be very tedious, so there are tables that can be used to simplify these calculations. A portion of a compound interest table is given in the Appendix.

Example 3
An investment of $650 pays 8% annual interest compounded semiannually. What is the interest earned in 5 years?

Strategy
To find the interest earned:
- Find the new principal by multiplying the original principal by the factor (1.48024) found in the compound interest table.
- Subtract the original principal from the new principal.

Solution
$650 \times 1.48024 \approx 962.16$

The new principal is $962.16.

$962.16 - 650 = 312.16$

The interest earned is $312.16.

You Try It 3
An investment of $1000 pays 6% annual interest compounded quarterly. What is the interest earned in 20 years?

Your strategy

Your solution

Solution on p. S15

6.3 Exercises

Objective A   Application Problems

1. To finance the purchase of 15 new cars, the Tropical Car Rental Agency borrowed $100,000 for 9 months at an annual interest rate of 9%. What is the simple interest due on the loan?

2. A home builder obtained a pre-construction loan of $50,000 for 8 months at an annual interest rate of 9.5%. What is the simple interest due on the loan? Round to the nearest cent.

3. The Mission Valley Credit Union charges its customers an interest rate of 2% per month on money that is transferred into an account that is overdrawn. Find the interest owed to the credit union for 1 month when $800 is transferred into an overdrawn account.

4. The Visa card that Francesca has charges her 1.6% per month on her unpaid balance. Find the interest owed to Visa when her unpaid balance for the month is $1250.

5. Action Machining Company purchased a robot-controlled lathe for $225,000 and financed the full amount at 8% simple annual interest for 4 years.
    a. Find the interest on the loan.
    b. Find the monthly payment.
    $$\left(\text{Monthly payment} = \frac{\text{loan amount} + \text{interest}}{\text{number of months}}\right)$$

6. For the purchase of an entertainment center, an $1800 loan is obtained for 2 years at a simple interest rate of 9.4%.
    a. Find the interest due on the loan.
    b. Find the monthly payment using the formula in part b of Exercise 5.

7. To attract new customers, Heller Ford is offering car loans at a simple interest rate of 4.5%.
    a. Find the interest charged to a customer who finances a car loan of $12,000 for 2 years.
    b. Find the monthly payment using the formula in part b of Exercise 5.

8. Cimarron Homes Inc. purchased a small plane for $57,000 and financed the full amount for 5 years at a simple annual interest rate of 9%.
    a. Find the interest due on the loan.
    b. Find the monthly payment using the formula in part b of Exercise 5.

9. Dennis Pappas decided to build onto an existing structure instead of buying a new home. He borrowed $42,000 for $3\frac{1}{2}$ years at a simple interest rate of 9.5%. Find the monthly payment.

Objective B   Application Problems

Solve. Use the table in the Appendix. Round to the nearest cent.

10. North Island Federal Credit Union pays 4% annual interest, compounded daily, on time savings deposits. Find the value of $750 deposited in this account after 1 year.

Solve. Use the table in the Appendix. Round to the nearest cent.

11. What is the value after 5 years of $1000 invested at 7% annual interest compounded quarterly?

12. An investment club invested $50,000 in a certificate of deposit that pays 5% annual interest compounded quarterly. Find the value of this investment after 10 years.

13. Tanya invested $2500 in a tax-sheltered annuity that pays 8% annual interest compounded daily. Find the value of her investment after 20 years.

14. Sal Trovato invested $3000 in a corporate retirement account that pays 6% annual interest compounded semiannually. Find the value of his investment after 15 years.

15. To replace equipment, a farmer invested $20,000 in an account that pays 7% annual interest compounded semiannually. What is the value of the investment after 5 years?

16. Green River Lodge invests $75,000 in a trust account that pays 8% interest compounded quarterly.
   a. What will the value of the investment be in 5 years?
   b. How much interest will be earned in the 5 years?

17. To save for retirement, a couple deposited $3000 in an account that pays 7% annual interest compounded daily.
   a. What will the value of the investment be in 10 years?
   b. How much interest will be earned in the 10 years?

18. To save for a child's college education, the Petersens deposited $2500 into an account that pays 6% annual interest compounded daily. Find the amount of interest earned in this account over a 20-year period.

APPLYING THE CONCEPTS

19. Explain the fundamental difference between simple interest and compound interest.

20. Visit a brokerage business and obtain information on annuities. Explain the advantages of an annuity as a retirement option.

21. Suppose you have a savings account that earns interest at the rate of 6% per year compounded monthly. On January 1, you open this account with a deposit of $100.
   a. On February 1, you deposit an additional $100 into the account. What is the value of the account after the deposit?
   b. On March 1, you deposit an additional $100 into the account. What is the value of the account after the deposit? *Note:* This type of savings plan, wherein equal amounts ($100) are saved at equal time intervals (every month), is called an annuity.

6.4 Real Estate Expenses

Objective A   ***To calculate the initial expenses of buying a home*** ....

One of the largest investments most people ever make is the purchase of a home. The major initial expense in the purchase is the down payment. The amount of the down payment is normally a percent of the purchase price. This percent varies among banks, but it usually ranges from 5% to 25%.

The **mortgage** is the amount that is borrowed to buy real estate. The mortgage amount is the difference between the purchase price and the down payment.

➡ A home is purchased for $140,000, and a down payment of $21,000 is made. Find the mortgage.

$$\boxed{\text{Purchase price}} - \boxed{\text{down payment}} = \boxed{\text{mortgage}}$$

$$140{,}000 \quad - \quad 21{,}000 \quad = \quad 119{,}000$$

The mortgage is $119,000.

Another large initial expense in buying a home is the loan origination fee, which is a fee that the bank charges for processing the mortgage papers. The loan origination fee is usually a percent of the mortgage and is expressed in **points,** which is the term banks use to mean percent. For example, "5 points" means "5 percent."

$$\boxed{\text{Points}} \times \boxed{\text{mortgage}} = \boxed{\text{loan origination fee}}$$

Example 1

A house is purchased for $125,000, and a down payment, which is 20% of the purchase price, is made. Find the mortgage.

Strategy

To find the mortgage:

- Find the down payment by solving the basic percent equation for *amount.*
- Subtract the down payment from the purchase price.

Solution

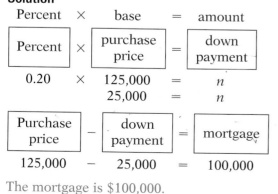

Percent × base = amount

$$\boxed{\text{Percent}} \times \boxed{\begin{array}{c}\text{purchase}\\\text{price}\end{array}} = \boxed{\begin{array}{c}\text{down}\\\text{payment}\end{array}}$$

$$0.20 \quad \times \quad 125{,}000 \quad = \quad n$$
$$25{,}000 \quad = \quad n$$

$$\boxed{\begin{array}{c}\text{Purchase}\\\text{price}\end{array}} - \boxed{\begin{array}{c}\text{down}\\\text{payment}\end{array}} = \boxed{\text{mortgage}}$$

$$125{,}000 \quad - \quad 25{,}000 \quad = \quad 100{,}000$$

The mortgage is $100,000.

You Try It 1

An office building is purchased for $216,000, and a down payment, which is 25% of the purchase price, is made. Find the mortgage.

Your strategy

Your solution

36250

Solution on p. S15

Example 2

A home is purchased with a mortgage of $65,000. The buyer pays a loan origination fee of $3\frac{1}{2}$ points. How much is the loan origination fee?

Strategy

To find the loan origination fee, solve the basic percent equation for *amount*.

Solution

$$\text{Percent} \times \text{base} = \text{amount}$$

$$\boxed{\text{Points}} \times \boxed{\text{mortgage}} = \boxed{\text{fee}}$$

$$0.035 \times 65,000 = n$$

$$2275 = n$$

The loan origination fee is $2275.

You Try It 2

The mortgage on a real estate investment is $80,000. The buyer paid a loan origination fee of $4\frac{1}{2}$ points. How much was the loan origination fee?

Your strategy

Your solution

Solution on p. S15

Objective B To calculate ongoing expenses of owning a home

Besides the initial expenses of buying a home, there are continuing monthly expenses involved in owning a home. The monthly mortgage payment, utilities, insurance, and taxes are some of these ongoing expenses. Of these expenses, the largest one is normally the monthly mortgage payment.

For a fixed-rate mortgage, the monthly mortgage payment remains the same throughout the life of the loan. The calculation of the monthly mortgage payment is based on the amount of the loan, the interest rate on the loan, and the number of years required to pay back the loan. Calculating the monthly mortgage payment is fairly difficult, so tables such as the one in the Appendix are used to simplify these calculations.

⇒ Find the monthly mortgage payment on a 30-year $60,000 mortgage at an interest rate of 9%. Use the monthly payment table in the Appendix.

$$60,000 \times \underset{\substack{\downarrow \\ \text{from the} \\ \text{table}}}{\underline{0.0080462}} \approx 482.77$$

The monthly mortgage payment is $482.77.

The monthly mortgage payment includes the payment of both principal and interest on the mortgage. The interest charged during any one month is charged on the unpaid balance of the loan. Therefore, during the early years of the mortgage, when the unpaid balance is high, most of the monthly mortgage payment is interest charged on the loan. During the last few years of a mortgage, when the unpaid balance is low, most of the monthly mortgage payment goes toward paying off the loan.

⇒ Find the interest paid on a mortgage during a month when the monthly mortgage payment is $186.26 and $58.08 of that amount goes toward paying off the principal.

$$\boxed{\text{Monthly mortgage payment}} - \boxed{\text{principal}} = \boxed{\text{interest}}$$

$$186.26 \quad - \quad 58.08 \quad = \quad 128.18$$

The interest paid on the mortgage is $128.18.

Property tax is another ongoing expense of owning a house. Property tax is normally an annual expense that may be paid on a monthly basis. The monthly property tax, which is determined by dividing the annual property tax by 12, is usually added to the monthly mortgage payment.

⇒ A homeowner must pay $534 in property tax annually. Find the property tax that must be added each month to the homeowner's monthly mortgage payment.

$$534 \div 12 = 44.5$$

Each month, $44.50 must be added to the monthly mortgage payment for property tax.

Example 3

Serge purchased some land for $120,000 and made a down payment of $25,000. The savings and loan association charges an annual interest rate of 8% on Serge's 25-year mortgage. Find the monthly mortgage payment.

Strategy

To find the monthly mortgage payment:

- Subtract the down payment from the purchase price to find the mortgage.
- Multiply the mortgage by the factor found in the monthly payment table in the Appendix.

Solution

$$\boxed{\begin{array}{c}\text{Purchase}\\\text{price}\end{array}} - \boxed{\begin{array}{c}\text{down}\\\text{payment}\end{array}} = \boxed{\begin{array}{c}\text{mort-}\\\text{gage}\end{array}}$$

$$120{,}000 \quad - \quad 25{,}000 \quad = \quad 95{,}000$$

$$95{,}000 \quad \times \quad \underset{\underset{\text{from the table}}{\uparrow}}{0.0077182} \quad \approx \quad 733.23$$

The monthly mortgage payment is $733.23.

You Try It 3

A new condominium project is selling townhouses for $75,000. A down payment of $15,000 is required, and a 20-year mortgage at an annual interest rate of 9% is available. Find the monthly mortgage payment.

Your strategy

Your solution

Solution on p. S15

Example 4

A home has a mortgage of $134,000 for 25 years at an annual interest rate of 7%. During a month when $375.88 of the monthly mortgage payment is principal, how much of the payment is interest?

Strategy

To find the interest:

- Multiply the mortgage by the factor found in the monthly payment table in the Appendix to find the monthly mortgage payment.
- Subtract the principal from the monthly mortgage payment.

Solution

$134,000 \times 0.0070678 \approx 947.09$

    ↑   ↑

   from the monthly mortgage
    table   payment

Monthly mortgage payment	−	principal	=	interest

 947.09 − 375.88 = 571.21

$571.21 is interest on the mortgage.

You Try It 4

An office building has a mortgage of $125,000 for 25 years at an annual interest rate of 9%. During a month when $492.65 of the monthly mortgage payment is principal, how much of the payment is interest?

Your strategy

Your solution

Example 5

The monthly mortgage payment for a home is $598.75. The annual property tax is $900. Find the total monthly payment for the mortgage and property tax.

Strategy

To find the monthly payment:

- Divide the annual property tax by 12 to find the monthly property tax.
- Add the monthly property tax to the monthly mortgage payment.

Solution

$900 \div 12 = 75$ (monthly property tax)

$598.75 + 75 = 673.75$

The total monthly payment is $673.75.

You Try It 5

The monthly mortgage payment for a home is $415.20. The annual property tax is $744. Find the total monthly payment for the mortgage and property tax.

Your strategy

Your solution

Solutions on p. S16

6.4 Exercises

· ·

Objective A   *Application Problems*

1. A condominium at Mt. Baldy Ski Resort was purchased for $97,000, and a down payment of $14,550 was made. Find the mortgage.

2. An insurance business was purchased for $173,000, and a down payment of $34,600 was made. Find the mortgage.

3. A building lot was purchased for $25,000. The lender requires a down payment of 30% of the purchase price. Find the down payment.

4. Ian Goldman purchased a new home for $88,500. The lender requires a down payment of 20% of the purchase price. Find the down payment.

5. Brian Stedman made a down payment of 25% of the $850,000 purchase price of an apartment building. How much was the down payment?

6. A clothing store was purchased for $125,000, and a down payment that was 25% of the purchase price was made. How much was the down payment?

7. A loan of $150,000 is obtained to purchase a home. The loan origination fee is $2\frac{1}{2}$ points. Find the amount of the loan origination fee.

8. Security Savings & Loan requires a borrower to pay $3\frac{1}{2}$ points for a loan. Find the amount of the loan origination fee for a loan of $90,000.

9. Baja Construction Inc. is selling homes for $150,000. A down payment of 5% is required.
    a. Find the down payment.
    b. Find the mortgage.

10. A cattle rancher purchased some land for $240,000. The bank requires a down payment of 15% of the purchase price.
    a. Find the down payment.
    b. Find the mortgage.

11. Vivian Tom purchased a home for $210,000. Find the mortgage if the down payment Vivian made is 10% of the purchase price.

12. A mortgage lender requires a down payment of 5% of the $80,000 purchase price of a condominium. How much is the mortgage?

Objective B   *Application Problems*

Solve. Use the monthly payment table in the Appendix. Round to the nearest cent.

13. An investor obtained a loan of $150,000 to buy a car wash business. The monthly mortgage payment was based on 25 years at 8%. Find the monthly mortgage payment.

14. A beautician obtained a 20-year mortgage of $90,000 to expand the business. The credit union charges an annual interest rate of 9%. Find the monthly mortgage payment.

Solve. Use the monthly payment table in the Appendix. Round to the nearest cent.

15. A couple interested in buying a home determines that they can afford a monthly mortgage payment of $800. Can they afford to buy a home with a 30-year $110,000 mortgage at 8% interest?

16. A lawyer is considering purchasing a new office building with a 20-year $400,000 mortgage at 9% interest. The lawyer can afford a monthly mortgage payment of $4000. Can the lawyer afford the monthly mortgage payment on the new office building?

17. The county tax assessor has determined that the annual property tax on a $125,000 house is $1348.20. Find the monthly property tax.

18. The annual property tax on a $155,000 home is $1992. Find the monthly property tax.

19. Abacus Imports Inc. has a warehouse with a 25-year mortgage of $200,000 at an annual interest rate of 9%.
  a. Find the monthly mortgage payment.
  b. During a month when $941.72 of the monthly mortgage payment is principal, how much of the payment is interest?

20. A vacation home has a mortgage of $135,000 for 30 years at an annual interest rate of 7%.
  a. Find the monthly mortgage payment.
  b. During a month when $392.47 of the monthly mortgage payment is principal, how much of the payment is interest?

21. The annual mortgage payment on a duplex is $10,844.40. The owner must pay an annual property tax of $948. Find the total monthly payment for the mortgage and property tax.

22. The monthly mortgage payment on a home is $716.40, and the homeowner pays an annual property tax of $792. Find the total monthly payment for the mortgage and property tax.

23. Maria Hernandez purchased a home for $210,000 and made a down payment of $15,000. The balance was financed for 30 years at an annual interest rate of 8%. Find the monthly mortgage payment.

24. A customer of a savings and loan purchased a $185,000 home and made a down payment of $20,000. The savings and loan charges its customers an annual interest rate of 7% for 30 years for a home mortgage. Find the monthly mortgage payment.

APPLYING THE CONCEPTS

25. A couple considering a mortgage of $100,000 have a choice of loans. One loan is an 8% loan for 20 years, and the other loan is at 8% for 30 years. Find the amount of interest that can be saved by choosing the 20-year loan.

26. Find out what an adjustable-rate mortgage is. What is the difference between this type of loan and a fixed-rate mortgage? List some of the advantages and disadvantages of each.

6.5 Car Expenses

Objective A *To calculate the initial expenses of buying a car* ....

The initial expenses in the purchase of a car usually include the down payment, the license fees, and the sales tax. The down payment may be very small or as much as 25% or 30% of the purchase price of the car, depending on the lending institution. License fees and sales tax are regulated by each state, so these expenses vary from state to state.

Example 1

A car is purchased for $8500, and the lender requires a down payment of 15% of the purchase price. Find the amount financed.

Strategy

To find the amount financed:

- Find the down payment by solving the basic percent equation for *amount*.
- Subtract the down payment from the purchase price.

Solution

Percent × base = amount

$$\boxed{\text{Percent}} \times \boxed{\begin{array}{c}\text{purchase}\\\text{price}\end{array}} = \boxed{\begin{array}{c}\text{down}\\\text{payment}\end{array}}$$

$$0.15 \quad \times \quad 8500 \quad = \quad n$$
$$1275 = n$$

$$8500 - 1275 = 7225$$

The amount financed is $7225.

You Try It 1

A down payment of 20% of the $9200 purchase price of a new car is made. Find the amount financed.

Your strategy

Your solution

Example 2

A sales clerk purchases a car for $6500 and pays a sales tax that is 5% of the purchase price. How much is the sales tax?

Strategy

To find the sales tax, solve the basic percent equation for *amount*.

Solution

Percent × base = amount

$$\boxed{\text{Percent}} \times \boxed{\begin{array}{c}\text{purchase}\\\text{price}\end{array}} = \boxed{\begin{array}{c}\text{sales}\\\text{tax}\end{array}}$$

$$0.05 \quad \times \quad 6500 \quad = \quad n$$
$$325 = n$$

The sales tax is $325.

You Try It 2

A car is purchased for $7350. The car license fee is 1.5% of the purchase price. How much is the license fee?

Your strategy

Your solution

Solutions on p. S16

408.45

Objective B   *To calculate ongoing expenses of owning a car* ....

Besides the initial expenses of buying a car, there are continuing expenses involved in owning a car. These ongoing expenses include car insurance, gas and oil, general maintenance, and the monthly car payment. The monthly car payment is calculated in the same manner as monthly mortgage payments on a home loan. A monthly payment table, such as the one in the Appendix, is used to simplify the calculation of monthly car payments.

Example 3

At a cost of $.27 per mile, how much does it cost to operate a car during a year in which the car is driven 15,000 miles?

Strategy

To find the cost, multiply the cost per mile by the number of miles driven.

Solution

$15,000 \times 0.27 = 4050$ The cost is $4050.

Example 4

During 1 month the total gasoline bill was $84 and the car was driven 1200 miles. What was the cost per mile for gasoline?

Strategy

To find the cost per mile for gasoline, divide the cost for gasoline by the number of miles driven.

Solution $84 \div 1200 = 0.07$

The cost per mile was $.07.

Example 5

A car is purchased for $8500 with a down payment of $1700. The balance is financed for 3 years at an annual interest rate of 9%. Find the monthly car payment.

Strategy

To find the monthly payment:

- Subtract the down payment from the purchase price to find the amount financed.
- Multiply the amount financed by the factor found in the monthly payment table in the Appendix.

Solution

$8500 - 1700 = 6800$

The amount financed is $6800.

$6800 \times 0.0317997 \approx 216.24$

The monthly payment is $216.24.

You Try It 3

At a cost of $.22 per mile, how much does it cost to operate a car during a year in which the car is driven 23,000 miles?

Your strategy

Your solution

You Try It 4

In a year in which the total car insurance bill was $360 and the car was driven 15,000 miles, what was the cost per mile for car insurance?

Your strategy

Your solution

You Try It 5

A truck is purchased for $15,900 with a down payment of $3975. The balance is financed for 4 years at an annual interest rate of 8%. Find the monthly payment.

Your strategy

Your solution

Solutions on p. S16

6.5 Exercises

· ·

Objective A   *Application Problems*

1. Amanda has saved $780 to make a down payment on a car. The car dealer requires a down payment of 12% of the purchase price. Does she have enough money to make the down payment on a used minivan that costs $7100?

2. A Ford Ranger was purchased for $23,500. A down payment of 15% of the purchase price was required. How much was the down payment?

3. A drapery installer bought a minivan to carry drapery samples. The purchase price of the van was $16,500, and a 4.5% sales tax was paid. How much was the sales tax?

4. A delivery truck for the Dixieline Lumber Company was purchased for $18,500. A sales tax of 4% of the purchase price was paid. Find the sales tax.

5. A license fee of 2% of the purchase price of a truck is to be paid on a pickup truck costing $12,500. How much is the license fee for the truck?

6. Your state charges a license fee of 1.5% on the purchase price of a car. How much is the license fee for a car that costs $6998?

7. An electrician bought a $12,000 flatbed truck. A state license fee of $175 and a sales tax of 3.5% of the purchase price are required.
   a. Find the sales tax.
   b. Find the total cost of the sales tax and the license fee.

8. A physical therapist bought a car for $9375 and made a down payment of $1875. The sales tax is 5% of the purchase price.
   a. Find the sales tax.
   b. Find the total cost of the sales tax and the down payment.

9. Martin bought a motorcycle for $2200 and made a down payment that is 25% of the purchase price.
   a. Find the down payment.
   b. Find the amount financed.

10. A carpenter bought a utility van for $14,900 and made a down payment that is 15% of the purchase price.
   a. Find the down payment.
   b. Find the amount financed.

11. An author bought a sports car for $35,000 and made a down payment of 20% of the purchase price. Find the amount financed.

12. Tania purchased a new car for $13,500 and made a down payment of 25% of the cost. Find the amount financed.

Objective B   *Application Problems*

Solve. Use the monthly payment table in the Appendix. Round to the nearest cent.

13. A rancher financed $14,000 for the purchase of a truck through a credit union at 9% interest for 4 years. Find the monthly truck payment.

14. A car loan of $8000 is financed for 3 years at an annual interest rate of 10%. Find the monthly car payment.

15. An estimate of the cost of owning a compact car is $.32 per mile. Using this estimate, how much does it cost to operate a car during a year in which the car is driven 16,000 miles?

16. An estimate of the cost of care and maintenance of automobile tires is $.015 per mile. Using this estimate, how much would it cost for care and maintenance of tires during a year in which the car is driven 14,000 miles?

17. A family spent $1600 on gas, oil, and car insurance during a period in which the car was driven 14,000 miles. Find the cost per mile for gas, oil, and car insurance.

18. Last year you spent $1050 for gasoline for your car. The car was driven 15,000 miles. What was your cost per mile for gasoline?

19. Elena's monthly car payment is $143.50. During a month in which $68.75 of the monthly payment is principal, how much of the payment is interest?

20. The cost for a pizza delivery truck for the year included $1870 in truck payments, $1200 for gasoline, and $675 for insurance. Find the total cost for truck payments, gasoline, and insurance for the year.

21. The city of Colton purchased a fire truck for $82,000 and made a down payment of $5400. The balance is financed for 5 years at an annual rate of 9%.
    a. Find the amount financed.
    b. Find the monthly truck payment.

22. A used car is purchased for $4995, and a down payment of $995 is made. The balance is financed for 3 years at an interest rate of 8%.
    a. Find the amount financed.
    b. Find the monthly car payment.

23. An artist purchased a new car costing $27,500 and made a down payment of $5500. The balance is financed for 3 years at an annual interest rate of 10%. Find the monthly car payment.

24. A half-ton truck with a camper is purchased for $19,500, and a down payment of $2500 is made. The balance is financed for 4 years at an annual interest rate of 9%. Find the monthly payment.

APPLYING THE CONCEPTS

25. One bank offers a 4-year car loan at an annual interest rate of 10% plus a loan application fee of $45. A second bank offers 4-year car loans at an annual interest rate of 11% but charges no loan application fee. If you need to borrow $5800 to purchase a car, which of the two bank loans has the lesser loan costs? Assume you keep the car for 4 years.

26. How much interest is paid on a 5-year car loan of $9000 if the interest rate is 9%?

6.6   Wages

Objective A   ***To calculate commissions, total hourly wages, and salaries*** ....

Commissions, hourly wage, and salary are three ways to receive payment for doing work.

Commissions are usually paid to salespersons and are calculated as a percent of total sales.

⇒ As a real estate broker, Emma Smith receives a commission of 4.5% of the selling price of a house. Find the commission she earned for selling a home for $75,000.

To find the commission Emma earned, solve the basic percent equation for *amount*.

Percent	×	base	=	amount
Commission rate	×	total sales	=	commission
0.045	×	75,000	=	3375

The commission is $3375.

An employee who receives an **hourly wage** is paid a certain amount for each hour worked.

⇒ A plumber receives an hourly wage of $13.25. Find the plumber's total wages for working 37 hours.

To find the plumber's total wages, multiply the hourly wage by the number of hours worked.

Hourly wage	×	number of hours worked	=	total wages
13.25	×	37	=	490.25

The plumber's total wages for working 37 hours are $490.25.

An employee who is paid a **salary** receives payment based on a weekly, biweekly (every other week), monthly, or annual time schedule. Unlike the employee who receives an hourly wage, the salaried worker does not receive additional pay for working more than the regularly scheduled workday.

⇒ Ravi Basar is a computer operator who receives a weekly salary of $395. Find his salary for 1 month (4 weeks).

To find Ravi's salary for 1 month, multiply the salary per pay period by the number of pay periods.

Salary per pay period	×	number of pay periods	=	total salary
395	×	4	=	1580

Ravi's total salary for 1 month is $1580.

Example 1

A pharmacist's hourly wage is $28. On Saturday, the pharmacist earns time and a half ($1\frac{1}{2}$ times the regular hourly wage). How much does the pharmacist earn for working 6 hours on Saturday?

Strategy

To find the pharmacist's earnings:

- Find the hourly wage for working on Saturday by multiplying the hourly wage by $1\frac{1}{2}$.
- Multiply the hourly wage by the number of hours worked.

Solution

$28 \times 1.5 = 42$ $42 \times 6 = 252$

The pharmacist earns $252.

You Try It 1

A construction worker's hourly wage is $8.50. The worker earns double time (2 times the regular hourly wage) for working overtime. How much does the worker earn for working 8 hours of overtime?

Your strategy

Your solution

Example 2

An efficiency expert received a contract for $3000. The consultant spent 75 hours on the project. Find the consultant's hourly wage.

Strategy

To find the hourly wage, divide the total earnings by the number of hours worked.

Solution

$3000 \div 75 = 40$

The hourly wage was $40.

You Try It 2

A contractor for a bridge project receives an annual salary of $28,224. What is the contractor's salary per month?

Your strategy

Your solution

Example 3

Dani Greene earns $18,500 per year plus a $5\frac{1}{2}$% commission on sales over $100,000. During one year, Dani sold $150,000 worth of computers. Find Dani's total earnings for the year.

Strategy

To find the total earnings:

- Find the commission earned by multiplying the commission rate by sales over $100,000.
- Add the commission to the annual pay.

Solution

$150,000 - 100,000 = 50,000$
$50,000 \times 0.055 = 2750$ commission
$18,500 + 2750 = 21,250$

Dani earned $21,250.

You Try It 3

An insurance agent earns $12,000 per year plus a $9\frac{1}{2}$% commission on sales over $50,000. During one year, the agent's sales totaled $175,000. Find the agent's total earnings for the year.

Your strategy

Your solution

Solutions on pp. S16–S17

6.6 Exercises

. . . .

Objective A   *Application Problems*

1. Lewis works in a clothing store and earns $7.50 per hour. How much does he earn in a 40-hour week?

2. Sasha pays a gardener an hourly wage of $9. How much does she pay the gardener for working 25 hours?

3. A real estate agent receives a 3% commission for selling a house. Find the commission that the agent earned for selling a house for $131,000.

4. Ron Caruso works as an insurance agent and receives a commission of 40% of the first year's premium. Find Ron's commission for selling a life insurance policy with a first-year premium of $1050.

5. A stockbroker receives a commission of 1.5% of the price of stock that is bought or sold. Find the commission on 100 shares of stock that were bought for $5600.

6. The owner of the Carousel Art Gallery receives a commission of 20% on paintings that are sold on consignment. Find the commission on a painting that sold for $22,500.

7. Keisha Brown receives an annual salary of $38,928 as an Italian Language teacher. How much does Keisha receive each month?

8. An apprentice plumber receives an annual salary of $27,900. How much does the plumber receive per month?

9. An electrician's hourly wage is $15.80. For working overtime, the electrician earns double time. What is the electrician's hourly wage for working overtime?

10. Carlos receives a commission of 12% of his weekly sales as a sales representative for a medical supply company. Find the commission he earned during a week in which sales were $4500.

11. A golf pro receives a commission of 25% for selling a golf set. Find what commission the pro earned for selling a golf set costing $450.

12. Steven receives $1.75 per square yard to install carpet. How much does he receive for installing 160 square yards of carpet?

13. A typist charges $1.75 per page for typing technical material. How much does the typist earn for typing a 225-page book?

14. A nuclear chemist received $15,000 in consulting fees while working on a nuclear power plant. The chemist worked 120 hours on the project. Find the consultant's hourly wage.

15. Maxine received $3400 for working on a project as a computer consultant for 40 hours. Find her hourly wage.

16. Gil Stratton's hourly wage is $10.78. For working overtime, he receives double time.
    a. What is Gil's hourly wage for working overtime?
    b. How much does he earn for working 16 hours of overtime?

17. Mark is a lathe operator and receives an hourly wage of $12.90. When working on Saturday, he receives time and a half.
    a. What is Mark's hourly wage on Saturday?
    b. How much does he earn for working 8 hours on Saturday?

18. A stock clerk at a supermarket earns $8.20 an hour. For working the night shift, the clerk's wage increases by 15%.
    a. What is the increase in hourly pay for working the night shift?
    b. What is the clerk's hourly wage for working the night shift?

19. A nurse earns $16.50 an hour. For working the night shift, the nurse receives a 10% increase in pay.
    a. What is the increase in hourly pay for working the night shift?
    b. What is the hourly pay for working the night shift?

20. Tony's hourly wage as a service station attendant is $6.40. For working the night shift, his wage is increased 25%. What is Tony's hourly wage for working the night shift?

21. Nicole Tobin, a door-to-door salesperson, receives a salary of $150 per week plus a commission of 15% on all sales over $1500. Find her earnings during a week in which sales totaled $3000.

APPLYING THE CONCEPTS

The table at the right shows the top five and bottom five starting salaries for recent college graduates (Source: Michigan State University). Use this table for Exercises 22 to 25.

22. What was the amount of increase in the starting salary for journalism majors from the previous year? Round to the nearest dollar.

23. What was the starting salary in the previous year for an industrial engineer? Round to the nearest dollar.

24. Between electrical engineers and computer scientists, which received the larger amount of increase in starting salary from the previous year?

25. Between telecommunications majors and liberal arts majors, which received the smaller amount of increase in starting salary from the previous year?

Estimated Starting Salaries
Top 5

Bachelor's Degree	Estimated Starting Salary	% Change from Previous Year
Chemical Engineering	$42,758	4.3%
Mechanical Engineering	$39,852	4.5%
Electrical Engineering	$38,811	4.0%
Industrial Engineering	$37,732	4.0%
Computer Science	$36,964	4.5%

Bottom 5

Liberal Arts	$24,102	3.5%
Natural Resources	$22,950	3.5%
Home Economics	$22,916	3.5%
Telecommunications	$22,447	4.0%
Journalism	$22,102	4.0%

6.7 | Bank Statements

Objective A   ***To calculate checkbook balances*** ....

A checking account can be opened at most banks or savings and loan associations by depositing an amount of money in the bank. A checkbook contains checks and deposit slips and a checkbook register in which to record checks written and amounts deposited in the checking account. Each time a check is written, the amount of the check is subtracted from the amount in the account. When a deposit is made, the amount deposited is added to the amount in the account.

A portion of a checkbook register is shown below. The account holder had a balance of $587.93 before writing two checks, one for $286.87 and the other for $102.38, and making one deposit of $345.00.

		RECORD ALL CHARGES OR CREDITS THAT AFFECT YOUR ACCOUNT					BALANCE	
NUMBER	DATE	DESCRIPTION OF TRANSACTION	PAYMENT/DEBIT (-)	√ T	FEE (IF ANY) (-)	DEPOSIT/CREDIT (+)	$ 587	93
108	8/4	Plumber	$ 286 87		$	$	301	06
109	8/10	Car Payment	102 38				198	68
	8/14	Deposit				345 00	543	68

To find the current checking account balance, subtract the amount of each check from the previous balance. Then add the amount of the deposit.

The current checking account balance is $543.68.

Example 1 A mail carrier had a checking account balance of $485.93 before writing two checks, one for $18.98 and another for $35.72, and making a deposit of $250. Find the current checking account balance.

You Try It 1 A cement mason had a checking account balance of $302.46 before writing a check for $20.59 and making two deposits, one in the amount of $176.86 and another in the amount of $94.73. Find the current checking account balance.

Strategy To find the current balance:
- Subtract the amount of each check from the old balance.
- Add the amount of the deposit.

Your strategy

Solution

```
  485.93
−  18.98   first check
─────────
  466.95
−  35.72   second check
─────────
  431.23
+ 250.00   deposit
─────────
  681.23
```

The current checking account balance is $681.23.

Your solution

Solution on p. S17

Objective B   To balance a checkbook ....

Each month a bank statement is sent to the account holder. The bank statement shows the checks that the bank has paid, the deposits received, and the current bank balance.

A bank statement and checkbook register are shown on the next page.

Balancing the checkbook, or determining if the checking account balance is accurate, requires a number of steps.

1. In the checkbook register, put a check mark (√) by each check paid by the bank and each deposit recorded by the bank.

RECORD ALL CHARGES OR CREDITS THAT AFFECT YOUR ACCOUNT

NUMBER	DATE	DESCRIPTION OF TRANSACTION	PAYMENT/DEBIT (-)		√ T	FEE (IF ANY) (-)	DEPOSIT/CREDIT (+)		BALANCE $ 840	27
263	5/20	Dentist	$ 25	00	√	$	$		815	27
264	5/22	Meat Market	33	61	√				781	66
265	5/22	Gas Company	67	14					714	52
	5/29	Deposit			√		192	00	906	52
266	5/29	Pharmacy	18	95	√				887	57
267	5/30	Telephone	43	85					843	72
268	6/2	Groceries	43	19	√				800	53
	6/3	Deposit			√		215	00	1015	53
269	6/7	Insurance	103	00	√				912	53
	6/10	Deposit					225	00	1137	53
270	6/15	Clothing Store	16	63	√				1120	90
271	6/18	Newspaper	7	00					1113	90

CHECKING ACCOUNT Monthly Statement   Account Number: 924-297-8

Date	Transaction	Amount	Balance
5/20	OPENING BALANCE		840.27
5/21	CHECK	25.00	815.27
5/23	CHECK	33.61	781.66
5/29	DEPOSIT	192.00	973.66
6/1	CHECK	18.95	954.71
6/1	INTEREST	4.47	959.18
6/3	CHECK	43.19	915.99
6/3	DEPOSIT	215.00	1130.99
6/9	CHECK	103.00	1027.99
6/16	CHECK	16.63	1011.36
6/20	SERVICE CHARGE	3.00	1008.36
6/20	CLOSING BALANCE		1008.36

2. Add to the current checkbook balance all checks that have been written but have not yet been paid by the bank and any interest paid on the account.

3. Subtract any service charges and any deposits not yet recorded by the bank. This is the checkbook balance.

4. Compare the balance with the bank balance listed on the bank statement. If the two numbers are equal, the bank statement and checkbook balance.

Current checkbook balance:	1113.90
Checks: 265	67.14
267	43.85
271	7.00
Interest:	+ 4.47
	1236.36
Service charge:	− 3.00
	1233.36
Deposit:	− 225.00
Checkbook balance:	1008.36

Checking bank balance from bank statement	Checkbook balance
$1008.36	= $1008.36

The bank statement and checkbook balance.

		RECORD ALL CHARGES OR CREDITS THAT AFFECT YOUR ACCOUNT								BALANCE	
NUMBER	DATE	DESCRIPTION OF TRANSACTION	PAYMENT/DEBIT (−)		√ T	FEE (IF ANY) (−)	DEPOSIT/CREDIT (+)		$	1620	42
413	3/2	Car Payment	$ 132	15	√	$	$			1488	27
414	3/2	Utility	67	14	√					1421	13
415	3/5	Restaurant - Dinner for 4	78	14						1342	99
	3/8	Deposit			√		1842	66		3185	65
416	3/10	House Payment	672	14	√					2513	51
417	3/14	Insurance	177	10						2336	41

CHECKING ACCOUNT Monthly Statement			Account Number: 924-297-8
Date	Transaction	Amount	Balance
3/1	OPENING BALANCE		1620.42
3/4	CHECK	132.15	1488.27
3/5	CHECK	67.14	1421.13
3/8	DEPOSIT	1842.66	3263.79
3/10	INTEREST	6.77	3270.56
3/12	CHECK	672.14	2598.42
3/25	SERVICE CHARGE	2.00	2596.42
3/30	CLOSING BALANCE		2596.42

Balance the bank statement shown above.

1. In the checkbook register, put a check mark (√) by each check paid by the bank and each deposit recorded by the bank.

2. Add to the current checkbook balance all checks that have been written but have not yet been paid by the bank and any interest paid on the account.

3. Subtract any service charges and any deposits not yet recorded by the bank. This is the checkbook balance.

4. Compare the balance with the bank balance listed on the bank statement. If the two numbers are equal, the bank statement and checkbook balance.

Current checkbook balance:	2336.41
Checks: 415	78.14
417	177.10
Interest:	+ 6.77
	2598.42
Service charge:	− 2.00
Checkbook balance:	2596.42

Closing bank balance from bank statement	Checkbook balance
$2596.42	= $2596.42

The bank statement and checkbook balance.

NUMBER	DATE	DESCRIPTION OF TRANSACTION	PAYMENT/DEBIT (-)		√ T	FEE (IF ANY) (-)	DEPOSIT/CREDIT (+)		BALANCE $ 412 64	
		RECORD ALL CHARGES OR CREDITS THAT AFFECT YOUR ACCOUNT								
345	1/14	Phone Bill	$ 34	75	√	$	$		377	89
346	1/19	Magazine	8	98	√				368	91
347	1/23	Theatre Tickets	45	00					323	91
	1/31	Deposit			√		947	00	1270	91
348	2/5	Cash	250	00	√				1020	91
349	2/12	Rent	440	00					580	91

CHECKING ACCOUNT Monthly Statement   Account Number: 924-297-8

Date	Transaction	Amount	Balance
1/10	OPENING BALANCE		412.64
1/18	CHECK	34.75	377.89
1/23	CHECK	8.98	368.91
1/31	DEPOSIT	947.00	1315.91
2/1	INTEREST	4.52	1320.43
2/10	CHECK	250.00	1070.43
2/10	CLOSING BALANCE		1070.43

Example 2

Balance the bank statement shown above.

Solution

Current checkbook balance:	580.91
Checks: 347	45.00
349	440.00
Interest:	+ 4.52
	1070.43
Service charge:	− 0.00
	1070.43
Deposit:	− 0.00
Checkbook balance:	1070.43

Closing bank balance from bank statement: $1070.43

Checkbook balance: $1070.43

The bank statement and checkbook balance.

		RECORD ALL CHARGES OR CREDITS THAT AFFECT YOUR ACCOUNT								BALANCE	
NUMBER	DATE	DESCRIPTION OF TRANSACTION	PAYMENT/DEBIT (-)		√ T	FEE (IF ANY) (-)		DEPOSIT/CREDIT (+)		$	603	17
	2/15	*Deposit*	$			$	$	523	84	1127	01
234	2/20	*Mortgage*	473	21						653	80
235	2/27	*Cash*	200	00						453	80
	3/1	*Deposit*						523	84	977	64
236	3/12	*Insurance*	275	50						702	14
237	3/12	*Telephone*	48	73				-		653	41

CHECKING ACCOUNT Monthly Statement			Account Number: 314-271-4	
Date	Transaction		Amount	Balance
2/14	OPENING BALANCE			603.17
2/15	DEPOSIT		523.84	1127.01
2/21	CHECK		473.21	653.80
2/28	CHECK		200.00	453.80
3/1	INTEREST		2.11	455.91
3/14	CHECK		275.50	180.41
3/14	CLOSING BALANCE			180.41

You Try It 2

Balance the bank statement shown above.

Your solution

Solution on p. S17

6.7 Exercises

· ·

Objective A   *Application Problems*

1. You had a checking account balance of $342.51 before making a deposit of $143.81. What is your new checking account balance?

2. Carmen had a checking account balance of $493.26 before writing a check for $48.39. What is the current checking account balance?

3. A real estate firm had a balance of $2431.76 in its rental property checking account. What is the balance in this account after a check for $1209.29 has been written?

4. The business checking account for R and R Tires showed a balance of $1536.97. What is the balance in this account after a deposit of $439.21 has been made?

5. A nutritionist had a checking account balance of $1204.63 before writing one check for $119.27 and another check for $260.09. Find the current checkbook balance.

6. Sam had a checking account balance of $3046.93 before writing a check for $1027.33 and making a deposit of $150.00. Find the current checkbook balance.

7. The business checking account for Rachael's Dry Cleaning had a balance of $3476.85 before a deposit of $1048.53 was made. The store manager then wrote checks, one for $848.37 and another for $676.19. Find the current checkbook balance.

8. Joel had a checking account balance of $427.38 before a deposit of $127.29 was made. Joel then wrote two checks, one for $43.52 and one for $249.78. Find the current checkbook balance.

9. A carpenter had a checkbook balance of $104.96 before making a deposit of $350 and writing a check for $71.29. Is there enough money in the account to purchase a refrigerator for $375?

10. A taxi driver had a checkbook balance of $149.85 before making a deposit of $245 and writing a check for $387.68. Is there enough money in the account for the bank to pay the check?

11. A sporting goods store has the opportunity to buy downhill skis and cross-country skis at a manufacturer's closeout sale. The downhill skis will cost $3500, and the cross-country skis will cost $2050. There is currently $5625.42 in the sporting goods store's checking account. Is there enough money in the account to make both purchases by check?

12. A lathe operator's current checkbook balance is $643.42. The operator wants to purchase a utility trailer for $225 and a used piano for $450. Is there enough money in the account to make the two purchases?

Objective B   *Application Problems*

13. Balance the checkbook.

		RECORD ALL CHARGES OR CREDITS THAT AFFECT YOUR ACCOUNT							BALANCE	
NUMBER	DATE	DESCRIPTION OF TRANSACTION	PAYMENT/DEBIT (-)		√ T	FEE (IF ANY) (-)	DEPOSIT/CREDIT (+)		$ 466	79
223	3/2	Groceries	$ 67	32		$	$		399	47
	3/5	Deposit					560	70	960	17
224	3/5	Rent	460	00					500	17
225	3/7	Gas & Electric	42	35					457	82
226	3/7	Cash	100	00					357	82
227	3/7	Insurance	118	44					239	38
228	3/7	Credit Card	119	32					120	06
229	3/12	Dentist	42	00					78	06
230	3/13	Drug Store	17	03					61	03
	3/19	Deposit					560	70	621	73
231	3/22	Car Payment	141	35					480	38
232	3/25	Cash	100	00					380	38
233	3/25	Oil Company	66	40					313	98
234	3/28	Plumber	55	73					258	25
235	3/29	Department Store	88	39					169	86

CHECKING ACCOUNT Monthly Statement			Account Number: 122-345-1
Date	Transaction	Amount	Balance
3/1	OPENING BALANCE		466.79
3/5	DEPOSIT	560.70	1027.49
3/7	CHECK	67.32	960.17
3/8	CHECK	460.00	500.17
3/8	CHECK	100.00	400.17
3/9	CHECK	42.35	357.82
3/12	CHECK	118.44	239.38
3/14	CHECK	42.00	197.38
3/18	CHECK	17.03	180.35
3/19	DEPOSIT	560.70	741.05
3/25	CHECK	141.35	599.70
3/27	CHECK	100.00	499.70
3/29	CHECK	55.73	443.97
3/30	INTEREST	13.22	457.19
4/1	CLOSING BALANCE		457.19

14. Balance the checkbook.

RECORD ALL CHARGES OR CREDITS THAT AFFECT YOUR ACCOUNT

NUMBER	DATE	DESCRIPTION OF TRANSACTION	PAYMENT/DEBIT (-)		√ T	FEE (IF ANY) (-)	DEPOSIT/CREDIT (+)		BALANCE $ 219 43	
	5/1	Deposit	$			$	$ 219	14	438	57
515	5/2	Electric Bill	22	35					416	22
516	5/2	Groceries	55	14					361	08
517	5/4	Insurance	122	17					238	91
518	5/5	Theatre Tickets	24	50					214	41
	5/8	Deposit					219	14	433	55
519	5/10	Telephone	17	39					416	16
520	5/12	Newspaper	12	50					403	66
	5/15	Interest					7	82	411	48
	5/15	Deposit					219	14	630	62
521	5/20	Hotel	172	90					457	72
522	5/21	Credit Card	113	44					344	28
523	5/22	Eye Exam	42	00					302	28
524	5/24	Groceries	77	14					225	14
525	5/24	Deposit					219	14	444	28
526	5/25	Oil Company	44	16					400	12
527	5/30	Car Payment	88	62					311	50
528	5/30	Doctor	37	42					274	08

CHECKING ACCOUNT Monthly Statement			Account Number: 122-345-1	
Date	Transaction		Amount	Balance
5/1	OPENING BALANCE			219.43
5/1	DEPOSIT		219.14	438.57
5/3	CHECK		55.14	383.43
5/4	CHECK		22.35	361.08
5/6	CHECK		24.50	336.58
5/8	CHECK		122.17	214.41
5/8	DEPOSIT		219.14	433.55
5/15	INTEREST		7.82	441.37
5/15	CHECK		17.39	423.98
5/15	DEPOSIT		219.14	643.12
5/23	CHECK		42.00	601.12
5/23	CHECK		172.90	428.22
5/24	CHECK		77.14	351.08
5/24	DEPOSIT		219.14	570.22
5/30	CHECK		88.62	481.60
6/1	CLOSING BALANCE			481.60

15. Balance the checkbook.

NUMBER	DATE	DESCRIPTION OF TRANSACTION	PAYMENT/DEBIT (-)		√ T	FEE (IF ANY) (-)	DEPOSIT/CREDIT (+)		BALANCE $ 1035	18
		RECORD ALL CHARGES OR CREDITS THAT AFFECT YOUR ACCOUNT								
218	7/2	*Mortgage*	$ 284	60		$	$		750	58
219	7/4	*Telephone*	23	36					727	22
220	7/7	*Cash*	200	00					527	22
	7/12	*Deposit*					792	60	1319	82
221	7/15	*Insurance*	192	30					1127	52
222	7/18	*Investment*	100	00					1027	52
223	7/20	*Credit Card*	214	83					812	69
	7/26	*Deposit*					792	60	1605	29
224	7/27	*Department Store*	113	37					1491	92

CHECKING ACCOUNT Monthly Statement		Account Number: 122-345-1	
Date	Transaction	Amount	Balance
7/1	OPENING BALANCE		1035.18
7/1	INTEREST	5.15	1040.33
7/4	CHECK	284.60	755.73
7/6	CHECK	23.36	732.37
7/12	DEPOSIT	792.60	1524.97
7/20	CHECK	192.30	1332.67
7/24	CHECK	100.00	1232.67
7/26	DEPOSIT	792.60	2025.27
7/28	CHECK	200.00	1825.27
7/30	CLOSING BALANCE		1825.27

APPLYING THE CONCEPTS

16. When a check is written, the amount is _____ from the balance.

17. When a deposit is made, the amount is _____ to the balance.

18. In checking the bank statement, _____ to the checkbook balance all checks that have been written but not processed.

19. In checking the bank balance, _____ any service charge and any deposits not yet recorded.

20. Define the words *credit* and *debit* as they apply to checkbooks.

Focus on Problem Solving

Counterexamples   An example that is given to show that a statement is not true is called a **counterexample.** For instance, suppose someone makes the statement "All colors are red." A counterexample to that statement would be to show someone the color blue or some other color.

If a statement is *always* true, there are no counterexamples. The statement "All even numbers are divisible by 2" is always true. It is not possible to give an example of an even number that is not divisible by 2.

In mathematics, statements that are always true are called *theorems,* and mathematicians are always searching for theorems. Sometimes a conjecture by a mathematician appears to be a theorem, that is, the statement appears to be always true, but later on someone finds a counterexample.

> **TAKE NOTE**
>
> Recall that a prime number is a natural number greater than 1 that can be divided by only itself and 1. For instance, 17 is a prime number. 12 is not a prime number because 12 is divisible by numbers other than 1 and 12, for example, 4.

One example of this occurred when the French mathematician Pierre de Fermat (1601–1665) conjectured that $2^{(2^n)} + 1$ was always a prime number for any natural number n. For instance, when $n = 3$, we have $2^{(2^3)} + 1 = 2^8 + 1 = 257$ and 257 is a prime number. However, in 1732 Leonard Euler (1707–1783) showed that when $n = 5$, $2^{(2^5)} + 1 = 4,294,967,297$ and that $4,294,967,297 = 641 \cdot 6,700,417$—without a calculator! Since 4,294,967,297 was the product of two numbers (other than itself and 1), it was not a prime number. This counterexample showed that Fermat's conjecture was not a theorem.

For Exercises 1 and 5, find at least one counterexample.

1. All numbers are positive.

2. All prime numbers are odd numbers.

3. The square of any number is always bigger than the number.

4. The reciprocal of a number is always less than 1.

5. A number ending in 9 is always larger than a number ending in 3.

When a problem is posed, it may not be known whether the problem statement is true or false. For instance, Christian Goldbach (1690–1764) stated that every even number greater than 2 can be written as the sum of two prime numbers. For example,

$$12 = 5 + 7 \qquad 32 = 3 + 29$$

Although this problem is approximately 250 years old, mathematicians have not been able to prove it is a theorem, nor have they been able to find a counterexample.

For Exercises 6 to 9, answer true if the statement is always true. If there is an instance when the statement is false, give a counterexample.

6. The sum of two positive numbers is always larger than either of the two numbers.

7. The product of two positive numbers is always larger than either of the two numbers.

8. Percents always represent a number less than or equal to 1.

9. It is never possible to divide by zero.

Projects and Group Activities

Annuities

Suppose you buy a car and finance $4300 for three years at an annual interest rate of 9%. To completely repay the loan, you must make 36 monthly payments of $136.74. A series of equal payments ($136.74) at regular intervals (monthly in this case) is called an **annuity**.

The mortgage payments and car payments that you calculated in this chapter are examples of annuities. These calculations were accomplished by using the tables in the Appendix. It is possible, however, to use a formula to calculate the amount of a monthly payment.

$$\text{Payment} = B \times \left[\frac{i}{1 - \dfrac{1}{(1 + i)^n}} \right]$$

where B is the amount borrowed, $i = \dfrac{\text{annual interest rate as a decimal}}{\text{number of payments per year}}$, and n is the total number of payments.

Although the formula looks quite complicated, it can be evaluated by using a scientific calculator. Here are some keystrokes that will work on most scientific calculators.

B ⨉ i ÷ (1 − 1 ÷ (1 + i) y^x n) = Payment

For the car payment above, calculate $i = \dfrac{0.09}{12} = 0.0075$ and $n = 3 \times 12 = 36$. Then the payment is calculated as

4300 ⨉ .0075 ÷ (1 − 1 ÷ (1 + .0075) y^x 36) =

The result will be 136.73885, which is $136.74 rounded to the nearest cent. The advantage of having a formula is that you can calculate the result for any interest rate and time period. You are not restricted to the values in a table.

If you were to trade in your car for a new one before the end of the loan, you would have to *pay off* the remaining amount owed. A modification of the formula above can be used to calculate the payoff.

$$\text{Payoff} = \text{Payment} \div \left[\frac{i}{1 - \dfrac{1}{(1 + i)^n}} \right]$$

In this case, n is the number of *remaining* payments and i is as before.

For instance, suppose you have kept the car for 2 years (24 months) and decide to trade it in for a new car. Then you have 12 payments remaining ($12 = 36 - 24$). The payoff is calculated as

136.74 ÷ (.0075 ÷ (1 − 1 ÷ (1 + .0075) y^x 12)) =

The result is $1563.61. This is the amount still owed on the car loan.

1. Ford Motor Company offered a loan rate of 1.9% for 3 years on selected models of a new car. Find the monthly payment for a loan of $12,000 on one of these cars.

2. The median price of a home in the United States is approximately $118,000. If you purchase a home at the median price and make a 20% down payment, what are the monthly payments for a 30-year loan for which the annual interest rate is 7.5%?

3. Suppose you keep the home in Exercise 2 for 10 years and then decide to sell it.
   a. How much do you still owe on the house?
   b. How much of the loan have you repaid?
   c. You have owned the home for $\frac{1}{3}$ of the 30-year period. Have you repaid $\frac{1}{3}$ of the loan?
   d. By experimenting with various values of *n*, try to determine how many months you must own the home before you have repaid $\frac{1}{2}$ of the loan amount.

Credit Card Finance Charges All credit card companies charge a *fee* (finance charge) when a credit card balance is not paid within a certain number of days of the *billing date* (the date the credit card bill is sent). There may also be an annual fee. The table below shows the charges for five banks in June of 1997. (If you have Internet access, you can get current rates by visiting http://www.bankrate.com.)

Bank	Annual Interest Rate	Annual Fee
Pulaski Bank and Trust	7.99%	$35
Oak Brook Bank	8.45%	$85
Huntington National Bank	8.50%	$70
AFBA Industrial Bank	11.40%	$0
Pullman Bank & Trust	12.50%	$0

The amount of the monthly finance charge is based (usually) on the average daily balance. For instance, using Huntington National Bank, if your average daily balance for one month was $275.89, then the monthly finance charge is calculated using the simple interest formula.

Interest = principal × annual interest rate × time

$$= 275.89 \times 0.085 \times \frac{1}{12}$$

• 1 month = $\frac{1}{12}$ year.

$$\approx 1.95$$

The finance charge is $1.95.

1. Suppose you have an average daily balance of $321.65 for 12 months. With which bank will your *annual* finance charge (including the annual fee) be least?

2. Suppose you have an average daily balance of $725.91 for 12 months. With which bank will your *annual* finance charge (including the annual fee) be least?

Chapter Summary

Key Words The *unit cost* is the cost of one item.

Percent increase is used to show how much a quantity has increased over its original value.

Cost is the price a business pays for a product.

Selling price is the price at which a business sells a product to a customer.

Markup is the difference between selling price and cost.

Markup rate is the markup expressed as a percent of a product's cost.

Percent decrease is used to show how much a quantity has decreased from its original value.

Sale price is the price that has been reduced from the regular price.

Discount is the difference between the regular price and the sale price.

Discount rate is the discount as a percent of a product's regular price.

Interest is the amount of money paid for the privilege of using someone else's money.

Principal is the amount of money originally deposited or borrowed.

The percent used to determine the amount of interest is the *interest rate*.

Interest computed on the original amount is called *simple interest*.

Compound interest is computed not only on the original principal but also on interest already earned.

The *mortgage* is the amount that is borrowed to buy real estate.

The loan origination fee is usually a percent of the mortgage and is expressed in *points*.

Commissions are usually paid to salespersons and are calculated as a percent of total sales.

An employee who receives an *hourly wage* is paid a certain amount for each hour worked.

An employee who is paid a *salary* receives payment based on a weekly, biweekly, monthly, or annual time schedule.

Essential Rules	*To Find Unit Cost*	To find the unit cost, divide the total cost by the number of units.
	To Find Total Cost	To find the total cost, multiply the unit cost by the number of units.
	Basic Markup Equations	Selling price = cost + markup
		Markup = markup rate × cost
	Basic Discount Equations	Sale price = regular price − discount
		Discount = discount rate × regular price
	Annual Simple Interest Equation	$\text{Principal} \times \dfrac{\text{annual}}{\text{interest rate}} \times \dfrac{\text{time}}{\text{in years}} = \text{interest}$

Chapter Review

1. A 20-ounce box of cereal costs $2.90. Find the unit cost.

2. An account executive had car expenses of $1025.58 for insurance, $605.82 for gas, $37.92 for oil, and $188.27 for maintenance during a year in which 15,320 miles were driven. Find the cost per mile for these four items. Round to the nearest tenth of a cent.

3. An oil stock was bought for 42\frac{3}{8}$ per share. Six months later, the stock was selling for 55\frac{1}{4}$ per share. Find the percent increase in the price of the stock for the 6 months. Round to the nearest tenth of a percent.

4. A sporting goods store uses a markup rate of 40%. What is the markup on a ski suit that costs the store $180?   72

5. A contractor borrowed $100,000 from a credit union for 9 months at an annual interest rate of 9%. What is the simple interest due on the loan?

6. A computer programmer invested $25,000 in a retirement account that pays 6% interest, compounded daily. What is the value of the investment in 10 years? Use the table in the Appendix. Round to the nearest cent. 45,550.75

7. Last year an oil company had earnings of $4.12 per share. This year the earnings are $4.73 per share. What is the percent increase in earnings per share? Round to the nearest percent.   .61   61%

8. The monthly mortgage payment for a condominum is $523.67. The owner must pay an annual property tax of $658.32. Find the total monthly payment for the mortgage and property tax.

9. A pickup truck with a slide-in camper is purchased for $14,450. A down payment of 8% is made, and the remaining cost is financed for 4 years at an annual interest rate of 9%. Find the monthly payment. Use the monthly schedule in the Appendix. Round to the nearest cent.

10. A fast-food restaurant invested $50,000 in an account that pays 7% annual interest compounded quarterly. What is the value of the investment in 1 year? Use the table in the Appendix.

11. Paula Mason purchased a home for $125,000. The lender requires a down payment of 15%. Find the amount of the down payment.

12. A plumber bought a truck for $13,500. A state license of $315 and a sales tax of 6.25% of the purchase price are required. Find the total cost of the sales tax and the license fee.

13. Techno-Center uses a markup rate of 35% on all computer systems. Find the selling price of a computer system that costs the store $1540.

14. Mien pays a monthly car payment of $122.78. During a month in which $25.45 is principal, how much of the payment is interest?

15. The manager of the retail store at a ski resort receives a commission of 3% on all sales at the alpine shop. Find the total commission received during a month in which the shop had $108,000 in sales.

16. A suit that regularly costs $235 is on sale for 40% off the regular price. Find the sale price.

17. Luke had a checking account balance of $1568.45 before writing checks for $123.76, $756.45, and $88.77. He then deposited a check for $344.21. Find Luke's current checkbook balance.

18. Pros' Sporting Goods borrowed $30,000 at an annual interest rate of 8% for 6 months. Find the simple interest due on the loan.

19. A credit union requires a borrower to pay $2\frac{1}{2}$ points for a loan. Find the origination fee for a loan of $75,000.

20. Twenty-four ounces of a mouthwash cost $3.49. A 60-ounce container of the same kind of mouthwash costs $8.40. Which is the better buy?

21. The Sweeneys bought a home for $156,000. The family made a 10% down payment and financed the remainder with a 30-year loan with an annual interest rate of 7%. Find the monthly mortgage payment. Use the monthly payment table in the Appendix. Round to the nearest cent.

22. Richard Valdez receives $12.60 per hour for working 40 hours a week and time and a half for working over 40 hours. Find his total income during a week in which he worked 48 hours.

23. The business checking account of a donut shop showed a balance of $9567.44 before checks of $1023.55, $345.44, and $23.67 were written and checks of $555.89 and $135.91 were deposited. Find the current checkbook balance.

24. A professional baseball player received a salary of $1 million last year. This year the player signed a contract paying $12 million over 4 years. Find the yearly percent increase in the player's salary.

Chapter Test

1. Twenty feet of lumber cost $138.40. What is the cost per foot?

2. Find the more economical purchase: 5 pounds of tomatoes for $1.65, or 8 pounds for $2.72.

3. Red snapper costs $4.15 per pound. Find the cost of $3\frac{1}{2}$ pounds. Round to the nearest cent.

4. An exercise bicycle increased in price from $415 to $498. Find the percent increase in the cost of the exercise bicycle.

5. Fifteen years ago a painting was priced at $6000. Today the same painting has a value of $15,000. Find the percent increase in the price of the painting during the 15 years.

6. A department store uses a 40% markup rate. Find the selling price of a compact disk player that the store purchased for $215.

7. A bookstore bought a paperback book for $5 and used a markup rate of 25%. Find the selling price of the book.

8. The price of gold dropped from $390 per ounce to $360 per ounce. What percent decrease does this amount represent? Round to the nearest tenth of a percent.

9. The price of a video camera dropped from $1120 to $896. What percent decrease does this price drop represent?

10. A corner hutch with a regular price of $299 is on sale for 30% off the regular price. Find the sale price.

11. A box of stationery that regularly sells for $4.50 is on sale for $2.70. Find the discount rate.

12. A construction company borrowed $75,000 for 4 months at an annual interest rate of 8%. Find the simple interest due on the loan.

13. Jorge, who is self-employed, placed $30,000 in an account that pays 6% annual interest compounded quarterly. How much interest was earned in 10 years? Use the table in the Appendix.

14. A savings and loan institution is giving mortgage loans that have a loan origination fee of $2\frac{1}{2}$ points. Find the loan origination fee on a home purchased with a loan of $134,000.

15. A new housing development offers homes with a mortgage of $222,000 for 25 years at an annual interest rate of 8%. Find the monthly mortgage payment. Use the table in the Appendix.

16. A Chevrolet Blazer was purchased for $23,750, and a 20% down payment was made. Find the amount financed.

17. A rancher purchased a GMC Jimmy for $23,714 and made a down payment of 15% of the cost. The balance was financed for 4 years at an annual interest rate of 7%. Find the monthly truck payment. Use the table in the Appendix.

18. Shaney receives an hourly wage of $13.40 an hour as an emergency room nurse. When called in at night, she receives time and a half. How much does Shaney earn in a week when she works 30 hours at normal rates and 15 hours during the night?

19. The business checking account for a pottery store had a balance of $7349.44 before checks for $1349.67 and $344.12 were written. The store manager then made a deposit of $956.60. Find the current checkbook balance.

20. Balance the checkbook shown.

RECORD ALL CHARGES OR CREDITS THAT AFFECT YOUR ACCOUNT

NUMBER	DATE	DESCRIPTION OF TRANSACTION	PAYMENT/DEBIT (-)	√ T	FEE (IF ANY) (-)	DEPOSIT/CREDIT (+)	BALANCE $ 422 13
	8/1	House Payment	$ 213 72		$	$	208 41
	8/4	Deposit				552 60	761 01
	8/5	Plane Tickets	162 40				598 61
	8/6	Groceries	66 44				532 17
	8/10	Car Payment	122 37				409 80
	8/15	Deposit				552 60	962 40
	8/16	Credit Card	213 45				748 95
	8/18	Doctor	92 14				656 81
	8/22	Utilities	72 30				584 51
	8/28	T. V. Repair	78 20				506 31

CHECKING ACCOUNT Monthly Statement		Account Number: 122-345-1	
Date	Transaction	Amount	Balance
8/1	OPENING BALANCE		422.13
8/3	CHECK	213.72	208.41
8/4	DEPOSIT	552.60	761.01
8/8	CHECK	66.44	694.57
8/8	CHECK	162.40	532.17
8/15	DEPOSIT	552.60	1084.77
8/23	CHECK	72.30	1012.47
8/24	CHECK	92.14	920.33
9/1	CLOSING BALANCE		920.33

Cumulative Review

1. Simplify $12 - (10 - 8)^2 \div 2 + 3$.

2. Add: $3\frac{1}{3} + 4\frac{1}{8} + 1\frac{1}{12}$

3. Find the difference between $12\frac{3}{16}$ and $9\frac{5}{12}$.

4. Find the product of $5\frac{5}{8}$ and $1\frac{9}{15}$.

5. Divide: $3\frac{1}{2} \div 1\frac{3}{4}$

6. Simplify $\left(\frac{3}{4}\right)^2 \div \left(\frac{3}{8} - \frac{1}{4}\right) + \frac{1}{2}$.

7. Divide: $0.059\overline{)3.0792}$
   Round to the nearest tenth.

8. Convert $\frac{17}{12}$ to a decimal. Round to the nearest thousandth.

9. Write "$410 in 8 hours" as a unit rate.

10. Solve the proportion $\frac{5}{n} = \frac{16}{35}$.
    Round to the nearest hundredth.

11. Write $\frac{5}{8}$ as a percent.

12. Find 6.5% of 420.

13. Write 18.2% as a decimal.

14. What percent of 20 is 8.4?

15. 30 is 12% of what?

16. 65 is 42% of what? Round to the nearest hundredth.

17. A series of late summer storms produced rainfall of $3\frac{3}{4}$, $8\frac{1}{2}$, and $1\frac{2}{3}$ inches during a 3-week period. Find the total rainfall during the 3 weeks.

18. The Homer family pays $\frac{1}{5}$ of its total monthly income for taxes. The family has a total monthly income of $2850. Find the amount of the monthly income that the Homers pay in taxes.

19. In 5 years, the cost of a scientific calculator went from $75 to $30. What is the ratio of the decrease in price to the original price?

20. A compact car was driven 417.5 miles on 12.5 gallons of gasoline. Find the number of miles driven per gallon of gasoline.

21. A 14-pound turkey costs $12.96. Find the unit cost. Round to the nearest cent.

22. Eighty shares of a stock paid a dividend of $112. At the same rate, find the dividend on 200 shares of the stock.

23. A video camera that regularly sells for $900 is on sale for 20% off the regular price. What is the sale price?

24. A department store bought a portable disk player for $85 and used a markup rate of 40%. Find the selling price of the disk player.

25. Sook Kim, an elementary school teacher, received an increase in salary from $2800 per month to $3024 per month. Find the percent increase in her salary.

26. A contractor borrowed $120,000 for 6 months at an annual interest rate of 10%. How much simple interest is due on the loan?

27. A red Ford Mustang was purchased for $26,900, and a down payment of $2000 was made. The balance is financed for 3 years at an annual interest rate of 9%. Find the monthly payment. Use the table in the Appendix. Round to the nearest cent.

28. A family had a checking account balance of $1846.78. A check of $568.30 was deposited into the account, and checks of $123.98 and $47.33 were written. Find the new checking account balance.

29. During one year, Anna Gonzalez spent $840 on gasoline and oil, $520 on insurance, $185 on tires, and $432 on repairs. Find the cost per mile to drive the car 10,000 miles during the year. Round to the nearest cent.

30. A house has a mortgage of $72,000 for 20 years at an annual interest rate of 11%. Find the monthly mortgage payment. Use the table in the Appendix. Round to the nearest cent.

7

Statistics

A sports statistician records and analyzes data for various sports. Data are kept on the number of strikes a pitcher throws, the number of double faults a tennis player makes, the number of times a golfer's drive hits the fairway, and many other pieces of information. This information can assist the player in working on weaknesses while maintaining strengths.

Objectives

Section 7.1
To read a pictograph
To read a circle graph

Section 7.2
To read a bar graph
To read a broken-line graph

Section 7.3
To read a histogram
To read a frequency polygon

Section 7.4
To find the mean, median, and mode of a distribution
To graph a box-and-whiskers plot

Frequencies of Letters

ZH WKH SHRSOH

The above phrase is a cryptogram. For this phrase to be read, the cryptogram has to be decoded.

Cryptology is the study of encrypting and decrypting messages. Encrypting means writing the message in code; decrypting means breaking a secret code. One of the methods the cryptologist uses in breaking a code is statistics.

Statistics is the study of the organization and analysis of data. A cryptologist uses statistics by analyzing ordinary text, such as that in a novel or a newspaper, and determining how frequently different letters of the alphabet occur. For example, in English, the letter "e" is the most frequently occurring letter. A table of the approximate frequencies of each letter is given below:

A—7.3%	J—0.2%	S—6.3%
B—0.9%	K—0.3%	T—9.3%
C—3.0%	L—3.6%	U—2.7%
D—4.3%	M—2.5%	V—1.3%
E—13.0%	N—7.8%	W—1.6%
F—2.7%	O—7.4%	X—0.6%
G—1.7%	P—2.7%	Y—1.8%
H—3.4%	Q—0.3%	Z—0.1%
I—7.5%	R—7.3%	

Knowing these frequencies, the cryptologist reasons that the most frequently occurring letters in a coded message correspond to the most frequently occurring letters in an ordinary message. Thus, to decode the phrase above, a cryptologist might guess that the letter H in the coded message corresponds to the letter E in an ordinary message. This guess may not be correct, but it is a good first choice.

See if you can decode the above phrase.

Answer: WE THE PEOPLE. The phrase was coded by taking the letter three spaces beyond the original letter. For example, A gets coded as D, B gets coded as E, C gets coded as F, and so on. This method of coding a message is called the Caesar Cipher, after Julius Caesar, who used this method.

7.1 Pictographs and Circle Graphs

Objective A *To read a pictograph* ....

Statistics is the branch of mathematics concerned with **data,** or numerical information. **Graphs** are displays that provide a pictorial representation of data. The advantage of graphs is that they present information in a way that is easily read. The disadvantage of graphs is that they can be misleading. (See "Projects and Group Activities" at the end of this chapter.)

A **pictograph** uses symbols to represent information. The pictograph in Figure 1 represents how the approximately 14,000,000 ounces of gold produced in the United States each year are used.

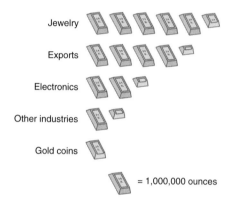

Figure 1   Uses of gold mined in the United States
Source: *USA Today,* April 3, 1997

From the pictograph, we can determine that the United States exported more than 4,000,000 ounces of gold.

 The pictograph in Figure 2 represents the responses of 600 young Americans when asked what they would like to have with them on a desert island.

➡ Use the basic percent equation to determine what percent of the responses were books.

The base is 600 (the total number of responses), and the amount is 90 (the number responding books).

percent × base = amount

$$n \times 600 = 90$$

$$n = \frac{90}{600}$$

$$n = 0.15$$

15% of the respondents wanted books on a desert island.

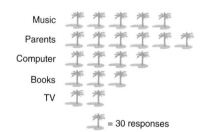

Figure 2   What 600 young
Americans want on a
desert island
Source: *Time,* June 30, 1997

The pictograph in Figure 3 shows the number of new cellular phones purchased in a particular city during a 4-month period.

The ratio of the number of cellular phones purchased in March to the number purchased in January is

$$\frac{3000}{4500} = \frac{2}{3}$$

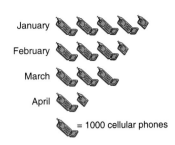

Figure 3 Monthly cellular phone purchases

Example 1
Use Figure 3 to find the total number of cellular phones purchased during the 4-month period.

Strategy
To find the total number of cellular phones purchased in the 4-month period:

• Read the pictograph to determine the number of cellular phones purchased each month.
• Add the four numbers.

Solution
Purchases for January: 4500
Purchases for February: 3500
Purchases for March: 3000
Purchases for April: 1500

Total purchases for the 4-month period:

$$\begin{array}{r} 4{,}500 \\ 3{,}500 \\ 3{,}000 \\ \underline{1{,}500} \\ 12{,}500 \end{array}$$

There were 12,500 cellular phones purchased in the 4-month period.

You Try It 1
Use Figure 3 to find what percent of the total number of cellular phone purchases the number of March cellular phone purchases represents.

Your strategy

Your solution

Solution on p. S17

Objective B *To read a circle graph* .... (10) CT

A **circle graph** represents data by the size of the sectors. The circle graph in Figure 4 represents the amount of energy from various sources consumed by Americans during one year. The complete circle graph represents the total amount of energy consumed, 90.4 quadrillion Btu. Each sector of the circle represents the consumption of energy from a different source.

To find the percent of the total energy consumed that originated from petroleum, solve the basic percent equation for percent (n). The base is 90.4 quadrillion Btu, and the amount is 34.6 quadrillion Btu.

Percent × base = amount
$$n \times 90.4 = 34.6$$
$$n = 34.6 \div 90.04 \approx 0.38274$$

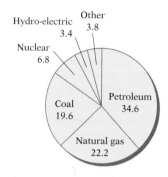

Figure 4 Annual energy consumption in the United States

Source: *Information Please* (1997)

TAKE NOTE

One quadrillion is 1,000,000,000,000,000.

To the nearest tenth of a percent, the percent of energy consumed from petroleum is 38.3%.

The circle graph can also be used to find the ratio of the amount of energy consumed from one source to the amount consumed from a second source. For instance, the ratio of the amount of nuclear energy to the amount of hydroelectric energy is $\frac{6.8}{3.4} = \frac{2}{1}$. This means that 2 times as much nuclear energy is consumed as hydroelectric energy.

The circle graph in Figure 5 shows the percents of the $17.8 billion that the top 25 companies spent for national advertising in one year that go to the various advertising media. The complete circle graph represents 100% of all the money spent by these companies. Each sector of the graph represents the percent of the total spent for a particular media.

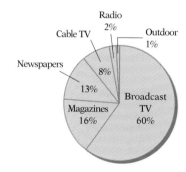

Figure 5 Distribution of advertising dollars for 25 companies

Source: Interep research

➡ How much money was spent for magazine advertising? Round to the nearest hundred million dollars.

To find the amount spent for magazine advertising, use the basic percent equation. The base is $17.8 billion, and the percent is 16%.

Percent × base = amount
$$0.16 \times 17.8 = 2.848$$

The amount spent was $2.848 billion or $2,848,000,000. Rounded to the nearest hundred million, the amount spent for magazine advertising was $2,800,000,000.

The circle graph in Figure 6, based on data from IntelliChoice, shows typical annual expenses of owning, operating, and financing a new car.

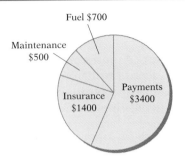

Figure 6   Annual expenses of $6000 for owning, operating, and financing a car

Source: Based on data from IntelliChoice

Example 2

Use Figure 6 to find the ratio of the annual insurance expense to the total annual cost of the car.

Strategy   To find the ratio:

- Locate the annual insurance expense in the circle graph.
- Write the ratio of the annual insurance expense to the total annual cost of operating the car in simplest form.

Solution   Annual insurance expense: $1400

$$\frac{1400}{6000} = \frac{7}{30}$$

The ratio is $\frac{7}{30}$.

The circle graph in Figure 7 shows the distribution of an employee's gross monthly income.

Example 3

Use Figure 7 to find the employee's take-home pay.

Strategy   To find the take-home pay:

- Locate the percent of the distribution that is take-home pay.
- Solve the basic percent equation for amount.

Solution   Take-home pay: 54%

Percent × base = amount
  0.54 × 2900 = 1566

The employee's take-home pay is $1566.

You Try It 2

Use Figure 6 to find the ratio of the annual cost of fuel to the annual cost of maintenance.

Your strategy

Your solution

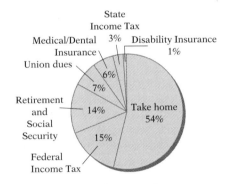

Figure 7   Distribution of gross monthly income of $2900

You Try It 3

Use Figure 7 to find the amount paid for medical/dental insurance.

Your strategy

Your solution

Solutions on pp. S17–S18

7.1 Exercises

Objective A

The pictograph in Figure 8 shows the approximate gross revenues in the United States from four Walt Disney animated movies.

1. Find the total gross revenues from the four movies.

2. Find the ratio of the gross revenue of *Beauty and the Beast* to the gross revenue of *The Hunchback of Notre Dame*.

3. Find the percent of the total gross revenue that was earned by *The Lion King*. Round to the nearest tenth of a percent.

Figure 8   Gross revenues of four Walt Disney animated movies

Source: *Time*, June 20, 1997

The pictograph in Figure 9 is based on a survey of adults who were asked whether they agreed with each statement.

4. Find the ratio of the number of people who agree that space exploration impacts daily life to the number of people who agree that space will be colonized in their lifetime.

5. How many more people agreed that humanity should explore planets than agreed that space exploration impacts daily life?

6. Is the number of people who agreed that they would travel in space more than twice the number of people who agreed that space would be colonized in their lifetime?

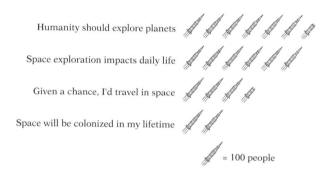

Figure 9   Number of adults who agree with the statement

Source: Opinion Research for Space Day Partners

The pictograph in Figure 10 is based on a survey of children aged 7 through 12. The percent of children's responses to the survey are shown. Assuming that 500 children were surveyed, solve Exercises 7 to 9.

7. Find the number of children who said they hid vegetables under a napkin.

8. What is the difference between the number of children who fed vegetables to the dog and the number who dropped them on the floor?

9. Were the responses given in the graph the only responses given by the children? Explain your answer.

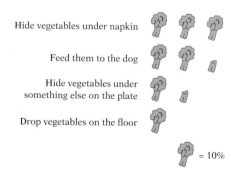

Figure 10   How children try to hide vegetables

Source: Strategic Consulting and Research for Del Monte

Objective B

An accounting major recorded the number of units required in each discipline to graduate with a degree in accounting. The results are shown in the circle graph in Figure 11.

10. How many units are required to graduate with a degree in accounting?

11. What is the ratio of the number of units in finance to the number of units in accounting?

12. What percent of the units required to graduate are taken in accounting? Round to the nearest tenth of a percent.

13. What percent of the units required to graduate are taken in mathematics? Round to the nearest tenth of a percent.

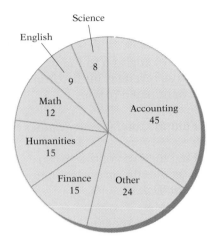

Figure 11 Number of units required to graduate with an Accounting degree

The circle graph in Figure 12 shows the population of seven regions.

14. Find the total population of the seven regions.

15. What is the ratio of the population of Asia to the population of Africa?

16. What is the ratio of the population of North America to the population of Asia?

17. What is the ratio of the population of North America to the population of South America?

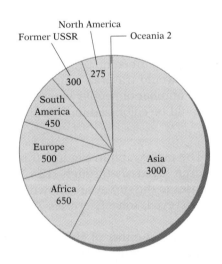

Figure 12 Population in millions of people

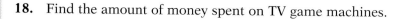 The circle graph in Figure 13 shows the breakdown of the approximately $3,100,000,000 that Americans spent on home video game equipment in one year.

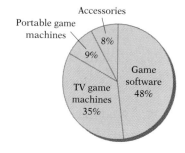

18. Find the amount of money spent on TV game machines.

19. Find the amount of money spent on portable game machines.

Figure 13 Percents of $3,100,000,000 spent annually on home video games

Source: The NPD Group, Toy Manufacturers of America

20. What fractional amount of the total money spent was spent on accessories?

21. Is the amount spent for TV game machines more than three times the amount spent for portable game machines?

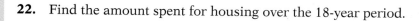 In *Numbers* by Andrea Sutcliff (HarperCollins, 1996), an estimate of $98,000 is given as the total cost of raising a child for the first 18 years of life. The circle graph in Figure 14 shows the percents that are spent for various categories.

22. Find the amount spent for housing over the 18-year period.

Figure 14 Distribution of expenses to raise a child

23. Find the amount spent for food over the 18-year period.

24. Find the amount spent for transportation and clothing over the 18-year period.

25. Find the total amount spent for housing and education for the 18-year period.

The circle graph in Figure 15 shows the land area of each of the seven continents in square miles.

26. Find the total land area of the seven continents.

27. Find the ratio of the land area of North America to the land area of South America.

28. What percent of the total land area is the land area of Asia? Round to the nearest tenth of a percent.

29. What percent of the total land area is the land area of Australia? Round to the nearest tenth of a percent.

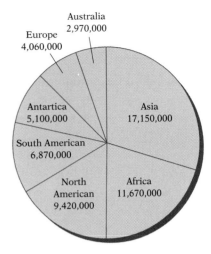

Figure 15 Land area of the seven continents in square miles

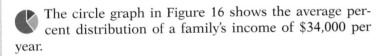 The circle graph in Figure 16 shows the average percent distribution of a family's income of $34,000 per year.

30. How much of the family's income was spent on food?

31. How much of the family's income was spent on entertainment?

32. How much more of the family's income was spent on medical needs than was spent on clothing?

33. Was the amount spent for housing more than twice the amount spent for food?

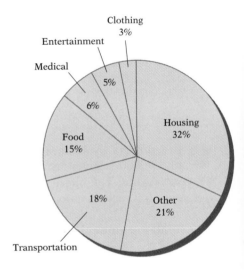

Figure 16 Percent distribution of a family's income

Source: Consumer Expenditure Survey for the Bureau of Labor Statistics

APPLYING THE CONCEPTS

34. What are the advantages of presenting data in the form of a pictograph? What are the disadvantages?

35. Make out a budget for your expenses. Record these expenses in a circle graph.

36. Pick out a typical day, and record in a circle graph the amount of time you spent on different activities.

7.2 Bar Graphs and Broken-Line Graphs

Objective A   To read a bar graph ···

A **bar graph** represents data by the height of the bars. The bar graph in Figure 17 shows temperature data recorded for Cincinnati, Ohio, for the months March through November. For each month, the height of the bar indicates the normal daily high temperature during that month. The jagged line near the bottom of the graph indicates that the vertical scale is missing the numbers between 0 and 50. (Source: U.S. Weather Bureau.)

The daily high temperature in September was 78°F. Because the bar for July is the tallest, the daily high temperature was highest in July.

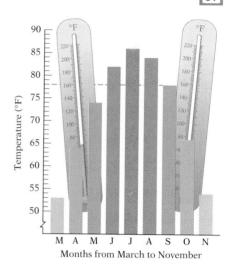

Figure 17 Daily high temperatures in Cincinnati, Ohio.

A **double-bar graph** is used to display data for purposes of comparison. The double-bar graph in Figure 18 shows the sales of new cars in June 1996 and June 1997 for four car companies. (Source: Ward's Communications.)

In June 1996, General Motors sold approximately 435,000 cars.

Only Ford had greater sales in June 1997 than it did in June 1996.

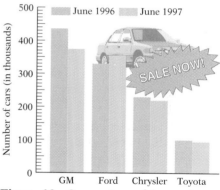

Figure 18 Comparison of June sales.

TAKE NOTE

The bar for General Motors in 1996 is halfway between the mark for 430 and for 440. Therefore, we estimate that the sales are halfway between those two numbers, or 435,000.

Example 1

Use Figure 18 to find the difference between June sales in 1996 and June sales in 1997 for Chrysler.

Strategy   To find the difference:

- Read the double-bar graph to find the sales for Chrysler in June of both years.
- Subtract to find the difference.

Solution

June 1996 Chrysler sales: 230,000
June 1997 Chrysler sales: 220,000
230,000 − 220,000 = 10,000
The difference in sales was 10,000 cars.

You Try It 1

Use Figure 18 to determine which company had the largest decrease in sales from June 1996 to June 1997.

Your strategy

Your solution

Solution on p. S18

Objective B   *To read a broken-line graph* .... CT

A **broken-line graph** represents data by the position of the lines and is used to show trends. The broken-line graph in Figure 19 shows the CD singles by American record companies for a five-year period. The height of each dot indicates the approximate number of CD singles sold in that year.

In 1995, 22 million CD singles were sold. In 1996, 43 million CD singles were sold.

For the years shown, sales increased more between 1995 and 1996 than between any other two years.

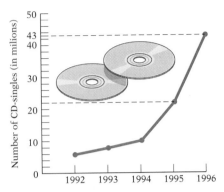

Figure 19   Number of CD singles sold by American record companies

Source: Recording Industry Association of America

Two broken-line graphs are often shown in the same figure for comparison. Figure 20 shows the net incomes of two software companies, Math Associates and MatheMentors, before their merger.

Several things can be determined from the graph:

The net income for Math Associates in 1997 was $8 million.

The net income for MatheMentors declined from 1994 to 1995.

The net income for Math Associates increased for each year shown.

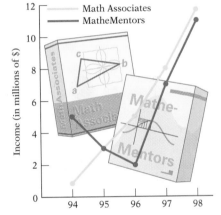

Figure 20   Net incomes of Math Associates and Mathementors

Example 2
Use Figure 20 to approximate the difference between the net income of Math Associates and MatheMentors in 1996.

Strategy
To find the difference:

* Read the line graph to determine the net income of Math Associates and MatheMentors in 1996.
* Subtract to find the difference between the net incomes.

Solution
Net income for Math Associates: $5 million.
Net income for MatheMentors: $2 million.
5 − 2 = 3
The difference between net incomes in 1996 was $3 million.

You Try It 2
Use Figure 20 to determine between which two years the net income of Math Associates increased the most.

Your strategy

Your solution

Solution on p. S18

7.2 Exercises

. . . .

Objective A

The bar graph in Figure 21 shows the number of days each year that the Pollution Standard Index (PSI) was greater than 100 in a large city. (An index greater than 100 indicates less than moderate air quality.)

1. How many days had a PSI greater than 100 in 1993?

2. What was the difference between the number of days with a PSI greater than 100 in 1995 and in 1996?

3. Between which two consecutive years did the PSI decrease the most?

4. Between which two consecutive years was the percent decrease in the PSI the greatest?

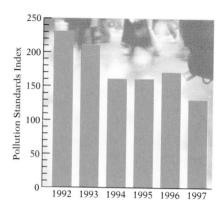

Figure 21   Air quality in a city

The double-bar graph in Figure 22 shows some crime statistics for the city of Dallas, Texas, for the years 1992 and 1996.

5. How many burglaries were committed in Dallas in 1992?

6. In which crime category did the number of crimes decrease the most?

7. In which crime category was the percent decrease in the number of crimes the greatest?

8. For the crime categories listed, did any category show an increase in the number of crimes?

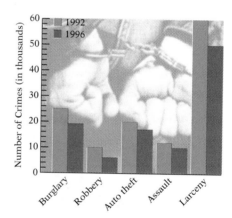

Figure 22   Statistics for some major crimes

Source: Dallas Police Department

The double-bar graph in Figure 23 shows maximum salaries for police officers in selected cities and the corresponding maximum salaries for officers in the suburbs of that city.

9. Estimate the difference between the maximum salaries of police officers in the suburbs and the city for New York.

10. Is there a city for which the maximum salary of a police officer in the city is greater than the salary in the suburbs?

11. For which city is the difference between the maximum salary in the suburbs and in the city the greatest?

12. Of the cities shown on the graph, which city has the lowest maximum salary for police officers in the suburbs?

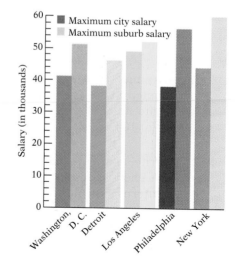

Figure 23   Maximum salaries of police officers in the city and the suburbs

Source: *USA Today*, May 20, 1997

Objective B

The broken-line graph in Figure 24 shows the average monthly snowfall during ski season around Aspen, Colorado.

13. What was the amount of snowfall during January?

14. During which month was the snowfall the greatest?

15. What was the total snowfall during March and April?

16. Find the ratio of the amount of snowfall in November to the amount of snowfall in December.

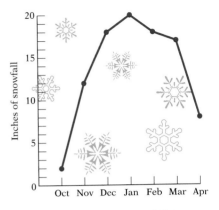

Figure 24   Average snowfall in Aspen, CO

Source: *Weather America*, by Alfred Garwood (Toucan Valley Publications, July 1996)

The double-broken-line graph in Figure 25 shows the recommended number of Calories per day that should be consumed by women and men in various age groups.

17. What is the difference between the number of Calories recommended for men and the number recommended for women 19–22 years of age?

18. What age and gender has the lowest recommended number of Calories?

19. Find the ratio of the number of Calories recommended for 15 to 18-year-old women to the number recommended for 51 to 74-year-old women.

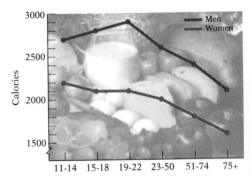

Figure 25   Recommended number of Calories per day for women and men

Source: *Numbers* by Andrea Sutcliffe (HarperCollins).

APPLYING THE CONCEPTS

The broken-line graph in Figure 26 shows U.S. energy consumption patterns for the years 1850–1990.

20. What two fuels provided the energy in the United States in 1850?

21. Estimate the percent of each fuel that the United States used in 1990. Does your estimate total 100%? Should your estimate total 100%?

22. Write a paragraph analyzing the patterns in the energy consumption graph. What do the patterns indicate about the future consumption of petroleum and natural gas?

23. Discuss what might be our energy consumption and needs in the year 2020 if the trends continue?

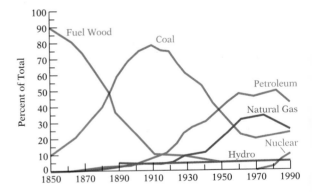

Figure 26   United States energy consumption patterns, 1850–1990

7.3 Histograms and Frequency Polygons

Objective A   *To read a histogram* ·· CT

A research group measured the fuel usage of 92 cars. The results are recorded in the histogram in Figure 27. A **histogram** is a special type of bar graph. The width of each bar corresponds to a range of numbers called a **class interval.** The height of each bar corresponds to the number of occurrences of data in each class interval and is called the **class frequency.**

Class Intervals (Miles per Gallon)	Class Frequencies (Number of Cars)
18–20	12
20–22	19
22–24	24
24–26	17
26–28	15
28–30	5

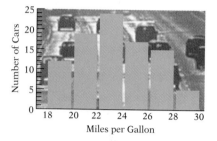

Figure 27

Twenty-four cars get between 22 and 24 miles per gallon.

A precision tool company has 85 employees. Their hourly wages are recorded in the histogram in Figure 28.

The ratio of the number of employees whose hourly wage is between $12 and $14 to the total number of employees is $\dfrac{17 \text{ employees}}{85 \text{ employees}} = \dfrac{1}{5}$.

Figure 28

Example 1
Use Figure 28 to find the number of employees whose hourly wage is between $14 and $18.

Strategy
To find the number of employees:

- Read the histogram to find the number of employees whose hourly wage is between $14 and $16 and the number whose wage is between $16 and $18.
- Add the two numbers.

Solution   Number whose wage is
        between $14 and $16: 20;
        between $16 and 18: 14.

        20 + 14 = 34

34 employees have an hourly wage between $14 and $18.

You Try It 1
Use Figure 28 to find the number of employees whose hourly wage is between $8 and $12.

Your strategy

Your solution

Solution on p. S18

Objective B   *To read a frequency polygon* .... CT

The speeds of 70 cars on a highway were measured by radar. The results are recorded in the frequency polygon in Figure 29. A **frequency polygon** is a graph that displays information in a manner similarly to a histogram. A dot is placed above the center of each class interval at a height corresponding to that class's frequency. The dots are then connected to form a broken-line graph. The center of a class interval is called the **class midpoint.**

Class Interval (Miles per Hour)	Class Midpoint	Class Frequency
30–40	35	7
40–50	45	13
50–60	55	25
60–70	65	21
70–80	75	4

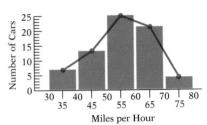

Figure 29

Twenty-five cars were traveling between 50 and 60 miles per hour.

In 1996, about 210,000 people scored at least 1200 (out of a maximum of 1600) on the SAT exam. Their scores are recorded in the frequency polygon in Figure 30.

The ratio of the number of people scoring between 1400 and 1500 to the total number of people represented is $\frac{30,000}{210,000} = \frac{1}{7}$.

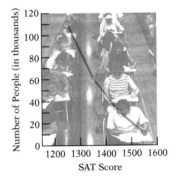

Figure 30

Source: Educational Testing Service

Example 2

Use Figure 30 to find the number of people who scored between 1400 and 1600 on the exam.

Strategy

To find the number of people who scored between 1400 and 1600 on the exam:

- Read the frequency polygon to find the number of people who scored between 1400 and 1500 and the number of people who scored between 1500 and 1600 on the exam.
- Add the two numbers.

Solution

The number who scored between 1400 and 1500: 30,000; between 1500 and 1600: 10,000.

30,000 + 10,000 = 40,000

40,000 people scored between 1400 and 1600.

You Try It 2

Use Figure 30 to find the number of people who scored between 1200 and 1400 on the exam.

Your strategy

Your solution

Solution on p. S18

7.3 Exercises

Objective A

The annual tuition for undergraduate college students attending four-year institutions varies depending on the college. The histogram in Figure 31 shows the tuition amounts for a representative sample of 120 students from various parts of the United States.

1. How many students have a tuition that is between $3000 and $6000 per year?

2. What is the ratio of the number of students whose tuition is between $9000 per year and $12,000 per year to the total number of students represented?

3. How many students pay more than $12,000 annually for tuition?

4. What percent of the total number of students spend less than $6000 annually?

The histogram in Figure 32 is based on data from the American Automobile Manufacturers Association. It shows the ages of a sample of 1000 cars in a typical city in the United States.

5. How many cars are between 6 and 12 years old?

6. Find the ratio of the number of cars between 12 and 15 years old to the total number of cars.

7. Find the number of cars more than 12 years old.

8. Find the percent of cars that are less than 9 years old.

According to a Maritz AmeriPoll, the average U.S. adult goes to a shopping mall about two times a month. The histogram shows the average time 100 adults spent in the mall per trip.

9. Find the number of adults who spend between 1 and 2 hours at the mall.

10. Find the number of adults who spend between 3 and 4 hours at the mall.

11. What percent of the adults spend less than 1 hour at the mall?

12. What percent of the adults spend 5 or more hours at the mall?

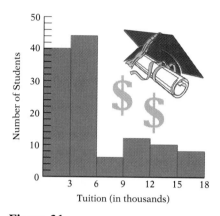

Figure 31

Source: Educational Testing Service

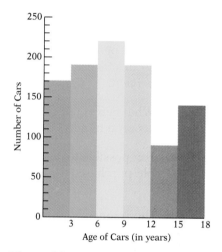

Figure 32

Source: American Automobile Manufacturers Association

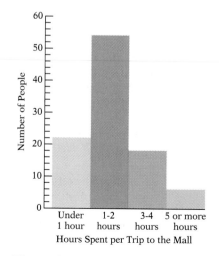

Figure 33

Source: Maritz AmeriPoll

Objective B

As reported in *Runner's World*, a total of 28 runners competed in the preliminaries for the 1997 U.S. track and field championship men's 200-meter dash. The results are recorded in the frequency polygon in Figure 34.

13. How many runners ran the race in less than 21 seconds?

14. Find the ratio of the number of runners who ran the race in a time between 20 and 21 seconds to the number who ran the race in a time between 21 and 22 seconds.

15. What percent of the runners ran the race in between 20.5 and 21 seconds? Round to the nearest tenth of a percent.

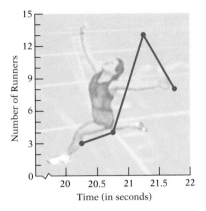

Figure 34

The frequency polygon in Figure 35 is based on data from a Gallup poll survey of 74 people who purchased lottery tickets.

16. How many people purchased between 1 and 10 tickets?

17. What percent of the people purchased between 20 and 30 tickets each month? Round to the nearest tenth of a percent.

18. What percent of the people purchased more than 10 tickets each month? Round to the nearest tenth of a percent.

19. Is it possible to determine from the graph how many people purchased 15 lottery tickets? Explain.

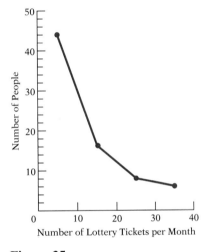

Figure 35

The frequency polygon in Figure 36 shows the distribution of scores of the approximately 1,080,000 students who took an SAT exam.

20. How many students scored between 1200 and 1400 on the exam?

21. What percent of the number of students who took the exam scored between 800 and 1000? Round to the nearest tenth of a percent.

22. How many students scored below 1000?

23. How many students scored above 800?

APPLYING THE CONCEPTS

24. Write a paragraph explaining the difference between a histogram and a bar graph.

25. In your own words, describe a frequency table.

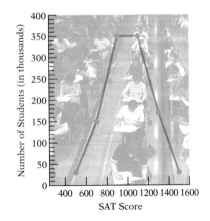

Figure 36

Source: Educational Testing Service

7.4 Statistical Measures

Objective A   *To find the mean, median, and mode of a distribution* ....

The average score on the math portion of the SAT was 432. The EPA estimates that a 1997 Eagle Talon averages 28 miles per gallon on the highway. The average rainfall for portions of Kauai is 350 inches per year. Each of these statements uses one number to describe an entire collection of numbers. Such a number is called an *average*.

In statistics there are various ways to calculate an average. Three of the most common, *mean*, *median*, and *mode*, are discussed here.

An automotive engineer tests the miles-per-gallon ratings of 15 cars and records the results as follows.

Miles per Gallon Ratings of 15 Cars														
25	22	21	27	25	35	29	31	25	26	21	39	34	32	28

The **mean** of the data is the sum of the measurements divided by the number of measurements. The symbol for the mean is $\bar{x}$.

> **Formula for the Mean**
>
> $$\bar{x} = \frac{\text{sum of the data values}}{\text{number of data values}}$$

To find the mean for the data above, add the numbers and then divide by 15.

$$\bar{x} = \frac{25 + 22 + 21 + 27 + 25 + 35 + 29 + 31 + 25 + 26 + 21 + 39 + 34 + 32 + 28}{15}$$

$$= \frac{420}{15} = 28$$

The mean number of miles per gallon for the 15 cars tested was 28 miles per gallon.

The mean is one of the most frequently computed averages. It is the one that is commonly used to calculate a student's performance in a class.

➡ The test scores for a student taking American history were 78, 82, 91, 87, and 93. What was the mean score for this student?

To find the mean, add the test scores. Then divide by 5, the number of scores.

$$\bar{x} = \frac{78 + 82 + 91 + 87 + 93}{5}$$

$$= \frac{431}{5} = 86.2$$

The mean score for the history student was 86.2.

The **median** of data is the number that separates the data into two equal parts when the numbers are arranged from smallest to largest (or largest to smallest). There are an equal number of values above the median and below the median.

To find the median of a set of numbers, first arrange the numbers from smallest to largest. The median is the number in the middle. The result of arranging the miles-per-gallon ratings given on the previous page from smallest to largest is shown below.

21 21 22 25 25 25 26 27 28 29 31 32 34 35 39

| 7 values below the median | Middle number **Median** | 7 values above the median |

The median is 27.

If the data contain an *even* number of values, the median is the mean of the two middle numbers.

➡ The selling price of the last six homes sold by a real estate agent were $175,000, $150,000, $250,000, $130,000, $245,000, and $190,000. Find the median selling price of these homes.

Arrange the numbers from smallest to largest. Because there is an even number of values, the median is the mean of the two middle numbers.

130,000 150,000 175,000 190,000 245,000 250,000

Middle 2 numbers

$$\text{Median} = \frac{175,000 + 190,000}{2} = 182,500$$

The median selling price was $182,500.

The **mode** of a set of numbers is the value that occurs most frequently. If a set of numbers has no number occurring more than once, then the data have no mode.

Here again are the data for the gasoline mileage ratings of cars.

Miles per Gallon Ratings of 15 Cars

25 22 21 27 25 35 29 31 25 26 21 39 34 32 28

25 is the number that occurs most frequently. The mode is 25.

Example 1
Twenty students were asked the number of units in which they were enrolled. The responses were:

| 15 | 12 | 13 | 15 | 17 | 18 | 13 | 20 | 9 | 16 |
| 14 | 10 | 15 | 12 | 17 | 16 | 6 | 14 | 15 | 12 |

Find the mean number of units taken by these students.

Strategy
To find the mean number of units:

- Determine the sum of the numbers.
- Divide the sum by 20.

Solution   The sum of the numbers is 279.

$$\bar{x} = \frac{279}{20} = 13.95$$

The mean is 13.95 units.

You Try It 1
The amounts spent by 12 customers at a McDonald's restaurant were:

| 5.26 | 7.23 | 4.09 | 7.11 | 6.50 | 5.69 |
| 4.66 | 3.89 | 4.25 | 8.36 | 5.75 | 6.05 |

Find the mean amount spent by these customers. Round to the nearest cent.

Your strategy

Your solution

Solution on p. S19

Example 2

The starting hourly wages for an apprentice electrician for 6 different work locations were $7.90, $8.25, $7.10, $8.08, $8.56, and $7.55. Find the median starting hourly wage.

Strategy

To find the median hourly wage:

- Arrange the numbers from smallest to largest.
- Because there is an even number of values, the median is the mean of the two middle numbers.

Solution

$7.10, $7.55, $7.90, $8.08, $8.25, $8.56

$$\text{Median} = \frac{7.90 + 8.08}{2} = 7.99$$

The median starting hourly wage was $7.99.

You Try It 2

The amounts of weight lost, in pounds, by 10 participants in a 6-month weight reduction program were 22, 16, 31, 14, 27, 16, 29, 31, 40, and 10. Find the median weight loss for these participants.

Your strategy

Your solution

Solution on p. S19

Objective B   To graph a box-and-whiskers plot ⋯⋯⋯⋯⋯⋯⋯⋯⋯⋯⋯⋯⋯⋯⋯⋯

The purpose of calculating a mean or median is to obtain one number that describes a group of measurements. That one number alone, however, may not adequately represent the data. A **box-and-whiskers plot** is a graph that gives a more complete picture of the data. A box-and-whiskers plot shows five numbers: the smallest value, the *first quartile*, the median, the *third quartile*, and the greatest value.

The **first quartile,** symbolized by Q_1, is the number that one-quarter of the data lie *below*. The **third quartile,** symbolized by Q_3, is the number that one-quarter of the data lie *above*. Another way to look at quartiles is that Q_1 is the median of the lower half of the data values, and Q_3 is the median of the upper half of the data values.

➡ Find the first quartile Q_1 and the third quartile Q_3 for the prices of 15 half-gallon cartons of deluxe ice cream.

Cost of Half-Gallon Cartons of Ice Cream

| 3.26 | 4.71 | 4.18 | 4.45 | 5.49 | 3.18 | 3.86 | 3.58 | 4.29 | 5.44 | 4.83 | 4.56 | 4.36 | 2.66 | 2.39 |

To find the quartiles, first arrange the data from the smallest value to the largest value. Then find the median.

| 2.39 | 2.66 | 3.18 | 3.26 | 3.58 | 3.86 | 4.18 | 4.29 | 4.36 | 4.45 | 4.56 | 4.71 | 4.83 | 5.44 | 5.49 |

The median is $4.29.

Now separate the data into two groups: those values below the median and those values above the median.

Values Less than the Median

| 2.39 | 2.66 | 3.18 | 3.26 | 3.58 | 3.86 | 4.18 |

Q_1

Values Greater than the Median

| 4.36 | 4.45 | 4.56 | 4.71 | 4.83 | 5.44 | 5.49 |

Q_3

The first quartile Q_1 is the median of the lower half of the data: $Q_1 = 3.26$.

The third quartile Q_3 is the median of the upper half of the data: $Q_3 = 4.71$.

The **interquartile range** is the difference between the third quartile Q_3 and the first quartile Q_1.

$$\text{Interquartile range} = Q_3 - Q_1 = 4.71 - 3.26 = 1.45$$

Fifty percent of the data in a distribution lie in the interquartile range.

A box-and-whiskers plot shows the interquartile range as a box. The box-and-whiskers plot for the data on the cost of ice cream is shown below.

The box-and-whiskers plot labels five values: the smallest, 2.39; the first quartile Q_1, 3.26; the median, 4.29; the third quartile Q_3, 4.71; and the largest value, 5.49. The **range** of the data is the difference between the largest and smallest values.

$$\text{Range} = 5.49 - 2.39 = 3.10.$$

For Example 3 and You Try It 3, use the data in the following table, which gives the number of people who have registered for a software training program.

Participants in Software Training

30	45	54	24	48	38	43	38	46	53	62	64	40	35

Example 3

Find the first quartile Q_1, the third quartile Q_3, and the interquartile range for the data in the software training table.

Strategy

- Arrange the data from smallest to largest. Then find the median.
- Find Q_1, the median of the lower half of the data.
- Find Q_3, the median of the upper half of the data.
- Interquartile range $= Q_3 - Q_1$.

Solution

24	30	35	**38**	38	40	**43**
45	46	48	**53**	54	62	64

$$\text{Median} = \frac{43 + 45}{2} = 44$$

$Q_1 = 38$ • The median of the top row of data.
$Q_3 = 53$ • The median of the bottom row of data.

Interquartile range $= Q_3 - Q_1 = 53 - 38 = 15$

You Try It 3

Draw the box-and-whiskers plot for the data in the software training table and determine the range.

Your strategy

Your solution

Solution on p. S19

7.4 Exercises

. . . .

Objective A

1. The number of big-screen televisions sold each month for one year was recorded by an electronics store. For 1997, the results were 15, 12, 20, 20, 19, 17, 22, 24, 17, 20, 15, and 27. Calculate the mean, the median, and the mode of the number of televisions sold per month.

2. The number of seats occupied on a jet for 16 transatlantic flights was recorded. The numbers were 309, 422, 389, 412, 401, 352, 367, 319, 410, 391, 330, 408, 399, 387, 411, and 398. Calculate the mean, the median, and the mode of the number of seats occupied per flight.

3. The times, in seconds, for a 100-meter dash at a college track meet were 10.45, 10.23, 10.57, 11.01, 10.26, 10.90, 10.74, 10.64, 10.52, and 10.78. Calculate the mean and the median times for the 100-meter dash.

4. A consumer research group purchased identical items in 8 grocery stores. The costs for the purchased items were $45.89, $52.12, $41.43, $40.67, $48.73, $42.45, $47.81, and $45.82. Calculate the mean and the median costs of the purchased items.

5. Your scores on six history tests were 78, 92, 95, 77, 94, and 88. If an "average score" of 90 receives an A for the course, which average, the mean or the median, would you prefer that the instructor use?

6. One measure of a computer's hard drive speed is called access time; this is measured in milliseconds (thousandths of a second). Find the mean (to the nearest hundredth), the median, and the mode times for 11 hard drives whose access times were 18, 17, 16, 17, 18, 19, 20, 19, 14, 17, and 17.

7. Eight health maintenance organizations (HMOs) presented group health insurance plans to a company. The monthly rates per employee were $423, $390, $405, $396, $426, $355, $404, and $430. Calculate the mean, the median, and the mode of the monthly rates.

8. The number of yards gained by a college running back for 6 games was recorded. The numbers were 98, 105, 120, 90, 111, and 104. Find the mean (to the nearest hundredth) and the median yards gained.

9. The monthly utility bills for 8 homes are $86.48, $92.81, $48.92, $74.16, $112.53, $61.92, $86.48, and $97.92. Find the mean and median monthly utility bills for these 8 homes.

10. According to the U.S. Census Bureau International Data Base, the estimated populations, in thousands, of the 10 largest cities in the world in the year 2000 are given at the right. Find the mean and the median population for these cities.

Tokyo-Yokohama, Japan	29,971
Mexico City, Mexico	27,872
Sao Paulo, Brazil	25,354
Seoul, South Korea	21,976
Bombay, India	15,357
New York, United States	14,648
Osaka-Kobe-Kyoto, Japan	14,287
Tehran, Iran	14,251
Rio de Janeiro, Brazil	14,169
Calcutta, India	14,088

11. The life expectancies, in years, in 10 selected Central and South American countries are given at the right. Find the mean and median life expectancy in these countries.

Brazil	62
Chile	75
Costa Rica	78
Ecuador	70
Guatemala	64
Panama	75
Peru	66
Trinidad and Tobago	71
Uruguay	74
Venezuela	73

12. The lengths of the terms, in years, of all the former Supreme Court chief justices are given in the table below. Find the mean and median length of term for the chief justices.

5	0	4	34	28	8	14	21
10	8	11	4	7	15	17	

Objective B

13. The hourly wage for an entry-level position at various firms was recorded by a labor research firm. Find the range, the first quartile and the third quartile, and the interquartile range for these data.

Starting Hourly Wages for 16 Companies

7.09	10.50	6.46	6.70	8.85	8.03	10.40	8.31
9.35	6.45	6.35	7.64	8.02	7.12	9.05	7.94

14. The cholesterol levels for 14 adults are recorded in the table below. Find the range, the first quartile and the third quartile, and the interquartile range for these data.

Cholesterol Level for 14 Adults

375	185	254	221	183	251	258
292	214	172	233	208	198	211

15. The gasoline consumption of 19 cars was tested and the results recorded in a table. Find the first quartile and the third quartile, and draw a box-and-whiskers plot of the data.

Miles per Gallon for 19 Cars

33	21	30	32	20	31	25	20	16	24
22	31	30	28	26	19	21	17	26	

16. The ages of the accountants who passed the Certified Public Accountant (CPA) exam at one test center are recorded in the table below. Find the first quartile and the third quartile, and draw a box-and-whiskers plot of the data.

Ages of Accountants Passing the CPA exam

24	42	35	26	24	37	27	26	28
34	43	46	29	34	25	30	28	

17. The times required for new employees to learn how to assemble a toy are recorded in the table below. Draw a box-and-whiskers plot of the data. What is the interquartile range?

Time to Train Employees (in hours)

4.3	3.1	5.3	8.0	2.6	3.5	4.9	4.3
6.2	6.8	5.4	6.0	5.1	4.8	5.3	6.7

18. A manufacturer of light bulbs tested the life of 20 light bulbs. The results are recorded in the table below. Draw a box-and-whiskers plot of the data. What is the interquartile range?

Life of 20 Light Bulbs (in hours)

1010	1235	1200	998	1400	789	986	905	1050	1100
1180	1020	1381	992	1106	1298	1268	1390	1390	890

19. The box-and-whiskers plot below shows the distribution of median incomes for the 50 states and the District of Columbia.

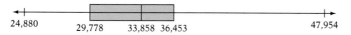

24,880   29,778   33,858 36,453   47,954

Identify Q_1, the median, and Q_3.

20. The box-and-whiskers plot below shows the distribution of the ages of presidents of the United States when they were inaugarated. Identify Q_1, the median, and Q_3.

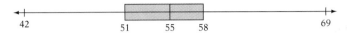

APPLYING THE CONCEPTS

21. For Exercise 19, between which two values do 50% of the median incomes of the United States fall?

22. Using Exercise 20, 50% of the ages of U.S. presidents at the time of their inauguration fall between which two values?

23. Using the three sets of data given at the right, answer the questions below.

Set 1: 3, 4, 5, 6, 7
Set 2: 1, 3, 4, 5, 6
Set 3: 3, 4, 5, 6, 8

   a. The mean of a set of data is always equal to the median of the data.

   b. The mean of a set of data is always less than the median of the data.

   c. The mean of a set of data is always greater than the median of the data.

24. Rita received scores of 82, 78, 91, and 80 on four tests. Elyssa received scores of 87, 83, 96, and 85 (exactly 5 points higher on each test). Are the means of the two students' test scores the same? If not, what is the relationship between the means of the two students' scores?

25. Jason received scores of 89, 85, 94, 11, and 91 on 5 tests. Which measurement, the mean or the median, gives a better representation of his performance? Explain.

For Exercises 26 and 27, answer true or false. If the answer is false, change the statement to make it true.

26. The range of the data for Exercise 20 is 42 years to 69 years.

27. There are equal numbers of data below the mean and above the mean.

Focus on Problem Solving

Inductive Reasoning   Suppose that, beginning in January, you save $25 each month. The total amount you have saved at the end of each month can be described by a list of numbers.

25	50	75	100	125	150	175	
Jan	Feb	Mar	Apr	May	June	July	...

The list of numbers that indicates your total savings is an *ordered* list of numbers called a **sequence**. Each of the numbers in a sequence is called a **term** of the sequence. The list is ordered because the position of a number in the list indicates the month in which that total amount has been saved. For example, the 7th term of the sequence (indicating July) is 175. This number means that a total of $175 has been saved by the end of the 7th month.

Now consider a person who has a different savings plan. The total amount saved by this person for the first seven months is given by the sequence

$$20, 35, 50, 65, 80, 95, 110, ...$$

The process you use to discover the next number in the above sequence is *inductive reasoning*. **Inductive reasoning** involves making generalizations from specific examples; in other words, we reach a conclusion by making observations about particular facts or cases. In the case of the above sequence, the person saved $15 per month after the first month.

Here is another example of inductive reasoning. Find the next two letters of the sequence A, B, E, F, I, J, ...

By trying different patterns, we can determine that a pattern for this sequence is

$$\underline{A, B}, C, D, \underline{E, F}, G, H, \underline{I, J}, ...$$

That is, write two letters, skip two letters, write two letters, skip two letters, and so on. The next two letters are M, N.

Use inductive reasoning to solve the problems below.

1. What is the next term of the sequence, ban, ben, bin, bon, ... ?

2. Using a calculator, determine the decimal representation of several proper fractions that have a denominator of 99. For instance, you may use $\frac{8}{99}$, $\frac{23}{99}$, and $\frac{75}{99}$. Now use inductive reasoning to explain the pattern and use your reasoning to find the decimal representation of $\frac{53}{99}$ without a calculator.

3. Find the next number in the sequence 1, 1, 2, 3, 5, 8, 13, 21, ...

4. The decimal representation of a number begins 0.10100100010000100000... . What are the next 10 digits in this number.

5. The first 7 rows of a triangle of numbers called Pascal's triangle are given below. Find the next row.

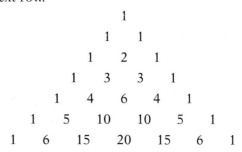

Projects and Group Activities

Deceptive Graphs   A graphical representation of data can sometimes be misleading. Consider the graphs shown below. A financial advisor with an investment firm claims that an investment with the firm will grow as shown in the graph on the left, whereas an investment with a competitor will grow as shown in the graph on the right. Apparently, you would accumulate more money by choosing the investment on the left.

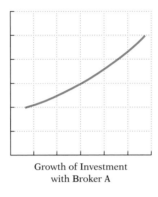

Growth of Investment
with Broker A

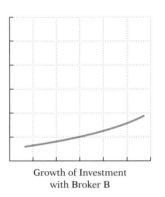

Growth of Investment
with Broker B

However, these graphs have a serious flaw. There are no labels on the horizontal and vertical axes. Therefore, it is impossible to tell which investment increased more or over what time interval. When labels are not placed on the axes of a graph, the data that graph represents are meaningless. This is one way in which advertisers use a visual impact to distort the true meaning of data.

The graphs below are the same as those drawn above except that scales have been drawn along each axis. Now it is possible to tell how each investment has performed. Note that each one turned in exactly the same performance.

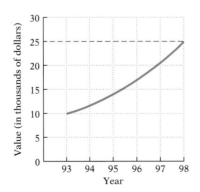

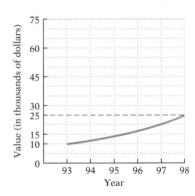

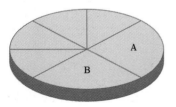

Drawing a circle graph as an oval is another way of distorting data. This is especially true if a three-dimensional representation is given. From the appearance of the circle graph at the left, one would think that region A is larger than region B. However, that isn't true. Measure the angle of each sector to see this for yourself. As you read newspapers and magazines, find examples of graphs that may distort the actual data. Discuss how these graphs should be drawn to be more accurate.

Average Daily Balance

A partial credit card statement and the calculation of the average daily balance are shown below.

Previous unpaid balance: $275		
New Purchases		
Date	Description	Charges
5/3	Shirt	$45
5/7	Gas	$20
5/15	Food	$35
5/20	Payment	$150 CR
5/27	Gift	$40

For this example, we are assuming that only a partial payment was made the previous month and that there is an unpaid balance of $275. We will assume that the next payment is due on 6/1 and the periodic interest rate is 1.5%.

Date	Charges or payments	Balance	Number of days balance has been owed	Balance × days
5/1–5/2		275	2	275 × 2 = 550
5/3–5/6	45	320 = 275 + 45	4	320 × 4 = 1280
5/7–5/14	20	340 = 320 + 20	8	340 × 8 = 2720
5/15–5/19	35	375 = 340 + 35	5	375 × 5 = 1875
5/20–5/26	150 CR	225 = 375 − 150	7	225 × 7 = 1575
5/27–5/31	40	265 = 225 + 40	5	265 × 5 = 1325

Total = 9325

$$\text{Average daily balance} = \frac{9325}{31} \approx 300.81$$

Days in May

TAKE NOTE

Average daily balance is similar to the calculation of grade point average in that it is a weighted average.

To calculate the finance charge, multiply the average daily balance by the periodic (monthly) interest rate.

$$\text{Finance charge} = 300.81 \times 0.015 \approx 4.51$$

The balance due is calculated as

TAKE NOTE

The new charges are $45 + 20 + 35 + 40 = 140$.

Balance due = previous balance + new charges + finance charge − payments
Balance due = 275 + 140 + 4.51 − 150 = 269.51

1. For the partial credit card statement below, calculate the balance due. Assume that the billing period ended on 3/31 and that the next billing period ends on 4/30. The periodic interest rate is 1.3%.

Previous unpaid balance: $425		
New Purchases		
Date	Description	Charges
4/5	Dinner	$55
4/9	Repair	$78
4/16	Payment	$250 CR
4/17	Gas	$14
4/24	Dentist	$62

2. If you have a credit card on which there is an unpaid balance, calculate the finance charge. This may be a challenging exercise. To begin, find the due date of the bill. The number of days the balance was owed begins with the day after the due date. You will also need to determine the periodic interest rate.

3. Suppose you have a credit card balance of $500 and you pay $475 by the due date. For the next month (30 days), you do not make any credit card purchases. If the monthly interest rate is 1.5% and the average daily balance method is used, how much interest is owed for not paying the entire bill? What percent of the balance that was due ($25) is the interest owed?

Chapter Summary

Key Words   *Statistics* is the branch of mathematics concerned with *data,* or numerical information.

A *graph* provides a pictorial representation of data. A *pictograph* uses symbols to represent information.

A *circle graph* represents data by the size of the sectors.

A *bar graph* represents data by the height of the bars.

A *broken-line graph* represents data by the position of the lines and shows trends and comparisons.

A *histogram* is a special kind of bar graph. In a histogram, the width of each bar corresponds to a range of numbers called a *class interval.* The height of each bar corresponds to the number of occurrences of data in each class interval and is called the *class frequency.*

A *frequency polygon* is a graph that displays information in a manner similar to a histogram. A dot is placed above the center of each class interval at a height corresponding to that class's frequency.

The *mean* of a set of data is the sum of the numbers in the set divided by the number of items in the set.

The *median* separates a list of numbers so that there are the same number of values below the median as there are above the median.

The *first quartile* Q_1 separates a list of numbers so that one-fourth of the data are below that number.

The *third quartile* Q_3 separates a list of numbers so that one-fourth of the data are above that number.

The *interquartile range* is the difference between Q_3 and Q_1.

A *box-and-whiskers plot* shows five numbers of a data set: the lowest number, the first quartile, the median, the third quartile, and the largest number.

Essential Rules   *To Find the Mean*

To find the mean of a set of numbers, divide the sum of the numbers by the number of addends.

$$\text{Mean} = \frac{\text{sum of numbers}}{\text{number of addends}}$$

To Find the Median

To find the median, arrange the numbers from smallest to largest and locate the middle number. When there are two middle numbers, the median is the average of those two numbers.

To Find Q_1

Arrange the numbers from smallest to largest and locate the median. Q_1 is the median of the lower half of the data.

To Find Q_3

Arrange the numbers from smallest to largest and locate the median. Q_3 is the median of the upper half of the data.

To Find the Interquartile range

Interquartile range $= Q_3 - Q_1$

Chapter Review

The circle graph in Figure 37 shows the approximate amount of money government agencies spent on maintaining Internet Web sites for a 3-year period.

1. Find the total amount of money these agencies spent on maintaining Web sites.

2. What is the ratio of the amount spent by the Department of Commerce to the amount spent by the EPA?

3. What percent of the total money spent did NASA spend? Round to the nearest tenth of a percent.

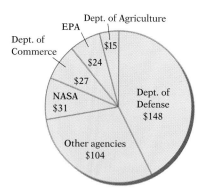

Figure 37 Millions of dollars federal agencies spend on Web sites

Source: General Accounting Office

The double-broken-line graph in Figure 38 shows the approximate prices for 1 ounce of gold and 1 ounce of platinum for a 4-year period.

4. Find the difference in price per ounce between gold and platinum in 1993.

5. What was the price of 1 ounce of gold and 1 ounce of platinum in 1996?

6. Find the ratio of the price of gold in 1995 to the price of platinum in 1995.

Figure 38 Price of gold and platinum

The frequency polygon in Figure 39 shows the range of scores for the first 80 games of a season for the New York Knicks basketball team.

7. Find the number of games in which fewer than 100 points were scored by the Knicks.

8. What is the ratio of the number of games in which 90 to 100 points were scored to the number of games in which 110 to 120 points were scored?

9. In what percent of the games were 110 points or more scored? Round to the nearest tenth of a percent.

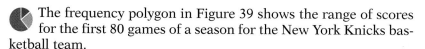

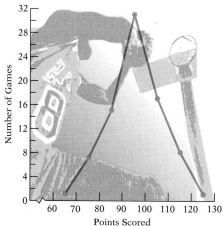

Figure 39

Source: *Sports Illustrated* Web site at http://CNNSI.com/

The pictograph in Figure 40 shows the number of athletes from Russia who earned a medal in the 1996 Summer Olympic games.

10. Find the total number of athletes from Russia earning medals at the Olympic games.

11. What is the ratio of the number of athletes receiving a gold medal to the number receiving a bronze medal?

12. What percent of the total number of Russian athletes received a silver medal? Round to the nearest tenth of a percent.

The double bar graph in Figure 41 shows the total days of operation and the days of full operation of ski resorts in different regions of the country.

13. Find the difference between the total days of operation and the days of full operation for Midwest ski areas.

14. What percent of the total days of operation was the days of full operation for the Rocky Mountain ski areas?

15. Which region had the lowest number of days of full operation? How many days of full operation did this region have?

Based on a Gallup poll, the number of hours 46 surveyed people slept during a typical weekday night are shown in the histogram in Figure 42.

16. How many people slept 8 hours or more?

17. Find the ratio of the number of people who slept 6 or fewer hours to the number of people who slept 9 or more hours.

18. What percent of the surveyed people slept 7 hours? Round to the nearest tenth of a percent.

19. The heart rates of 24 women tennis players were measured after each of them had run one-quarter of a mile. The results are listed in the table below.

80	82	99	91	93	87	103	94	73	96	86	80
97	94	108	81	100	109	91	84	78	96	96	100

Find the mean, median, and mode for this distribution.

20. For the data in Exercise 19, find the range and the interquartile range.

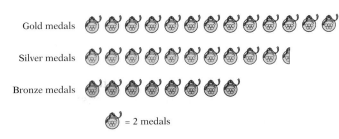

Gold medals
Silver medals
Bronze medals

= 2 medals

Figure 40 Russian Olympic medal winners

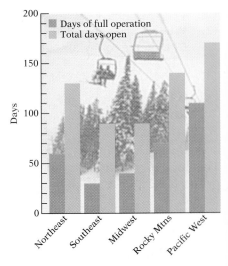

Figure 41

Source: Economic Analysis of United States Ski Areas

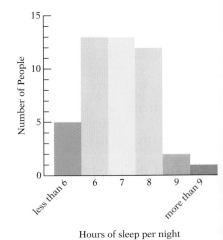

Hours of sleep per night

Figure 42

Chapter Test

Forty college students were surveyed to see how much money they spent each week on dining out in restaurants. The results are recorded in the frequency polygon shown in Figure 43.

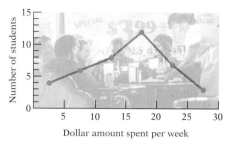

Figure 43

1. How many students spent between $15 and $25 per week?

2. Find the ratio of the number of students who spent between $10 and $15 to the number who spent between $15 and $20.

3. What percent of the students surveyed spent less than $15 per week?

The pictograph in Figure 44 is based on the results of a Gallup poll survey of married couples. Each individual was asked to give a letter grade to the marriage.

4. Find the total number of people who were surveyed.

5. Find the ratio of the number of people who gave their marriage a B to those who gave it a C.

6. What percent of the total number of people surveyed gave their marriage an A?

Figure 44 Survey of married couples rating their marriage

The double-bar graph in Figure 45 shows the number of trucks sold in the United States during the 4 quarters of 1995 and 1996.

7. Find the number of trucks sold in the third quarter of 1995.

8. Find the difference between the number of trucks sold in the second quarter of 1996 and the second quarter of 1995.

9. Were more trucks sold in the United States in 1995 or in 1996?

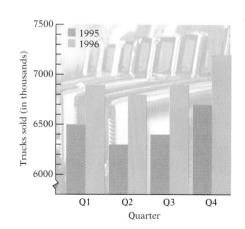

Figure 45

Source: American Automobile Manufacturers Association

The circle graph in Figure 46 shows the number of people in different generations in the United States.

10. Using this graph, determine the population of the United States.

11. What percent of the U.S. population belongs to Generation X? Round to the nearest tenth of a percent.

12. Which is the larger segment of the population: those born before 1965 or those born in 1965 or later?

The histogram in Figure 47 shows the per capita incomes in the United States for all 50 states.

13. How many states have per capita incomes between $16,000 and $22,000?

14. What percent of the states have a per capita income that is between $19,000 and $22,000?

15. What percent of the states have a per capita income that is $25,000 or more?

The double-broken-line graph in Figure 48 shows the quarterly income for Nordstrom department stores for the years 1995 and 1996.

16. What was Nordstrom's third-quarter income for 1995?

17. In which quarters was Nordstrom's quarterly income in 1996 less than the quarterly income in 1995?

18. Find the difference between Nordstrom's fourth-quarter income in 1995 and the income in the fourth quarter of 1996.

19. The length of time (in days) that various batteries operated a portable CD player continuously are given in the table below.

| 2.9 | 2.4 | 3.1 | 2.5 | 2.6 | 2.0 | 3.0 | 2.3 | 2.4 | 2.7 |
| 2.0 | 2.4 | 2.6 | 2.7 | 2.1 | 2.9 | 2.8 | 2.4 | 2.0 | 2.8 |

Find the mean and median for this distribution.

20. For the data in Exercise 19, draw a box-and-whiskers plot.

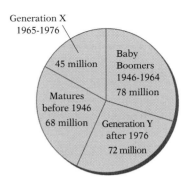

Figure 46 Number of people in United States by year born

Source: *Time* Magazine, June 9, 1997

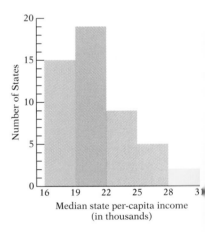

Figure 47

Source: Bureau of Labor Statistics

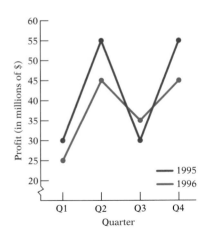

Figure 48 Quarterly income for Nordstrom's

Cumulative Review

1. Simplify: $2^2 \cdot 3^3 \cdot 5$

2. Simplify: $3^2 \cdot (5 - 2) \div 3 + 5$

3. Find the LCM of 24 and 40.

4. Write $\frac{60}{144}$ in simplest form.

5. Find the total of $4\frac{1}{2}$, $2\frac{3}{8}$, and $5\frac{1}{5}$.

6. Subtract: $12\frac{5}{8} - 7\frac{11}{12}$

7. Multiply: $\frac{5}{8} \times 3\frac{1}{5}$

8. Find the quotient of $3\frac{1}{5}$ and $4\frac{1}{4}$.

9. Simplify: $\frac{5}{8} \div \left(\frac{3}{4} - \frac{2}{3}\right) + \frac{3}{4}$

10. Write two hundred nine and three hundred five thousandths in standard form.

11. Find the product of 4.092 and 0.69.

12. Convert $16\frac{2}{3}$ to a decimal. Round to the nearest hundredth.

13. Write "330 miles on 12.5 gallons of gas" as a unit rate.

14. Solve the proportion: $\frac{n}{5} = \frac{16}{25}$

15. Write $\frac{4}{5}$ as a percent.

16. 8 is 10% of what?

17. What is 38% of 43?

18. What percent of 75 is 30?

19. Tanim Kamal, a salesperson at a department store, receives $100 per week plus 2% commission on sales. Find the income for a week in which Tanim had $27,500 in sales.

20. A life insurance policy costs $4.15 for every $1000 of insurance. At this rate, what is the cost for $50,000 of life insurance?

21. A contractor borrowed $125,000 for 6 months at an annual simple interest rate of 11%. Find the interest due on the loan.

22. A compact disk player with a cost of $180 is sold for $279. Find the mark-up rate.

23. The circle graph in Figure 49 shows how a family's monthly income of $3000 is budgeted. How much is budgeted for food?

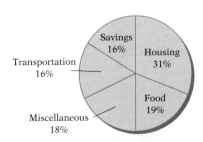

Figure 49   Budget for a monthly income of $3000

24. The double-broken-line graph in Figure 50 shows two students' scores on 5 math tests of 30 problems each. Find the difference between the numbers of problems the two students answered correctly on Test 1.

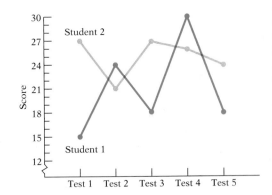

Figure 50

25. The average daily high temperatures for a week in Newtown were 56°, 72°, 80°, 75°, 68°, 62°, and 74°. Find the mean high temperature for the week. Round to the nearest tenth of a degree.

26. The salaries for six teachers in a small school are $27,000, $31,000, $38,500, $32,300, $30,200, and $35,000. Find the median salary.

8.1 Length

Objective A   *To convert measurements of length in the U.S. Customary System* ·· CT

POINT OF INTEREST

The ancient Greeks devised the foot measurement, which they usually divided into 16 fingers. It was the Romans who subdivided the foot into 12 units called inches. The word *inch* is derived from the Latin word *uncia,* meaning a twelfth part.

The Romans also used a unit called "pace" which equaled two steps. One thousand paces equaled one mile. The word for mile is derived from the Latin word *mille,* which means 1000.

A **measurement** includes a number and a unit.

$$
\begin{array}{cc}
3 & \text{feet} \\
7 & \text{miles} \\
12 & \text{yards} \\
\underbrace{} & \underbrace{} \\
\text{number} & \text{unit}
\end{array}
$$

Standard units of measurement have been established to simplify trade and commerce.

The unit of length, or distance, that is called the **yard** was originally defined as the length of a specified bronze bar located in London.

The standard U.S. Customary System units of length are **inch, foot, yard,** and **mile.** Equivalences between units of length in the U.S. Customary System are

$$
\begin{aligned}
12 \text{ inches (in.)} &= 1 \text{ foot (ft)} \\
3 \text{ ft} &= 1 \text{ yard (yd)} \\
36 \text{ in.} &= 1 \text{ yard (yd)} \\
5280 \text{ ft} &= 1 \text{ mile (mi)}
\end{aligned}
$$

These equivalences can be used to form conversion rates to change one unit of measurement to another. For example, because 3 ft = 1 yd, the conversion rates $\frac{3 \text{ ft}}{1 \text{ yd}}$ and $\frac{1 \text{ yd}}{3 \text{ ft}}$ are each equivalent to 1.

➡ Convert 27 ft to yards.

$$27 \text{ ft} = 27 \text{ ft} \times \boxed{\frac{1 \text{ yd}}{3 \text{ ft}}}$$

$$= 27 \text{ ft} \times \frac{1 \text{ yd}}{3 \text{ ft}}$$

$$= \frac{27 \text{ yd}}{3}$$

$$= 9 \text{ yd}$$

➡ Convert 5 yd to feet.

$$5 \text{ yd} = 5 \text{ yd} \times \boxed{\frac{3 \text{ ft}}{1 \text{ yd}}}$$

$$= 5 \text{ yd} \times \frac{3 \text{ ft}}{1 \text{ yd}}$$

$$= \frac{15 \text{ ft}}{1}$$

$$= 15 \text{ ft}$$

Note that in the conversion rate chosen, the unit in the numerator is the same as the unit desired in the answer. The unit in the denominator is the same as the unit in the given measurement.

Example 1   Convert 40 in. to feet.

Solution $40 \text{ in.} = 40 \text{ in.} \times \dfrac{1 \text{ ft}}{12 \text{ in.}} = 3\dfrac{1}{3} \text{ ft}$

You Try It 1   Convert 60 in. to feet.

Your solution

Example 2   Convert 36 ft to yards.

Solution $36 \text{ ft} = 36 \text{ ft} \times \dfrac{1 \text{ yd}}{3 \text{ ft}} = 12 \text{ yd}$

You Try It 2   Convert 14 ft to yards.

Your solution

Example 3   Convert $3\dfrac{1}{4}$ yd to feet.

Solution $3\dfrac{1}{4} \text{ yd} = 3\dfrac{1}{4} \text{ yd} \times \dfrac{3 \text{ ft}}{1 \text{ yd}} = 9\dfrac{3}{4} \text{ ft}$

You Try It 3   Convert 9800 ft to miles.

Your solution

Solutions on p. S19

Objective B   *To perform arithmetic operations with measurements of length* ....

When performing arithmetic operations with measurements of length, write the answer in simplest form. For example, 1 ft 14 in. should be written as 2 ft 2 in.

➡ Convert: 50 in. = _____ ft _____ in.

$$\begin{array}{r} 4 \text{ ft } 2 \text{ in.} \\ 12 \overline{)\ 50} \\ -48 \\ \hline 2 \end{array}$$

* Because 12 in. = 1 ft, divide 50 in. by 12. The whole-number part of the quotient is the number of feet. The remainder is the number of inches.

50 in. = 4 ft 2 in.

Example 4   Convert:
17 in. = _____ ft _____ in.

Solution
$$\begin{array}{r} 1 \text{ ft } 5 \text{ in.} \\ 12 \overline{)\ 17} \\ -12 \\ \hline 5 \end{array}$$

17 in. = 1 ft 5 in.

You Try It 4   Convert:
42 in. = _____ ft _____ in.

Your solution

Example 5   Convert:
31 ft = _____ yd _____ ft

Solution
$$\begin{array}{r} 10 \text{ yd } 1 \text{ ft} \\ 3 \overline{)\ 31} \\ -30 \\ \hline 1 \end{array}$$

31 ft = 10 yd 1 ft

You Try It 5   Convert:
14 ft = _____ yd _____ ft

Your solution

Solutions on p. S19

Example 6 Find the sum of 4 ft 4 in. and 1 ft 11 in.

Solution
$$\begin{array}{r} 4 \text{ ft} \quad 4 \text{ in.} \\ +\ 1 \text{ ft} \ 11 \text{ in.} \\ \hline 5 \text{ ft } 15 \text{ in.} = 6 \text{ ft } 3 \text{ in.} \end{array}$$

You Try It 6 Find the sum of 3 ft 5 in. and 4 ft 9 in.

Your solution

Example 7 Subtract: 9 ft 6 in. − 3 ft 8 in.

Solution

$$\begin{array}{r} \overset{8 \text{ ft}}{\cancel{9}} \text{ft} \ \overset{18 \text{ in.}}{\cancel{6}\text{in.}} \\ -\ 3 \text{ ft} \quad 8 \text{ in.} \\ \hline 5 \text{ ft } 10 \text{ in.} \end{array}$$

• **Borrow 1 ft (12 in.) from 9 ft and add to 6 in.**

You Try It 7 Subtract: 4 ft 2 in. − 1 ft 8 in.

Your solution

Example 8 Multiply: 3 yd 2 ft × 4

Solution
$$\begin{array}{r} 3 \text{ yd } 2 \text{ ft} \\ \times \qquad 4 \\ \hline 12 \text{ yd } 8 \text{ ft} = 14 \text{ yd } 2 \text{ ft} \end{array}$$

You Try It 8 Multiply: 4 yd 1 ft × 8

Your solution

Example 9 Find the quotient of 4 ft 3 in. and 3.

Solution

$$\begin{array}{r} 1 \text{ ft} \qquad 5 \text{ in.} \\ 3 \overline{)\ 4 \text{ ft} \qquad 3 \text{ in.}} \\ -\ 3 \text{ ft} \\ \hline 1 \text{ ft} = 12 \text{ in.} \\ 15 \text{ in.} \\ -15 \text{ in.} \\ \hline 0 \end{array}$$

You Try It 9 Find the quotient of 7 yd 1 ft and 2.

Your solution

Example 10 Multiply: $2\frac{3}{4}$ ft × 3

Solution
$$2\frac{3}{4} \text{ ft} \times 3 = \frac{11}{4} \text{ ft} \times 3$$
$$= \frac{33}{4} \text{ ft}$$
$$= 8\frac{1}{4} \text{ ft}$$

You Try It 10 Subtract: $6\frac{1}{4}$ ft − $3\frac{2}{3}$ ft

Your solution

Solutions on pp. S19–S20

Objective C   To solve application problems ·································

Example 11
A concrete block is 9 in. high. How many rows of blocks are required for a retaining wall that is 6 ft high?

Strategy
To find the number of rows of blocks, convert 9 in. to feet. Then divide the height of the wall (6 ft) by the height of each block.

Solution

9 in. $= \dfrac{9 \text{ in.}}{1} \cdot \dfrac{1 \text{ ft}}{12 \text{ in.}} = 0.75$ ft

$\dfrac{6 \text{ ft}}{0.75 \text{ ft}} = 8$

The wall will have 8 rows of blocks.

You Try It 11
The floor of a storage room is being tiled. Eight tiles, each a 9-inch square, fit across the width of the floor. Find the width in feet of the storage room.

Your strategy

Your solution

Example 12
A plumber used 3 ft 9 in., 2 ft 6 in., and 11 in. of copper tubing to install a sink. Find the total length of copper tubing used.

Strategy
To find the total length of copper tubing used, add the three lengths of copper tubing (3 ft 9 in., 2 ft 6 in., and 11 in.).

Solution

```
   3 ft   9 in.
   2 ft   6 in.
+         11 in.
   5 ft 26 in. = 7 ft 2 in.
```

The plumber used 7 ft 2 in. of copper tubing.

You Try It 12
A board 9 ft 8 in. is cut into four pieces of equal length. How long is each piece?

Your strategy

Your solution

Solutions on p. S20

8.1 Exercises

· ·

Objective A

Convert.

1. 6 ft = _____ in.

2. 9 ft = _____ in.

3. 30 in. = _____ ft

4. 64 in. = _____ ft

5. 13 yd = _____ ft

6. $4\frac{1}{2}$ yd = _____ ft

7. 16 ft = _____ yd

8. $4\frac{1}{2}$ ft = _____ yd

9. $2\frac{1}{3}$ yd = _____ in.

10. 5 yd = _____ in.

11. 120 in. = _____ yd

12. 66 in. = _____ yd

13. 2 mi = _____ ft

14. $1\frac{1}{2}$ mi = _____ ft

15. $7\frac{1}{2}$ in. = _____ ft

Objective B

Perform the arithmetic operation.

16. 100 in. =
___ ft ___ in.

17. 6400 ft =
___ mi ___ ft

18. 15 in. =
___ ft ___ in.

19.   6 ft 7 in.
  + 3 ft 4 in.

20.   9 ft 11 in.
  + 3 ft 6 in.

21.   5 ft 3 in.
  − 2 ft 6 in.

22.   9 yd 1 ft
  − 3 yd 2 ft

23.   2 ft 5 in.
  ×   6

24. $3\frac{2}{3}$ ft × 4

25. 2)‾5‾f‾t‾4‾i‾n‾.

26. $12\frac{1}{2}$ in. ÷ 3

27. $4\frac{2}{3}$ ft + $6\frac{1}{2}$ ft

28.   3 yd 2 ft
  + 6 yd 2 ft

29.   1 mi 4200 ft
  + 2 mi 3600 ft

30.   5 yd 1 ft
  − 2 yd 2 ft

Objective C   *Application Problems*

31. A kitchen counter is to be covered with tile that is 4 in. square. How many tiles can be placed along one row of a counter top that is 4 ft 8 in. long?

32. Thirty-two yards of material were used for making pleated draperies. How many feet of material were used?

33. Find the missing dimension.

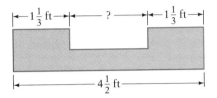

34. Find the total length of the shaft.

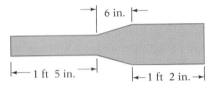

35. What length of material is needed to drill two holes 3 in. in diameter and leave $\frac{1}{2}$ in. between the holes and on either side as shown in the diagram?

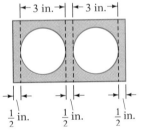

36. Find the missing dimension in the figure.

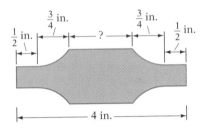

37. A board $6\frac{2}{3}$ ft long is cut into four equal pieces. How long is each piece?

38. How long must a board be if four pieces, each 3 ft 4 in. long, are to be cut from it?

39. A picture is 1 ft 9 in. high and 1 ft 6 in. wide. Find the length of framing needed to frame the picture.

40. You bought 32 ft of baseboard to install in the kitchen of your house. How many inches of baseboard did you purchase?

41. Forty-five bricks, each 9 in. long, are laid end to end to make the base for a wall. Find the length of the wall in feet.

42. A roof is constructed with nine rafters, each 8 ft 4 in. long. Find the total number of feet of material needed to build the rafters.

APPLYING THE CONCEPTS

43. There are approximately 2 billion adults living on Earth. If an average adult is 19 in. in width (from shoulder to shoulder) and all the adults are standing shoulder to shoulder, could the line reach around Earth at the equator, a distance of approximately 25,000 mi?

44. How good are you at estimating lengths or distances? Estimate the length of a pencil, the width of your room, the length of a block, and the distance to the grocery store. Then measure the lengths and compare the results with your estimates.

8.2   Weight

Objective A   *To convert measurements of weight in the U.S. Customary System* ....

Weight is a measure of how strongly the earth is pulling on an object. The unit of weight called the **pound** is defined as the weight of a standard solid kept at the Bureau of Standards in Washington, D.C. The U.S. Customary System units of weight are **ounce, pound,** and **ton.**

Equivalences between units of weight in the U.S. Customary System are

$$16 \text{ ounces (oz)} = 1 \text{ pound (lb)}$$
$$2000 \text{ lb} = 1 \text{ ton}$$

These equivalences can be used to form conversion rates to change one unit of measurement to another. For example, because 16 oz = 1 lb, the conversion rates $\frac{16 \text{ oz}}{1 \text{ lb}}$ and $\frac{1 \text{ lb}}{16 \text{ oz}}$ are each equivalent to 1.

➡ Convert 62 oz to pounds.

$$62 \text{ oz} = 62 \text{ oz} \times \boxed{\frac{1 \text{ lb}}{16 \text{ oz}}}$$

$$= \frac{62 \text{ oz}}{1} \times \frac{1 \text{ lb}}{16 \text{ oz}}$$

$$= \frac{62 \text{ lb}}{16}$$

$$= 3\frac{7}{8} \text{ lb}$$

• The conversion rate must contain lb (the unit desired in the answer) in the numerator and oz (the original unit) in the denominator.

Example 1   Convert $3\frac{1}{2}$ tons to pounds.

Solution $3\frac{1}{2} \text{ tons} = 3\frac{1}{2} \text{ tons} \times \frac{2000 \text{ lb}}{1 \text{ ton}}$

$= 7000 \text{ lb}$

You Try It 1   Convert 3 lb to ounces.

Your solution

Example 2   Convert 42 oz to pounds.

Solution $42 \text{ oz} = 42 \text{ oz} \times \frac{1 \text{ lb}}{16 \text{ oz}}$

$= \frac{42 \text{ lb}}{16} = 2\frac{5}{8} \text{ lb}$

You Try It 2   Convert 4200 lb to tons.

Your solution

Solutions on p. S20

Objective B   *To perform arithmetic operations with*
measurements of weight ....

When performing arithmetic operations with measurements of weight, write the answer in simplest form. For example, 1 lb 22 oz should be written 2 lb 6 oz.

Example 3   Find the difference between
14 lb 5 oz and 8 lb 14 oz.

Solution

$$
\begin{array}{r}
\overset{13\text{ lb}}{14\text{ lb}}\ \overset{21\text{ oz}}{5\text{ oz}} \\
-\ \ 8\text{ lb }14\text{ oz} \\
\hline
5\text{ lb }\ \ 7\text{ oz}
\end{array}
$$

• Borrow 1 lb
(16 oz) from
14 lb and add
to 5 oz.

Example 4   Divide: 7 lb 14 oz ÷ 3

Solution

$$
\begin{array}{r}
2\text{ lb}\ \ \ \ 10\text{ oz} \\
3\overline{)\ 7\text{ lb}\ \ \ \ 14\text{ oz}} \\
-6\text{ lb} \\
\hline
1\text{ lb}\ =\ 16\text{ oz} \\
\hline
30\text{ oz} \\
-30\text{ oz} \\
\hline
0
\end{array}
$$

You Try It 3   Find the difference between
7 lb 1 oz and 3 lb 4 oz.

Your solution

You Try It 4   Multiply: 3 lb 6 oz × 4

Your solution

Solutions on p. S20

Objective C   *To solve application problems* ....

Example 5
Sirina Jasper purchased 4 lb 8 oz of oat bran and 2 lb 11 oz of wheat bran. She plans to blend the two brans and then repackage the mixture in 3-ounce packages for a diet supplement. How many 3-oz packages can she make?

Strategy
To find the number of 3-oz packages:

• Add the amount of oat bran (4 lb 8 oz) to the amount of wheat bran (2 lb 11 oz).
• Convert the sum to ounces.
• Divide the total ounces by the weight of each package (3 oz).

Solution

$$
\begin{array}{l}
4\text{ lb }\ \ 8\text{ oz} \\
2\text{ lb }11\text{ oz} \\
\hline
6\text{ lb }19\text{ oz} = 7\text{ lb }3\text{ oz} = 115\text{ oz}
\end{array}
$$

$$\frac{115\text{ oz}}{3\text{ oz}} \cong 38.3$$

She can make 38 packages.

You Try It 5
Find the weight in pounds of 12 bars of soap. Each bar weighs 9 oz.

Your strategy

Your solution

Solution on p. S20

8.2 Exercises

. . . .

Objective A

Convert.

1. 64 oz = _____ lb

2. 36 oz = _____ lb

3. 4 lb = _____ oz

4. 7 lb = _____ oz

5. 3200 lb = _____ tons

6. 7000 lb = _____ tons

7. 6 tons = _____ lb

8. $1\frac{1}{4}$ tons = _____ lb

9. 66 oz = _____ lb

10. 90 oz = _____ lb

11. $1\frac{1}{2}$ lb = _____ oz

12. $2\frac{5}{8}$ lb = _____ oz

13. $1\frac{3}{10}$ tons = _____ lb

14. $\frac{4}{5}$ ton = _____ lb

15. 500 lb = _____ ton

16. 5000 lb = _____ tons

17. 180 oz = _____ lb

18. 12 oz = _____ lb

Objective B

Perform the arithmetic operation.

19. 9000 lb =
_____ tons _____ lb

20. 85 oz =
_____ lb _____ oz

21. 40 oz =
_____ lb _____ oz

22. $\begin{array}{r} 4\text{ lb }7\text{ oz} \\ +\ 3\text{ lb }12\text{ oz} \\ \hline \end{array}$

23. $\begin{array}{r} 1\text{ ton }800\text{ lb} \\ +\ 3\text{ tons }1600\text{ lb} \\ \hline \end{array}$

24. $\begin{array}{r} 7\text{ lb }5\text{ oz} \\ -\ 3\text{ lb }8\text{ oz} \\ \hline \end{array}$

25. $\begin{array}{r} 3\text{ tons }500\text{ lb} \\ -\ 1\text{ ton }\ 800\text{ lb} \\ \hline \end{array}$

26. $\begin{array}{r} 3\text{ lb }6\text{ oz} \\ \times\ \ \ \ \ 4 \\ \hline \end{array}$

27. $5\frac{1}{2}$ lb × 6

28. $2\overline{)3\text{ lb }8\text{ oz}}$

29. $4\frac{2}{3}$ lb × 3

30. $\begin{array}{r} 7\text{ lb }7\text{ oz} \\ +\ 6\text{ lb }9\text{ oz} \\ \hline \end{array}$

31. $\begin{array}{r} 6\frac{1}{2}\text{ oz} \\ +\ 2\frac{1}{2}\text{ oz} \\ \hline \end{array}$

32. $\begin{array}{r} 6\frac{3}{8}\text{ lb} \\ -\ 2\frac{5}{6}\text{ lb} \\ \hline \end{array}$

33. 5 lb 12 oz ÷ 4

Objective C   *Application Problems*

34. A machinist has 25 iron rods to mill. Each rod weighs 20 oz. Find the total weight of the rods in pounds.

35. A fireplace brick weighs $2\frac{1}{2}$ lb. What is the weight of a load of 800 bricks?

36. A college bookstore received 1200 textbooks, each weighing 9 oz. Find the total weight of the 1200 textbooks in pounds.

37. A 4 × 4-inch tile weighs 7 oz. Find the weight in pounds of a package of 144 tiles.

38. A farmer ordered 20 tons of feed for 100 cattle. After 15 days, the farmer has 5 tons of feed left. How many pounds of food has each cow eaten per day?

39. A case of soft drink contains 24 cans, each weighing 6 oz. Find the weight, in pounds, of the case of soft drink.

40. A baby weighed 7 lb 8 oz at birth. At 6 months of age, the baby weighed 15 lb 13 oz. Find the baby's increase in weight during the 6 months.

41. Shampoo weighing 5 lb 4 oz is divided equally and poured into four containers. How much shampoo is in each container?

42. A steel rod weighing 16 lb 11 oz is cut into three pieces. Find the weight of each piece of steel rod.

43. Find the cost of a ham roast weighing 5 lb 10 oz if the price per pound is $2.40.

44. A candy store buys candy weighing 12 lb for $14.40. The candy is repackaged and sold in 6-ounce packages for $1.15 each. Find the markup on the 12 lb of candy.

45. A manuscript weighing 2 lb 3 oz is mailed at the postage rate of $.25 per ounce. Find the cost of mailing the manuscript.

APPLYING THE CONCEPTS

46. Write a paragraph describing the growing need for precision in our measurements as civilization progressed. Include a discussion of the need for precision in the space industry.

47. Estimate the weight of a nickel, a textbook, a friend, and a car. Then find the actual weights and compare them with your estimates.

8.3 Capacity

Objective A   To convert measurements of capacity in the U.S. Customary System ....

Liquid substances are measured in units of **capacity.** The standard U.S. Customary units of capacity are the **fluid ounce, cup, pint, quart,** and **gallon.** Equivalences between units of capacity in the U.S. Customary System are

$$8 \text{ fluid ounces (fl oz)} = 1 \text{ cup (c)}$$
$$2 \text{ c} = 1 \text{ pint (pt)}$$
$$2 \text{ pt} = 1 \text{ quart (qt)}$$
$$4 \text{ qt} = 1 \text{ gallon (gal)}$$

These equivalences can be used to form conversion rates to change one unit of measurement to another. For example, because 8 fl oz = 1 c, the conversion rates $\frac{8 \text{ fl oz}}{1 \text{ c}}$ and $\frac{1 \text{ c}}{8 \text{ fl oz}}$ are each equivalent to 1.

➡ Convert 36 fl oz to cups.

$$36 \text{ fl oz} = 36 \text{ fl oz} \times \boxed{\frac{1 \text{ c}}{8 \text{ fl oz}}}$$

$$= \frac{36 \text{ fl oz}}{1} \times \frac{1 \text{ c}}{8 \text{ fl oz}}$$

$$= \frac{36 \text{ c}}{8}$$

$$= 4\frac{1}{2} \text{ c}$$

- The conversion rate must contain c in the numerator and fl oz in the denominator.

➡ Convert 3 qt to cups.

$$3 \text{ qt} = 3 \text{ qt} \times \boxed{\frac{2 \text{ pt}}{1 \text{ qt}}} \times \boxed{\frac{2 \text{ c}}{1 \text{ pt}}}$$

$$= \frac{3 \text{ qt}}{1} \times \frac{2 \text{ pt}}{1 \text{ qt}} \times \frac{2 \text{ c}}{1 \text{ pt}}$$

$$= \frac{12 \text{ c}}{1}$$

$$= 12 \text{ c}$$

- The direct equivalence is not given above. Use two conversion rates. First convert quarts to pints and then convert pints to cups. The unit in the denominator of the second conversion rate and the unit in the numerator of the first conversion rate must be the same in order to cancel.

Example 1   Convert 42 c to quarts.

Solution $42 \text{ c} = 42 \text{ c} \times \frac{1 \text{ pt}}{2 \text{ c}} \times \frac{1 \text{ qt}}{2 \text{ pt}}$

$$= \frac{42 \text{ qt}}{4} = 10\frac{1}{2} \text{ qt}$$

You Try It 1   Convert 18 pt to gallons.

Your solution

Solution on p. S20

Objective B   ***To perform arithmetic operations with
measurements of capacity*** ....

When performing arithmetic operations with measurements of capacity, write
the answer in simplest form. For example, 1 c 12 fl oz should be written as 2 c
4 fl oz.

Example 2   What is 4 gal 1 qt decreased by
2 gal 3 qt?

Solution

$$
\begin{array}{r}
\overset{3 \text{ gal}}{\cancel{4 \text{ gal}}} \ \overset{5 \text{ qt}}{\cancel{1 \text{ qt}}} \\
-\ 2 \text{ gal } 3 \text{ qt} \\
\hline
1 \text{ gal } 2 \text{ qt}
\end{array}
$$

• **Borrow 1 gal
(4 qt) from
4 gal and add
to 1 qt.**

You Try It 2   Find the quotient of
4 gal 2 qt and 3.

Your solution

Solution on p. S20

Objective C   ***To solve application problems*** ....

Example 3
A can of apple juice contains 25 fl oz. Find
the number of quarts of apple juice in a case
of 24 cans.

Strategy
To find the number of quarts of apple juice
in one case:

• Multiply the number of cans (24) by the
number of fluid ounces per can (25) to
find the total number of fluid ounces in
the case.
• Convert the number of fluid ounces in the
case to quarts.

Solution
24 × 25 fl oz = 600 fl oz

$$
600 \text{ fl oz} = \frac{600 \ \cancel{\text{fl oz}}}{1} \cdot \frac{1 \ \cancel{c}}{8 \ \cancel{\text{fl oz}}} \cdot \frac{1 \ \cancel{\text{pt}}}{2 \ \cancel{c}} \cdot \frac{1 \text{ qt}}{2 \ \cancel{\text{pt}}}
$$

$$
= \frac{600 \text{ qt}}{32} = 18\frac{3}{4} \text{ qt}
$$

One case of apple juice contains $18\frac{3}{4}$ qt.

You Try It 3
Five students are going backpacking in the
desert. Each student requires 3 qt of water
per day. How many gallons of water should
they take for a 3-day trip?

Your strategy

Your solution

Solution on p. S20

8.3 Exercises

. . . .

Objective A

Convert.

1. 60 fl oz = _____ c

2. 48 fl oz = _____ c

3. 3 c = _____ fl oz

4. $2\frac{1}{2}$ c = _____ fl oz

5. 8 c = _____ pt

6. 5 c = _____ pt

7. $3\frac{1}{2}$ pt = _____ c

8. 12 pt = _____ qt

9. 22 qt = _____ gal

10. 10 qt = _____ gal

11. $2\frac{1}{4}$ gal = _____ qt

12. 7 gal = _____ qt

13. $7\frac{1}{2}$ pt = _____ qt

14. $3\frac{1}{2}$ qt = _____ pt

15. 20 fl oz = _____ pt

16. $1\frac{1}{2}$ pt = _____ fl oz

17. 17 c = _____ qt

18. $1\frac{1}{2}$ qt = _____ c

Objective B

Perform the arithmetic operation.

19. 14 qt =
_____ gal _____ qt

20. 9 pt =
_____ qt _____ pt

21. 5 pt =
_____ qt _____ pt

22. 　3 gal 2 qt
　+ 4 gal 3 qt

23. 　4 qt 1 pt
　+ 2 qt 1 pt

24. 　3 gal 1 qt
　− 1 gal 2 qt

25. 　3 c 3 fl oz
　− 2 c 5 fl oz

26. 　2 qt 1 pt
　× 　　5

27. $3\frac{1}{2}$ pt × 5

28. 5)$\overline{6\text{ gal }1\text{ qt}}$

29. $3\frac{1}{2}$ gal ÷ 4

30. 　5 c 3 fl oz
　+ 3 c 6 fl oz

Perform the arithmetic operation.

31.   3 gal 3 qt
        + 1 gal 2 qt

32.   4 c 6 fl oz
        − 2 c 7 fl oz

33.   3 gal
        − 1 gal 2 qt

34. $1\frac{1}{2}$ pt + $2\frac{2}{3}$ pt

35. $4\frac{1}{2}$ gal − $1\frac{3}{4}$ gal

36. 2)3 gal 2 qt

Objective C   *Application Problems*

37. Sixty adults will attend a church social. Each adult will drink 2 c of coffee. How many gallons of coffee should be prepared?

38. The Bayside Playhouse serves punch during intermission. Assume that 200 people will each drink 1 c of punch. How many gallons of punch should be ordered?

39. A solution needed for a class of 30 chemistry students required 72 fl oz of water, 16 fl oz of one solution, and 48 fl oz of another solution. Find the number of quarts of the final solution.

40. A cafeteria sold 124 cartons of milk in 1 day. Each carton contained 1 c of milk. How many quarts of milk were sold that day?

41. A farmer changed the oil in the tractor seven times during the year. Each oil change required 5 qt of oil. How many gallons of oil did the farmer use in the seven oil changes?

42. There are 24 cans in a case of tomato juice. Each can contains 10 fl oz of tomato juice. Find the number of 1-cup servings in the case of tomato juice.

43. One brand of orange juice costs $1.20 for 1 qt. Another brand costs $.96 for 24 fl oz. Which is the more economical purchase?

44. Mandy carried 6 qt of water for 3 days of desert camping. Water weighs 8 1/3 lb per gallon. Find the weight of water that she carried.

45. A department store bought hand lotion in 5-quart containers and then repackaged the lotion in 8-fluid-ounce bottles. The lotion and bottles cost $41.50, and each 8-fluid-ounce bottle was sold for $4.25. How much profit was made on each 5-quart package of lotion?

46. Orlando bought oil in 50-gallon containers for changing the oil in his customers' cars. He paid $80 for the 50 gal of oil and charged customers $1.05 per quart. Find the profit Orlando made on one 50-gallon container of oil.

APPLYING THE CONCEPTS

47. Define the following units: grain, dram, furlong, and rod. Give an example where each would be used.

48. Assume that you wanted to invent a new measuring system. Discuss some of the features that would have to be incorporated in the system.

8.4   Energy and Power

Objective A   *To use units of energy in the U.S. Customary System* ....

Energy can be defined as the ability to do work. Energy is stored in coal, in gasoline, in water behind a dam, and in one's own body.

One **foot-pound** (ft · lb) of energy from your body is required to lift 1 pound a distance of 1 foot.

To lift 50 lb a distance of 5 ft requires
$50 \times 5 = 250$ ft · lb of energy.

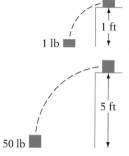

Consumer items that use energy, such as furnaces, stoves, and air conditioners, are rated in **British thermal units** (Btu).

A furnace with a rating of 35,000 Btu per hour releases 35,000 Btu of energy in one hour (1 h).

$$1 \text{ Btu} = 778 \text{ ft} \cdot \text{lb}$$

Therefore, the following conversion rate, equivalent to 1, can be written:

$$\frac{778 \text{ ft} \cdot \text{lb}}{1 \text{ Btu}} = 1$$

Example 1
Convert 250 Btu to foot-pounds.

Solution

$250 \text{ Btu} = 250 \ \cancel{\text{Btu}} \times \dfrac{778 \text{ ft} \cdot \text{lb}}{1 \ \cancel{\text{Btu}}}$

$\qquad = 194,500 \text{ ft} \cdot \text{lb}$

Example 2
Find the energy required for a 125-pound person to climb a mile-high mountain.

Solution
In climbing the mountain, the person is lifting 125 lb a distance of 5280 ft.

$\text{Energy} = 125 \text{ lb} \times 5280 \text{ ft}$

$\qquad\quad = 660,000 \text{ ft} \cdot \text{lb}$

You Try It 1
Convert 4.5 Btu to foot-pounds.

Your solution

You Try It 2
Find the energy required for a motor to lift 800 lb through a distance of 16 ft.

Your solution

Solutions on p. S21

Example 3
A furnace is rated at 80,000 Btu per hour.
How many foot-pounds of energy are
released in 1 h?

Solution

$$80,000 \text{ Btu} = 80,000 \text{ Btu} \times \frac{778 \text{ ft} \cdot \text{lb}}{1 \text{ Btu}}$$

$$= 62,240,000 \text{ ft} \cdot \text{lb}$$

You Try It 3
A furnace is rated at 56,000 Btu per hour.
How many foot-pounds of energy are
released in 1 h?

Your solution

Solution on p. S21

Objective B   To use units of power in the U.S. Customary System ....

Power is the rate at which work is done, or the rate at which energy is released.

Power is measured in **foot-pounds per second** $\left(\frac{\text{ft} \cdot \text{lb}}{\text{s}}\right)$. In each of the following examples, the amount of energy released is the same, but the time taken to release the energy is different; thus the power is different.

100 lb is lifted 10 ft in 10 s.

$$\text{Power} = \frac{10 \text{ ft} \times 100 \text{ lb}}{10 \text{ s}} = 100 \frac{\text{ft} \cdot \text{lb}}{\text{s}}$$

100 lb is lifted 10 ft in 5 s.

$$\text{Power} = \frac{10 \text{ ft} \times 100 \text{ lb}}{5 \text{ s}} = 200 \frac{\text{ft} \cdot \text{lb}}{\text{s}}$$

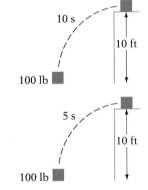

The U.S. Customary unit of power is the **horsepower.** A horse doing average work can pull 550 lb a distance of 1 ft in 1 s and can continue this work all day.

$$1 \text{ horsepower (hp)} = 550 \frac{\text{ft} \cdot \text{lb}}{\text{s}}$$

Example 4
Find the power needed to raise 300 lb a
distance of 30 ft in 15 s.

Solution $\text{Power} = \dfrac{30 \text{ ft} \times 300 \text{ lb}}{15 \text{ s}}$

$$= 600 \frac{\text{ft} \cdot \text{lb}}{\text{s}}$$

You Try It 4
Find the power needed to raise 1200 lb a
distance of 90 ft in 24 s.

Your solution

Example 5
A motor has a power of 2750 $\frac{\text{ft} \cdot \text{lb}}{\text{s}}$. Find the
horsepower of the motor.

Solution $\dfrac{2750}{550} = 5 \text{ hp}$

You Try It 5
A motor has a power of 3300 $\frac{\text{ft} \cdot \text{lb}}{\text{s}}$. Find the
horsepower of the motor.

Your solution

Solutions on p. S21

8.4 Exercises

· ·

Objective A

1. Convert 25 Btu to foot-pounds.

2. Convert 6000 Btu to foot-pounds.

3. Convert 25,000 Btu to foot-pounds.

4. Convert 40,000 Btu to foot-pounds.

5. Find the energy required to lift 150 lb a distance of 10 ft.

6. Find the energy required to lift 300 lb a distance of 16 ft.

7. Find the energy required to lift a 3300-pound car a distance of 9 ft.

8. Find the energy required to lift a 3680-pound elevator a distance of 325 ft.

9. Three tons are lifted 5 ft. Find the energy required in foot-pounds.

10. Seven tons are lifted 12 ft. Find the energy required in foot-pounds.

11. A construction worker carries 3-pound blocks up a 10-foot flight of stairs. How many foot-pounds of energy are required to carry 850 blocks up the stairs?

12. A crane lifts an 1800-pound steel beam to the roof of a building 36 ft high. Find the amount of energy the crane requires in lifting the beam.

13. A furnace is rated at 45,000 Btu per hour. How many foot-pounds of energy are released by the furnace in 1 h?

14. A furnace is rated at 22,500 Btu per hour. How many foot-pounds of energy does the furnace release in 1 h?

15. Find the amount of energy in foot-pounds given off when 1 lb of coal is burned. One pound of coal gives off 12,000 Btu of energy when burned.

16. Find the amount of energy in foot-pounds given off when 1 lb of gasoline is burned. One pound of gasoline gives off 21,000 Btu of energy when burned.

Objective B

17. Convert $1100 \frac{\text{ft} \cdot \text{lb}}{\text{s}}$ to horsepower.

18. Convert $6050 \frac{\text{ft} \cdot \text{lb}}{\text{s}}$ to horsepower.

19. Convert $4400 \frac{\text{ft} \cdot \text{lb}}{\text{s}}$ to horsepower.

20. Convert $1650 \frac{\text{ft} \cdot \text{lb}}{\text{s}}$ to horsepower.

21. Convert 5 hp to foot-pounds per second.

22. Convert 3 hp to foot-pounds per second.

23. Convert 7 hp to foot-pounds per second.

24. Convert 2 hp to foot-pounds per second.

25. Find the power in foot-pounds per second needed to raise 125 lb a distance of 12 ft in 3 s.

26. Find the power in foot-pounds per second needed to raise 500 lb a distance of 60 ft in 8 s.

27. Find the power in foot-pounds per second needed to raise 3000 lb a distance of 40 ft in 25 s.

28. Find the power in foot-pounds per second needed to raise 12,000 lb a distance of 40 ft in 60 s.

29. Find the power in foot-pounds per second of an engine that can raise 180 lb to a height of 40 ft in 5 s.

30. Find the power in foot-pounds per second of an engine that can raise 1200 lb to a height of 18 ft in 30 s.

31. A motor has a power of $1650 \frac{\text{ft} \cdot \text{lb}}{\text{s}}$. Find the horsepower of the motor.

32. A motor has a power of $16,500 \frac{\text{ft} \cdot \text{lb}}{\text{s}}$. Find the horsepower of the motor.

33. A motor has a power of $6600 \frac{\text{ft} \cdot \text{lb}}{\text{s}}$. Find the horsepower of the motor.

APPLYING THE CONCEPTS

34. Pick out some source of energy. Write an article about this form of energy. Include the source, pollution, and future prospects associated with this form of energy.

Focus on Problem Solving

Applying Solutions to Other Problems

Problem solving in the previous chapters concentrated on solving specific problems. After a problem is solved, there is an important question to be asked: "Does the solution to this problem apply to other types of problems?"

To illustrate this extension of problem solving, we will consider *triangular numbers*, which were studied by ancient Greek mathematicians. The numbers 1, 3, 6, 10, 15, and 21 are the first six triangular numbers. What is the next triangular number?

To answer this question, note in the diagram below that a triangle can be formed using the number of dots that correspond to a triangular number.

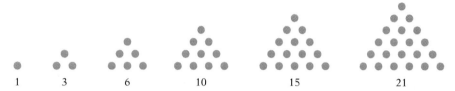

Observe that the number of dots in each row is one more than the number of dots in the row above. The total number of dots can be found by addition.

The pattern suggests that the next triangular number (the seventh one) is the sum of the first 7 natural numbers. The seventh triangular number is 28. The diagram at the right shows the seventh triangular number.

Using the pattern for triangular numbers, the tenth triangular number is

$$1 + 2 + 3 + 4 + 5 + 6 + 7 + 8 + 9 + 10 = 55$$

Now consider a situation that may seem to be totally unrelated to triangular numbers. Suppose you are in charge of scheduling softball games for a league. There are seven teams in the league, and each team must play every other team once. How many games must be scheduled?

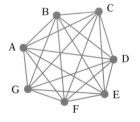

We label the teams A, B, C, D, E, F, and G. (See the figure at the left.) A line between two teams indicates that the two teams play each other. Beginning with A, there are 6 lines for the 6 teams that A must play. There are 6 teams that B must play, but the line between A and B has already been drawn, so there are only 5 remaining games to schedule for B. Now move on to C. The lines between C and A and between C and B have already been drawn, so there are only 4 additional lines to be drawn to represent the teams C will play. Moving on to D, the lines between D and A, D and B, and D and C have already been drawn, so there are 3 more lines to be drawn to represent the teams D will play.

Note that as we move from team to team, one fewer line needs to be drawn. When we reach F, there is only one line to be drawn, the one between F and G. The total number of lines drawn is 6 + 5 + 4 + 3 + 2 + 1 = 21, the sixth triangular number. For a league with 7 teams, the number of games that must be scheduled so that each team plays every other team once is the sixth triangular number. If there were 10 teams in the league, the number of games that must be scheduled would be the ninth triangular number, which is 45.

A college chess team wants to schedule a match so that each of its 15 members plays each other member of the team twice. How many matches must be scheduled?

Projects and Group Activities

Parsecs   Although one mile may seem like a long distance, for astronomers this measurement is inadequate for the vastness of space. Another measurement of distance called the *light-year* is more useful. A **light-year** is the distance a ray of light can travel in one year. One light-year is approximately 5,870,000,000,000 miles. This is certainly a long distance. However, the vastness of space is so large that even this distance is not useful for some measurements. To measure even greater distances, a *parsec* is used.

1. Use a reference find the distance (in miles) of a parsec.
2. What is the distance, in parsecs, from our solar system to the Andromeda galaxy?
3. What is the distance, in parsecs, from our solar system to the Clouds of Magellan?

Nomographs

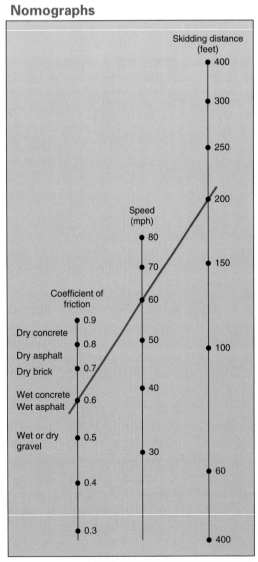

The chart at the left is a *nomograph*. A **nomograph** is a chart representing numerical relationships among variables. A chart is another tool that is used in problem solving.

One of the details a traffic accident investigator checks when looking into a car accident is the length of the skid marks of the car. This length can help the investigator determine the speed of the car when the brakes were applied.

An equation is one method that can be used to detemine the speed. The difficulty with this method is that the investigator may have forgotten the equation, or, even if the equation is remembered, it may be very difficult to solve.

The nomograph at the left can be used to determine the speed of a car under given conditions. It shows the relationship among the speed of the car, the skidding distance, and the *coefficient of friction*.

The coefficient of friction is an experimentally obtained value that considers how easy or hard it is to drag one object over another. For instance, it is easier to drag a box across ice than it is to drag it across a carpet. The coefficient of friction is smaller for the box and ice than it is for the box and carpet.

To use the nomograph at the left, an investigator would draw a line from the coefficient of friction to the skidding distance. The point at which the line crosses the speed line shows how fast the car was going when the brakes were applied. The line from 0.6 to 200 intersects the speed line at 60. This indicates that a car that skids 200 feet on wet asphalt or concrete was traveling at 60 mph.

1. Use the nomograph to determine the speed of a car when the brakes were applied for a car traveling on gravel and for skid marks of 100 feet.
2. Use the nomograph to determine the speed of a car when the brakes were applied for a car traveling on dry concrete and for skid marks of 150 feet.

Averages If two towns are 150 miles apart and you drive between the two towns in 3 hours, then your

$$Average\ speed = \frac{total\ distance}{total\ time} = \frac{150}{3} = 50\ mi/h$$

It is highly unlikely that your speed was *exactly* 50 mi/h the entire time of the trip. Sometimes you will have traveled faster than 50 mi/h, and other times slower than 50 mi/h. Dividing the total distance you traveled by the total time it took to go that distance is an example of calculating an average.

There are many other averages that may be calculated. For instance, the Environmental Protection Agency calculates an estimated mpg (miles per gallon) for new cars. Miles per gallon is an average calculated from the formula

$$\frac{Gallons\ of\ gasoline}{Miles\ traveled}$$

For instance, the mpg for a car that travels 308 miles on 11 gallons of gas is $\frac{308}{11} = 28$ mpg.

A pilot would not use miles per gallon as a measure of fuel efficiency. Rather, pilots use gallons per hour. A plane that travels 5 hours and uses 400 gallons of fuel has an average that is calculated as

$$\frac{Gallons\ of\ fuel}{Hours\ flown} = \frac{400}{5} = 80\ gal/h$$

Using the examples above, calculate the following averages.

1. Determine the average speed of a car that travels 355 miles in 6 hours. Round to the nearest tenth.

2. Determine the mpg of a car that can travel 405 miles on 12 gallons of gasoline. Round to the nearest tenth.

3. If a plane flew 2000 miles in 5 hours and used 1000 gallons of fuel, determine the average number of gallons per hour used by the plane.

Another type of average is grade-point average (GPA). It is calculated by multiplying the units for each class by the grade point for that class, adding the results, and dividing by the total number of units taken. Here is an example using the grading scale A = 4, B = 3, C = 2, D = 1, and F = 0.

Class	Units	Grade
Math	4	B (= 3)
English	3	A (= 4)
French	5	C (= 2)
Biology	3	B (= 3)

$$GPA = \frac{4 \cdot 3 + 3 \cdot 4 + 5 \cdot 2 + 3 \cdot 3}{4 + 3 + 5 + 3} = \frac{43}{15} \approx 2.87$$

4. A grading scale that provides for plus or minus grades uses A = 4, A− = 3.7, B+ = 3.3, B = 3, B− = 2.7, C+ = 2.3, C = 2, C− = 1.7, D+ = 1.3, D = 1, D− = 0.7, and F = 0. Calculate the GPA of the student whose grades are given below.

Class	Units	Grade
Math	5	B+
English	3	C+
Spanish	5	A−
Physical Science	3	B−

Chapter Summary

Key Words   A *measurement* includes a number and a unit.

The U.S. Customary units of length are *inch, foot, yard,* and *mile.*

Weight is a measure of how strongly the earth is pulling on an object.

The U.S. Customary units of weight are *ounce, pound,* and *ton.*

Liquid substances are measured in units of *capacity.*

The U.S. Customary units of capacity are *fluid ounce, cup, pint, quart,* and *gallon.*

Energy is the ability to do work.

One *foot-pound* of energy is the energy necessary to lift 1 pound a distance of 1 foot.

Furnaces, stoves, and air conditioners are rated in energy units called *British thermal units* (Btu).

Power is the rate at which work is done.

The U.S. Customary unit of power is the *horsepower* (hp).

Essential Rule   A conversion unit is used to convert one unit of measurement to another. For example, the conversion unit $\frac{12 \text{ in.}}{1 \text{ ft}}$ is used to convert feet to inches.

Chapter Review

1. Convert 4 ft to inches.

2. What is 7 ft 6 in. divided by 3?

3. Find the energy needed to lift 200 lb a distance of 8 ft.

4. Convert $2\frac{1}{2}$ pt to fluid ounces.

5. Convert 14 ft to yards.

6. Convert 2400 lb to tons.

7. Find the quotient of 7 lb 5 oz and 3.

8. Convert $3\frac{3}{8}$ lb to ounces.

9. Add: 3 ft 9 in.
            + 5 ft 6 in.

10. Subtract: 3 tons 500 lb
                   − 1 ton 1500 lb

11. Add: 5 lb 11 oz
             + 3 lb 8 oz

12. Subtract: 5 yd 1 ft
                   − 3 yd 2 ft

13. Convert 12 c to quarts.

14. Find the product of 2 ft 8 in. and 5.

15. Convert 2.5 hp to foot-pounds per second.

16. Multiply: 5 lb 8 oz
$$\times \quad 8$$

17. Convert 50 Btu to foot-pounds. (1 Btu = 778 ft · lb.)

18. Convert 3850 $\frac{\text{ft} \cdot \text{lb}}{\text{s}}$ to horsepower. $\left(1 \text{ hp} = 550 \frac{\text{ft} \cdot \text{lb}}{\text{s}}. \right)$

19. A board 6 ft 11 in. is cut from a board 10 ft 5 in. long. Find the length of the remaining piece of board.

20. A book weighing 2 lb 3 oz is mailed at the postage rate of $.18 per ounce. Find the cost of mailing the book.

21. A can of pineapple juice contains 18 fl oz. Find the number of quarts in a case of 24 cans.

22. A cafeteria sold 256 cartons of milk in one school day. Each carton contains 1 c of milk. How many gallons of milk were sold that day?

23. A furnace is rated at 35,000 Btu per hour. How many foot-pounds of energy does the furnace release in 1 h? (1 Btu = 778 ft · lb.)

24. Find the power in foot-pounds per second of an engine that can raise 800 lb to a height of 15 ft in 25 s.

Chapter Test

1. Convert $2\frac{1}{2}$ ft to inches.

2. Subtract: 4 ft 2 in. − 1 ft 9 in.

3. A board $6\frac{2}{3}$ ft long is cut into five equal pieces. How long is each piece?

4. Seventy-two bricks, each 8 in. long, are laid end to end to make the base for a wall. Find the length of the wall in feet.

5. Convert $2\frac{7}{8}$ lb to ounces.

6. Convert: 40 oz = ____ lb ____ oz

7. Find the sum of 9 lb 6 oz and 7 lb 11 oz.

8. Divide: 6 lb 12 oz ÷ 4

9. A college bookstore received 1000 workbooks, each weighing 12 oz. Find the total weight of the 1000 workbooks in pounds.

10. An elementary school class gathered 800 aluminum cans for recycling. Four aluminum cans weigh 3 oz. Find the amount the class received if the rate of pay was $.75 per pound for the aluminum cans. Round to the nearest cent.

11. Convert 13 qt to gallons.

12. Convert $3\frac{1}{2}$ gal to pints.

13. What is $1\frac{3}{4}$ gal times 7?

14. Add: 5 gal 2 qt + 2 gal 3 qt

15. A can of grapefruit juice contains 20 fl oz. Find the number of cups of grapefruit juice in a case of 24 cans.

16. Nick, a mechanic, bought oil in 40-gallon containers for changing the oil in customers' cars. He paid $90 for the 40 gallons of oil and charged customers $1.35 per quart. Find the profit Nick made on one 40-gallon container of oil.

17. Find the energy required to lift 250 lb a distance of 15 ft.

18. A furnace is rated at 40,000 Btu per hour. How many foot-pounds of energy are released by the furnace in 1 h? (1 Btu = 778 ft · lb.)

19. Find the power needed to lift 200 lb a distance of 20 ft in 25 s.

20. A motor has a power of 2200 $\frac{\text{ft} \cdot \text{lb}}{\text{s}}$. Find the motor's horsepower. $\left(1 \text{ hp} = 550 \frac{\text{ft} \cdot \text{lb}}{\text{s}}.\right)$

Cumulative Review

1. Find the LCM of 9, 12, and 15.

2. Write $\frac{43}{8}$ as a mixed number.

3. Subtract: $5\frac{7}{8} - 2\frac{7}{12}$

4. What is $5\frac{1}{3}$ divided by $2\frac{2}{3}$?

5. Simplify $\frac{5}{8} \div \left(\frac{3}{8} - \frac{1}{4}\right) - \frac{5}{8}$.

6. Round 2.0972 to the nearest hundredth.

7. Multiply: $\begin{array}{r} 0.0792 \\ \times\ \ \ 0.49 \\ \hline \end{array}$

8. Solve the proportion: $\frac{n}{12} = \frac{44}{60}$

9. Find $2\frac{1}{2}\%$ of 50.

10. 18 is 42% of what? Round to the nearest hundredth.

11. A 7.2-pound roast costs $15.48. Find the unit cost.

12. Add: $3\frac{2}{5}$ in. $+ 5\frac{1}{3}$ in.

13. Convert: 24 oz = ___ lb ___ oz

14. Multiply: 3 lb 8 oz × 9

15. Subtract: $4\frac{1}{3}$ qt $- 1\frac{5}{6}$ qt

16. Find 2 lb 10 oz less than 4 lb 6 oz.

17. An investor receives a dividend of $56 from 40 shares of stock. At the same rate, find the dividend that would be received from 200 shares of stock.

18. Anna had a balance of $578.56 in her checkbook. She wrote checks of $216.98 and $34.12 and made a deposit of $315.33. What is her new checking balance?

19. An account executive receives a salary of $800 per month plus a commission of 2% on all sales over $25,000. Find the total monthly income of an account executive who has monthly sales of $140,000.

20. A health inspector found that 3% of a shipment of carrots were spoiled and could not be sold. Find the amount of carrots from a shipment of 2500 lb that could be sold.

21. The scores on the final exam of a trigonometry class are recorded in the histogram in the figure. What percent of the class received a score between 80% and 90%? Round to the nearest percent.

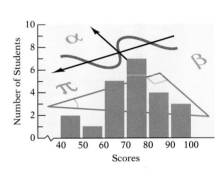

22. Hayes Department Store uses a markup rate of 40% on all merchandise. What is the selling price of a compact disk player that cost the store $220?

23. A construction firm received a loan of $200,000 for 8 months at a simple interest rate of 11%. Find the interest paid on the loan.

24. Six college students spent several weeks panning for gold during their summer vacation. The students obtained 1 lb 3 oz of gold. After selling the gold for $400 per ounce, how much money did each student receive? Round to the nearest dollar.

25. Four books were mailed at the rate of $.15 per ounce. The books weighed 1 lb 3 oz, 13 oz, 1 lb 8 oz, and 1 lb. Find the cost of mailing the books.

26. One brand of yogurt costs $.61 for 8 oz; 36 oz of another brand can be bought for $2.70. Which purchase is the better buy?

27. A contractor can buy a 4000-gallon tank of gasoline for $3600. The pump price of the gasoline is $1.17 per gallon. How much does the contractor save by buying the 4000 gal of gasoline?

28. Find the energy required to lift 400 lb a distance of 8 ft.

29. Find the power in foot-pounds per second needed to raise 600 lb a distance of 8 ft in 12 s.

9

The Metric System of Measurement

Nurses use the metric system to determine the amount of medication to administer to a patient. Also, a nurse uses a sphygmomanometer to measure a person's blood pressure. A measurement of 120 over 80 means that when the heart is contracting, it can force mercury in a glass tube to rise 120 millimeters, and when the heart is relaxing, the mercury reaches a height of 80 millimeters.

Objectives

Section 9.1
To convert units of length in the metric system of measurement
To solve application problems

Section 9.2
To convert units of mass in the metric system of measurement
To solve application problems

Section 9.3
To convert units of capacity in the metric system of measurement
To solve application problems

Section 9.4
To use units of energy in the metric system of measurement

Section 9.5
To convert U.S. Customary units to metric units
To convert metric units to U.S. Customary units

Is a Pound a Pound?

Which is heavier, a pound of feathers or a pound of gold? It would seem that a pound is a pound, whether it is gold or feathers. However, this is not the case.

The weights of metals, such as gold and silver, are measured using the troy weight system, whereas the weights of feathers, meat, people, and other nonmetal quantities are measured using the avoirdupois weight system. Each system is part of the U.S. Customary System of measurement.

One grain is a small weight in the U.S. Customary System; it is approximately 0.02 ounce. A pound of feathers weighs 7000 grains, but a pound of gold weighs only 5760 grains. Therefore, a pound of feathers weighs more than a pound of gold.

To complicate matters, 1 avoirdupois pound contains 16 ounces, but 1 troy pound contains 12 ounces, which means that there are 437.5 grains in 1 avoirdupois ounce but 480 grains in a troy ounce. Thus an ounce of feathers weighs less than an ounce of gold.

To summarize, a pound of feathers weighs more than a pound of gold, but an ounce of feathers weighs less than an ounce of gold. This kind of confusion is one reason why the metric system of measurement was developed.

9.1 Length

Objective A **To convert units of length in the metric system of measurement** ....

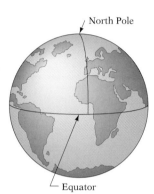

North Pole

Equator

In 1789, an attempt was made to standardize units of measurement internationally in order to simplify trade and commerce between nations. A commission in France developed a system of measurement known as the **metric system.** The basic unit of length in the metric system is the **meter.** One meter is approximately the distance from a doorknob to the floor.

All units of length in the metric system are derived from the meter. Prefixes to the basic unit denote the length of each unit. For example, the prefix "centi-" means one-hundredth, so 1 centimeter is 1 one-hundredth of a meter.

kilo- = 1000	1 kilometer (km) = 1000 meters (m)
hecto- = 100	1 hectometer (hm) = 100 m
deca- = 10	1 decameter (dam) = 10 m
	1 meter (m) = 1 m
deci- = 0.1	1 decimeter (dm) = 0.1 m
centi- = 0.01	1 centimeter (cm) = 0.01 m
milli- = 0.001	1 millimeter (mm) = 0.001 m

Conversion between units of length in the metric system involves moving the decimal point to the right or to the left. Listing the units in order from largest to smallest will indicate how many places to move the decimal point and in which direction.

To convert 4200 cm to meters, write the units in order from largest to smallest.

km   hm   dam   m   dm   cm   mm

2 positions

Converting cm to m requires moving 2 positions to the left.

4200 cm = 42.00 m

2 places

Move the decimal point the same number of places and in the same direction.

A metric measurement involving two units is customarily written in terms of one unit. Convert the smaller unit to the larger unit and then add.

To convert 8 km 32 m to kilometers, first convert 32 m to kilometers.

km   hm   dam   m   dm   cm   mm

* Converting m to km requires moving 3 positions to the left.

32 m = 0.032 km

* Move the decimal point the same number of places and in the same direction.

8 km 32 m = 8 km + 0.032 km
       = 8.032 km

* Add the result to 8 km.

Example 1   Convert 0.38 m to millimeters.

Solution   0.38 m = 380 mm

Example 2   Convert 4 m 62 cm to meters.

Solution   62 cm = 0.62 m

4 m 62 cm = 4 m + 0.62 m
= 4.62 m

You Try It 1   Convert 3.07 m to centimeters.

Your solution

You Try It 2   Convert 3 km 750 m to kilometers.

Your solution

Solutions on p. S21

Objective B   *To solve application problems* ....

TAKE NOTE

Although in this text we will always change units to the larger unit, it is possible to perform the calculation by changing to the smaller unit.

2 m − 85 cm
= 200 cm − 85 cm
= 115 cm

Note that 115 cm = 1.15 m.

In the application problems in this section, we perform arithmetic operations with the measurements of length in the metric system. It is important to remember that before measurements can be added or subtracted, they must be expressed in terms of the same unit. In this textbook, unless otherwise stated, the units should be changed to the larger unit before the arithmetic operation is performed.

To subtract 85 cm from 2 m, convert 85 cm to meters.

$$2 \text{ m} - 85 \text{ cm} = 2 \text{ m} - 0.85 \text{ m}$$
$$= 1.15 \text{ m}$$

Example 3
A piece measuring 142 cm is cut from a board 4.20 m long. Find the length of the remaining piece.

Strategy
To find the length of the remaining piece:
• Convert the length of the piece cut (142 cm) to meters.
• Subtract the length of the piece cut from the original length.

Solution
142 cm = 1.42 m

4.20 m − 142 cm = 4.20 m − 1.42 m
= 2.78 m

The length of the piece remaining is 2.78 m.

You Try It 3
A bookcase 175 cm long has four shelves. Find the cost of the shelves when the price of the lumber is $15.75 per meter.

Your strategy

Your solution

Solution on p. S21

9.1 Exercises

. . . .

Objective A

Convert.

1. 42 cm = _____ mm

2. 62 cm = _____ mm

3. 81 mm = _____ cm

4. 68.2 mm = _____ cm

5. 6804 m = _____ km

6. 3750 m = _____ km

7. 2.109 km = _____ m

8. 32.5 km = _____ m

9. 432 cm = _____ m

10. 61.7 cm = _____ m

11. 0.88 m = _____ cm

12. 3.21 m = _____ cm

13. 7038 m = _____ km

14. 2589 m = _____ km

15. 3.5 km = _____ m

16. 9.75 km = _____ m

17. 260 cm = _____ m

18. 705 cm = _____ m

19. 1.685 m = _____ cm

20. 0.975 m = _____ cm

21. 14.8 cm = _____ mm

22. 6 m 42 cm = _____ m

23. 62 m 7 cm = _____ m

24. 42 cm 6 mm = _____ cm

25. 31 cm 9 mm = _____ cm

26. 62 km 482 m = _____ km

27. 8 km 75 m = _____ km

Objective B   *Application Problems*

28. How many shelves, each 140 cm long, can be cut from a board that is 4.20 m in length? Find the length of the board remaining after the shelves are cut.

29. Find the missing dimension, in centimeters, in the diagram at the right.

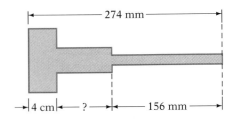

30. A walk-a-thon had two checkpoints. One checkpoint was 1400 m from the starting point. The second checkpoint was 1200 m from the first checkpoint. The second checkpoint was 1800 m from the finish line. How long was the walk? Express the answer in kilometers.

31. Twenty rivets are used to fasten two steel plates together. The plates are 3.4 m long, and the rivets are equally spaced, with a rivet at each end. Find the distance between the rivets. Round to the nearest tenth of a centimeter.

32. Find the total length, in centimeters, of the shaft in the diagram at the right.

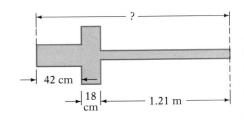

33. You purchase a 50-meter roll of fencing, at a cost of $14.95 per meter, in order to build a dog run that is 340 cm wide and 1380 cm long. After you cut the four pieces of fencing from the roll, how much of the fencing is left on the roll?

34. Carmine is a member of a group that has adopted 10 km of highway. During this week, Carmine cleaned up litter along the highway for 2500 m, 1500 m, 1200 m, 1300 m, and 1400 m. Find the average number of kilometers Carmine cleaned up on each of the 5 days this week.

35. The distance between Earth and the sun is 150,000,000 km. Light travels 300,000,000 m in 1 s. How long does it take for light to reach Earth from the sun?

36. The circumference of Earth is 40,000 km. How long would it take to travel the circumference of Earth at a speed of 85 km per hour? Round to the nearest tenth.

37. Light travels 300,000 km in 1 s. How far does light travel in 1 day?

APPLYING THE CONCEPTS

38. Explain the meaning of "parsec" and how this unit is used in measuring astronomical distances.

39. Write a short history of the metric system.

9.2 Mass

Objective A   To convert units of mass in the metric system of measurement ....

Mass and weight are closely related. Weight is a measure of how strongly the earth is pulling on an object. Therefore, an object's weight is less in space than on the earth's surface. However, the amount of material in the object, its **mass,** remains the same. On the surface of the earth, mass and weight can be used interchangeably.

The basic unit of mass in the metric system is the **gram.** If a box that is 1 cm long on a side is filled with water, then the mass of that water is 1 gram.

1 gram = the mass of water in the box

The gram is a very small unit of mass. A paper clip weighs about 1 gram. The kilogram (1000 grams) is a more useful unit of mass in consumer applications. This textbook weighs about 1 kilogram.

The units of mass in the metric system have the same prefixes as the units of length:

$$1 \text{ kilogram (kg)} = 1000 \text{ grams (g)}$$
$$1 \text{ hectogram (hg)} = 100 \text{ g}$$
$$1 \text{ decagram (dag)} = 10 \text{ g}$$
$$1 \text{ gram (g)} = 1 \text{ g}$$
$$1 \text{ decigram (dg)} = 0.1 \text{ g}$$
$$1 \text{ centigram (cg)} = 0.01 \text{ g}$$
$$1 \text{ milligram (mg)} = 0.001 \text{ g}$$

Conversion between units of mass in the metric system involves moving the decimal point to the right or to the left. Listing the units in order from largest to smallest will indicate how many places to move the decimal point and in which direction.

To convert 324 g to kilograms, first write the units in order from largest to smallest.

kg hg dag g dg cg mg   Converting g to kg requires moving
⌣⌣⌣   3 positions to the left.
3 positions

324 g = 0.324 kg   Move the decimal point the same number of
⌣⌣   places and in the same direction.
3 places

Example 1   Convert 4.23 g to milligrams.

Solution   4.23 g = 4230 mg

You Try It 1   Convert 42.3 mg to grams.

Your solution

Solution on p. S21

Example 2   Convert 2 kg 564 g to kilograms.

Solution   564 g = 0.564 kg

2 kg 564 g = 2 kg + 0.564 kg
= 2.564 kg

You Try It 2   Convert 3 g 54 mg to grams.

Your solution

Solution on p. S21

Objective B   *To solve application problems* ······················· CT

In the application problems in this section, we perform arithmetic operations with the measurements of mass in the metric system. Remember that before measurements can be added or subtracted, they must be expressed in terms of the same unit. In this textbook, unless otherwise stated, the units should be changed to the larger unit before the arithmetic operation is performed.

To subtract 750 g from 3 kg, convert 750 g to kilograms.

$$3 \text{ kg} - 750 \text{ g} = 3 \text{ kg} - 0.750 \text{ kg}$$
$$= 2.250 \text{ kg}$$

Example 3

Find the cost of three packages of ground meat weighing 540 g, 670 g, and 890 g if the price per kilogram is $9.89. Round to the nearest cent.

Strategy

To find the cost of the meat:

• Find the total weight of the 3 packages.
• Convert the total weight to kilograms.
• Multiply the weight by the cost per kilogram ($9.89).

Solution

540 g + 670 g + 890 g = 2100 g

2100 g = 2.1 kg

2.1 × 9.89 = 20.769

The cost of the meat is $20.77.

You Try It 3

How many kilograms of fertilizer are required to fertilize 400 trees in an apple orchard if 300 g of fertilizer are used for each tree?

Your strategy

Your solution

Solution on p. S21

9.2 Exercises

. . . .

Objective A

Convert.

1. 420 g = _____ kg

2. 7421 g = _____ kg

3. 127 mg = _____ g

4. 43 mg = _____ g

5. 4.2 kg = _____ g

6. 0.027 kg = _____ g

7. 0.45 g = _____ mg

8. 325 g = _____ mg

9. 1856 g = _____ kg

10. 8900 g = _____ kg

11. 4057 mg = _____ g

12. 1970 mg = _____ g

13. 1.37 kg = _____ g

14. 5.1 kg = _____ g

15. 0.0456 g = _____ mg

16. 0.2 g = _____ mg

17. 18,000 g = _____ kg

18. 0.87 kg = _____ g

19. 3 kg 922 g = _____ kg

20. 1 kg 47 g = _____ kg

21. 7 g 891 mg = _____ g

22. 209 g 42 mg = _____ g

23. 4 kg 63 g = _____ kg

24. 18 g 5 mg = _____ g

_____

Objective B   Application Problems

25. A 1.19-kg container of Quaker Oats contains 30 servings. Find the number of grams in one serving of the oatmeal. Round to the nearest gram.

26. A patient is advised to supplement her diet with 2 g of calcium per day. The calcium tablets she purchases contain 500 mg of calcium per tablet. How many tablets per day should the patient take?

27. a. One egg contains 274 mg of cholesterol. How many grams of cholesterol are in one dozen eggs?
   b. One glass of milk contains 33 mg of cholesterol. How many grams of cholesterol are in four glasses of milk?

28. A carat is a unit of weight equal to 200 mg. Find the weight in grams of a 10-carat precious stone.

29. The nutrition label for a corn bread mix is shown at the right.
   a. How many kilograms of mix are in the package?
   b. How many grams of sodium are contained in two servings of the corn bread?

Nutrition Facts

Serving Size ⅙ pkg. (31g mix)
Servings Per Container 6

Amount Per Serving	Mix	Prepared
Calories	110	160
Calories from Fat	10	50

	% Daily Value*	
Total Fat 1g	1%	9%
Saturated Fat 0g	0%	7%
Cholesterol 0mg	0%	12%
Sodium 210mg	9%	11%
Total Carbohydrate 24g	8%	8%
Sugars 6g		
Protein 2g		

30. Find the cost of three packages of ground meat weighing 470 g, 680 g, and 590 g if the price per kilogram is $5.40.

31. Eighty grams of grass seed are used for every 100 m² of lawn. How many kilograms of grass seed are needed to cover 2000 m²?

32. A commuter flight charges $7.95 for each kilogram or part of a kilogram over 15 kg of luggage weight. How much extra must be paid for three pieces of luggage weighing 6450 g, 5850 g, and 7500 g?

33. A health food store buys nuts in 10-kilogram containers and repackages the nuts for resale. The store packages the nuts in 200-gram bags, costing $.04 each, and sells them for $1.89 per bag. Find the profit on a 10-kilogram container of nuts costing $50.

34. A train car is loaded with 15 automobiles weighing 1405 kg each. Find the total weight of the automobiles.

35. During one year the United States exported 37,141 million kg of wheat, 2680 million kg of rice, and 40,365 million kg of corn. What percent of the total of these grain exports was corn? Round to the nearest tenth of a percent.

APPLYING THE CONCEPTS

36. Define a metric ton. Convert the weights in Exercise 35 to metric tons.

37. Discuss the advantages and disadvantages of the U.S. Customary and metric systems of measurement.

9.3   Capacity

Objective A   *To convert units of capacity in the metric system*
of measurement ....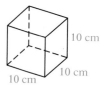

The basic unit of capacity in the metric system is the
liter. One **liter** is defined as the capacity of a box
that is 10 cm long on each side.

The units of capacity in the metric system have the same prefixes as the units
of length:

$$1 \text{ kiloliter (kl)} = 1000 \text{ L}$$
$$1 \text{ hectoliter (hl)} = 100 \text{ L}$$
$$1 \text{ decaliter (dal)} = 10 \text{ L}$$
$$1 \text{ liter (L)} = 1 \text{ L}$$
$$1 \text{ deciliter (dl)} = 0.1 \text{ L}$$
$$1 \text{ centiliter (cl)} = 0.01 \text{ L}$$
$$1 \text{ milliliter (ml)} = 0.001 \text{ L}$$

The milliliter is equal to
1 cubic centimeter (cm^3).

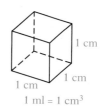

$1 \text{ ml} = 1 \text{ cm}^3$

Conversion between units of capacity in the metric system involves moving the
decimal point to the right or to the left. Listing the units in order from largest to
smallest will indicate how many places to move the decimal point and in which
direction.

To convert 824 ml to liters, first write the units in order from largest to smallest.

kl hl dal L dl cl ml
            3 positions

Converting ml to L requires moving 3 positions to the left.

$824 \text{ ml} = 0.824 \text{ L}$
        3 places

Move the decimal point the same number of places and in the same direction.

Example 1   Convert 4 L 32 ml to liters

Solution $32 \text{ ml} = 0.032 \text{ L}$

$4 \text{ L } 32 \text{ ml} = 4 \text{ L} + 0.032 \text{ L}$
$= 4.032 \text{ L}$

You Try It 1   Convert 2 kl 167 L to liters.

Your solution

Solution on p. S21

Example 2   Convert 1.23 L to cubic centimeters.

Solution   1.23 L = 1230 ml = 1230 cm³

You Try It 2   Convert 325 cm³ to liters.

Your solution

Solution on p. S21

Objective B   *To solve application problems* ....

In the application problems in this section, we perform arithmetic operations with the measurements of capacity in the metric system. Remember that before measurements can be added or subtracted, they must be expressed in terms of the same unit. In this textbook, unless otherwise stated, the units should be changed to the larger unit before the arithmetic operation is performed.

To add 2.5 kl and 875 L, convert 875 L to kiloliters.

$$2.5 \text{ kl} + 875 \text{ L} = 2.5 \text{ kl} + 0.875 \text{ kl}$$
$$= 3.375 \text{ kl}$$

Example 3
A laboratory assistant is in charge of ordering acid for three chemistry classes of 30 students each. Each student requires 80 ml of acid. How many liters of acid should be ordered? (The assistant must order by the whole liter.)

Strategy
To find the number of liters to be ordered:

- Find the number of milliliters of acid needed by multiplying the number of classes (3) by the number of students per class (30) by the number of milliliters of acid required by each student (80).
- Convert milliliters to liters.
- Round up to the nearest whole number.

Solution
3(30)(80) = 7200 ml

7200 ml = 7.2 L

7.2 rounded up to the nearest whole number is 8.

The assistant should order 8 L of acid.

You Try It 3
For $99.50, a cosmetician buys 5 L of moisturizer and repackages it in 125-milliliter jars. Each jar costs the cosmetician $.35. Each jar of moisturizer is sold for $5.95. Find the profit on the 5 L of moisturizer.

Your strategy

Your solution

Solution on p. S21

9.3 Exercises

· ·

Objective A

Convert.

1. 4200 ml = _____ L

2. 7.5 ml = _____ L

3. 3.42 L = _____ ml

4. 0.037 L = _____ ml

5. 423 ml = _____ cm³

6. 0.32 ml = _____ cm³

7. 642 cm³ = _____ ml

8. 0.083 cm³ = _____ ml

9. 42 cm³ = _____ L

10. 3075 cm³ = _____ L

11. 0.435 L = _____ cm³

12. 2.57 L = _____ cm³

13. 4.62 kl = _____ L

14. 0.035 kl = _____ L

15. 1423 L = _____ kl

16. 897 L = _____ kl

17. 1.267 L = _____ cm³

18. 4.105 L = _____ cm³

19. 3 L 42 ml = _____ L

20. 1 L 127 ml = _____ L

21. 3 kl 4 L = _____ kl

22. 6 kl 32 L = _____ kl

23. 8 L 200 ml = _____ L

24. 9 kl 505 L = _____ kl

Objective B   *Application Problems*

25. The air in Earth's atmosphere is 78% nitrogen and 21% oxygen.
   a. Without calculating, is the amount of oxygen in 50 L of air more or less than 25 L?
   b. Find the amount of oxygen in 50 L of air.

26. A can of tomato juice contains 1.36 L. How many 170-milliliter servings are in one can of tomato juice?

27. An athletic club uses 800 ml of chlorine each day for its swimming pool. How many liters of chlorine are used in a month of 30 days?

28. The printed label from a container of milk is shown at the right. How many 230-milliliter servings are in the container? Round to the nearest whole number.

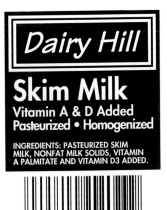

29. A flu vaccine is being given for the coming winter season. A medical corporation buys 12 L of flu vaccine. How many patients can be immunized if each person receives 3 cm^3 of the vaccine?

1 GAL. (3.78 L)

30. A chemistry experiment requires 12 ml of an acid solution. How many liters of acid should be ordered when 4 classes of 90 students each are going to perform the experiment? (The acid must be ordered by the whole liter.)

31. A case of 12 one-liter bottles of apple juice costs $19.80. A case of 24 cans, each can containing 340 ml of apple juice, costs $14.50. Which case of apple juice is the better buy?

32. For $95, a pharmacist purchases 5 L of cough syrup and repackages it in 250-milliliter bottles. Each bottle costs the pharmacist $.25. Each bottle of cough syrup is sold for $7.89. Find the profit on the 5 L of cough syrup.

33. A service station operator bought 85 kl of gasoline for $19,250. The gasoline was sold for $.329 per liter. Find the profit on the 85 kl of gasoline.

34. A wholesale distributor purchased 32 kl of cooking oil for $44,480. The wholesaler repackaged the cooking oil in 1.25-liter bottles. The bottles cost $.21 each. Each bottle of cooking oil was sold for $2.97. Find the distributor's profit on the 32 kl of cooking oil.

APPLYING THE CONCEPTS

35. After a 280-milliliter serving is taken from a 3-liter bottle of water, how much water remains in the container? Write the answer in three different ways.

36. Write an essay describing problems in trade and manufacturing that arise between the United States and Europe because they use different systems of measurement.

9.4 Energy

Objective A *To convert units of energy in the metric system of measurement*..

Two commonly used units of energy in the metric system are the calorie and the watt-hour.

Heat is commonly measured in units called calories, or in larger units called Calories (with a capital C). A **Calorie** is 1000 calories and should be called a kilo-calorie, but it is common practice in nutritional references and food labeling to simply call it a Calorie. A Calorie is the amount of heat required to raise the temperature of 1 kg of water 1 degree Celsius. One Calorie is also the energy required to lift 1 kg a distance of 427 m.

⇒ Swimming uses 480 Calories per hour. How many Calories are used by swimming $\frac{1}{2}$ h each day for 30 days?

Strategy To find the number of Calories used:

- Find the number of hours spent swimming.
- Multiply the number of hours spent swimming by the Calories used per hour.

Solution $\frac{1}{2} \times 30 = 15$

$15(480) = 7200$

7200 Calories are used by swimming $\frac{1}{2}$ h each day for 30 days.

The **watt-hour** is used for measuring electrical energy. One watt-hour is the amount of energy required to lift 1 kg a distance of 370 m. A light bulb rated at 100 watts (W) will emit 100 watt-hours (Wh) of energy each hour.

1000 watt-hours (Wh) = 1 kilowatt-hour (kWh)

⇒ A 150-watt bulb is on for 8 h. At 8¢ per kWh, find the cost of the energy used.

Strategy To find the cost:

- Find the number of watt-hours used.
- Convert to kilowatt-hours.
- Multiply the number of kilowatt-hours used by the cost per kilo-watt-hour.

Solution $150 \times 8 = 1200$

$1200 \text{ Wh} = 1.2 \text{ kWh}$

$1.2 \times 0.08 = 0.096$

The cost of the energy used is $.096.

Example 1
Walking uses 180 Calories per hour. How many Calories will you burn off by walking $5\frac{1}{4}$ h during one week?

Strategy
To find the number of Calories, multiply the number of hours spent walking by the Calories used per hour.

Solution
$5\frac{1}{4} \times 180 = \frac{21}{4} \times 180 = 945$

You will burn off 945 Calories.

Example 2
An iron is rated at 1200 W. If the iron is used for 1.5 h, how much energy, in kilowatt-hours, is used?

Strategy
To find the energy used, multiply to find the number of watt-hours used. Convert the watt-hours to kilowatt-hours.

Solution
1200 W × 1.5 h = 1800 Wh = 1.8 kWh

1.8 kWh of energy are used.

Example 3
A TV set rated at 1800 W is on an average of 3.5 h per day. At 7.2¢ per kilowatt-hour, find the cost of operating the set for one week.

Strategy
To find the cost:
- Multiply to find the total number of hours the set is used.
- Multiply the product by the number of watts to find the watt-hours. Convert the watt-hours to kilowatt-hours.
- Multiply the number of kilowatt-hours by the cost per kilowatt-hour.

Solution
$3.5 \times 7 = 24.5$ h

$24.5 \times 1800 = 44,100$ Wh = 44.1 kWh

$44.1 \times \$.072 = \$3.1752$

The cost is \$3.1752.

You Try It 1
Housework requires 240 Calories per hour. How many Calories are burned off by doing $4\frac{1}{2}$ h of housework?

Your strategy

Your solution

You Try It 2
Find the number of kilowatt-hours of energy used when a 150-watt light bulb burns for 200 h.

Your strategy

Your solution

You Try It 3
A microwave oven rated at 500 W is used an average of 20 min per day. At 8.7¢ per kilowatt-hour, find the cost of operating the oven for 30 days.

Your strategy

Your solution

Solutions on p. S22

9.4 Exercises

· ·

Objective A   *Application Problems*

1. How many Calories can be eliminated from your diet if you omit one slice of bread per day for 30 days? One slice of bread contains 110 Calories.

2. How many Calories can be omitted from your diet in two weeks by omitting 400 Calories per day?

3. A nutrition label from a package of crisp bread is shown at the right.

   a. How many Calories are in $1\frac{1}{2}$ servings?

   b. How many Calories from fat are in 6 slices of the bread?

4. Moderately active people need 20 Calories per pound of body weight to maintain their weight. How many Calories should a 150-lb moderately active person consume per day to maintain that weight?

5. People whose daily activities would be described as light activity need 15 Calories per pound of body weight to maintain their weight. How many Calories should a 135-pound lightly active person consume per day to maintain that weight?

6. For a healthy diet, it is recommended that 55% of the daily intake of Calories come from carbohydrates. Find the daily intake of Calories from carbohydrates if you want to limit your Calorie intake to 1600 Calories.

7. Playing singles tennis requires 450 Calories per hour. How many Calories do you burn in 30 days playing 45 min per day?

8. After playing golf for 3 h, Ruben had a banana split containing 550 Calories. Playing golf uses 320 Calories per hour.

   a. Without doing the calculations, did the banana split contain more or fewer Calories than Ruben burned off playing golf?

   b. Find the number of Calories Ruben gained or lost from these two activities.

9. Hiking requires approximately 315 Calories per hour. How many hours would you have to hike to burn off the Calories in a 375-Calorie sandwich, a 150-Calorie soda, and a 280-Calorie ice cream cone? Round to the nearest tenth.

10. Riding a bicycle requires 265 Calories per hour. How many hours would Shawna have to ride a bicycle to burn off the Calories in a 320-Calorie milkshake, a 310-Calorie cheeseburger, and a 150-Calorie apple? Round to the nearest tenth.

Nutrition Facts

Serving Size 2 Slices (18g)
Servings Per Container about 15

Amount Per Serving

Calories 60	Calories from Fat 10

	% Daily Value*
Total Fat 1g	2%
Saturated Fat 0g	0%
Polyunsaturated Fat 0.5g	
Monounsaturated Fat 0.5g	
Cholesterol 0mg	0%
Sodium 60mg	3%
Total Carbohydrate 10g	3%
Dietary Fiber 3g	10%
Sugars 1g	
Protein 2g	

Vitamin A 0%	•	Vitamin C 0%
Calcium 0%	•	Iron 4%

* Percent Daily Values are based on a 2,000 calorie diet. Your daily values may be higher or lower depending on your calorie needs.

	Calories:	2,000	2,500
Total Fat	Less than	65g	80g
Saturated Fat	Less than	20g	25g
Cholesterol	Less than	300mg	300mg
Sodium	Less than	2,400mg	2,400mg
Total Carbohydrate		300g	375g
Dietary Fiber		25g	30g

Calories per gram:
Fat 9 • Carbohydrate 4 • Protein 4

11. An oven uses 500 W of energy. How many watt-hours of energy are used to cook a 5-kilogram roast for $2\frac{1}{2}$ h?

12. A 21-inch color TV set is rated at 90 W. The TV is used an average of $3\frac{1}{2}$ h each day for a week. How many kilowatt-hours of energy are used during the week?

13. A fax machine is rated at 9 W when the machine is in standby mode and at 36 W when in operation. How many kilowatt-hours of energy are used during a week in which the fax machine is in standby mode for 39 h and in operation for 6 h?

14. A 120-watt CD player is on an average of 2 h a day. Find the cost of listening to the CD player for 2 weeks at a cost of 9.4¢ per kilowatt-hour. Round to the nearest cent.

15. How much does it cost to run a 2200-watt air conditioner for 8 h at 9¢ per kilowatt-hour? Round to the nearest cent.

16. A space heater is used for 3 h. The heater uses 1400 W per hour. Electricity costs 11.1¢ per kilowatt-hour. Find the cost of using the electric heater. Round to the nearest cent.

17. A 60-watt Sylvania Long Life Soft White Bulb has a light output of 835 lumens and an average life of 1250 h. A 34-watt Sylvania Energy Saver Bulb has a light output of 400 lumens and an average life of 1500 h.
    a. Is the light output of the Energy Saver Bulb more or less than half that of the Long Life Soft White Bulb?
    b. If electricity costs 10.8¢ per kilowatt-hour, what is the difference in cost between using the Long Life Soft White Bulb for 150 h and using the Energy Saver Bulb for 150 h? Round to the nearest cent.

18. A house is insulated to save energy. The house used 265 kWh of electrical energy per month before insulation and saves 45 kWh of energy per month after insulation. What percent decrease does this amount represent? Round to the nearest tenth.

19. A welder uses 6.5 kW of energy each hour. Find the cost of using the welder for 6 h a day for 30 days. The cost is 9.4¢ per kilowatt-hour.

APPLYING THE CONCEPTS

20. Write an essay on how to improve the energy efficiency of a home.

21. A maintenance intake of Calories allows a person to neither gain nor lose weight. Consult a book on nutrition in order to make a table of weights and the corresponding maintenance intake of Calories. Then for each weight, add another column indicating the appropriate Calorie intake when an individual at that weight wants to lose 1 lb per week.

9.5 Conversion Between the U.S. Customary and the Metric Systems of Measurement

Objective A *To convert U.S. Customary units to metric units* ....

POINT OF INTEREST

The definition of one inch has been changed as a consequence of the wide acceptance of the metric system. One inch is now exactly 25.4 mm.

More than 90% of the world's population use the metric system of measurement. Therefore, converting U.S. Customary units to metric units is essential in trade and commerce—for example, in importing foreign goods and exporting domestic goods. Approximate equivalences between the two systems follow.

Units of Length	Units of Weight	Units of Capacity
1 in. = 2.54 cm	1 oz ≈ 28.35 g	1 L ≈ 1.06 qt
1 m ≈ 3.28 ft	1 lb ≈ 454 g	1 gal ≈ 3.79 L
1 m ≈ 1.09 yd	1 kg ≈ 2.2 lb	
1 mi ≈ 1.61 km		

These equivalences can be used to form conversion rates to change one unit of measurement to another. For example, because 1 mi ≈ 1.61 km, the conversion rates $\frac{1 \text{ mi}}{1.61 \text{ km}}$ and $\frac{1.61 \text{ km}}{1 \text{ mi}}$ are each approximately equal to 1.

➡ Convert 55 mi to kilometers.

$$55 \text{ mi} \approx 55 \text{ mi} \times \boxed{\frac{1.61 \text{ km}}{1 \text{ mi}}}$$

* The conversion rate must contain km in the numerator and mi in the denominator.

$$= \frac{55 \text{ mi}}{1} \times \frac{1.61 \text{ km}}{1 \text{ mi}}$$

$$= \frac{88.55 \text{ km}}{1}$$

$$55 \text{ mi} \approx 88.55 \text{ km}$$

Example 1
Convert 45 mi/h to kilometers per hour.

Solution
$$\frac{45 \text{ mi}}{\text{h}} \approx \frac{45 \text{ mi}}{\text{h}} \times \frac{1.61 \text{ km}}{1 \text{ mi}}$$

$$\approx 72.45 \text{ km/h}$$

You Try It 1
Convert 60 ft/s to meters per second. Round to the nearest hundredth.

Your solution

Solution on p. S22

Example 2
The price of gasoline is $1.39/gal. Find the cost per liter. Round to the nearest tenth of a cent.

Solution
$$\frac{\$1.39}{\text{gal}} \approx \frac{\$1.39}{\text{gal}} \times \frac{1 \text{ gal}}{3.79 \text{ L}}$$
$$\approx \$.367/\text{L}$$

You Try It 2
The price of milk is $2.19/gal. Find the cost per liter. Round to the nearest cent.

Your solution

Solution on p. S22

Objective B   To convert metric units to U.S. Customary units ....

Metric units are already being used in the United States today. Cereal is sold by the gram, 35-mm film is available, and soda is sold by the liter. The same conversion rates used in Objective A are used for converting metric units to U.S. customary units.

Example 3
Convert 200 m to feet.

Solution
$$200 \text{ m} \approx 200 \text{ m} \times \frac{3.28 \text{ ft}}{1 \text{ m}}$$
$$\approx 656 \text{ ft}$$

You Try It 3
Convert 45 cm to inches. Round to the nearest hundredth.

Your solution

Example 4
Convert 90 km/h to miles per hour. Round to the nearest hundredth.

Solution
$$\frac{90 \text{ km}}{\text{h}} \approx \frac{90 \text{ km}}{\text{h}} \times \frac{1 \text{ mi}}{1.61 \text{ km}}$$
$$\approx 55.90 \text{ mi/h}$$

You Try It 4
Express 75 km/h in miles per hour. Round to the nearest hundredth.

Your solution

Example 5
The price of gasoline is $.372/L. Find the cost per gallon. Round to the nearest cent.

Solution
$$\frac{\$.372}{1 \text{ L}} \approx \frac{\$.372}{1 \text{ L}} \times \frac{3.79 \text{ L}}{1 \text{ gal}}$$
$$\approx \$1.41/\text{gal}$$

You Try It 5
The price of ice cream is $1.75/L. Find the cost per gallon. Round to the nearest cent.

Your solution

Solutions on p. S22

9.5 Exercises

· ·

Objective A

Convert. Round to the nearest hundredth.

1. Convert the 100-yard dash to meters.

2. Find the weight in kilograms of a 145-pound person.

3. Find the height in meters of a person 5 ft 8 in. tall.

4. Find the number of cups in 2 L of soda.

5. How many kilograms does a 15-pound turkey weigh?

6. Find the number of liters in 14.3 gal of gasoline.

7. Find the number of milliliters in 1 c.

8. The winning long jump at a track meet was 29 ft 2 in. Convert this distance to meters.

9. Express 65 mi/h in kilometers per hour.

10. Express 30 mi/h in kilometers per hour.

11. Fat-free hot dogs cost $3.49/lb. Find the cost per kilogram.

12. Seedless watermelon costs $.59/lb. Find the cost per kilogram.

13. The cost of gasoline is $1.47/gal. Find the cost per liter.

14. Deck stain costs $24.99/gal. Find the cost per liter.

15. Gary is planning a 5-day backpacking trip and decides to hike an average of 5 h each day. Hiking requires an extra 320 Calories per hour. How many pounds will he lose during the trip if he consumes an extra 900 Calories each day? (3500 Calories is equivalent to 1 lb.)

16. Swimming requires 550 Calories per hour. How many pounds could be lost by swimming $1\frac{1}{2}$ h each day for 5 days if no extra calories were consumed? (3500 Calories is equivalent to 1 lb.)

17. The distance around the earth is 24,887 mi. Convert this distance to kilometers.

18. The distance from the earth to the sun is 93,000,000 mi. Convert this distance to kilometers.

Objective B

Convert. Round to the nearest hundredth.

19. Convert the 100-meter dash to feet.

20. Find the weight in pounds of a 86-kilogram person.

21. Find the number of gallons in 6 L of antifreeze.

22. Find the height in inches of a person 1.85 m tall.

23. Find the distance of the 1500-meter race in feet.

24. Find the weight in ounces of 327 g of cereal.

25. How many gallons of water does a 24-liter aquarium hold?

26. Find the width in inches of 35-mm film.

27. Express 80 km/h in miles per hour.

28. Express 30 m/s in feet per second.

29. Gasoline costs $.385/L. Find the cost per gallon.

30. A 5-kilogram ham costs $5/kg. Find the cost per pound.

31. A backpack tent weighs 2.1 kg. Find its weight in pounds.

32. A 2.5-kilogram bag of grass seed costs $7.89. Find the cost per pound.

33. The speed of light is 300,000 km/s. Convert this speed to miles per second.

APPLYING THE CONCEPTS

34. For the following U.S. Customary units, make an estimate of the metric equivalent. Then perform the conversion and see how close you came to the actual measurement.

60 mi/h ≈   120 lb ≈   6 ft ≈

1 mi ≈   1 gal ≈   1 quarter-mile ≈

35. Determine whether the statement is true or false.
  a. A liter is more than a gallon.
  b. A meter is less than a yard.
  c. 30 mi/h is less than 60 km/h.
  d. A kilogram is greater than a pound.
  e. An ounce is less than a gram.

36. Should the United States keep the U.S. Customary system or convert to the metric system? Justify your position.

Focus on Problem Solving

Working Backward

Sometimes the solution to a problem can be found by *working backward*. This problem-solving technique can be used to find a winning strategy for a game called Nim.

There are many variations of this game. For our game, there are two players, Player A and Player B, who alternately place 1, 2, or 3 matchsticks in a pile. The object of the game is to place the 32nd matchstick in the pile. Is there a strategy that Player A can use to guarantee winning the game?

Working backward, if there are 29, 30, or 31 matchsticks in the pile when it is A's turn to play, A can win by placing 3 matchsticks (29 + 3 = 32), 2 matchsticks, (30 + 2 = 32), or 1 (31 + 1 = 32) matchstick on the pile. If there are to be 29, 30, or 31 matchsticks in the pile when it is A's turn, there must be 28 matchsticks in the pile when it is B's turn.

Working backward from 28, if there are to be 28 matches in the pile at B's turn, there must be 25, 26, or 27 at A's turn. Player A can then add 3 matchsticks, 2 matchsticks, or 1 matchstick to the pile to bring the number to 28. For there to be 25, 26, or 27 matchsticks in the pile at A's turn, there must be 24 matchsticks at B's turn.

Now working backward from 24, if there are to be 24 matches in the pile at B's turn, there must be 21, 22, or 23 at A's turn. Player A can then add 3 matchsticks, 2 matchsticks, or 1 matchstick to the pile to bring the number to 24. For there to be 21, 22, or 23 matchsticks in the pile at A's turn, there must be 20 matchsticks at B's turn.

So far, we have found that for Player A to win, there must be 28, 24, or 20 matchsticks in the pile when it is B's turn to play. Note that each time, the number is decreasing by 4. Continuing this pattern, Player A will win if there are 16, 12, 8, or 4 matchsticks in the pile when it is B's turn.

Player A can guarantee winning by making sure that the number of matchsticks in the pile is a multiple of 4. To ensure this, Player A allows Player B to go first and then adds exactly enough matchsticks to the pile to bring the total to a multiple of 4.

For example, suppose B places 3 matchsticks in the pile; then A places 1 matchstick (3 + 1 = 4). Now B places 2 matchsticks in the pile. The total is now 6 matchsticks. Player A then places 2 matchsticks in the pile to bring the total to 8, a multiple of 4. If play continues in this way, Player A will win.

Here are some variations of Nim. See whether you can develop a winning strategy for Player A. (*Hint:* It may not be possible.)

1. Suppose the goal is to place the last matchstick in a pile of 30 matches.

2. Suppose the players make two piles of matchsticks, with the maximum number of matchsticks in each pile to be 20.

3. In this variation of Nim, there are 40 matchsticks in a pile. Each player alternately selects 1, 2, or 3 matches from the pile. The player who selects the last match wins.

Projects and Group Activities

Name That Metric Unit

What unit in the metric system would be used to measure each of the following? If you are working in a group, be sure that each member agrees on the unit to be used and understands why that unit is used before going on to the next item.

the distance from Los Angeles to New York

the weight of a truck

a person's waist

the amount of coffee in a mug

the weight of a thumbtack

the amount of water in a swimming pool

the distance a baseball player hits a baseball

a person's hat size

the amount of protein needed daily

a person's weight

the amount of maple syrup served with pancakes

the amount of water in a water cooler

the amount of medication in an aspirin

the distance to the grocery store

the width of a hair

a person's height

the amount of water a family uses monthly

the weight of a lawnmower

Deductive Reasoning

Suppose that during the last week of your math class, your instructor tells you that if you receive an A on the final exam, you will earn an A in the course. When the final exam grades are posted, you learn that you received an A on the final exam. You can then assume that you will earn an A in the course.

The process used to determine your grade in the math course is deductive reasoning. **Deductive reasoning** involves drawing a conclusion that is based on given facts. The problems below require deductive reasoning.

1. Given that $\Delta\Delta\Delta = \Diamond\Diamond\Diamond\Diamond$ and $\Diamond\Diamond\Diamond\Diamond = \acute{O}\acute{O}$, then $\Delta\Delta\Delta\Delta\Delta\Delta = $ how many $\acute{O}$s?

2. Given that $\ddagger\ddagger = \bullet\bullet\bullet$ and $\bullet\bullet\bullet = \Lambda$, then $\ddagger\ddagger\ddagger\ddagger = $ how many Λs?

3. Given that $\acute{O}\acute{O}\acute{O} = \Omega\Omega$ and $¤ = \Omega\Omega$, then $¤¤ = $ how many $\acute{O}$s?

4. Given that $\int\int\int\int\int = \partial\partial$ and $\partial\partial\partial\partial = ¥¥¥$, then $¥¥¥¥¥¥ = $ how many $\int$s?

5. Given that $\hat{O}\hat{O}\hat{O}\hat{O}\hat{O} = \square\square\square$ and $\square\square\square\square\square\square = \S\S\S\S$, then $\S\S\S\S\S\S = $ how many $\hat{O}$s?

6. Chris, Dana, Leslie, and Pat are neighbors. Each drives a different type of vehicle: a compact car, a sedan, a sports car, or a station wagon. From the following statements, determine which type of vehicle each of the neighbors drives. It may be helpful to use the chart provided below.
   a. Although the vehicle owned by Chris has more mileage on it than does either the sedan or the sports car, it does not have the highest mileage of all four cars.
   b. Pat and the owner of the sports car live on one side of the street, and Leslie and the owner of the compact car live on the other side of the street.
   c. Leslie owns the vehicle with the most mileage on it.

TAKE NOTE

To use the chart to solve this problem, write an X in a box to indicate that a possibility has been eliminated. Write a $\checkmark$ to show that a match has been found. When a row or column has 3 Xs, a $\checkmark$ is written in the remaining open box in that row or column of the chart.

	Compact	Sedan	Sports Car	Wagon
Chris				
Dana				
Leslie				
Pat				

7. The Ontkeans, Kedrovas, McIvers, and Levinsons are neighbors. Each of the four families specializes in a different national cuisine (Chinese, French, Italian, or Mexican). From the following statements, determine which cuisine each family specializes in.
   a. The Ontkeans invited the family that specializes in Chinese cuisine and the family that specializes in Mexican cuisine for dinner last night.
   b. The McIvers live between the family that specializes in Italian cuisine and the Ontkeans. The Levinsons live between the Kedrovas and the family that specializes in Chinese cuisine.
   c. The Kedrovas and the family that specializes in Italian cuisine both subscribe to the same culinary magazine.

Search the World Wide Web Use the Internet to find information regarding the metric system. You might enter "metric" as the word to search for.

Find professional organizations whose members are in careers related to your major. For example, we found information regarding the metric system and architecture, traffic safety services, cooking, surveying, and transportation.

The process of changing our system of measurement to the metric system is called **metrication** or **metric transition.** Find at least two associations involved in metrication.

Describe one way in which a country that has changed to the metric system helped its citizens in the transition to the metric system. For example, one Web site shows metric-conversion postal stamps printed in Australia.

Chapter Summary

Key Words The *metric system of measurement* is a system of measurement based on the decimal system.

The basic unit of measurement of length in the metric system is the *meter.*

The basic unit of mass in the metric system is the *gram.*

The basic unit of capacity in the metric system is the *liter.*

Heat is commonly measured in units called *Calories.*

The *watt-hour* is used in the metric system for measuring electrical energy.

Essential Rules Prefixes to the basic unit denote the magnitude of each unit in the metric system

kilo-	1000
hecto-	100
deca-	10
deci-	0.1
centi-	0.01
milli-	0.001

Conversion between units in the metric system involves moving the decimal point:
1. When converting from a larger unit to a smaller unit, move the decimal point to the **right.**
2. When converting from a smaller unit to a larger unit, move the decimal point to the **left**.

Chapter Review

1. Convert 1.25 km to meters.

2. Convert 0.450 g to milligrams.

3. Convert 0.0056 L to milliliters.

4. Convert the 1000-meter run to yards. Round to the nearest tenth.

5. Convert 79 mm to centimeters.

6. Convert 5 m 34 cm to meters.

7. Convert 990 g to kilograms.

8. Convert 2550 ml to liters.

9. Convert 4870 m to kilometers.

10. Convert 0.37 cm to millimeters.

11. Convert 6 g 829 mg to grams.

12. Convert 1.2 L to cubic centimeters.

13. Convert 4.050 kg to grams.

14. Convert 8.7 m to centimeters.

15. Convert 192 ml to cubic centimeters.

16. Convert 356 mg to grams.

17. Convert 372 cm to meters.

18. Convert 8.3 kl to liters.

19. Convert 2 L 89 ml to liters.

20. Convert 5410 cm^3 to liters.

21. Convert 3792 L to kiloliters.

22. Convert 468 cm^3 to milliliters.

23. Three pieces of wire are cut from a 50-meter roll. The three pieces measure 240 cm, 560 cm, and 480 cm. How much wire fence is left on the roll after the three pieces are cut?

24. Find the total cost of three packages of chicken weighing 790 g, 830 g, and 655 g if the cost is $2.79 per kilogram.

25. Ham costs $3.40 per pound. Find the cost per kilogram.

26. One hundred twenty-five guests are expected to attend a reception. Assuming that each person drinks 400 ml of coffee, how many liters of coffee should be prepared?

27. A large egg contains approximately 90 Calories. How many Calories can be eliminated from your diet in a 30-day month by eliminating one large egg per day from your usual breakfast?

28. A TV uses 240 W of energy. The set is on an average of 5 h a day in a 30-day month. At a cost of 9.5¢ per kilowatt-hour, how much does it cost to run the set for 30 days?

29. A backpack weighs 1.90 kg. Find the weight in pounds. Round to the nearest hundredth.

30. Cycling burns up approximately 400 Calories per hour. How many hours of cycling are necessary to lose 1 lb? (3500 Calories is equivalent to 1 lb.)

31. Six liters of liquid soap were bought for $11.40 per liter. The soap was repackaged in 150-milliliter plastic containers. The cost of each container was $.26. Each container of soap sold for $3.29 per bottle. Find the profit on the 6 L of liquid soap.

32. A color TV is rated at 80 W. The TV is used an average of 2 h each day for a week. How many kilowatt-hours of energy are used during the week?

33. How many kilograms of fertilizer are required to fertilize 500 trees in an orchard if 250 g of fertilizer are used for each tree?

Chapter Test

1. Convert 2.96 km to meters.

2. Convert 0.378 g to milligrams.

3. Convert 0.046 L to milliliters.

4. Convert 919 cm³ to milliliters.

5. Convert 42.6 mm to centimeters.

6. Convert 7 m 96 cm to meters.

7. Convert 847 g to kilograms.

8. Convert 3920 ml to liters.

9. Convert 5885 m to kilometers.

10. Convert 1.5 cm to millimeters.

11. Convert 3 g 89 mg to grams.

12. Convert 1.6 L to cubic centimeters.

13. Convert 3.29 kg to grams.

14. Convert 4.2 m to centimeters.

15. Convert 96 ml to cubic centimeters.

16. Convert 1375 mg to grams.

17. Convert 402 cm to meters.

18. Convert 8.92 kl to liters.

19. Convert 5 km 38 m to meters.

20. Convert 6020 L to kiloliters.

21. A carpenter needs 30 rafters, each 380 cm long. Find the total length of the rafters in meters.

22. A tile measuring 20 × 20 cm weighs 250 g. Find the weight, in kilograms, of a box of 144 tiles.

23. The community health clinic is giving flu shots for the coming flu season. Each flu shot contains 2 cm³ of vaccine. How many liters of vaccine are needed to inoculate 2600 people?

24. Convert 35 mi/h to kilometers per hour. Round to the nearest tenth. (1 mi ≈ 1.61 km)

25. Twenty-five rivets are used to fasten two steel plates together. The plates are 4.20 m long, and the rivets are equally spaced, with a rivet at each end. Find the distance, in centimeters, between the rivets.

26. Two hundred grams of fertilizer are used for each tree in an orchard containing 1200 trees. At $2.75 per kilogram of fertilizer, how much does it cost to fertilize the orchard?

27. An air conditioner rated at 1600 W is operated an average of 4 h per day. Electrical energy costs 8.5¢ per kilowatt-hour. How much does it cost to operate the air conditioner for 30 days?

28. A laboratory assistant is in charge of ordering acid for three chemistry classes of 40 students each. Each student requires 90 ml of acid. How many liters of acid should be ordered? (The assistant must order by the whole liter.)

29. The record ski jump for women is 547 ft. Convert this distance to meters. Round to the nearest hundredth. (1 m ≈ 3.28 ft)

30. The record ski jump for men is 204 m. Convert this distance to feet. Round to the nearest hundredth. (1 m ≈ 3.28 ft)

Cumulative Review

1. Simplify: $12 - 8 \div (6 - 4)^2 \cdot 3$

2. Find the total of $5\frac{3}{4}$, $1\frac{5}{6}$, and $4\frac{7}{9}$.

3. Subtract: $4\frac{2}{9} - 3\frac{5}{12}$

4. Divide: $5\frac{3}{8} \div 1\frac{3}{4}$

5. Simplify: $\left(\frac{2}{3}\right)^4 \cdot \left(\frac{9}{4}\right)^2$

6. Subtract: $12.0072 - 9.937$

7. Solve the proportion $\frac{5}{8} = \frac{n}{50}$. Round to the nearest tenth.

8. Write $1\frac{3}{4}$ as a percent.

9. 6.09 is 4.2% of what number?

10. Convert 18 pt to gallons.

11. Convert 875 cm to meters.

12. Convert 3420 m to kilometers.

13. Convert 5.05 kg to grams.

14. Convert 3 g 672 mg to grams.

15. Convert 6 L to milliliters.

16. Convert 2.4 kl to liters.

17. The Guerrero family has a monthly income of $2244 per month. The family spends one-fourth of its monthly income on rent. How much money is left after the rent is paid?

18. The state income tax on a business is $620 plus 0.08 times the profit the business makes. The business made a profit of $82,340.00 last year. Find the amount of state income tax the business paid.

19. The property tax on a $45,000 home is $900. At the same rate, what is the property tax on a home worth $75,000?

20. A car dealer offers new-car buyers a 12% rebate on some models. What rebate would a new-car buyer receive on a car that cost $13,500?

21. Rob Akullian received a dividend of $533 on an investment of $8200. What percent of the investment is the dividend?

22. You received grades of 78, 92, 45, 80, and 85 on five English exams. Find your average grade.

23. Karla Perella, a ski instructor, receives a salary of $22,500. Her salary will increase by 12% next year. What will be her salary next year?

24. A sporting goods store has regularly priced $80 fishing rods on sale for $62.40. What is the discount rate?

25. Forty-eight blocks, each 9 in. long, are laid end to end to make the base for a wall. Find the length of the wall in feet.

26. A jar of apple juice contains 24 oz. Find the number of quarts of apple juice in a case of 16 jars.

27. A garage mechanic bought oil in a 40-gallon container. The mechanic bought the oil for $4.88 per gallon and sold the oil for $1.99 per quart. Find the profit on the 40-gallon container of oil.

28. A school swimming pool uses 1200 ml of chlorine each school day. How many liters of chlorine are used for 20 days during the month?

29. A 1200-watt hair dryer is used an average of 30 min a day. At a cost of 10.5¢ per kilowatt-hour, how much does it cost to operate the hair dryer for 30 days?

30. Convert 60 mi/h to kilometers per hour. Round to the nearest tenth. (1.61 km = 1 mi)

10

Rational Numbers

Computer designers use negative numbers to measure the voltage in a circuit. By changing the voltage in a circuit, the behavior of the circuit changes. Some of the circuits created by these computer designers are called gates. Using a combination of gates produces circuits that enable a computer to perform operations such as addition, subtraction, multiplication, and division.

Objectives

Section 10.1
To identify the order relation between two integers
To evaluate expressions that contain the absolute-value symbol

Section 10.2
To add integers
To subtract integers
To solve application problems

Section 10.3
To multiply integers
To divide integers
To solve application problems

Section 10.4
To add or subtract rational numbers
To multiply or divide rational numbers
To solve application problems

Section 10.5
To write a number in scientific notation
To use the Order of Operations Agreement to simplify expressions

History of Negative Numbers

When a temperature is "below zero," that temperature is represented by placing the symbol − before the number. Thus −4 degrees means that the temperature is 4 degrees below zero. The number −4 is read "negative four" and is an example of a negative number.

The earliest evidence for the use of negative numbers dates from China, about 250 B.C. The Chinese used two sets of calculating rods, one red for positive numbers and one black for negative numbers. The idea seems to have remained with the Chinese and did not spread quickly to the Middle East or to Europe.

Between the years 300 B.C. and A.D. 1500, there were a few further attempts to deal with negative numbers. Then, in 1500, negative numbers began appearing more and more frequently. In most cases, however, the numbers were considered "fictitious" numbers or "false" numbers. The idea of using a negative number to refer to a quantity below zero was still not an accepted idea.

By the 18th century, negative numbers were discussed in most mathematics textbooks. However, operations such as multiplying two negative numbers were not included in some books.

As the 18th century came to a close, some 2000 years after the first evidence of negative numbers from the Chinese, negative numbers were finally accepted. This concept, like many other mathematical ideas, took a long time to develop. Do you suppose some mathematical idea is floating around today that will take 2000 years to become accepted?

10.1 Introduction to Integers

Objective A   *To identify the order relation*
between two integers ....

Thus far in the text, we have encountered only zero and the numbers greater than zero. The numbers greater than zero are called **positive numbers.** However, the phrases "12 degrees below zero," "$25 in debt," and "15 feet below sea level" refer to numbers less than zero. These numbers are called **negative numbers.**

The **integers** are... −4, −3, −2, −1, 0, 1, 2, 3, 4,... .

Each integer can be shown on a number line. The integers to the left of zero on the number line are called **negative integers** and are represented by a negative sign (−) placed in front of the number. The integers to the right of zero are called **positive integers.** The positive integers are also called natural numbers. Zero is neither a positive nor a negative integer.

POINT OF INTEREST

Among the slang words for zero are *zilch, zip,* and *goose egg.* The word *love* for zero in scoring a tennis game comes from the French for "the egg," *l'oeuf.*

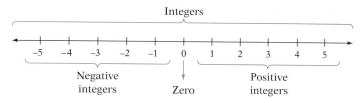

A number line can be used to visualize the order relation of two integers. A number that appears to the left of a given number is less than (<) the given number. A number that appears to the right of a given number is greater than (>) the given number.

2 is greater than negative 4.

2 > −4

Negative 5 is less than negative 3.

−5 < −3

Example 1
The temperature at the North Pole was recorded as 87 degrees below zero. Represent this temperature as an integer.

Solution   −87 degrees

You Try It 1
The surface of the Salton Sea is 232 ft below sea level. Represent this depth by a signed number.

Your solution

Example 2
Graph −2 on the number line.

Solution

You Try It 2
Graph −4 on the number line.

Your solution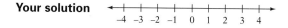

Example 3
Place the correct symbol, < or >, between the two numbers.

   a. −5   −7   **b.** 1   −2

Solution   **a.** −5 > −7   **b.** 1 > −2

You Try It 3
Place the correct symbol, < or >, between the two numbers.

   a. −12   −8   **b.** −5   0

Your solution

Solutions on p. S23

Objective B **To evaluate expressions that contain the absolute-value symbol** ··············

Two numbers that are the same distance from zero on the number line but on opposite sides of zero are called **opposites.**

−4 is the opposite of 4

and

4 is the opposite of −4.

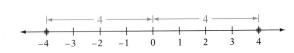

Note that a negative sign can be read as "the opposite of."

−(4) = −4   The opposite of positive 4 is negative 4.

−(−4) = 4   The opposite of negative 4 is positive 4.

The **absolute value** of a number is the distance between zero and the number on the number line. Therefore, the absolute value of a number is a positive number or zero. The symbol for absolute value is "| |".

The distance from 0 to 4 is 4. Thus, $|4| = 4$ (the absolute value of 4 is 4).

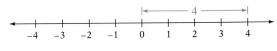

The distance from 0 to −4 is 4. Thus $|-4| = 4$ (the absolute value of −4 is 4).

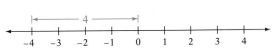

The absolute value of a positive number is the number itself. The absolute value of a negative number is the opposite of the negative number. The absolute value of zero is zero.

Example 4   Find the absolute value of 2 and −3.

Solution $|2| = 2$
$|-3| = 3$

You Try It 4   Find the absolute value of −7 and 21.

Your solution

Example 5   Evaluate $|-34|$ and $|0|$.

Solution $|-34| = 34$
$|0| = 0$

You Try It 5   Evaluate $|2|$ and $|-9|$.

Your solution

Example 6   Evaluate $-|-4|$.

Solution $-|-4| = -4$
The minus sign *in front of* the absolute-value sign is not affected by the absolute-value sign.

You Try It 6   Evaluate $-|-12|$.

Your solution

Solutions on p. S23

10.1 Exercises

· ·

Objective A

Represent the quantity by a signed number.

1. A lake 120 ft below sea level

2. A temperature that is 15° below zero

3. A share of stock up 2 points

4. A loss of 324 dollars

Graph the numbers on the number line.

5. 3 and −3

6. −2 and 0

7. −4 and 1

8. 4 and −1

Place the correct symbol between the two numbers.

9. −2   −5

10. −6   −1

11. −16   1

12. −2   13

13. 3   −7

14. 5   −6

15. −11   −8

16. −4   −10

17. 35   28

18. 42   19

19. −42   27

20. −36   49

21. 21   −34

22. 53   −46

23. −27   −39

24. −51   −20

25. −87   63

26. −75   92

27. 86   −79

28. 95   −71

29. −62   −84

30. −91   −70

31. −131   101

32. 127   −150

Objective B

Find the opposite number.

33. 4   **34.** 16   **35.** -2 **36.** -3 **37.** 22

38. 45   **39.** -31 **40.** -59 **41.** 70   **42.** -88

Evaluate.

43. $|2|$ **44.** $|-2|$ **45.** $|-6|$ **46.** $|6|$ **47.** $|8|$

48. $|5|$ **49.** $|-9|$ **50.** $|-1|$ **51.** $-|-1|$ **52.** $-|-5|$

53. $-|0|$ **54.** $|16|$ **55.** $|19|$ **56.** $|-12|$ **57.** $|-22|$

58. $-|29|$ **59.** $-|20|$ **60.** $-|-14|$ **61.** $-|-18|$ **62.** $|-15|$

63. $|-23|$ **64.** $-|33|$ **65.** $-|27|$ **66.** $|32|$ **67.** $|25|$

68. $-|-42|$ **69.** $|-74|$ **70.** $|-61|$ **71.** $-|88|$ **72.** $-|52|$

APPLYING THE CONCEPTS

73. The graph at the right shows the lowest recorded temperatures, in degrees Fahrenheit, for selected states in the United States. Which state has the lowest recorded temperature?

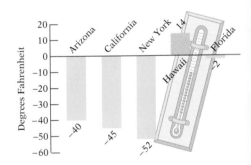

Lowest recorded temperatures

74. **a.** Name two numbers that are 5 units from 3 on the number line.
b. Name two numbers that are 3 units from -1 on the number line.

75. **a.** Find a number that is halfway between -7 and -5.
b. Find a number that is halfway between -10 and -6.
c. Find a number that is one-third of the way between -12 and -3.

76. In your own words, describe **(a)** the opposite of a number, and **(b)** the absolute value of a number.

10.2 Addition and Subtraction of Integers

Objective A *To add integers* ....

An integer can be graphed as a dot on a number line, as shown in Section 10.1. An integer also can be represented anywhere along a number line by an arrow. A positive number is represented by an arrow pointing to the right. A negative number is represented by an arrow pointing to the left. The absolute value of the number is represented by the length of the arrow. The integers 5 and −4 are shown on the number line in the figure below.

The sum of two integers can be shown on a number line. To add two integers, use arrows to represent the addends, with the first arrow starting at zero. The sum is the number directly below the tip of the arrow that represents the second addend.

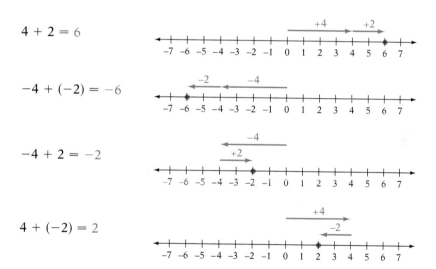

$4 + 2 = 6$

$-4 + (-2) = -6$

$-4 + 2 = -2$

$4 + (-2) = 2$

The sums of the integers shown above can be categorized by the signs of the addends.

The addends have the same sign.

$4 + 2$ *positive* 4 plus *positive* 2
$-4 + (-2)$ *negative* 4 plus *negative* 2

The addends have different signs.

$-4 + 2$ *negative* 4 plus *positive* 2
$4 + (-2)$ *positive* 4 plus *negative* 2

The rule for adding two integers depends on whether the signs of the addends are the same or different.

> **Rule for Adding Two Integers**
>
> To add integers with the same sign, add the absolute values of the numbers. Then attach the sign of the addends.
>
> To add integers with different signs, find the difference between the absolute values of the numbers. Then attach the sign of the addend with the larger absolute value.

➡ Add: $(-4) + (-9)$

$$|-4| = 4, |-9| = 9$$
$$4 + 9 = 13$$

- Because the signs of the addends are the same, add the absolute values of the numbers.

$$(-4) + (-9) = -13$$

- Then attach the sign of the addends.

➡ Add: $6 + (-13)$

$$|6| = 6, |-13| = 13$$
$$13 - 6 = 7$$

- Because the signs of the addends are different, subtract the smaller absolute value from the larger absolute value.

POINT OF INTEREST

Although mathematical symbols are fairly standard in every country, that has not always been true. Italian mathematicians in the 15th century used a "p" to indicate plus. The "p" was from the Italian word *piu*.

$$6 + (-13) = -7$$

- Then attach the sign of the number with the larger absolute value. Because $|-13| > |6|$, attach the negative sign.

➡ Add: $162 + (-247)$

$$162 + (-247) = -85$$

- Because the signs are different, find the difference between the absolute values of the numbers and attach the sign of the number with the greater absolute value.

➡ Find the sum of -14 and -47.

$$-14 + (-47) = -61$$

- Because the signs are the same, add the absolute values of the numbers and attach the sign of the addends.

CALCULATOR NOTE

To add $-14 + (-47)$ on your calculator, enter the following:

14 [+/−] [+] 47 [+/−] [=]

When adding more than two integers, start from the left and add the first two numbers. Then add the sum to the third number. Continue this process until all the numbers have been added.

➡ Add: $(-4) + (-6) + (-8) + 9$

$$\begin{aligned}(-4) + (-6) + (-8) + 9 &= (-10) + (-8) + 9 \\ &= (-18) + 9 \\ &= -9\end{aligned}$$

- Add the first two numbers.
- Add the sum to the next number.
- Continue adding until all numbers have been added.

Example 1   What is -162 added to 98?

Solution $-162 + 98 = -64$

You Try It 1   Add: $-154 + (-37)$

Your solution

Solution on p. S23

Example 2

Add: $-2 + (-7) + 4 + (-6)$

Solution

$$-2 + (-7) + 4 + (-6) = -9 + 4 + (-6)$$
$$= -5 + (-6)$$
$$= -11$$

You Try It 2

Add: $-5 + (-2) + 9 + (-3)$

Your solution

Solution on p. S23

Objective B   To subtract integers ....

Before the rules for subtracting two integers are explained, look at the translation into words of an expression that is the difference of two integers:

$9 - 3$	positive 9 minus positive 3
$(-9) - 3$	negative 9 minus positive 3
$9 - (-3)$	positive 9 minus negative 3
$(-9) - (-3)$	negative 9 minus negative 3

Note that the sign $-$ is used in two different ways. One way is as a negative sign, as in (-9), *negative* 9. The second way is to indicate the operation of subtraction, as in $9 - 3$, 9 *minus* 3.

Look at the next four subtraction expressions and decide whether the second number in each expression is a positive number or a negative number:

1. $(-10) - 8$ **2.** $(-10) - (-8)$ **3.** $10 - (-8)$ **4.** $10 - 8$

In expressions 1 and 4, the second number is a positive 8. In expressions 2 and 3, the second number is a negative 8.

> **Rule for Subtracting Two Integers**
>
> To subtract two integers, add the opposite of the second integer to the first integer.

This rule states that to subtract two integers, we rewrite the subtraction expression as the sum of the first number and the opposite of the second number.

Here are some examples:

First number	$-$	second number	$=$	first number	$+$	the opposite of the second number	
8	$-$	15	$=$	8	$+$	(-15)	$= -7$
8	$-$	(-15)	$=$	8	$+$	15	$= 23$
(-8)	$-$	15	$=$	(-8)	$+$	(-15)	$= -23$
(-8)	$-$	(-15)	$=$	(-8)	$+$	15	$= 7$

CALCULATOR NOTE

The $\boxed{+/-}$ key on your calculator is used to find the opposite of a number. The $\boxed{-}$ is used to perform the operation of subtraction.

➡ Subtract: $(-15) - 75$

$$(-15) - 75 = (-15) + (-75)$$
$$= -90$$

• To subtract, add the opposite of the second number to the first number.

⇨ Subtract: $27 - (-32)$

$$27 - (-32) = 27 + 32$$
$$= 59$$

• To subtract, add the opposite of the second number to the first number.

When subtraction occurs several times in an expression, rewrite each subtraction as addition of the opposite and then add.

⇨ Subtract: $-13 - 5 - (-8)$

$$-13 - 5 - (-8) = -13 + (-5) + 8$$
$$= -18 + 8$$
$$= -10$$

• Rewrite each subtraction as the addition of the opposite and then add.

Example 3
Find 8 less than -12.

Solution
$$-12 - 8 = -12 + (-8)$$
$$= -20$$

You Try It 3
Find -8 less 14.

Your solution

Example 4
Subtract: $6 - (-20)$

Solution
$$6 - (-20) = 6 + 20$$
$$= 26$$

You Try It 4
Subtract: $3 - (-15)$

Your solution

Example 5
Subtract: $-8 - 30 - (-12) - 7$

Solution
$$-8 - 30 - (-12) - 7$$
$$= -8 + (-30) + 12 + (-7)$$
$$= -38 + 12 + (-7)$$
$$= -26 + (-7)$$
$$= -33$$

You Try It 5
Subtract: $4 - (-3) - 12 - (-7) - 20$

Your solution

Solutions on p. S23

Objective C   **To solve application problems** ··························

Example 6
Find the temperature after an increase of 9°C from -6°C.

Strategy
To find the temperature, add the increase (9) to the previous temperature (-6).

Solution
$$-6 + 9 = 3$$

The temperature is 3°C.

You Try It 6
Find the temperature after an increase of 12°C from -10°C.

Your strategy

Your solution

Solution on p. S23

10.2 Exercises

. . . .

Objective A

Name the negative integers in the list of numbers.

1. $-14, 28, 0, -\dfrac{5}{7}, -364, -9.5$

2. $-37, 90, -\dfrac{7}{10}, -88.8, 42, -561$

Add.

3. $3 + (-5)$ **4.** $-4 + 2$ **5.** $8 + 12$ **6.** $16 + 23$

7. $-3 + (-8)$ **8.** $-12 + (-1)$ **9.** $-4 + (-5)$ **10.** $-12 + (-12)$

11. $6 + (-9)$ **12.** $4 + (-9)$ **13.** $-6 + 7$ **14.** $-12 + 6$

15. $2 + (-3) + (-4)$ **16.** $7 + (-2) + (-8)$ **17.** $-3 + (-12) + (-15)$

18. $9 + (-6) + (-16)$ **19.** $-17 + (-3) + 29$ **20.** $13 + 62 + (-38)$

21. $-3 + (-8) + 12$ **22.** $-27 + (-42) + (-18)$

23. $13 + (-22) + 4 + (-5)$ **24.** $-14 + (-3) + 7 + (-6)$

25. $-22 + 10 + 2 + (-18)$ **26.** $-6 + (-8) + 13 + (-4)$

27. $-16 + (-17) + (-18) + 10$ **28.** $-25 + (-31) + 24 + 19$

29. $-126 + (-247) + (-358) + 339$ **30.** $-651 + (-239) + 524 + 487$

31. What is -8 more than -12?   **32.** What is -5 more than 3?

33. What is −7 added to −16?

34. What is 7 added to −25?

35. What is −4 plus 2?

36. What is −22 plus −17?

37. Find the sum of −2, 8, and −12.

38. Find the sum of 4, −4, and −6.

39. What is the total of 2, −3, 8, and −13?

40. What is the total of −6, −8, 13, and −2?

Objective B

Subtract.

41. $16 - 8$

42. $12 - 3$

43. $7 - 14$

44. $6 - 9$

45. $-7 - 2$

46. $-9 - 4$

47. $7 - (-29)$

48. $3 - (-4)$

49. $-6 - (-3)$

50. $-4 - (-2)$

51. $6 - (-12)$

52. $-12 - 16$

53. $-4 - 3 - 2$

54. $4 - 5 - 12$

55. $12 - (-7) - 8$

56. $-12 - (-3) - (-15)$

57. $4 - 12 - (-8)$

58. $13 - 7 - 15$

59. $-6 - (-8) - (-9)$

60. $7 - 8 - (-1)$

61. $-30 - (-65) - 29 - 4$

62. $42 - (-82) - 65 - 7$

63. $-16 - 47 - 63 - 12$

64. $42 - (-30) - 65 - (-11)$

65. $47 - (-67) - 13 - 15$

66. $-18 - 49 - (-84) - 27$

67. $167 - 432 - (-287) - 359$

68. $-521 - (-350) - 164 - (-299)$

69. Subtract -8 from -4.

70. Subtract -12 from 3.

71. What is the difference between -8 and 4?

72. What is the difference between 8 and -3?

73. What is -4 decreased by 8?

74. What is -13 decreased by 9?

75. Find -2 less than 1.

76. Find -3 less than -5.

Objective C *Application Problems*

77. Find the temperature after a rise of 7°C from -8°C.

78. Find the temperature after a rise of 5°C from -19°C.

79. During a card game of Hearts, Nick had a score of 11 points before his opponent "shot the moon," subtracting a score of 26 from Nick's total. What was Nick's score after his opponent shot the moon?

80. In a card game of Hearts, Monique had a score of -19 before she shot the moon, entitling her to add 26 points to her score. What was Monique's score after she shot the moon?

81. The price of Byplex Corporation's stock fell each trading day of the first week of June 1998. Use the figure at the right to find the change in the price of Byplex stock over the week's time.

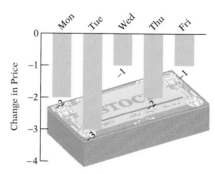

82. The average temperature on the sunlit side of the moon is approximately 215°F. On the dark side, it is approximately -250°F. Find the difference between the temperature on the sunlit side of the moon and on the dark side of the moon.

Change in price of Byplex Corporation Stock.

83. The average temperature throughout Earth's stratosphere is -70°F. The temperature on Earth's surface is 57°F. Find the difference between these average temperatures.

The elevation, or height, of places on the earth is measured in relation to sea level, or the average level of the ocean's surface. The table below shows height above sea level as a positive number and depth below sea level as a negative number. Use the table for Exercises 84 to 86.

Continent	Highest Elevation (in feet)		Lowest Elevation (in feet)	
Africa	Mt. Kilimanjaro	19,340	Lake Assal	−512
Asia	Mt. Everest	29,028	Dead Sea	−1312
North America	Mt. McKinley	20,320	Death Valley	−282
South America	Mt. Aconcagua	22,834	Valdes Peninsula	−131

84. What is the difference in elevation between Mt. Kilimanjaro and Lake Assal?

85. What is the difference in elevation between Mt. Aconcagua and the Valdes Peninsula?

86. For which continent shown is the difference between the highest and lowest elevations **(a)** greatest? **(b)** smallest?

The figure at the right shows the highest and lowest temperatures ever recorded for selected regions of the world. Use this graph for Exercises 87 to 89.

87. What is the difference between the highest and lowest temperatures recorded in Africa?

88. What is the difference between the highest and lowest temperatures recorded in South America?

89. What is the difference between the lowest temperature recorded in Europe and the lowest temperature recorded in Asia?

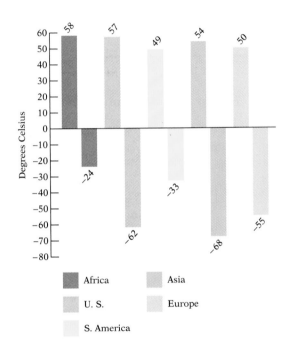

Highest and lowest temperatures recorded (in degrees Celsius)

APPLYING THE CONCEPTS

90. Consider the numbers 4, −7, −5, 13, and −9. What is the largest difference that can be obtained by subtracting one number in the list from another number in the list? Find the smallest positive difference.

91. Fill in the blank squares at the right with integers so that the sum of the integers along any row, column, or diagonal is zero.

92. The sum of two negative integers is −8. Find the integers.

93. Explain the difference between the words *negative* and *minus*.

10.3 Multiplication and Division of Integers

Objective A   *To multiply integers* .... (13) CT

Multiplication is the repeated addition of the same number.

Several different symbols are used to indicate multiplication:

$$3 \times 2 = 6 \qquad\qquad 3 \cdot 2 = 6 \qquad\qquad (3)(2) = 6$$

When 5 is multiplied by a sequence of decreasing integers, each product decreases by 5.

$$5 \times 3 = 15$$
$$5 \times 2 = 10$$
$$5 \times 1 = 5$$
$$5 \times 0 = 0$$

The pattern developed can be continued so that 5 is multiplied by a sequence of negative numbers. The resulting products must be negative in order to maintain the pattern of decreasing by 5.

$$5 \times (-1) = -5$$
$$5 \times (-2) = -10$$
$$5 \times (-3) = -15$$
$$5 \times (-4) = -20$$

This example illustrates that the product of a positive number and a negative number is negative.

When -5 is multiplied by a sequence of decreasing integers, each product increases by 5.

$$-5 \times 3 = -15$$
$$-5 \times 2 = -10$$
$$-5 \times 1 = -5$$
$$-5 \times 0 = 0$$

The pattern developed can be continued so that -5 is multiplied by a sequence of negative numbers. The resulting products must be positive in order to maintain the pattern of increasing by 5.

$$-5 \times (-1) = 5$$
$$-5 \times (-2) = 10$$
$$-5 \times (-3) = 15$$
$$-5 \times (-4) = 20$$

This example illustrates that the product of two negative numbers is positive.

The pattern for multiplication shown above is summarized in the following rules for multiplying integers.

CALCULATOR NOTE

To multiply $(-4)(-8)$ on your calculator, enter the following:

4 [+/−] [×] 8 [+/−] [=]

Rule for Multiplying Two Numbers

To multiply numbers with the same sign, multiply the absolute values of the factors. The product is positive.

$$4 \cdot 8 = 32$$
$$(-4)(-8) = 32$$

To multiply numbers with different signs, multiply the absolute values of the factors. The product is negative.

$$-4 \cdot 8 = -32$$
$$(4)(-8) = -32$$

➡ Multiply: $2(-3)(-5)(-7)$

$$2(-3)(-5)(-7) = -6(-5)(-7)$$

$$= 30(-7)$$

$$= -210$$

- To multiply more than two numbers, multiply the first two numbers.
- Then multiply the product by the third number.
- Continue until all the numbers have been multiplied.

Example 1
Multiply: $(-2)(6)$

Solution
$(-2)(6) = -12$ • The signs are different. The product is negative.

Example 2
Find the product of -42 and 62.

Solution
$-42 \cdot 62 = -2604$

Example 3
Multiply: $-5(-4)(6)(-3)$

Solution
$$-5(-4)(6)(-3) = 20(6)(-3)$$
$$= 120(-3)$$
$$= -360$$

You Try It 1
Multiply: $(-3)(-5)$

Your solution

You Try It 2
Find -38 multiplied by 51.

Your solution

You Try It 3
Multiply: $-7(-8)(9)(-2)$

Your solution

Solutions on p. S23

Objective B   To divide integers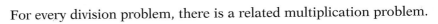

For every division problem, there is a related multiplication problem.

Division: $\dfrac{8}{2} = 4$ Related multiplication: $4 \cdot 2 = 8$

This fact can be used to illustrate the rules for dividing signed numbers.

Rule for Dividing Two Numbers

To divide numbers with the same sign, divide the absolute values of the numbers. The quotient is positive.

To divide integers with different signs, divide the absolute values of the numbers. The quotient is negative.

$\dfrac{8}{2} = 4$ because $4 \cdot 2 = 8$

$\dfrac{-8}{-2} = 4$ because $4(-2) = -8$

$\dfrac{8}{-2} = -4$ because $-4(-2) = 8$

$\dfrac{-8}{2} = -4$ because $-4(2) = -8$

Note that $\frac{8}{-2}$, $\frac{-8}{2}$, and $-\frac{8}{2}$ are all equal to -4.

If a and b are two integers, then $\frac{a}{-b} = \frac{-a}{b} = -\frac{a}{b}$.

Properties of Zero and One in Division

Zero divided by any number other than zero is zero.

Any number other than zero divided by itself is 1.

Any number divided by 1 is the number.

Division by zero is not defined.

$\frac{0}{a} = 0$ because $0 \cdot a = 0$

$\frac{a}{a} = 1$ because $1 \cdot a = a$

$\frac{a}{1} = a$ because $a \cdot 1 = a$

$\frac{4}{0} = ?$ $? \cdot 0 = 4$

There is no number whose product with zero is 4.

The examples below illustrate these properties of division.

$$\frac{0}{-8} = 0 \qquad \frac{-7}{-7} = 1 \qquad \frac{-9}{1} = -9 \qquad \frac{-3}{0} \text{ is undefined.}$$

Example 4
Divide: $(-120) \div (-8)$

Solution
$(-120) \div (-8) = 15$ • The signs are the same.
The quotient is positive.

You Try It 4
Divide: $(-135) \div (-9)$

Your solution

Example 5
Divide: $95 \div (-5)$

Solution
$95 \div (-5) = -19$ • The signs are different.
The quotient is negative.

You Try It 5
Divide: $84 \div (-6)$

Your solution

Example 6
Find the quotient of -81 and 3.

Solution
$-81 \div 3 = -27$

You Try It 6
What is -72 divided by 4?

Your solution

Example 7
Divide: $0 \div (-24)$

Solution
$0 \div (-24) = 0$ • Zero divided by a nonzero number is zero.

You Try It 7
Divide: $-39 \div 0$

Your solution

Solutions on p. S23

Objective C   To solve application problems ....

Example 8

The combined scores of the top five golfers in a tournament equaled -10 (10 under par). What was the average score of the five golfers?

Strategy

To find the average score, divide the combined scores (-10) by the number of golfers (5).

Solution

$-10 \div 5 = -2$

The average score was -2.

You Try It 8

The melting point of mercury is $-38°C$. The melting point of argon is five times the melting point of mercury. Find the melting point of argon.

Your strategy

Your solution

Example 9

The daily high temperatures during one week were recorded as follows: $-9°$, $3°$, $0°$, $-8°$, $2°$, $1°$, $4°$. Find the average daily high temperature for the week.

Strategy

To find the average daily high temperature:

- Add the seven temperature readings.
- Divide by 7.

Solution

$-9 + 3 + 0 + (-8) + 2 + 1 + 4 = -7$

$-7 \div 7 = -1$

The average daily high temperature was $-1°$.

You Try It 9

The daily low temperatures during one week were recorded as follows: $-6°$, $-7°$, $1°$, $0°$, $-5°$, $-10°$, $-1°$. Find the average daily low temperature for the week.

Your strategy

Your solution

Solutions on p. S23

10.3 Exercises

· ·

Objective A

Multiply.

1. 14×3

2. 62×9

3. $-4 \cdot 6$

4. $-7 \cdot 3$

5. $-2 \cdot (-3)$

6. $-5 \cdot (-1)$

7. $(9)(2)$

8. $(3)(8)$

9. $5(-4)$

10. $4(-7)$

11. $-8(2)$

12. $-9(3)$

13. $(-5)(-5)$

14. $(-3)(-6)$

15. $(-7)(0)$

16. -32×4

17. -24×3

18. $19 \cdot (-7)$

19. $6(-17)$

20. $-8(-26)$

21. $-4(-35)$

22. $-5 \cdot (23)$

23. $-6 \cdot (38)$

24. $9(-27)$

25. $8(-40)$

26. $-7(-34)$

27. $-4(39)$

28. $4 \cdot (-8) \cdot 3$

29. $5 \times 7 \times (-2)$

30. $8 \cdot (-6) \cdot (-1)$

31. $(-9)(-9)(2)$

32. $-8(-7)(-4)$

33. $-5(8)(-3)$

Multiply.

34. $(-6)(5)(7)$

35. $-1(4)(-9)$

36. $6(-3)(-2)$

37. $4(-4) \cdot 6(-2)$

38. $-5 \cdot 9(-7) \cdot 3$

39. $-9(4) \cdot 3(1)$

40. $8(8)(-5)(-4)$

41. $(-6) \cdot 7 \cdot (-10)(-5)$

42. $-9(-6)(11)(-2)$

43. What is -5 multiplied by -4?

44. What is 6 multiplied by -5?

45. What is -8 times 6?

46. What is -8 times -7?

47. Find the product of -4, 7, and -5.

48. Find the product of -2, -4, and -7.

Objective B

Divide.

49. $12 \div (-6)$

50. $18 \div (-3)$

51. $(-72) \div (-9)$

52. $(-64) \div (-8)$

53. $0 \div (-6)$

54. $-49 \div 7$

55. $45 \div (-5)$

56. $-24 \div 4$

57. $-36 \div 4$

58. $-56 \div 7$

59. $-81 \div (-9)$

60. $-40 \div (-5)$

61. $72 \div (-3)$

62. $44 \div (-4)$

63. $-60 \div 5$

64. $-66 \div 6$

65. $-93 \div (-3)$

66. $-98 \div (-7)$

67. $(-85) \div (-5)$

68. $(-60) \div (-4)$

69. $120 \div 8$

Divide.

70. $144 \div 9$ **71.** $78 \div (-6)$ **72.** $84 \div (-7)$

73. $-72 \div 4$ **74.** $-80 \div 5$ **75.** $-114 \div (-6)$

76. $-91 \div (-7)$ **77.** $-104 \div (-8)$ **78.** $-126 \div (-9)$

79. $57 \div (-3)$ **80.** $162 \div (-9)$ **81.** $-136 \div (-8)$

82. $-128 \div 4$ **83.** $-130 \div (-5)$ **84.** $(-280) \div 8$

85. $(-92) \div (-4)$ **86.** $-196 \div (-7)$ **87.** $-150 \div (-6)$

88. $(-261) \div 9$ **89.** $204 \div (-6)$ **90.** $165 \div (-5)$

91. $-132 \div (-12)$ **92.** $-156 \div (-13)$ **93.** $-182 \div 14$

94. $-144 \div 12$ **95.** $143 \div 11$ **96.** $168 \div 14$

97. $-180 \div (-15)$ **98.** $-169 \div (-13)$ **99.** $154 \div (-11)$

100. Find the quotient of -132 and -11.   **101.** Find the quotient of 182 and -13.

102. What is -60 divided by -15?   **103.** What is 144 divided by -24?

104. Find the quotient of -135 and 15.   **105.** Find the quotient of -88 and 22.

Objective C   *Application Problems*

106. The daily low temperatures during one week were recorded as follows: 4°, −5°, 8°, −1°, −12°, −14°, −8°. Find the average daily low temperature for the week.

107. The daily high temperatures during one week were recorded as follows: −6°, −11°, 1°, 5°, −3°, −9°, −5°. Find the average daily high temperature for the week.

108. The graph at the right shows the boiling point of three chemical elements. The boiling point of neon is seven times the highest boiling point shown in the table.
a. Without actually calculating the boiling point, determine whether the boiling point of neon is above 0°C or below 0°C.
b. What is the boiling point of neon?

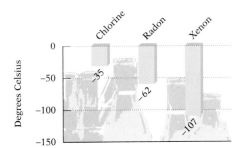

109. The combined scores of the top ten golfers in a tournament equaled −20 (20 under par). What was the average score of the ten golfers?

110. The combined scores of the top four golfers in a tournament equaled −12 (12 under par). What was the average score of the four golfers?

111. The wind chill factor when the temperature is −15°F and the wind is blowing at 20 mph is five times the wind chill factor when the temperature is 25°F and the wind is blowing at 35 mph. If the wind chill factor at 25°F with a 35-mph wind is −12°F, what is the wind chill factor at −15°F with a 20-mph wind?

112. To discourage guessing on a multiple-choice exam, an instructor graded the test by giving 5 points for a correct answer, −2 points for an answer left blank, and −5 points for an incorrect answer. How many points did a student score who answered 20 questions correctly, answered 5 questions incorrectly, and left 2 questions blank?

APPLYING THE CONCEPTS

113. **a.** Find the largest possible product of two negative integers whose sum is −10.
b. Find the smallest possible sum of two negative integers whose product is 16.

114. Use repeated addition to show that the product of two integers with different signs is a negative number.

115. Determine whether the statement is true or false.
a. The product of a nonzero number and its opposite is negative.
b. The square of a negative number is a positive number.

116. 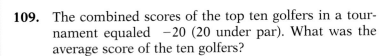 In your own words, describe the rules for multiplying and dividing integers.

10.4 Operations with Rational Numbers

Objective A   ***To add or subtract rational numbers*** ....

In this section, operations with rational numbers are discussed. A **rational number** is the quotient of two integers.

> **Rational Numbers**
>
> A rational number is a number that can be written in the form $\dfrac{a}{b}$, where a and b are integers and $b \neq 0$.

Each of the three numbers shown at the right is a rational number.

$$\frac{3}{4} \qquad \frac{-2}{9} \qquad \frac{13}{-5}$$

An integer can be written as the quotient of the integer and 1. Therefore, **every integer is a rational number.**

$$6 = \frac{6}{1} \qquad -8 = \frac{-8}{1}$$

A mixed number can be written as the quotient of two integers. Therefore, **every mixed number is a rational number.**

$$1\frac{4}{7} = \frac{11}{7} \qquad 3\frac{2}{5} = \frac{17}{5}$$

Recall from Section 3.6 that every fraction can be written as a decimal by dividing the numerator of the fraction by the denominator. The result is either a terminating decimal or a repeating decimal.

We can write the fraction $\dfrac{3}{4}$ as the terminating decimal 0.75.

TAKE NOTE

The fraction bar can be read "divided by."

$\dfrac{3}{4} = 3 \div 4$

$$\begin{array}{r} 0.75 \\ 4\overline{)3.00} \\ -2\,8 \\ \hline 20 \\ -20 \\ \hline 0 \end{array}$$

This is a **terminating decimal.**

The remainder is zero.

We can write the fraction $\dfrac{2}{3}$ as the repeating decimal $0.\overline{6}$.

$$\begin{array}{r} 0.666 = 0.\overline{6} \\ 3\overline{)2.000} \\ -1\,8 \\ \hline 20 \\ -18 \\ \hline 20 \\ -18 \\ \hline 2 \end{array}$$

This is a **repeating decimal.**
The bar over the digit 6 in $0.\overline{6}$ is used to show that this digit repeats.

The remainder is never zero.

All terminating and repeating decimals are rational numbers.

To add or subtract rational numbers in fractional form, first find the least common multiple (LCM) of the denominators.

➡ Add: $-\dfrac{7}{8} + \dfrac{5}{6}$

$8 = 2 \cdot 2 \cdot 2$
$6 = 2 \cdot 3$
$\text{LCM} = 2 \cdot 2 \cdot 2 \cdot 3 = 24$

• Find the LCM of the denominators.

$-\dfrac{7}{8} + \dfrac{5}{6} = -\dfrac{21}{24} + \dfrac{20}{24}$

• Rewrite each fraction using the LCM of the denominators as the common denominator.

$= \dfrac{-21 + 20}{24}$

• Add the numerators.

$= \dfrac{-1}{24} = -\dfrac{1}{24}$

TAKE NOTE

In this text, answers that are negative fractions are written with the negative sign in front of the fraction.

➡ Subtract: $-\dfrac{7}{9} - \dfrac{5}{12}$

$9 = 3 \cdot 3$
$12 = 2 \cdot 2 \cdot 3$
$\text{LCM} = 2 \cdot 2 \cdot 3 \cdot 3 = 36$

• Find the LCM of the denominators.

$-\dfrac{7}{9} - \dfrac{5}{12} = -\dfrac{28}{36} - \dfrac{15}{36}$

• Rewrite each fraction using the LCM of the denominators as the common denominator.

$= \dfrac{-28}{36} + \dfrac{-15}{36}$

• Rewrite subtraction as addition of the opposite. Rewrite negative fractions with the negative sign in the numerator.

$= \dfrac{-28 + (-15)}{36}$

• Add the numerators.

$= \dfrac{-43}{36} = -\dfrac{43}{36} = -1\dfrac{7}{36}$

To add or subtract rational numbers in decimal form, use the sign rules for adding integers.

➡ Add: $47.034 + (-56.91)$

$\begin{array}{r} 56.910 \\ -47.034 \\ \hline 9.876 \end{array}$

• The signs are different. Find the difference between the absolute values of the numbers.

$47.034 + (-56.91)$
$= -9.876$

• Attach the sign of the number with the greater absolute value.

➡ Subtract: $-39.09 - 102.98$

$$-39.09 - 102.98$$
$$= -39.09 + (-102.98)$$

• Rewrite subtraction as addition of the opposite number.

$$\begin{array}{r} 39.09 \\ +102.98 \\ \hline 142.07 \end{array}$$

• The signs of the addends are the same. Find the sum of the absolute values of the numbers.

$$-39.09 - 102.98 = -142.07$$

• Attach the sign of the addends.

Example 1

Subtract: $\dfrac{5}{16} - \dfrac{7}{40}$

Solution

The LCM of 16 and 40 is 80.

$$\frac{5}{16} - \frac{7}{40} = \frac{25}{80} - \frac{14}{80}$$

$$= \frac{25}{80} + \frac{-14}{80}$$

$$= \frac{25 + (-14)}{80} = \frac{11}{80}$$

You Try It 1

Subtract: $\dfrac{5}{9} - \dfrac{11}{12}$

Your solution

Example 2

Simplify: $-\dfrac{3}{4} + \dfrac{1}{6} - \dfrac{5}{8}$

Solution

The LCM of 4, 6, and 8 is 24.

$$-\frac{3}{4} + \frac{1}{6} - \frac{5}{8} = -\frac{18}{24} + \frac{4}{24} - \frac{15}{24}$$

$$= \frac{-18}{24} + \frac{4}{24} + \frac{-15}{24}$$

$$= \frac{-18 + 4 + (-15)}{24}$$

$$= \frac{-29}{24} = -\frac{29}{24} = -1\frac{5}{24}$$

You Try It 2

Simplify: $-\dfrac{7}{8} - \dfrac{5}{6} + \dfrac{2}{3}$

Your solution

Example 3

Subtract: $42.987 - 98.61$

Solution

$$42.987 - 98.61 = 42.987 + (-98.61)$$

$$\begin{array}{r} 98.610 \\ -42.987 \\ \hline 55.623 \end{array}$$

$$42.987 - 98.61 = -55.623$$

You Try It 3

Subtract: $16.127 - 67.91$

Your solution

Solutions on p. S24

Example 4
Simplify: $1.02 + (-3.6) + 9.24$

Solution
$$1.02 + (-3.6) + 9.24 = -2.58 + 9.24$$
$$= 6.66$$

You Try It 4
Simplify: $2.7 + (-9.44) + 6.2$

Your solution

Solution on p. S24

Objective B   *To multiply or divide rational numbers* ....

The product of two rational numbers written as fractions is the product of the numerators over the product of the denominators. Use the sign rules for multiplying integers.

➡ Simplify: $-\dfrac{3}{8} \times \dfrac{12}{17}$

$$-\frac{3}{8} \times \frac{12}{17} = -\left(\frac{3 \cdot 12}{8 \cdot 17}\right) = -\frac{9}{34}$$

• The signs are different.
  The product is negative.

To divide rational numbers written as fractions, invert the divisor and then multiply.

➡ Simplify: $-\dfrac{3}{10} \div \left(-\dfrac{18}{25}\right)$

$$-\frac{3}{10} \div \left(-\frac{18}{25}\right) = \frac{3}{10} \times \frac{25}{18} = \frac{3 \cdot 25}{10 \cdot 18} = \frac{5}{12}$$

• The signs are the same.
  The quotient is positive.

To multiply or divide rational numbers written in decimal form, use the sign rules for integers.

➡ Simplify: $(-6.89) \times (-0.00035)$

$$
\begin{array}{r}
6.89 \\
\times \quad 0.00035 \\
\hline
3445 \\
2067 \quad\;\; \\
\hline
0.0024115 \\
\end{array}
$$

2 decimal places
5 decimal places

7 decimal places

• The signs are the same. Multiply
  the absolute values.

$$(-6.89) \times (-0.00035) = 0.0024115$$

• The product is positive.

⇒ Divide $1.32 \div (-0.27)$. Round to the nearest tenth.

$$
\begin{array}{r}
4.88 \approx 4.9 \\
0.27.\overline{)1.32.00} \\
-1\ 08 \\
\hline
24\ 0 \\
-21\ 6 \\
\hline
2\ 40 \\
-2\ 16 \\
\hline
24
\end{array}
$$

• Divide the absolute values. Move the decimal point two places in the divisor and then in the dividend. Place the decimal point in the quotient.

$$1.32 \div (-0.27) \approx -4.9$$

• The signs are different. The quotient is negative.

Example 5   Multiply: $-\dfrac{7}{12} \times \dfrac{9}{14}$

Solution   The product is negative.

$$-\frac{7}{12} \times \frac{9}{14} = -\left(\frac{7 \cdot 9}{12 \cdot 14}\right)$$

$$= -\frac{3}{8}$$

You Try It 5   Multiply: $\left(-\dfrac{2}{3}\right)\left(-\dfrac{9}{10}\right)$

Your solution

Example 6   Divide: $-\dfrac{3}{8} \div \left(-\dfrac{5}{12}\right)$

Solution   The quotient is positive.

$$-\frac{3}{8} \div \left(-\frac{5}{12}\right) = \frac{3}{8} \times \frac{12}{5}$$

$$= \frac{3 \cdot 12}{8 \cdot 5}$$

$$= \frac{9}{10}$$

You Try It 6   Divide: $-\dfrac{5}{8} \div \dfrac{5}{40}$

Your solution

Example 7   Multiply: -4.29×8.2

Solution   The product is negative.

$$
\begin{array}{r}
4.29 \\
\times\ \ \ 8.2 \\
\hline
858 \\
3432 \\
\hline
35.178
\end{array}
$$

$$-4.29 \times 8.2 = -35.178$$

You Try It 7   Multiply: -5.44×3.8

Your solution

Solutions on p. S24

Example 8   Multiply: $-3.2 \times (-0.4) \times 6.9$

Solution $-3.2 \times (-0.4) \times 6.9$
$= 1.28 \times 6.9$
$= 8.832$

You Try It 8   Multiply: $3.44 \times (-1.7) \times 0.6$

Your solution

Example 9   Divide: $-0.0792 \div (-0.42)$
Round to the nearest
hundredth.

Solution

$$
\begin{array}{r}
0.188 \approx 0.19 \\
0.42.\overline{)0.07.920} \\
\underline{-4\,2} \\
3\,72 \\
\underline{-3\,36} \\
360 \\
\underline{-336} \\
24
\end{array}
$$

$-0.0792 \div (-0.42) \approx 0.19$

You Try It 9   Divide: $-0.394 \div 1.7$
Round to the nearest
hundredth.

Your solution

Solutions on p. S24

Objective C   To solve application problems ....

Example 10
In Fairbanks, Alaska, the average
temperature during the month of July is
61.5°F. During the month of January, the
average temperature in Fairbanks is
-12.7°F. What is the difference between the
average temperature in Fairbanks during
July and the average temperature during
January?

Strategy
To find the difference, subtract the average
temperature in January (-12.7) from the
average temperature in July (61.5).

Solution
$61.5 - (-12.7) = 61.5 + 12.7 = 74.2$

The difference between the average
temperature during July and the average
temperature during January in Fairbanks
is 74.2°F.

You Try It 10
On January 10, 1911, in Rapid City, South
Dakota, the temperature fell from 12.78°C at
7:00 A.M. to -13.33°C at 7:15 A.M. How
many degrees did the temperature fall
during the 15-minute period?

Your strategy

Your solution

Solution on p. S24

10.4 Exercises

. . . .

Objective A

Simplify.

1. $\dfrac{5}{8} - \dfrac{5}{6}$

2. $\dfrac{1}{9} - \dfrac{5}{27}$

3. $-\dfrac{5}{12} - \dfrac{3}{8}$

4. $-\dfrac{5}{6} - \dfrac{5}{9}$

5. $-\dfrac{6}{13} + \dfrac{17}{26}$

6. $-\dfrac{7}{12} + \dfrac{5}{8}$

7. $-\dfrac{5}{8} - \left(-\dfrac{11}{12}\right)$

8. $-\dfrac{7}{12} - \left(-\dfrac{7}{8}\right)$

9. $\dfrac{5}{12} - \dfrac{11}{15}$

10. $\dfrac{2}{5} - \dfrac{14}{15}$

11. $-\dfrac{3}{4} - \dfrac{5}{8}$

12. $-\dfrac{2}{3} - \dfrac{5}{8}$

13. $-\dfrac{5}{2} - \left(-\dfrac{13}{4}\right)$

14. $-\dfrac{7}{3} - \left(-\dfrac{3}{2}\right)$

15. $-\dfrac{3}{8} - \dfrac{5}{12} - \dfrac{3}{16}$

16. $-\dfrac{5}{16} + \dfrac{3}{4} - \dfrac{7}{8}$

17. $\dfrac{1}{2} - \dfrac{3}{8} - \left(-\dfrac{1}{4}\right)$

18. $\dfrac{3}{4} - \left(-\dfrac{7}{12}\right) - \dfrac{7}{8}$

19. $\dfrac{1}{3} - \dfrac{1}{4} - \dfrac{1}{5}$

20. $\dfrac{5}{16} + \dfrac{1}{8} - \dfrac{1}{2}$

21. $\dfrac{1}{2} + \left(-\dfrac{3}{8}\right) + \dfrac{5}{12}$

22. $-\dfrac{3}{8} + \dfrac{3}{4} - \left(-\dfrac{3}{16}\right)$

23. $3.4 + (-6.8)$

24. $-4.9 + 3.27$

25. $-8.32 + (-0.57)$

26. $-3.5 + 7$

27. $-4.8 + (-3.2)$

Simplify.

28. $6.2 + (-4.29)$

29. $-4.6 + 3.92$

30. $7.2 + (-8.42)$

31. $-45.71 + (-135.8)$

32. $-35.274 + 12.47$

33. $4.2 + (-6.8) + 5.3$

34. $6.7 + 3.2 + (-10.5)$

35. $-4.5 + 3.2 + (-19.4)$

36. $2.09 - 6.72 - 5.4$

37. $-18.39 + 4.9 - 23.7$

38. $19 - (-3.72) - 82.75$

39. $-3.09 - 4.6 - 27.3$

40. $-3.89 + (-2.9) + 4.723 + 0.2$

41. $-4.02 + 6.809 - (-3.57) - (-0.419)$

42. $0.0153 + (-1.0294) + (-1.0726)$

43. $0.27 + (-3.5) - (-0.27) + (-5.44)$

Objective B

Simplify.

44. $\dfrac{1}{2} \times \left(-\dfrac{3}{4}\right)$

45. $-\dfrac{2}{9} \times \left(-\dfrac{3}{14}\right)$

46. $\left(-\dfrac{3}{8}\right)\left(-\dfrac{4}{15}\right)$

47. $\left(-\dfrac{3}{4}\right)\left(-\dfrac{8}{27}\right)$

48. $-\dfrac{1}{2} \times \dfrac{8}{9}$

49. $\dfrac{5}{12} \times \left(-\dfrac{8}{15}\right)$

50. $\left(-\dfrac{5}{12}\right)\left(\dfrac{42}{65}\right)$

51. $\left(\dfrac{3}{8}\right)\left(-\dfrac{15}{41}\right)$

52. $\left(-\dfrac{15}{8}\right)\left(-\dfrac{16}{3}\right)$

53. $\left(-\dfrac{5}{7}\right)\left(-\dfrac{14}{15}\right)$

54. $\dfrac{5}{8} \times \left(-\dfrac{7}{12}\right) \times \dfrac{16}{25}$

55. $\left(\dfrac{1}{2}\right)\left(-\dfrac{3}{4}\right)\left(-\dfrac{5}{8}\right)$

Simplify.

56. $\dfrac{1}{3} \div \left(-\dfrac{1}{2}\right)$

57. $-\dfrac{3}{8} \div \dfrac{7}{8}$

58. $\left(-\dfrac{3}{4}\right) \div \left(-\dfrac{7}{40}\right)$

59. $\dfrac{5}{6} \div \left(-\dfrac{3}{4}\right)$

60. $-\dfrac{5}{12} \div \dfrac{15}{32}$

61. $-\dfrac{5}{16} \div \left(-\dfrac{3}{8}\right)$

62. $\left(-\dfrac{3}{8}\right) \div \left(-\dfrac{5}{12}\right)$

63. $\left(-\dfrac{8}{19}\right) \div \dfrac{7}{38}$

64. $\left(-\dfrac{2}{3}\right) \div 4$

65. $-6 \div \dfrac{4}{9}$

66. $-6.7 \times (-4.2)$

67. $-8.9 \times (-3.5)$

68. -1.6×4.9

69. -14.3×7.9

70. $(-0.78)(-0.15)$

71. $(-1.21)(-0.03)$

72. $(-8.919) \div (-0.9)$

73. $-77.6 \div (-0.8)$

74. $59.01 \div (-0.7)$

75. $(-7.04) \div (-3.2)$

76. $(-84.66) \div 1.7$

77. $-3.312 \div (0.8)$

78. $1.003 \div (-0.59)$

79. $26.22 \div (-6.9)$

 Divide. Round to the nearest hundredth.

80. $(-19.08) \div 0.45$

81. $21.792 \div (-0.96)$

82. $(-38.665) \div (-9.5)$

83. $(-3.171) \div (-45.3)$

84. $27.738 \div (-60.3)$

85. $(-13.97) \div (-25.4)$

___

Objective C *Application Problems*

86. ◐ On January 23, 1916, the temperature in Browing, Montana, was 6.67°C. On January 24, 1916, the temperature in Browing was −48.9°C. Find the difference between the temperatures in Browing on these two days.

87. ◔ On January 22, 1943, in Spearfish, South Dakota, the temperature fell from 12.22°C at 9 A.M. to −20°C at 9:27 A.M. How many degrees did the temperature fall during the 27-minute period?

88. The boiling point of nitrogen is −195.8°C and the melting point is −209.86°C. Find the difference between the boiling point and the melting point of nitrogen.

89. The boiling point of oxygen is −182.962°C. Oxygen's melting point is −218.4°C. What is the difference between the boiling point and the melting point of oxygen?

◑ The chart at the right shows the closing price of a share of stock on May 30, 1997, for each of five companies. Also shown is the change in the closing price from the previous day. To find the closing price on the previous day, subtract the change in price from the closing price on May 30. Use this chart for Exercises 90 and 91.

Company	Closing Price	Change in Price
Dole Food	$42\frac{1}{2}$	$+1\frac{5}{8}$
General Mills	$63\frac{1}{4}$	$-\frac{5}{8}$
Nabisco	$39\frac{5}{8}$	$-\frac{3}{8}$
Pepsico	$36\frac{3}{4}$	$-\frac{5}{8}$
Quaker Oats	$41\frac{1}{4}$	$+\frac{3}{8}$

90. Find the closing price on the previous day for **(a)** Dole Food and **(b)** Pepsico.

91. Find the closing price on the previous day for **(a)** Quaker Oats and **(b)** General Mills.

APPLYING THE CONCEPTS

92. Determine whether the statement is true or false.
   a. Every integer is a rational number.
   b. Every whole number is an integer.
   c. Every integer is a positive number.
   d. Every rational number is an integer.

93. Find a rational number between $-\frac{3}{4}$ and $-\frac{2}{3}$.

94. Find a rational number between **(a)** 0.1 and 0.2, **(b)** 1 and 1.1, and **(c)** 0 and 0.005.

95. ✏ Given any two different rational numbers, is it always possible to find a rational number between them? If so, explain how. If not, give an example of two different rational numbers for which there is no rational number between them.

10.5 Scientific Notation and the Order of Operations Agreement

Objective A *To write a number in scientific notation* ....

Scientific notation uses negative exponents. Therefore, we will discuss that topic before presenting scientific notation.

Look at the powers of 10 shown at the right. Note the pattern: The exponents are decreasing by 1, and each successive number on the right is one-tenth of the number above it. $(100,000 \div 10 = 10,000; \ 10,000 \div 10 = 1000;$ etc.)

$$10^5 = 100,000$$
$$10^4 = 10,000$$
$$10^3 = 1000$$
$$10^2 = 100$$
$$10^1 = 10$$

If we continue this pattern, the next exponent on 10 is $1 - 1 = 0$, and the number on the right side is $10 \div 10 = 1$.

$$10^0 = 1$$

The next exponent on 10 is $0 - 1 = -1$, and 10^{-1} is equal to $1 \div 10 = 0.1$.

$$10^{-1} = 0.1$$

The pattern is continued on the right. Note that a negative exponent does not indicate a negative number. Rather, each power of 10 with a negative exponent is equal to a number between 0 and 1. Also note that as the exponent on 10 decreases, so does the number it is equal to.

$$10^{-2} = 0.01$$
$$10^{-3} = 0.001$$
$$10^{-4} = 0.0001$$
$$10^{-5} = 0.00001$$
$$10^{-6} = 0.000001$$

Very large and very small numbers are encountered in the natural sciences. For example, the mass of an electron is 0.00000000000000000000000000000911 kg. Numbers such as this are difficult to read, so a more convenient system called **scientific notation** is used. In scientific notation, a number is expressed as the product of two factors, one a number between 1 and 10, and the other a power of 10.

To express a number in scientific notation, write it in the form $a \times 10^n$, where a is a number between 1 and 10 and n is an integer.

For numbers greater than 10, move the decimal point to the right of the first digit. The exponent n is positive and equal to the number of places the decimal point has been moved.

$$240,000 = 2.4 \times 10^5$$

$$93,000,000 = 9.3 \times 10^7$$

For numbers less than 1, move the decimal point to the right of the first nonzero digit. The exponent n is negative. The absolute value of the exponent is equal to the number of places the decimal point has been moved.

$$0.0003 = 3 \times 10^{-4}$$

$$0.0000832 = 8.32 \times 10^{-5}$$

Changing a number written in scientific notation to decimal notation also requires moving the decimal point.

When the exponent on 10 is positive, move the decimal point to the right the same number of places as the exponent.

$$3.45 \times 10^9 = 3{,}450{,}000{,}000$$

$$2.3 \times 10^8 = 230{,}000{,}000$$

When the exponent on 10 is negative, move the decimal point to the left the same number of places as the absolute value of the exponent.

$$8.1 \times 10^{-3} = 0.0081$$

$$6.34 \times 10^{-6} = 0.00000634$$

Example 1   Write 824,300,000,000 in scientific notation.

Solution   The number is greater than 10. Move the decimal point 11 places to the left. The exponent on 10 is 11.

$$824{,}300{,}000{,}000 = 8.243 \times 10^{11}$$

You Try It 1   Write 0.000000961 in scientific notation.

Your solution

Example 2   Write 6.8×10^{-10} in decimal notation.

Solution   The exponent on 10 is negative. Move the decimal point 10 places to the left.

$$6.8 \times 10^{-10} = 0.00000000068$$

You Try It 2   Write 7.329×10^6 in decimal notation.

Your solution

Solutions on p. S24

Objective B   ***To use the Order of Operations Agreement to simplify expressions*** ....

The Order of Operations Agreement has been used throughout this book. In simplifying expressions with rational numbers, the same Order of Operations Agreement is used. This agreement is restated here.

> **The Order of Operations Agreement**
>
> **Step 1**   Do all operations inside parentheses.
> **Step 2**   Simplify any expressions containing exponents.
> **Step 3**   Do multiplication and division as they occur from left to right.
> **Step 4**   Rewrite subtraction as addition of the opposite. Then do additions as they occur from left to right.

TAKE NOTE

In $(-3)^2$, we are squaring -3; multiply -3 times -3. In -3^2, we are finding the opposite of 3^2. The expression -3^2 is the same as $-(3^2)$.

Exponents may be confusing in expressions with signed numbers.

$$(-3)^2 = (-3) \times (-3) = 9$$
$$-3^2 = -(3)^2 = -(3 \times 3) = -9$$

Note that -3 is squared only when the negative sign is *inside* the parentheses.

➡ Simplify: $(-3)^2 - 2 \times (8 - 3) + (-5)$

$(-3)^2 - 2 \times \underbrace{(8 - 3)} + (-5)$ **1.** Perform operations inside parentheses.

$\underbrace{(-3)^2} - 2 \times 5 + (-5)$ **2.** Simplify expressions with exponents.

$9 - \underbrace{2 \times 5} + (-5)$ **3.** Do multiplications and divisions as they occur from left to right.

$9 - 10 + (-5)$

$\underbrace{9 + (-10)} + (-5)$ **4.** Rewrite subtraction as the addition of the opposite. Then add from left to right.

$\underbrace{(-1) + (-5)}$

-6

CALCULATOR NOTE

As shown above, the value of -3^2 is different from the value of $(-3)^2$. The keystrokes to evaluate each of these on your calculator are different. To evaluate -3^2, enter:

3 $\boxed{x^2}$ $\boxed{+/-}$

To evaluate $(-3)^2$, enter:

3 $\boxed{+/-}$ $\boxed{x^2}$

➡ Simplify: $\left(\dfrac{1}{4} - \dfrac{1}{2}\right)^2 \div \dfrac{3}{8}$

$\underbrace{\left(\dfrac{1}{4} - \dfrac{1}{2}\right)}^2 \div \dfrac{3}{8}$ **1.** Perform operations inside parentheses.

$\underbrace{\left(-\dfrac{1}{4}\right)^2} \div \dfrac{3}{8}$ **2.** Simplify expressions with exponents.

$\underbrace{\dfrac{1}{16} \div \dfrac{3}{8}}$ **3.** Do multiplication and division as they occur from left to right.

$\underbrace{\dfrac{1}{16} \times \dfrac{8}{3}}$

$\dfrac{1}{6}$

Example 3   Simplify: $8 - 4 \div (-2)$

Solution $8 - 4 \div (-2) = 8 - (-2)$
$= 8 + 2$
$= 10$

You Try It 3   Simplify: $9 - 9 \div (-3)$

Your solution

Solution on p. S24

Example 4   Simplify: $12 \div (-2)^2 + 5$

Solution $12 \div (-2)^2 + 5$
$= 12 \div 4 + 5$
$= 3 + 5$
$= 8$

You Try It 4   Simplify: $8 \div 4 \cdot 4 - (-2)^2$

Your solution

Example 5   Simplify: $12 - (-10) \div (8 - 3)$

Solution $12 - (-10) \div (8 - 3)$
$= 12 - (-10) \div 5$
$= 12 - (-2)$
$= 12 + 2$
$= 14$

You Try It 5   Simplify: $8 - (-15) \div (2 - 7)$

Your solution

Example 6   Simplify:
$(-3)^2 \times (5 - 7)^2 - (-9) \div 3$

Solution $(-3)^2 \times (5 - 7)^2 - (-9) \div 3$
$= (-3)^2 \times (-2)^2 - (-9) \div 3$
$= 9 \times 4 - (-9) \div 3$
$= 36 - (-9) \div 3$
$= 36 - (-3)$
$= 36 + 3$
$= 39$

You Try It 6   Simplify:
$(-2)^2 \times (3 - 7)^2 - (-16) \div (-4)$

Your solution

Example 7   Simplify: $3 \div \left(\dfrac{1}{2} - \dfrac{1}{4} \right) - 3$

Solution $3 \div \left(\dfrac{1}{2} - \dfrac{1}{4} \right) - 3$
$= 3 \div \dfrac{1}{4} - 3$
$= 3 \times \dfrac{4}{1} - 3$
$= 12 - 3$
$= 12 + (-3)$
$= 9$

You Try It 7   Simplify: $7 \div \left(\dfrac{1}{7} - \dfrac{3}{14} \right) - 9$

Your solution

Solutions on pp. S24–S25

10.5 Exercises

Objective A

Write the number in scientific notation.

1. 2,370,000

2. 75,000

3. 0.00045

4. 0.000076

5. 309,000

6. 819,000,000

7. 0.000000601

8. 0.00000000096

9. 57,000,000,000

10. 934,800,000,000

11. 0.000000017

12. 0.0000009217

Write the number in decimal notation.

13. 7.1×10^5

14. 2.3×10^7

15. 4.3×10^{-5}

16. 9.21×10^{-7}

17. 6.71×10^8

18. 5.75×10^9

19. 7.13×10^{-6}

20. 3.54×10^{-8}

21. 5×10^{12}

22. 1.0987×10^{11}

23. 8.01×10^{-3}

24. 4.0162×10^{-9}

Solve.

25. Light travels approximately 16,000,000,000 mi in one day. Write this number in scientific notation.

26. Write the mass of Earth, which is approximately 5,980,000,000,000,000,000,000,000 kg, in scientific notation.

27. The graph at the right shows the spending on Medicaid in 1990, 1993, and 1996. Write the dollar amount spent on Medicaid in 1996 in scientific notation.

28. The electric charge on an electron is 0.0000000000000000016 coulomb. Write this number in scientific notation.

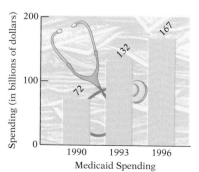

Medicaid Spending

Source: Health Care Financing Administration

29. The length of an ultraviolet light wave is approximately 0.0000037 m. Write this number in scientific notation.

30. One unit used to measure the speed of a computer is the picosecond. One picosecond is 0.000000001 of a second. Write one picosecond in scientific notation.

Objective B

Simplify.

31. $8 \div 4 + 2$

32. $3 - 12 \div 2$

33. $4 + (-7) + 3$

34. $-16 \div 2 + 8$

35. $4^2 - 4$

36. $6 - 2^2$

37. $2 \times (3 - 5) - 2$

38. $2 - (8 - 10) \div 2$

39. $4 - (-3)^2$

40. $(-2)^2 - 6$

41. $4 - (-3) - 5$

42. $6 + (-8) - (-3)$

43. $4 - (-2)^2 + (-3)$

44. $-3 + (-6)^2 - 1$

45. $3^2 - 4 \times 2$

46. $9 \div 3 - (-3)^2$

47. $3 \times (6 - 2) \div 6$

48. $4 \times (2 - 7) \div 5$

49. $2^2 - (-3)^2 + 2$

50. $3 \times (8 - 5) + 4$

51. $6 - 2 \times (1 - 5)$

52. $4 \times 2 \times (3 - 6)$

53. $(-2)^2 - (-3)^2 + 1$

54. $4^2 - 3^2 - 4$

55. $6 - (-3) \times (-3)^2$

56. $4 - (-5) \times (-2)^2$

57. $4 \times 2 - 3 \times 7$

58. $16 \div 2 - 9 \div 3$

59. $(-2)^2 - 5 \times 3 - 1$

60. $4 - 2 \times 7 - 3^2$

Simplify.

61. $7 \times 6 - 5 \times 6 + 3 \times 2 - 2 + 1$

62. $3 \times 2^2 + 5 \times (3 + 2) - 17$

63. $-4 \times 3 \times (-2) + 12 \times (3 - 4) + (-12)$

64. $3 \times 4^2 - 16 - 4 + 3 - (1 - 2)^2$

65. $-12 \times (6 - 8) + 1^2 \times 3^2 \times 2 - 6 \times 2$

66. $-3 \times (-2)^2 \times 4 \div 8 - (-12)$

67. $10 \times 9 - (8 + 7) \div 5 + 6 - 7 + 8$

68. $-27 - (-3)^2 - 2 - 7 + 6 \times 3$

69. $3^2 \times (4 - 7) \div 9 + 6 - 3 - 4 \times 2$

70. $16 - 4 \times 8 + 4^2 - (-18) \div (-9)$

71. $(-3)^2 \times (5 - 7)^2 - (-9) \div 3$

72. $-2 \times 4^2 - 3 \times (2 - 8) - 3$

73. $4 - 6(2 - 5)^3 \div (17 - 8)$

74. $5 + 7(3 - 8)^2 \div (-14 + 9)$

75. $(1.2)^2 - 4.1 \times 0.3$

76. $2.4 \times (-3) - 2.5$

77. $1.6 - (-1.6)^2$

78. $4.1 \times 8 \div (-4.1)$

79. $(4.1 - 3.9) - 0.7^2$

80. $1.8 \times (-2.3) - 2$

81. $(-0.4)^2 \times 1.5 - 2$

82. $(6.2 - 1.3) \times (-3)$

83. $4.2 - (-3.9) - 6$

Simplify.

84. $-\dfrac{1}{2} + \dfrac{3}{8} \div \left(-\dfrac{3}{4}\right)$

85. $\left(\dfrac{3}{4}\right)^2 - \dfrac{3}{8}$

86. $\left(\dfrac{1}{2}\right)^2 - \left(-\dfrac{1}{2}\right)^2$

87. $\dfrac{5}{16} - \dfrac{3}{8} + \dfrac{1}{2}$

88. $\dfrac{2}{7} \div \dfrac{5}{7} - \dfrac{3}{14}$

89. $\dfrac{1}{2} \times \dfrac{1}{4} \times \dfrac{1}{2} - \dfrac{3}{8}$

90. $\dfrac{2}{3} \times \dfrac{5}{8} \div \dfrac{2}{7}$

91. $\dfrac{1}{2} - \left(\dfrac{3}{4} - \dfrac{3}{8}\right) \div \dfrac{1}{3}$

92. $\dfrac{3}{8} \div \left(-\dfrac{1}{2}\right)^2 + 2$

APPLYING THE CONCEPTS

93. Place the correct symbol, < or >, between the two numbers.
   a. $3.45 \times 10^{-14} \;\square\; 3.45 \times 10^{-15}$
   b. $5.23 \times 10^{18} \;\square\; 5.23 \times 10^{17}$
   c. $3.12 \times 10^{12} \;\square\; 3.12 \times 10^{11}$

94. Light travels 3×10^8 m in 1 s. How far does light travel in 1 year? (Astronomers refer to this distance as 1 light-year.)

95. **a.** Evaluate $1^3 + 2^3 + 3^3 + 4^3$.
   b. Evaluate $(-1)^3 + (-2)^3 + (-3)^3 + (-4)^3$.
   c. Evaluate $1^3 + 2^3 + 3^3 + 4^3 + 5^3$.
   d. Based on your answers to parts a, b, and c, evaluate $(-1)^3 + (-2)^3 + (-3)^3 + (-4)^3 + (-5)^3$.

96. Evaluate $2^{(3^2)}$ and $(2^3)^2$. Are the answers the same? If not, which is larger?

97. Abdul, Becky, Carl, and Diana were being questioned by their teacher. One of the students had left an apple on the teacher's desk, but the teacher did not know which one. Abdul said it was either Becky or Diana. Diana said it was neither Becky nor Carl. If both those statements are false, who left the apple on the teacher's desk? Explain how you arrived at your solution.

98. In your own words, explain how you know that a number is written in scientific notation.

99. Express the mass of the sun and the mass of a neutron in kilograms using scientific notation.

Focus on Problem Solving

Drawing Diagrams How do you best remember something? Do you remember best what you hear? The word *aural* means *pertaining to the ear;* people with a strong aural memory remember best those things that they hear. The word *visual* means *pertaining to the sense of sight;* people with a strong visual memory remember best that which they see written down. Some people claim that their memory is in their writing hand—they remember something only if they write it down! The method by which you best remember something is probably also the method by which you can best learn something new.

In problem-solving situations, try to capitalize on your strengths. If you tend to understand the material better when you hear it spoken, read application problems aloud or have someone else read them to you. If writing helps you to organize ideas, rewrite application problems in your own words.

No matter what your main strength, visualizing a problem can be a valuable aid in problem solving. A drawing, sketch, diagram, or chart can be a useful tool in problem solving, just as calculators and computers are tools. A diagram can be helpful in gaining an understanding of the relationships inherent in a problem-solving situation. A sketch will help you to organize the given information, and can lead to your being able to focus on the method by which the solution can be determined.

A tour bus drives 5 mi south, then 4 mi west, then 3 mi north, then 4 mi east. How far is the tour bus from the starting point?

Draw a diagram of the given information.

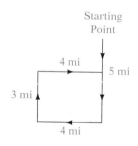

From the diagram, we can see that the solution can be determined by subtracting 3 from 5: $5 - 3 = 2$.

The bus is 2 mi from the starting point.

If you roll two ordinary six-sided dice and multiply the two numbers that appear on top, how many different products are there?

Make a chart of the possible products. In the chart below, repeated products are marked with an asterisk.

$1 \cdot 1 = 1$	$2 \cdot 1 = 2$ (*)	$3 \cdot 1 = 3$ (*)	$4 \cdot 1 = 4$ (*)	$5 \cdot 1 = 5$ (*)	$6 \cdot 1 = 6$ (*)
$1 \cdot 2 = 2$	$2 \cdot 2 = 4$ (*)	$3 \cdot 2 = 6$ (*)	$4 \cdot 2 = 8$ (*)	$5 \cdot 2 = 10$ (*)	$6 \cdot 2 = 12$ (*)
$1 \cdot 3 = 3$	$2 \cdot 3 = 6$ (*)	$3 \cdot 3 = 9$	$4 \cdot 3 = 12$ (*)	$5 \cdot 3 = 15$ (*)	$6 \cdot 3 = 18$ (*)
$1 \cdot 4 = 4$	$2 \cdot 4 = 8$	$3 \cdot 4 = 12$ (*)	$4 \cdot 4 = 16$	$5 \cdot 4 = 20$ (*)	$6 \cdot 4 = 24$ (*)
$1 \cdot 5 = 5$	$2 \cdot 5 = 10$	$3 \cdot 5 = 15$	$4 \cdot 5 = 20$	$5 \cdot 5 = 25$	$6 \cdot 5 = 30$ (*)
$1 \cdot 6 = 6$	$2 \cdot 6 = 12$	$3 \cdot 6 = 18$	$4 \cdot 6 = 24$	$5 \cdot 6 = 30$	$6 \cdot 6 = 36$

By counting the products that are not repeats, we can see that there are 18 different products.

Look at Sections 1 and 2 in this chapter. You will notice that number lines are used: to help you to visualize the integers, as an aid in ordering integers, to help you to understand the concepts of opposite and absolute value, and to illustrate addition of integers. As you begin your work with integers, you may find that sketching a number line may prove helpful in your understanding of a problem, or in working through a calculation involving integers.

Projects and Group Activities

Time Zones   In 1884, a system of standard time was adopted by the International Meridian Conference. The prime meridian is a semicircle passing through Greenwich, England, and labeled 0°, as shown in the diagram at the right.

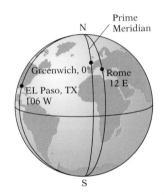

The other meridians are 15° apart, and each 15° width determines a time zone. The time zones to the east of the prime meridian are negative, and the zones to the west are positive, as shown below.

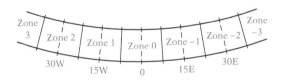

The table below gives the time zones for selected cities.

City	Time Zone	City	Time Zone
Athens	−2	London	0
Beijing	−8	Moscow	−3
Houston	6	Oslo	−1
Honolulu	11	Rio de Janeiro	3

To find the time for a city that is not in your time zone, subtract the time zone of the other city from the time zone of your city. Add that difference to the current time in your time zone. For example, say it is 2:00 P.M. in Athens. What time is it in Houston?

From the table above, the time zone in Athens is −2 and the time zone of Houston is 6.

Subtract 6 from −2. $-2 - 6 = -8$

Add that number to the current time $2:00 \text{ P.M.} + (-8) = 6:00 \text{ A.M.}$
in your time zone.

It is 6:00 A.M. in Houston.

1. Find the time in Beijing when the time in Oslo is 11:00 P.M.

2. Find the time in Moscow when the time in Honolulu is 8:00 A.M.

3. Find the time in Rio de Janeiro when the time in Beijing is 3:00 P.M.

4. An office in Athens is open from 9:00 A.M. to 5:00 P.M. What are the times in Houston that a call to Athens can be made during Athens office hours?

5. An office in Honolulu is open from 8:00 A.M. to 4:00 P.M. What are the times in Moscow that a call to Honolulu can be made during Honolulu office hours?

Closure The whole numbers are said to be *closed* with respect to addition because when two whole numbers are added, the result is a whole number. The whole numbers are not closed with respect to subtraction because, for example, 4 and 7 are whole numbers but $4 - 7 = -3$, and -3 is not a whole number. Complete the table below by entering a Y if the operation is closed for those numbers and an N if it is not closed. When we discuss whether multiplication and division are closed, zero is not included because division by zero is not defined.

	Add	*Subtract*	*Multiply*	*Divide*
Whole numbers	Y	N		
Integers				
Rational numbers				

www.fedstats.gov Information regarding the history of the federal budget can be found on the World Wide Web. Go to the Web site www.fedstats.gov. Click on Fast Facts and then on Frequently Requested Tables. You will see a table entitled "Federal Budget—Summary." When the federal budget table appears on the screen, look for the column that lists each year's surplus or deficit. You will see that a negative sign ($-$) is used to show a deficit. Note that the figures are in millions of dollars.

1. During which years shown in the table was there a surplus?

2. What was the first year during which the deficit was less than $-100{,}000$?

3. Since 1990, in what years was the deficit reduced from the previous year?

4. Use the figures in the table to write three word problems. Have a classmate solve them.

Chapter Summary

Key Words
Positive numbers are numbers greater than zero.

Negative numbers are numbers less than zero.

The integers are ... $-4, -3, -2, -1, 0, 1, 2, 3, 4, \ldots$.

Negative integers are integers to the left of zero on the number line.

Positive integers are integers to the right of zero on the number line.

The *absolute value* of a number is its distance from zero on a number line.

A *rational number* is a number that can be written as the ratio of two numbers.

In *scientific notation*, a number is expressed in the form $a \times 10^n$, where a is a number between 1 and 10 and n is an integer.

Essential Rules
Addition of Integers with the Same Sign
To add numbers with the same sign, add the absolute values of the numbers. Then attach the sign of the addends.

Addition of Integers with Different Signs
To add numbers with different signs, find the difference between the absolute values of the numbers. Then attach the sign of the number with the greater absolute value.

Subtraction of Integers
To subtract one integer from another, add the opposite of the second integer to the first integer.

Multiplication of Integers with the Same Sign
To multiply numbers with the same sign, multiply the absolute values of the numbers. The product is positive.

Multiplication of Integers with Different Signs
To multiply numbers with different signs, multiply the absolute values of the numbers. The product is negative.

Division of Integers with the Same Sign
The quotient of two numbers with the same sign is positive.

Division of Integers with Different Signs
The quotient of two numbers with different signs is negative.

Order of Operations Agreement

Step 1 Perform operations inside parentheses.

Step 2 Simplify exponential expressions.

Step 3 Do multiplication and division as they occur from left to right.

Step 4 Rewrite subtraction as the addition of the opposite. Then do additions as they occur from left to right.

Chapter Review

1. Find the opposite of 22.

2. Subtract: $-8 - (-2) - (-10) - 3$

3. Subtract: $\frac{5}{8} - \frac{5}{6}$

4. Simplify: $-0.33 + 1.98 - 1.44$

5. Multiply: $\left(-\frac{2}{3}\right)\left(\frac{6}{11}\right)\left(-\frac{22}{25}\right)$

6. Multiply: -0.08×16

7. Simplify: $12 - 6 \div 3$

8. Simplify: $\left(\frac{2}{3}\right)^2 - \frac{5}{6}$

9. Find the opposite of -4.

10. Place the correct symbol, $<$ or $>$, between the two numbers.
$0 \quad -3$

11. Evaluate $-|-6|$.

12. Divide: $-18 \div (-3)$

13. Add: $-\frac{3}{8} + \frac{5}{12} + \frac{2}{3}$

14. Multiply: $\frac{1}{3} \times \left(-\frac{3}{4}\right)$

15. Divide: $-\frac{7}{12} \div \left(-\frac{14}{39}\right)$

16. Simplify: $16 \div 4(8 - 2)$

17. Add: $-22 + 14 + (-18)$

18. Simplify: $3^2 - 9 + 2$

19. Write 0.0000397 in scientific notation.

20. Divide: $-1.464 \div 18.3$

21. Simplify: $-\dfrac{5}{12} + \dfrac{7}{9} - \dfrac{1}{3}$

22. Multiply: $\dfrac{6}{34} \times \dfrac{17}{40}$

23. Multiply: $1.2 \times (-0.035)$

24. Simplify: $-\dfrac{1}{2} + \dfrac{3}{8} \div \dfrac{9}{20}$

25. Evaluate $|-5|$.

26. Place the correct symbol, $<$ or $>$, between the two numbers.
$\quad$ 2 $\quad$ -40

27. Find 2 times -13.

28. Simplify: $-0.4 \times 5 - (-3.33)$

29. Add: $\dfrac{5}{12} + \left(-\dfrac{2}{3}\right)$

30. Simplify: $-33.4 + 9.8 - (-16.2)$

31. Divide: $\left(-\dfrac{3}{8}\right) \div \left(-\dfrac{4}{5}\right)$

32. Write 2.4×10^5 in decimal notation.

33. Find the temperature after a rise of $18°$ from $-22°$.

34. To discourage guessing on a multiple-choice exam, an instructor graded the test by giving 3 points for a correct answer, -1 point for an answer left blank, and -2 points for an incorrect answer. How many points did a student score who answered 38 questions correctly, answered 4 questions incorrectly, and left 8 questions blank?

35. The boiling point of mercury is 356.58°C. The melting point of mercury is $-38.87°$C. Find the difference between the boiling point and the melting point of mercury.

Chapter Test

1. Subtract: $-5 - (-8)$

2. Evaluate $-|-2|$.

3. Add: $-\frac{2}{5} + \frac{7}{15}$

4. Find the product of 0.032 and -1.9.

5. Place the correct symbol, $<$ or $>$, between the two numbers.
   $-8 \quad -10$

6. Add: $1.22 + (-3.1)$

7. Simplify: $4 \times (4 - 7) \div (-2) - 4 \times 8$

8. Multiply: $-5 \times (-6) \times 3$

9. What is -1.004 decreased by 3.01?

10. Divide: $-72 \div 8$

11. Find the sum of -2, 3, and -8.

12. Add: $-\frac{3}{8} + \frac{2}{3}$

13. Write 87,600,000,000 in scientific notation.

14. Find the product of -4 and 12.

15. Divide: $\frac{0}{-17}$

16. Subtract: $16 - 4 - (-5) - 7$

17. Find the quotient of $-\frac{2}{3}$ and $\frac{5}{6}$.

18. Place the correct symbol, $<$ or $>$, between the two numbers.
$$0 \quad -4$$

19. Add: $16 + (-10) + (-20)$

20. Simplify: $(-2)^2 - (-3)^2 \div (1 - 4)^2 \times 2 - 6$

21. Subtract: $-\frac{2}{5} - \left(-\frac{7}{10}\right)$

22. Write 9.601×10^{-8} in decimal notation.

23. Divide: $-15.64 \div (-4.6)$

24. Find the sum of $-\frac{1}{2}, \frac{1}{3}$, and $\frac{1}{4}$.

25. Multiply: $\frac{3}{8} \times \left(-\frac{5}{6}\right) \times \left(-\frac{4}{15}\right)$

26. Subtract: $2.113 - (-1.1)$

27. Find the temperature after a rise of 11°C from −4°C.

28. The melting point of radon is −71°C. The melting point of oxygen is three times the melting point of radon. Find the melting point of oxygen.

29. On December 24, 1924, in Fairfield, Montana, the temperature fell from 17.22°C at noon to −29.4°C at midnight. How many degrees did the temperature fall in the 12-hour period?

30. The daily low temperature readings for a 3-day period were as follows: −7°, 9°, −8°. Find the average low temperature for the 3-day period.

Cumulative Review

1. Simplify: $16 - 4 \cdot (3 - 2)^2 \cdot 4$

2. Find the difference between $8\frac{1}{2}$ and $3\frac{4}{7}$.

3. Divide: $3\frac{7}{8} \div 1\frac{1}{2}$

4. Simplify: $\frac{3}{8} \div \left(\frac{3}{8} - \frac{1}{4}\right) \div \frac{7}{3}$

5. Subtract: $2.907 - 1.09761$

6. Solve the proportion $\frac{7}{12} = \frac{n}{32}$. Round to the nearest hundredth.

7. 22 is 160% of what number?

8. Convert: 7 qt = _____ gal _____ qt

9. Convert: 6692 ml = _____ L

10. Convert 4.2 ft to meters. Round to the nearest hundredth. (1 m = 3.28 ft.)

11. Find 32% of 180.

12. Convert $3\frac{2}{5}$ to a percent.

13. Add: $-8 + 5$

14. Add: $3\frac{1}{4} + \left(-6\frac{5}{8}\right)$

15. Subtract: $-6\frac{1}{8} - 4\frac{5}{12}$

16. Simplify: $-12 - (-7) - 3(-8)$

17. What is -3.2 times -1.09?

18. Multiply: $-6 \times 7 \times \left(-\frac{3}{4}\right)$

19. Find the quotient of 42 and -6.

20. Divide: $-2\frac{1}{7} \div \left(-3\frac{3}{5}\right)$

21. Simplify: $3 \times (3 - 7) \div 6 - 2$

22. Simplify: $4 - (-2)^2 \div (1 - 2)^2 \times 3 + 4$

23. A board $5\frac{2}{3}$ ft long is cut from a board 8 ft long. What is the length of the board remaining?

24. Nimisha had a balance of $763.56 in her checkbook before writing checks for $135.88 and $47.81 and making a deposit of $223.44. Find her new checkbook balance.

25. A suit that regularly sells for $165 is on sale for $120. Find the percent decrease in price. Round to the nearest tenth of a percent.

26. A reception is planned for 80 guests. How many gallons of coffee should be prepared to provide 2 cups of coffee for each guest?

27. A stock selling for $82\frac{5}{8}$ per share pays a dividend of $1.50 per share. The dividend is increased by 12%. Find the dividend per share after the increase.

28. The hourly wages for five job classifications at a company are $9.40, $7.32, $13.25, $8.73, and $11.10. Find the median hourly pay.

29. A pre-election survey showed that 5 out of every 8 registered voters would cast ballots in a city election. At this rate, how many people would vote in a city of 960,000 registered voters?

30. The daily high temperature readings for a 4-day period were recorded as follows: $-19°$, $-7°$, $1°$, and $9°$. Find the average high temperature for the 4-day period.

CHAPTER

11

Introduction to Algebra

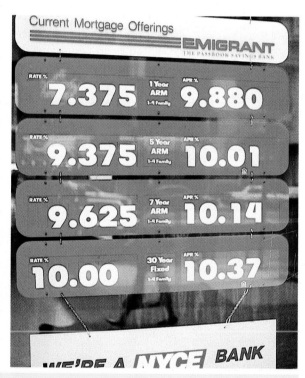

Current Mortgage Offerings

EMIGRANT
THE PASSBOOK SAVINGS BANK

RATE %		APR %
7.375	1 Year ARM 1-4 Family	9.880
9.375	5 Year ARM 1-4 Family	10.01
9.625	7 Year ARM 1-4 Family	10.14
10.00	30 Year Fixed 1-4 Family	10.37

WE'RE A NYCE BANK

Mortgage brokers assist people who are looking for a home loan. The broker, by solving an equation, can determine the monthly payment on home loans of different amounts of money and different interest rates. Part of the broker's job is then to ensure that the monthly payment on the home loan is within the financial means of the home buyer.

Objectives

Section 11.1
To evaluate variable expressions
To simplify variable expressions containing no parentheses
To simplify variable expressions containing parentheses

Section 11.2
To determine whether a given value is a solution of an equation
To solve an equation of the form $x + a = b$
To solve an equation of the form $ax = b$
To solve application problems

Section 11.3
To solve an equation of the form $ax + b = c$
To solve application problems

Section 11.4
To solve an equation of the form $ax + b = cx + d$
To solve an equation containing parentheses

Section 11.5
To translate a verbal expression into a mathematical expression given the variable
To translate a verbal expression into a mathematical expression by assigning the variable

Section 11.6
To translate a sentence into an equation and solve
To solve application problems

History of the Equals Sign

A portion of a page of the first book that used an equals sign, =, is shown at the left. This book was written in 1557 by Robert Recorde and was titled *The Whetstone of Witte*.

Notice, near the end of the paragraph in the illustration, the words, "bicause noe 2 thynges can be moare equalle." Recorde decided that two things could not be more equal than two parallel lines of the same length. Therefore it made sense to use this symbol to show equality.

This page also illustrates the use of the plus sign, +, and the minus sign, −. These symbols had been widely used for only about 100 years when this book was written.

11.1 Variable Expressions

Objective A *To evaluate variable expressions* ....

Often we discuss a quantity without knowing its exact value—for example, next year's inflation rate, the price of gasoline next summer, or the interest rate on a new-car loan next fall. In mathematics, a letter of the alphabet is used to stand for a quantity that is unknown or that can change or *vary*. The letter is called a **variable.** An expression that contains one or more variables is called a **variable expression.**

A company's business manager has determined that the company will make a $2 profit on each radio it sells. The manager wants to describe the company's total profit from the sale of radios. Because the number of radios that the company will sell is unknown, the manager lets the variable n stand for that number. Then the variable expression $2 \cdot n$, or simply $2n$, describes the company's profit from selling n radios.

The company's profit from selling n radios is $\$2 \cdot n = \$2n$.

If the company sells 12 radios, its profit is $\$2 \cdot 12 = \$24$.

If the company sells 75 radios, its profit is $\$2 \cdot 75 = \$150$.

Replacing the variable or variables in a variable expression and then simplifying the resulting numerical expression is called **evaluating the variable expression.**

➡ Evaluate $3x^2 + xy - z$ when $x = -2$, $y = 3$, and $z = -4$.

$3x^2 + xy - z$

$3(-2)^2 + (-2)(3) - (-4)$ • Replace each variable in the expression with the number it stands for.

$= 3 \cdot 4 + (-2)(3) - (-4)$ • Use the Order of Operations Agreement to simplify the resulting numerical expression.

$= 12 + (-6) - (-4)$

$= 12 + (-6) + 4$

$= 6 + 4$

$= 10$

The value of the variable expression $3x^2 + xy - z$ when $x = -2$, $y = 3$, and $z = -4$ is 10.

Example 1

Evaluate $3x - 4y$ when $x = -2$ and $y = 3$.

Solution

$3x - 4y$

$3(-2) - 4(3) = -6 - 12$
$\qquad\qquad\quad = -6 + (-12) = -18$

You Try It 1

Evaluate $6a - 5b$ when $a = -3$ and $b = 4$.

Your solution

Example 2

Evaluate $-x^2 - 6 \div y$ when $x = -3$ and $y = 2$.

Solution

$-x^2 - 6 \div y$

$-(-3)^2 - 6 \div 2 = -9 - 6 \div 2$
$\qquad\qquad\qquad\quad = -9 - 3$
$\qquad\qquad\qquad\quad = -9 + (-3) = -12$

You Try It 2

Evaluate $-3s^2 - 12 \div t$ when $s = -2$ and $t = 4$.

Your solution

Example 3

Evaluate $-\frac{1}{2}y^2 - \frac{3}{4}z$ when $y = 2$ and $z = -4$.

Solution

$-\frac{1}{2}y^2 - \frac{3}{4}z$

$-\frac{1}{2}(2)^2 - \frac{3}{4}(-4) = -\frac{1}{2} \cdot 4 - \frac{3}{4}(-4)$
$\qquad\qquad\qquad\qquad = -2 - (-3)$
$\qquad\qquad\qquad\qquad = -2 + (3) = 1$

You Try It 3

Evaluate $-\frac{2}{3}m + \frac{3}{4}n^3$ when $m = 6$ and $n = 2$.

Your solution

Example 4

Evaluate $-2ab + b^2 + a^2$ when $a = -\frac{3}{5}$ and $b = \frac{2}{5}$.

Solution

$-2ab + b^2 + a^2$

$-2\left(-\frac{3}{5}\right)\left(\frac{2}{5}\right) + \left(\frac{2}{5}\right)^2 + \left(-\frac{3}{5}\right)^2$

$= -2\left(-\frac{3}{5}\right)\left(\frac{2}{5}\right) + \left(\frac{4}{25}\right) + \left(\frac{9}{25}\right)$

$= \frac{12}{25} + \frac{4}{25} + \frac{9}{25} = \frac{25}{25} = 1$

You Try It 4

Evaluate $-3yz - z^2 + y^2$ when $y = -\frac{2}{3}$ and $z = \frac{1}{3}$.

Your solution

Solutions on p. S25

Objective B   **To simplify variable expressions containing no parentheses** .....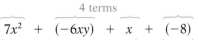

The **terms** of a variable expression are the addends of the expression. The variable expression at the right has four terms.

4 terms

$7x^2 \;+\; (-6xy) \;+\; x \;+\; (-8)$

variable terms   constant term

Three of the terms are **variable terms:** $7x^2$, $(-6xy)$, and x.

One of the terms is a **constant term:** (-8). A constant term has no variables.

Each variable term is composed of a **numerical coefficient** and a **variable part** (the variable or variables and their exponents). When the numerical coefficient is 1, the 1 is usually not written. $(1x = x)$

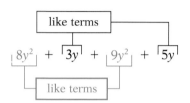

Like terms of a variable expression are the terms with the same variable part. (Because $y^2 = y \cdot y$, y^2 and y are not like terms.)

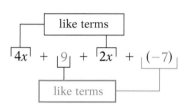

In variable expressions that contain constant terms, the constant terms are like terms.

The Commutative and Associative Properties of Addition are used to simplify variable expressions. These properties can be stated in general form using variables.

Commutative Property of Addition

If a and b are two numbers, then $a + b = b + a$.

Associative Property of Addition

If a, b, and c are three numbers, then $a + (b + c) = (a + b) + c$.

To **simplify a variable expression,** *combine* like terms by adding their numerical coefficients. For example, to simplify $2y + 3y$, think

$$2y + 3y = (y + y) + (y + y + y) = 5y$$

⇒ Simplify: $8z - 5 + 2z$

$8z - 5 + 2z = 8z + 2z - 5$ • Use the Commutative and Associative
$\qquad\qquad = 10z - 5$ Properties of Addition to group like terms.
Combine the like terms $8z + 2z = 10z$.

⟹ Simplify: $12a - 4b - 8a + 2b$

$$12a - 4b - 8a + 2b = 12a - 8a - 4b + 2b$$
$$= 4a - 2b$$

•   **Use the Commutative and Associative Properties of Addition to group like terms. Combine like terms.**

⟹ Simplify: $6z^2 + 3 - z^2 - 7$

$$6z^2 + 3 - z^2 - 7 = 6z^2 - z^2 + 3 - 7$$
$$= 5z^2 - 4$$

•   **Use the Commutative and Associative Properties to group like terms. Combine like terms. $6z^2 - z^2 = 6z^2 - 1z^2 = 5z^2$**

Example 5
Simplify: $6xy - 8x + 5x - 9xy$

Solution
$6xy - 8x + 5x - 9xy$
$= 6xy + (-8)x + 5x + (-9)xy$
$= 6xy + (-9)xy + (-8)x + 5x$
$= -3xy + (-3)x$
$= -3xy - 3x$

You Try It 5
Simplify: $5a^2 - 6b^2 + 7a^2 - 9b^2$

Your solution

Example 6
Simplify: $-4z^2 + 8 + 5z^2 - 3$

Solution
$-4z^2 + 8 + 5z^2 - 3$
$= -4z^2 + 8 + 5z^2 + (-3)$
$= -4z^2 + 5z^2 + 8 + (-3)$
$= z^2 + 5$

You Try It 6
Simplify: $-6x + 7 + 9x - 10$

Your solution

Example 7
Simplify: $\frac{1}{4}m^2 - \frac{1}{2}n^2 + \frac{1}{2}m^2$

Solution
$\frac{1}{4}m^2 - \frac{1}{2}n^2 + \frac{1}{2}m^2$

$= \frac{1}{4}m^2 + \frac{1}{2}m^2 - \frac{1}{2}n^2$

$= \frac{3}{4}m^2 - \frac{1}{2}n^2$

You Try It 7
Simplify: $\frac{3}{8}w + \frac{1}{2} - \frac{1}{4}w - \frac{2}{3}$

Your solution

Solutions on p. S25

Objective C   *To simplify variable expressions containing parentheses* ....

The Commutative and Associative Properties of Multiplication and the Distributive Property are used to simplify variable expressions that contain parentheses. These properties can be stated in general form using variables.

> **Commutative Property of Multiplication**
>
> If a and b are two numbers, then $a \cdot b = b \cdot a$.

> **Associative Property of Multiplication**
>
> If a, b, and c are three numbers, then $a \cdot (b \cdot c) = (a \cdot b) \cdot c$.

The Associative and Commutative Properties of Multiplication are used to simplify variable expressions such as the following.

➡ Simplify: $-5(4x)$

$$-5(4x) = (-5 \cdot 4)x$$ • Use the Associative Property of Multiplication.
$$= -20x$$

➡ Simplify: $(6y) \cdot 5$

$$(6y) \cdot 5 = 5 \cdot (6y)$$ • Use the Commutative Property of Multiplication.
$$= (5 \cdot 6)y = 30y$$ • Use the Associative Property of Multiplication.

The Distributive Property is used to remove parentheses from variable expressions that contain both multiplication and addition.

> **Distributive Property**
>
> If a, b, and c are three numbers, then $a(b + c) = ab + ac$.

➡ Simplify: $4(z + 5)$

$$4(z + 5) = 4z + 4(5)$$ • The Distributive Property is used to rewrite the
$$= 4z + 20$$ variable expression without parentheses.

➡ Simplify: $-3(2x + 7)$

$$-3(2x + 7) = -3(2x) + (-3)(7)$$ • Use the Distributive Property.
$$= -6x + (-21)$$
$$= -6x - 21$$ • Recall that $a + (-b) = a - b$.

The Distributive Property can also be stated in terms of subtraction.

$$a(b - c) = ab - ac$$

⇒ Simplify: $8(2r - 3s)$

$$8(2r - 3s) = 8(2r) - 8(3s)$$
$$= 16r - 24s$$

 • **Use the Distributive Property.**

⇒ Simplify: $-5(2x - 4y)$

$$-5(2x - 4y) = (-5)(2x) - (-5)(4y)$$
$$= -10x - (-20y)$$
$$= -10x + 20y$$

 • **Use the Distributive Property.**

 • **Recall that $a - (-b) = a + b$.**

⇒ Simplify: $12 - 5(m + 2) + 2m$

$$12 - 5(m + 2) + 2m = 12 - 5m + (-5)(2) + 2m$$
$$= 12 - 5m + (-10) + 2m$$

$$= -5m + 2m + 12 + (-10)$$

$$= -3m + 2$$

 • **Use the Distributive Property to simplify the expression $-5(m + 2)$.**

 • **Use the Commutative and Associative Properties to group like terms.**

 • **Combine like terms by adding their numerical coefficients. Add constant terms.**

The answer $-3m + 2$ can also be written as $2 - 3m$. In this text, we will write answers with variable terms first, followed by the constant term.

Example 8
Simplify: $4(x - 3)$

Solution
$$4(x - 3) = 4x - 4(3)$$
$$= 4x - 12$$

You Try It 8
Simplify: $5(a - 2)$

Your solution

Example 9
Simplify: $5n - 3(2n - 4)$

Solution
$$5n - 3(2n - 4) = 5n - 3(2n) - (-3)(4)$$
$$= 5n - 6n - (-12)$$
$$= 5n - 6n + 12$$
$$= -n + 12$$

You Try It 9
Simplify: $8s - 2(3s - 5)$

Your solution

Example 10
Simplify: $3(c - 2) + 2(c + 6)$

Solution
$$3(c - 2) + 2(c + 6) = 3c - 3(2) + 2c + 2(6)$$
$$= 3c - 6 + 2c + 12$$
$$= 3c + 2c - 6 + 12$$
$$= 5c + 6$$

You Try It 10
Simplify: $4(x - 3) - 2(x + 1)$

Your solution

Solutions on p. S25

11.1 Exercises

· ·

Objective A

Evaluate the variable expression when $a = -3$, $b = 6$, and $c = -2$.

1. $5a - 3b$ **2.** $4c - 2b$ **3.** $2a + 3c$ **4.** $2c + 4a$

5. $-c^2$ **6.** $-a^2$ **7.** $b - a^2$ **8.** $b - c^2$

9. $ab - c^2$ **10.** $bc - a^2$ **11.** $2ab - c^2$ **12.** $3bc - a^2$

13. $a - (b \div a)$ **14.** $c - (b \div c)$ **15.** $2ac - (b \div a)$ **16.** $4ac \div (b \div a)$

17. $b^2 - c^2$ **18.** $b^2 - a^2$ **19.** $b^2 \div (ac)$ **20.** $3c^2 \div (ab)$

21. $c^2 - (b \div c)$ **22.** $a^2 - (b \div a)$ **23.** $a^2 + b^2 + c^2$ **24.** $a^2 - b^2 - c^2$

25. $ac + bc + ab$ **26.** $ac - bc - cb$ **27.** $a^2 + b^2 - ab$ **28.** $b^2 + c^2 - bc$

29. $2b - (3c + a^2)$ **30.** $\frac{2}{3}b + \left(\frac{1}{2}c - a\right)$ **31.** $\frac{1}{3}a + \left(\frac{1}{2}b - \frac{2}{3}a\right)$

32. $-\frac{2}{3}b - \left(\frac{1}{2}c + a\right)$ **33.** $\frac{1}{6}b + \frac{1}{3}(c + a)$ **34.** $\frac{1}{2}c + \left(\frac{1}{3}b - a\right)$

Evaluate the variable expression when $a = -\frac{1}{2}$, $b = \frac{3}{4}$, and $c = \frac{1}{4}$.

35. $a + (b - c)$ **36.** $c + (b - 2c)$ **37.** $4a + (3b - c)$

38. $2b + (c - 3a)$ **39.** $2a - b^2 \div c$ **40.** $b \div (-c) + 2a$

🔲 Evaluate the variable expression when $a = 3.72$, $b = -2.31$, and $c = -1.74$.

41. $a^2 - b^2$

42. $a^2 - b \cdot c$

43. $3ac - (c \div a)$

44. $3b - (3b - a^2)$

45. $2c + (b^2 - c)$

46. $abc - 2(b \div c^2)$

Objective B

Simplify.

47. $7z + 9z$

48. $6x + 5x$

49. $12m - 3m$

50. $5y - 12y$

51. $5at + 7at$

52. $12mn + 11mn$

53. $-4yt + 7yt$

54. $-12yt + 5yt$

55. $-3x - 12y$

56. $-12y - 7y$

57. $3t^2 - 5t^2$

58. $7t^2 + 8t^2$

59. $6c - 5 + 7c$

60. $7x - 5 + 3x$

61. $2t + 3t - 7t$

62. $9x^2 - 5 - 3x^2$

63. $7y^2 - 2 - 4y^2$

64. $3w - 7u + 4w$

65. $6w - 8u + 8w$

66. $4 - 6xy - 7xy$

67. $10 - 11xy - 12xy$

68. $7t^2 - 5t^2 - 4t^2$

69. $3v^2 - 6v^2 - 8v^2$

70. $5ab - 7a - 10ab$

71. $-10ab - 3a + 2ab$

72. $-4x^2 - x + 2x^2$

73. $-3y^2 - y + 7y^2$

74. $4x^2 - 8y - x^2 + y$

75. $2a - 3b^2 - 5a + b^2$

76. $8y - 4z - y + 2z$

77. $3x^2 - 7x + 4x^2 - x$

78. $5y^2 - y + 6y^2 - 5y$

79. $6s - t - 9s + 7t$

80. $5w - 2v - 9w + 5v$

81. $4m + 8n - 7m + 2n$

82. $z + 9y - 4z + 3y$

Simplify.

83. $-5ab + 7ac + 10ab - 3ac$

84. $-2x^2 - 3x - 11x^2 + 14x$

85. $\frac{4}{9}a^2 - \frac{1}{5}b^2 + \frac{2}{9}a^2 + \frac{4}{5}b^2$

86. $\frac{6}{7}x^2 + \frac{2}{5}x - \frac{3}{7}x^2 - \frac{4}{5}x$

87. $4.235x - 0.297x + 3.056x$

88. $8.092y - 3.0793y + 0.063y$

89. $7.81m + 3.42n - 6.25m - 7.19n$

90. $8.34y^2 - 4.21y - 6.07y^2 - 5.39y$

Objective C

Simplify.

91. $5(x + 4)$

92. $3(m + 6)$

93. $(y - 3)4$

94. $(z - 3)7$

95. $-2(a + 4)$

96. $-5(b + 3)$

97. $3(5x + 10)$

98. $2(4m - 7)$

99. $5(3c - 5)$

100. $-4(w - 3)$

101. $-3(y - 6)$

102. $3m + 4(m + z)$

103. $5x + 2(x + 7)$

104. $6z - 3(z + 4)$

105. $8y - 4(y + 2)$

106. $7w - 2(w - 3)$

107. $9x - 4(x - 6)$

108. $-5m + 3(m + 4)$

109. $-2y + 3(y - 2)$

110. $5m + 3(m + 4) - 6$

111. $4n + 2(n + 1) - 5$

112. $8z - 2(z - 3) + 8$

113. $9y - 3(y - 4) + 8$

114. $6 - 4(a + 4) + 6a$

115. $3x + 2(x + 2) + 5x$

116. $7x + 4(x + 1) + 3x$

117. $-7t + 2(t - 3) - t$

Simplify.

118. $-3y + 2(y - 4) - y$

119. $z - 2(1 - z) - 2z$

120. $2y - 3(2 - y) + 4y$

121. $3(y - 2) - 2(y - 6)$

122. $7(x + 2) + 3(x - 4)$

123. $2(t - 3) + 7(t + 3)$

124. $3(y - 4) - 2(y - 3)$

125. $3t - 6(t - 4) + 8t$

126. $5x + 3(x - 7) - 9x$

APPLYING THE CONCEPTS

127. The square and the rectangle at the right can be used to illustrate algebraic expressions. The illustration below represents the expression $2x + 1$.

a. Using similar squares and rectangles, draw figures that represent the expressions $3 + 2x$, $4x + 6$, $3x + 2$, and $2x + 4$.

b. The illustration below represents the expression $3(x + 1)$. Rearrange these rectangles so that the x's are together and the 1's are together. Write a mathematical expression for the rearranged figure.

128. Using squares and rectangles similar to those in Exercise 127, draw figures that represent the expressions $2 + 3x$, $2(2x + 3)$, $4x + 3$, and $4x + 6$.
   a. Does the figure $2(2x + 3)$ equal the figure $4x + 6$? Explain how this relates to the Distributive Property.
   b. Does the figure $2 + 3x$ equal the figure $5x$? How is this related to combining like terms?

129. **a.** Simplifying variable expressions requires combining like terms. Give some examples of how this applies to everyday experience.
   b. It was stated in this section that the variable terms y^2 and y are not like terms. Use measurements of area and distance to show that these terms would not be combined as measurements.

130. Explain why the simplification of the expression $2 + 3(2x + 4)$ shown at the right is incorrect. What is the correct simplification.

Why is this incorrect?
$$2 + 3(2x + 4) = 5(2x + 4)$$
$$= 10x + 20$$

11.2 Introduction to Equations

Objective A *To determine whether a given value is a solution of an equation* ....

An **equation** expresses the equality of two mathematical expressions. The expressions can be either numerical or variable expressions.

$$5 + 4 = 9$$
$$3x + 13 = x - 8$$
$$y^2 + 4 = 6y + 1$$
$$x = -3$$
Equations

In the equation at the right, if the variable is replaced by 4, the equation is true.

$$x + 3 = 7$$
$$4 + 3 = 7 \quad \text{A true equation}$$

If the variable is replaced by 6, the equation is false.

$$6 + 3 = 7 \quad \text{A false equation}$$

A **solution** of an equation is a value of the variable that results in a true equation. 4 is a solution of the equation $x + 3 = 7$. 6 is not a solution of the equation $x + 3 = 7$.

➡ Is -2 a solution of the equation $x^2 + 1 = 2x + 9$?

$$\frac{x^2 + 1 = 2x + 9}{(-2)^2 + 1 \mid 2(-2) + 9}$$
$$4 + 1 \mid -4 + 9$$
$$5 = 5$$

• Replace the variable by the given value.

• Evaluate the numerical expressions.

• Compare the results. If the results are equal, the given value is a solution. If the results are not equal, the given value is not a solution.

Yes, -2 is a solution of the equation $x^2 + 1 = 2x + 9$.

Example 1 Is $\frac{1}{2}$ a solution of
$$2x(x + 2) = 3x + 1?$$

Solution
$$\frac{2x(x + 2) = 3x + 1}{2\left(\frac{1}{2}\right)\left(\frac{1}{2} + 2\right) \mid 3\left(\frac{1}{2}\right) + 1}$$
$$2\left(\frac{1}{2}\right)\left(\frac{5}{2}\right) \mid 3\left(\frac{1}{2}\right) + 1$$
$$\frac{5}{2} = \frac{5}{2}$$

Yes, $\frac{1}{2}$ is a solution.

You Try It 1 Is -2 a solution of
$$x(x + 3) = 4x + 6?$$

Your solution

Solution on p. S25

Example 2 Is 5 a solution of
$$(x - 2)^2 = x^2 - 4x + 2?$$

Solution
$$\begin{array}{c|c}
(x - 2)^2 & x^2 - 4x + 2 \\
\hline
(5 - 2)^2 & 5^2 - 4(5) + 2 \\
3^2 & 25 - 4(5) + 2 \\
9 & 25 - 20 + 2 \\
& 25 + (-20) + 2 \\
9 \neq 7 & (\neq \text{ means is not} \\
& \text{equal to})
\end{array}$$

No. 5 is not a solution.

You Try It 2 Is -3 a solution of
$$x^2 - x = 3x + 7?$$

Your solution

Solution on p. S25

Objective B **To solve an equation of the form $x + a = b$** ....

A solution of an equation is a value of the variable that, when substituted in the equation, results in a true equation. To **solve** an equation means to find a solution of the equation.

The simplest equation to solve is an equation of the form *variable = constant*. The constant is the solution of the equation.

If $x = 7$, then 7 is the solution of the equation because $7 = 7$ is a true equation.

In solving an equation of the form $x + a = b$, the goal is to simplify the given equation to one of the form *variable = constant*. The Addition Properties that follow are used to simplify equations to this form.

> **Addition Property of Zero**
>
> The sum of a term and zero is the term.
> $$a + 0 = a \qquad 0 + a = a$$

> **Addition Property of Equations**
>
> If a, b, and c are algebraic expressions, then the equations $a = b$ and $a + c = b + c$ have the same solutions.

The Addition Property of Equations states that the same quantity can be added to each side of an equation without changing the solution of the equation.

In solving an equation, the goal is to rewrite the given equation in the form *variable = constant*. The Addition Property of Equations is used to remove a term from one side of the equation by adding the opposite of that term to each side of the equation.

⟹ Solve: $x - 7 = -2$

$x - 7 = -2$

- The goal is to simplify the equation to one of the form *variable = constant.*

$x - 7 + 7 = -2 + 7$

$x + 0 = 5$

- Add the opposite of the constant term -7 to each side of the equation. After simplifying and using the Addition Property of Zero, the equation will be in the form *variable = constant.*

$x = 5$

The solution is 5.

Because subtraction is defined in terms of addition, the Addition Property of Equations allows the same number to be subtracted from each side of an equation.

⟹ Solve: $x + 8 = 5$

$x + 8 = 5$

- The goal is to simplify the equation to one of the form *variable = constant.*

$x + 8 - 8 = 5 - 8$

$x + 0 = -3$

- Add the opposite of the constant term 8 to each side of the equation. This procedure is equivalent to subtracting 8 from each side of the equation.

$x = -3$

The solution is -3. You should check this solution.

Example 3 Solve: $4 + m = -2$

Solution
$4 + m = -2$
$4 - 4 + m = -2 - 4$
$0 + m = -6$
$m = -6$

The solution is -6.

You Try It 3 Solve: $-2 + y = -5$

Your solution

Example 4 Solve: $3 = y - 2$

Solution
$3 = y - 2$
$3 + 2 = y - 2 + 2$
$5 = y + 0$
$5 = y$

The solution is 5.

You Try It 4 Solve: $7 = y + 8$

Your solution

Example 5 Solve: $\frac{2}{7} = \frac{5}{7} + t$

Solution
$\frac{2}{7} = \frac{5}{7} + t$
$\frac{2}{7} - \frac{5}{7} = \frac{5}{7} - \frac{5}{7} + t$
$-\frac{3}{7} = 0 + t$
$-\frac{3}{7} = t$

The solution is $-\frac{3}{7}$.

You Try It 5 Solve: $\frac{1}{5} = z + \frac{4}{5}$

Your solution

Solutions on pp. S25–S26

Objective C   To solve an equation of the form $ax = b$ ....

In solving an equation of the form $ax = b$, the goal is to simplify the given equation to one of the form *variable = constant*. The Multiplication Properties that follow are used to simplify equations to this form.

> **Multiplication Property of Reciprocals**
>
> The product of a nonzero term and its reciprocal equals 1.

$$a\left(\frac{1}{a}\right) = 1 \qquad \frac{1}{a}(a) = 1$$

$$\left(\frac{a}{b}\right)\left(\frac{b}{a}\right) = 1 \qquad \left(\frac{b}{a}\right)\left(\frac{a}{b}\right) = 1$$

> **Multiplication Property of One**
>
> The product of a term and 1 is the term.
> $$a \cdot 1 = a \qquad 1 \cdot a = a$$

> **Multiplication Property of Equations**
>
> If a, b, and c are algebraic expressions and $c \neq 0$, then the equation $a = b$ has the same solutions as the equation $ac = bc$.

The Multiplication Property of Equations states that each side of an equation can be multiplied by the same nonzero number without changing the solutions of the equation.

Recall that the goal of solving an equation is to rewrite the equation in the form *variable = constant*. The Multiplication Property of Equations is used to rewrite an equation in this form by multiplying each side of the equation by the reciprocal of the coefficient.

➡ Solve: $\frac{2}{3}x = 8$

$$\frac{2}{3}x = 8$$
$$\left(\frac{3}{2}\right)\left(\frac{2}{3}\right)x = \left(\frac{3}{2}\right)8$$
$$1 \cdot x = 12$$
$$x = 12$$

• Multiply each side of the equation by $\frac{3}{2}$, the reciprocal of $\frac{2}{3}$. After simplifying, the equation will be in the form *variable = constant*.

Check:
$$\frac{2}{3}x = 8$$
$$\left(\frac{2}{3}\right)12 \ \bigg| \ 8$$
$$8 = 8$$

The solution is 12.

Because division is defined in terms of multiplication, the Multiplication Property of Equations allows each side of an equation to be divided by the same nonzero quantity.

➡ Solve: $-4x = 24$

$$-4x = 24$$

- The goal is to rewrite the equation in the form *variable = constant*.

$$\frac{-4x}{-4} = \frac{24}{-4}$$
$$1x = -6$$
$$x = -6$$

- Multiply each side of the equation by the reciprocal of -4. This is equivalent to dividing each side of the equation by -4. Then simplify.

The solution is -6. You should check this solution.

When using the Multiplication Property of Equations, it is usually easier to multiply each side of the equation by the reciprocal of the coefficient when the coefficient is a fraction. Divide each side of the equation by the coefficient when the coefficient is an integer or a decimal.

Example 6 Solve: $-2x = 6$

Solution
$$-2x = 6$$
$$\frac{-2x}{-2} = \frac{6}{-2}$$
$$1x = -3$$
$$x = -3$$

The solution is -3.

You Try It 6 Solve: $4z = -20$

Your solution

Example 7 Solve: $-9 = \frac{3}{4}y$

Solution
$$-9 = \frac{3}{4}y$$
$$\left(\frac{4}{3}\right)(-9) = \left(\frac{4}{3}\right)\left(\frac{3}{4}y\right)$$
$$-12 = 1y$$
$$-12 = y$$

The solution is -12.

You Try It 7 Solve: $8 = \frac{2}{5}n$

Your solution

Example 8 Solve: $6z - 8z = -5$

Solution
$$6z - 8z = -5 \quad \text{Combine like terms}$$
$$-2z = -5$$
$$\frac{-2z}{-2} = \frac{-5}{-2}$$
$$1z = \frac{5}{2}$$
$$z = \frac{5}{2} = 2\frac{1}{2}$$

The solution is $\frac{5}{2}$ or $2\frac{1}{2}$.

You Try It 8 Solve: $\frac{2}{3}t - \frac{1}{3}t = -2$

Your solution

Solutions on p. S26

Objective D   To solve application problems .... (17)

Example 9

An accountant for an auto parts store found that the weekly profit for the store was $850 and that the total amount spent during the week was $1200. Use the formula $P = R - C$, where P is the profit, R is the revenue, and C is the amount spent, to find the revenue for the week.

Strategy

To find the revenue for the week, replace the variables P and C in the formula by the given values, and solve for R.

Solution

$$P = R - C$$
$$850 = R - 1200$$
$$850 + 1200 = R - 1200 + 1200$$
$$2050 = R + 0$$
$$2050 = R$$

The revenue for the week was $2050.

You Try It 9

A clothing store's sale price for a pair of slacks is $22. This is a discount of $8 off the regular price. Use the formula $S = R - D$, where S is the sale price, R is the regular price, and D is the discount, to find the regular price.

Your strategy

Your solution

Example 10

A store manager uses the formula $S = R - D \cdot R$, where S is the sale price, R is the regular price, and D is the discount rate. During a clearance sale, all items are discounted 20%. Find the regular price of a jacket that is on sale for $40.

Strategy

To find the regular price of the jacket, replace the variables S and D in the formula by the given values, and solve for R.

Solution

$$S = R - D \cdot R$$
$$40 = R - 0.20R$$
$$40 = 0.80R \qquad \bullet\ R - 0.20R = 1R - 0.20R$$
$$\frac{40}{0.80} = \frac{0.80R}{0.80}$$
$$50 = R$$

The regular price of the jacket is $50.

You Try It 10

Find the monthly payment when the total amount paid on a loan is $6840 and the loan is paid off in 24 months. Use the formula $A = MN$, where A is the total amount paid on a loan, M is the monthly payment, and N is the number of monthly payments.

Your strategy

Your solution

Solutions on p. S26

11.2 Exercises

Objective A

1. Is -3 a solution of
$2x + 9 = 3$?

2. Is -2 a solution of
$5x + 7 = 12$?

3. Is 2 a solution of
$4 - 2x = 8$?

4. Is 4 a solution of
$5 - 2x = 4x$?

5. Is 3 a solution of
$3x - 2 = x + 4$?

6. Is 2 a solution of
$4x + 8 = 4 - 2x$?

7. Is 3 a solution of
$x^2 - 5x + 1 = 10 - 5x$?

8. Is -5 a solution of
$x^2 - 3x - 1 = 9 - 6x$?

9. Is -1 a solution of
$2x(x - 1) = 3 - x$?

10. Is 2 a solution of
$3x(x - 3) = x - 8$?

11. Is 2 a solution of
$x(x - 2) = x^2 - 4$?

12. Is -4 a solution of
$x(x + 4) = x^2 + 16$?

13. Is $-\frac{2}{3}$ a solution of
$3x + 6 = 4$?

14. Is $\frac{1}{2}$ a solution of
$2x - 7 = -3$?

15. Is $\frac{1}{4}$ a solution of
$2x - 3 = 1 - 14x$?

16. Is $-\frac{1}{3}$ a solution of
$5x - 2 = 1 - 2x$?

17. Is $\frac{3}{4}$ a solution of
$3x(x - 2) = x - 4$?

18. Is $\frac{2}{5}$ a solution of
$5x(x + 1) = x + 3$?

19. Is 1.32 a solution of
$x^2 - 3x = -0.8776 - x$?

20. Is -1.9 a solution of
$x^2 - 3x = x + 3.8$?

21. Is 1.05 a solution of
$x^2 + 3x = x(x + 3)$?

Objective B

Solve.

22. $x + 3 = 9$

23. $x + 7 = 5$

24. $y - 6 = 16$

25. $z - 4 = 10$

26. $3 + n = 4$

27. $6 + x = 8$

28. $z + 7 = 2$

29. $w + 9 = 5$

Solve.

30. $x - 3 = -7$

31. $m - 4 = -9$

32. $y + 6 = 6$

33. $t - 3 = -3$

34. $v - 7 = -4$

35. $x - 3 = -1$

36. $1 + x = 0$

37. $3 + y = 0$

38. $x - 10 = 5$

39. $y - 7 = 3$

40. $x + 4 = -7$

41. $t - 3 = -8$

42. $w + 5 = -5$

43. $z + 6 = -6$

44. $x + 7 = -8$

45. $x + 2 = -5$

46. $x + \dfrac{1}{2} = -\dfrac{1}{2}$

47. $x - \dfrac{5}{6} = -\dfrac{1}{6}$

48. $y + \dfrac{7}{11} = -\dfrac{3}{11}$

49. $\dfrac{2}{5} + x = -\dfrac{3}{5}$

50. $\dfrac{7}{8} + y = -\dfrac{1}{8}$

51. $\dfrac{1}{3} + x = \dfrac{2}{3}$

52. $x + \dfrac{1}{2} = -\dfrac{1}{3}$

53. $y + \dfrac{3}{8} = \dfrac{1}{4}$

54. $y + \dfrac{2}{3} = -\dfrac{3}{8}$

55. $t + \dfrac{1}{4} = -\dfrac{1}{2}$

56. $x + \dfrac{1}{3} = \dfrac{5}{12}$

57. $y + \dfrac{2}{3} = -\dfrac{5}{12}$

Objective C

Solve.

58. $3y = 12$

59. $5x = 30$

60. $5z = -20$

61. $3z = -27$

62. $-2x = 6$

63. $-4t = 20$

64. $-5x = -40$

65. $-2y = -28$

66. $40 = 8x$

67. $24 = 3y$

68. $-24 = 4x$

69. $-21 = 7y$

70. $\dfrac{x}{3} = 5$

71. $\dfrac{y}{2} = 10$

72. $\dfrac{n}{4} = -2$

73. $\dfrac{y}{7} = -3$

Solve.

74. $-\dfrac{x}{4} = 1$

75. $\dfrac{-y}{3} = 5$

76. $\dfrac{2}{3}w = 4$

77. $\dfrac{5}{8}x = 10$

78. $\dfrac{3}{4}v = -3$

79. $\dfrac{2}{7}x = -12$

80. $-\dfrac{1}{3}x = -2$

81. $-\dfrac{1}{5}y = -3$

82. $\dfrac{3}{8}x = -24$

83. $\dfrac{5}{12}y = -16$

84. $-4 = -\dfrac{2}{3}z$

85. $-8 = -\dfrac{5}{6}x$

86. $-12 = -\dfrac{3}{8}y$

87. $-9 = \dfrac{5}{6}t$

88. $\dfrac{2}{3}x = -\dfrac{2}{7}$

89. $\dfrac{3}{7}y = \dfrac{5}{6}$

90. $4x - 2x = 7$

91. $3a - 6a = 8$

92. $\dfrac{4}{5}m - \dfrac{1}{5}m = 9$

93. $\dfrac{1}{3}b - \dfrac{2}{3}b = -1$

Objective D   *Application Problems*

In Exercises 94 to 97, use the formula $A = P + I$, where A is the value of the investment after 1 year, P is the original investment, and I is the increase in value of the investment.

94. The value of an investment in a high-tech company after 1 year was $17,700. The increase in value during the year was $2700. Find the amount of the original investment.

95. The value of an investment in a software company after 1 year was $26,440. The increase in value during the year was $2830. Find the amount of the original investment.

96. The original investment in a mutual fund was $8000. The value of the mutual fund after 1 year was $11,420. Find the increase in value of the investment.

97. The original investment in a money market fund was $7500. The value of the mutual fund after 1 year was $8690. Find the increase in value of the investment.

In Exercises 98 to 101, use the formula $D = M \cdot G$, where D is the distance, M is the miles per gallon, and G is the number of gallons. Round to the nearest tenth.

98. Julio, a sales executive, averages 28 mi/gal on a 621-mile trip. Find the number of gallons of gasoline used on the trip.

99. Over a three-day weekend, you take a 592-mile trip. If you average 32 mi/gal on the trip, how many gallons of gasoline did you use?

100. The manufacturer of a subcompact car estimates that the car can travel 560 mi on a 15-gallon tank of gas. Find the miles per gallon.

101. You estimate that your car can travel 410 mi on 12 gal of gasoline. Find the miles per gallon.

In Exercises 102 and 103, use the formula $S = C + M$, where S is the selling price, C is the cost, and M is the markup.

102. A computer store sells a computer for $2240. The computer has a markup of $420. Find the cost of the computer.

103. A department store buys shirts for $13.50 and sells the shirts for $19.80. Find the markup on each shirt.

In Exercises 104 and 105, use the formula $S = C + R \cdot C$, where S is the selling price, C is cost, and R is the markup rate.

104. A store manager uses a markup rate of 24% on all appliances. Find the cost of a blender that sells for $52.70.

105. A music store uses a markup rate of 30%. Find the cost of a compact disk that sells for $13.39.

APPLYING THE CONCEPTS

106. Write out the steps for solving the equation $x - 3 = -5$. Identify each property of real numbers and each property of equations as you use it.

107. Write out the steps for solving the equation $\frac{3}{4}x = 6$. Identify each property of real numbers and each property of equations as you use it.

108. Is 2 a solution of $x = x + 4$? Try $-2, 0, 3, 6$, and 10. Do you think there is a solution of this equation? Why or why not?

109. Write an equation of the form $x + a = b$ that has -4 as its solution.

110. Write an equation of the form $a - x = b$ that has -2 as its solution.

111. In your own words, state **(a)** the Addition Property of Equations and **(b)** the Multiplication Property of Equations.

11.3 General Equations: Part I

Objective A *To solve an equation of the form ax + b = c* ....

To solve an equation of the form $ax + b = c$, it is necessary to use both the Addition and the Multiplication Properties to simplify the equation to one of the form *variable = constant*.

➡ Solve: $\dfrac{x}{4} - 1 = 3$

$$\frac{x}{4} - 1 = 3$$

• The goal is to simplify the equation to one of the form *variable = constant*.

$$\frac{x}{4} - 1 + 1 = 3 + 1$$

$$\frac{x}{4} + 0 = 4$$

• Add the opposite of the constant term -1 to each side of the equation. Then simplify (Addition Properties).

$$\frac{x}{4} = 4$$

$$4 \cdot \frac{x}{4} = 4 \cdot 4$$
$$1x = 16$$
$$x = 16$$

• Multiply each side of the equation by the reciprocal of the numerical coefficient of the variable term. Then simplify (Multiplication Properties).

TAKE NOTE

$\dfrac{x}{4} = \dfrac{1}{4}x$

The reciprocal of $\dfrac{1}{4}$ is 4.

The solution is 16.

• Write the solution.

Example 1 Solve: $3x + 7 = 2$

Solution
$$3x + 7 = 2$$
$$3x + 7 - 7 = 2 - 7$$
$$3x = -5$$
$$\frac{3x}{3} = \frac{-5}{3}$$
$$x = -\frac{5}{3} = -1\frac{2}{3}$$

The solution is $-1\dfrac{2}{3}$.

You Try It 1 Solve: $5x + 8 = 6$

Your solution

Example 2 Solve: $5 - x = 6$

Solution
$$5 - x = 6$$
$$5 - 5 - x = 6 - 5$$
$$-x = 1$$
$$(-1)(-x) = (-1) \cdot 1$$
$$x = -1$$

The solution is -1.

You Try It 2 Solve: $7 - x = 3$

Your solution

Solutions on p. S26

Objective B   *To solve application problems* ··· (17) CT

Example 3

Find the Celsius temperature when the Fahrenheit temperature is 212°. Use the formula $F = \frac{9}{5}C + 32$, where F is the Fahrenheit temperature and C is the Celsius temperature.

Strategy

To find the Celsius temperature, replace the variable F in the formula by the given value and solve for C.

Solution

$$F = \frac{9}{5}C + 32$$

$$212 = \frac{9}{5}C + 32$$

$$212 - 32 = \frac{9}{5}C + 32 - 32$$

$$180 = \frac{9}{5}C$$

$$\frac{5}{9} \cdot 180 = \frac{5}{9} \cdot \frac{9}{5}C$$

$$100 = C$$

The Celsius temperature is 100°.

You Try It 3

Find the Celsius temperature when the Fahrenheit temperature is −22°. Use the formula $F = \frac{9}{5}C + 32$, where F is the Fahrenheit temperature and C is the Celsius temperature.

Your strategy

Your solution

Example 4

To find the total cost of production, an economist uses the formula $T = U \cdot N + F$, where T is the total cost, U is the cost per unit, N is the number of units made, and F is the fixed cost. Find the number of units made during a week when the total cost was $8000, the cost per unit was $16, and the fixed costs were $2000.

Strategy

To find the number of units made, replace the variables T, U, and F in the formula by the given values and solve for N.

Solution

$$T = U \cdot N + F$$

$$8000 = 16 \cdot N + 2000$$

$$8000 - 2000 = 16 \cdot N + 2000 - 2000$$

$$6000 = 16 \cdot N$$

$$\frac{6000}{16} = \frac{16 \cdot N}{16}$$

$$375 = N$$

The number of units made was 375.

You Try It 4

Find the cost per unit during a week when the total cost was $4500, the number of units produced was 250, and the fixed costs were $1500. Use the formula $T = U \cdot N + F$, where T is the total cost, U is the cost per unit, N is the number of units made, and F is the fixed cost.

Your strategy

Your solution

Solutions on pp. S26–S27

11.3 Exercises

Objective A

Solve.

1. $3x + 5 = 14$ **2.** $5z + 6 = 31$ **3.** $2n - 3 = 7$ **4.** $4y - 4 = 20$

5. $5w + 8 = 3$ **6.** $3x + 10 = 1$ **7.** $3z - 4 = -16$ **8.** $6x - 1 = -13$

9. $5 + 2x = 7$ **10.** $12 + 7x = 33$ **11.** $6 - x = 3$ **12.** $4 - x = -2$

13. $3 - 4x = 11$ **14.** $2 - 3x = 11$ **15.** $5 - 4x = 17$ **16.** $8 - 6x = 14$

17. $3x + 6 = 0$ **18.** $5x - 20 = 0$ **19.** $-3x - 4 = -1$ **20.** $-7x - 22 = -1$

21. $12x - 30 = 6$ **22.** $9x - 7 = 2$ **23.** $3x + 7 = 4$ **24.** $8x + 13 = 5$

25. $-2x + 11 = -3$ **26.** $-4x + 15 = -1$ **27.** $14 - 5x = 4$ **28.** $7 - 3x = 4$

29. $-8x + 7 = -9$ **30.** $-7x + 13 = -8$ **31.** $9x + 13 = 13$ **32.** $-2x + 7 = 7$

33. $7x - 14 = 0$ **34.** $5x + 10 = 0$ **35.** $4x - 4 = -4$ **36.** $-13x - 1 = -1$

37. $3x + 5 = 7$ **38.** $4x + 6 = 9$ **39.** $6x - 1 = 16$ **40.** $12x - 3 = 7$

Solve.

41. $2x - 3 = -8$

42. $5x - 3 = -12$

43. $-6x + 2 = -7$

44. $-3x + 9 = -1$

45. $-2x - 3 = -7$

46. $-5x - 7 = -4$

47. $3x + 8 = 2$

48. $2x - 9 = 8$

49. $3x - 7 = 0$

50. $7x - 2 = 0$

51. $-2x + 9 = 12$

52. $-7x + 3 = 1$

53. $\frac{1}{2}x - 2 = 3$

54. $\frac{1}{3}x + 1 = 4$

55. $\frac{3}{5}w - 1 = 2$

56. $\frac{2}{5}w + 5 = 6$

57. $\frac{2}{9}t - 3 = 5$

58. $\frac{5}{9}t - 3 = 2$

59. $\frac{y}{3} - 6 = -8$

60. $\frac{y}{2} - 2 = 3$

61. $\frac{x}{3} - 2 = -5$

62. $\frac{x}{4} - 3 = 5$

63. $\frac{5}{8}v + 6 = 3$

64. $\frac{2}{3}v - 4 = 3$

65. $\frac{4}{7}z + 10 = 5$

66. $\frac{3}{8}v - 3 = 4$

67. $\frac{2}{9}x - 3 = 5$

68. $\frac{1}{2}x + 3 = -8$

69. $\frac{3}{4}x - 5 = -4$

70. $\frac{2}{3}x - 5 = -8$

71. $1.5x - 0.5 = 2.5$

72. $2.5w - 1.3 = 3.7$

73. $0.8t + 1.1 = 4.3$

74. $0.3v + 2.4 = 1.5$

75. $0.4x - 2.3 = 1.3$

76. $1.2t + 6.5 = 2.9$

77. $3.5y - 3.5 = 10.5$

78. $1.9x - 1.9 = -1.9$

79. $0.32x + 4.2 = 3.2$

80. $5x - 3x + 2 = 8$

81. $6m + 2m - 3 = 5$

82. $4a - 7a - 8 = 4$

83. $3y - 8y - 9 = 6$

84. $x - 4x + 5 = 11$

85. $-2y + y - 3 = 6$

86. $-4y - y - 8 = 12$

87. $0.032x - 0.0194 = 0.139$

88. $-3.256x + 42.38 = -16.9$

89. $6.09x + 17.33 = 16.805$

90. $1.925x + 32.87 = -16.994$

Objective B   *Application Problems*

In Exercises 91 and 92, use the relationship between Fahrenheit temperature and Celsius temperature, which is given by the formula $F = \frac{9}{5}C + 32$, where F is the Fahrenheit temperature and C is the Celsius temperature.

91. Find the Celsius temperature when the Fahrenheit temperature is $-40°$.

92. Find the Celsius temperature when the Fahrenheit temperature is $72°$. Round to the nearest tenth of a degree.

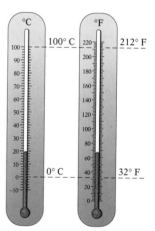

In Exercises 93 and 94, use the formula $V = V_0 + 32t$, where V is the final velocity of a falling object, V_0 is the starting velocity of a falling object, and t is the time for the object to fall.

93. Find the time required for an object to increase in velocity from 8 ft/s to 472 ft/s.

94. Find the time required for an object to increase in velocity from 16 ft/s to 128 ft/s.

In Exercises 95 and 96, use the formula $T = U \cdot N + F$, where T is the total cost, U is the cost per unit, N is the number of units made, and F is the fixed cost.

95. Find the number of units made during a week when the total cost was $25,000, the cost per unit was $8, and the fixed costs were $5000.

96. Find the cost per unit during a week when the total cost was $80,000, the total number of units produced was 500, and the fixed costs were $15,000.

In Exercises 97 and 98, use the formula $T = I \cdot R + B$, where T is the monthly tax, I is the monthly income, R is the income tax rate, and B is the base monthly tax.

97. The monthly tax that a mechanic pays is $476. The mechanic's monthly tax rate is 22%, and the base monthly tax is $80. Find the mechanic's monthly salary.

98. The monthly tax that Marcy, a teacher, pays is $770. Her monthly income is $3100, and the base monthly tax is $150. Find Marcy's income tax rate.

In Exercises 99 to 102, use the formula $M = S \cdot R + B$, where M is the monthly earnings, S is total sales, R is the commission rate, and B is the base monthly salary.

99. A book representative earns a base monthly salary of $600 plus a 9% commission on total sales. Find the total sales during a month in which the representative earned $3480.

100. A sales executive earns a base monthly salary of $1000 plus a 5% commission on total sales. Find the total sales during a month in which the executive earned $2800.

101. Miguel earns a base monthly salary of $750. Find his commission rate during a month in which total sales were $42,000 and he earned $2640.

102. Tina earns a base monthly salary of $500. Find her commission rate during a month when total sales were $42,500 and her earnings were $3560.

APPLYING THE CONCEPTS

103. Explain in your own words the steps you would take to solve the equation $\frac{2}{3}x - 4 = 10$. State the property of real numbers or the property of equations that is used at each step.

104. Make up an equation of the form $ax + b = c$ that has -3 as its solution.

105. Does the sentence "Solve $3x + 4(x - 3)$" make sense? Why or why not?

11.4   General Equations: Part II

Objective A   *To solve an equation of the form ax + b = cx + d* ....

When a variable occurs on each side of an equation, the Addition Properties are used to rewrite the equation so that variable terms are on one side of the equation and constant terms are on the other side of the equation. Then the Multiplication Properties are used to simplify the equation to one of the form *variable = constant*.

➡ Solve: $4x - 6 = 8 - 3x$

$$4x - 6 = 8 - 3x$$

• The goal is to write the equation in the form *variable = constant.*

$$4x + 3x - 6 = 8 - 3x + 3x$$
$$7x - 6 = 8 + 0$$
$$7x - 6 = 8$$

• Add 3x to each side of the equation. Then simplify (Addition Properties). Now only one variable term occurs in the equation.

$$7x - 6 + 6 = 8 + 6$$
$$7x + 0 = 14$$
$$7x = 14$$

• Add 6 to each side of the equation. Then simplify (Addition Properties). Now only one constant term occurs in the equation.

$$\frac{7x}{7} = \frac{14}{7}$$
$$1x = 2$$
$$x = 2$$

• Divide each side of the equation by the numerical coefficient of the variable term. Then simplify (Multiplication Properties).

The solution is 2.

• Write the solution.

Example 1

Solve: $\frac{2}{9}x - 3 = \frac{7}{9}x + 2$

Solution

$$\frac{2}{9}x - 3 = \frac{7}{9}x + 2$$

$$\frac{2}{9}x - \frac{7}{9}x - 3 = \frac{7}{9}x - \frac{7}{9}x + 2$$

$$-\frac{5}{9}x - 3 = 2$$

$$-\frac{5}{9}x - 3 + 3 = 2 + 3$$

$$-\frac{5}{9}x = 5$$

$$\left(-\frac{9}{5}\right)\left(-\frac{5}{9}\right)x = \left(-\frac{9}{5}\right)5$$

$$x = -9$$

The solution is -9.

You Try It 1

Solve: $\frac{1}{5}x - 2 = \frac{2}{5}x + 4$

Your solution

Solution on p. S27

Objective B **To solve an equation containing parentheses** ....

When an equation contains parentheses, one of the steps in solving the equation requires use of the Distributive Property.

$$a(b + c) = ab + ac$$

The Distributive Property is used to rewrite a variable expression without parentheses.

➡ Solve: $4(3 + x) - 2 = 2(x - 4)$

$4(3 + x) - 2 = 2(x - 4)$	• The goal is to write the equation in the form *variable = constant*.
$12 + 4x - 2 = 2x - 8$ $10 + 4x = 2x - 8$	• Use the Distributive Property to rewrite the equation without parentheses.
$10 + 4x - 2x = 2x - 2x - 8$ $10 + 2x = -8$	• Subtract $2x$ from each side of the equation.
$10 - 10 + 2x = -8 - 10$ $2x = -18$	• Subtract 10 from each side of the equation.
$\dfrac{2x}{2} = -\dfrac{18}{2}$ $x = -9$	• Divide each side of the equation by the numerical coefficient of the variable term.
The solution is -9.	• Write the solution.

Example 2   Solve: $3(x + 2) - x = 11$

Solution
$$3(x + 2) - x = 11$$
$$3x + 6 - x = 11$$
$$2x + 6 = 11$$
$$2x + 6 - 6 = 11 - 6$$
$$2x = 5$$
$$\frac{2x}{2} = \frac{5}{2}$$
$$x = \frac{5}{2}$$
$$x = 2\frac{1}{2}$$

The solution is $2\frac{1}{2}$.

You Try It 2   Solve: $4(x - 1) - x = 5$

Your solution

Solution on p. S27

11.4 Exercises

Objective A

Solve.

1. $6x + 3 = 2x + 5$

2. $7x + 1 = x + 19$

3. $3x + 3 = 2x + 2$

4. $6x + 3 = 3x + 6$

5. $5x + 4 = x - 12$

6. $3x - 12 = x - 8$

7. $7x - 2 = 3x - 6$

8. $2x - 9 = x - 8$

9. $9x - 4 = 5x - 20$

10. $8x - 7 = 5x + 8$

11. $2x + 1 = 16 - 3x$

12. $3x + 2 = -23 - 2x$

13. $5x - 2 = -10 - 3x$

14. $4x - 3 = 7 - x$

15. $2x + 7 = 4x + 3$

16. $7x - 6 = 10x - 15$

17. $x + 4 = 6x - 11$

18. $x - 6 = 4x - 21$

19. $3x - 7 = x - 7$

20. $2x + 6 = 7x + 6$

21. $3 - 4x = 5 - 3x$

22. $6 - 2x = 9 - x$

23. $7 + 3x = 9 + 5x$

24. $12 + 5x = 9 - 3x$

25. $5 + 2x = 7 + 5x$

26. $9 + x = 2 + 3x$

27. $8 - 5x = 4 - 6x$

28. $9 - 4x = 11 - 5x$

29. $6x + 1 = 3x + 2$

30. $7x + 5 = 4x + 7$

31. $5x + 8 = x + 5$

32. $9x + 1 = 3x - 4$

33. $2x - 3 = 6x - 4$

Solve.

34. $4 - 3x = 4 - 5x$

35. $6 - 3x = 6 - 5x$

36. $2x + 7 = 4x - 3$

37. $6x - 2 = 2x - 9$

38. $4x - 7 = -3x + 2$

39. $6x - 3 = -5x + 8$

40. $7x - 5 = 3x + 9$

41. $-6x - 2 = -8x - 4$

42. $-7x + 2 = 3x - 8$

43. $-3 - 4x = 7 - 2x$

44. $-8 + 5x = 8 + 6x$

45. $3 - 7x = -2 + 5x$

46. $3x - 2 = 7 - 5x$

47. $5x + 8 = 4 - 2x$

48. $4 - 3x = 6x - 8$

49. $12x - 9 = 3x + 12$

50. $4x + 13 = -6x + 9$

51. $\dfrac{5}{7}x - 3 = \dfrac{2}{7}x + 6$

52. $\dfrac{4}{5}x - 1 = \dfrac{1}{5}x + 5$

53. $\dfrac{3}{7}x + 5 = \dfrac{5}{7}x - 1$

54. $\dfrac{3}{4}x + 2 = \dfrac{1}{4}x - 9$

Objective B

Solve.

55. $6x + 2(x - 1) = 14$

56. $3x + 2(x + 4) = 13$

57. $-3 + 4(x + 3) = 5$

58. $8x - 3(x - 5) = 30$

59. $6 - 2(x + 4) = 6$

60. $5 - 3(x + 2) = 8$

61. $5 + 7(x + 3) = 20$

62. $6 - 3(x - 4) = 12$

63. $2x + 3(x - 5) = 10$

64. $3x - 4(x + 3) = 9$

65. $3(x - 4) + 2x = 3$

66. $4 + 3(x - 9) = -12$

Solve.

67. $2x - 3(x - 4) = 12$

68. $4x - 2(x - 5) = 10$

69. $2x + 3(x + 4) = 7$

70. $3(x + 2) + 7 = 12$

71. $3(x - 2) + 5 = 5$

72. $4(x - 5) + 7 = 7$

73. $3x + 7(x - 2) = 5$

74. $-3x - 3(x - 3) = 3$

75. $4x - 2(x + 9) = 8$

76. $3x - 6(x - 3) = 9$

77. $3x + 5(x - 2) = 10$

78. $3x - 5(x - 1) = -5$

79. $3x + 4(x + 2) = 2(x + 9)$

80. $5x + 3(x + 4) = 4(x + 2)$

81. $2x - 3(x - 4) = 2(x + 6)$

82. $3x - 4(x - 1) = 3(x - 2)$

83. $7 - 2(x - 3) = 3(x - 1)$

84. $4 - 3(x + 2) = 2(x - 4)$

85. $6x - 2(x - 3) = 11(x - 2)$

86. $9x - 5(x - 3) = 5(x + 4)$

87. $6x - 3(x + 1) = 5(x + 2)$

88. $2x - 7(x - 2) = 3(x - 4)$

89. $7 - (x + 1) = 3(x + 3)$

90. $12 + 2(x - 9) = 3(x - 12)$

Solve.

91. $2x - 3(x + 4) = 2(x - 5)$

92. $3x + 2(x - 7) = 7(x - 1)$

93. $x + 5(x - 4) = 3(x - 8) - 5$

94. $2x - 2(x - 1) = 3(x - 2) + 7$

95. $9x - 3(x - 4) = 13 + 2(x - 3)$

96. $3x - 4(x - 2) = 15 - 3(x - 2)$

97. $3(x - 4) + 3x = 7 - 2(x - 1)$

98. $2(x - 6) + 7x = 5 - 3(x - 2)$

99. $3.67x - 5.3(x - 1.932) = 6.99$

100. $4.06x + 4.7(x + 3.22) = 1.774$

101. $8.45(x - 10) = 3(x - 3.854)$

102. $4(x - 1.99) - 3.92 = 3(x - 1.77)$

APPLYING THE CONCEPTS

103. If $2x - 2 = 4x + 6$, what is the value of $3x^2$?

104. If $3 + 2(4a - 3) = 4$ and $4 - 3(2 - 3b) = 11$, which is larger, a or b?

105. Explain what is wrong with the demonstration at the right, which suggests that $4 = 5$.

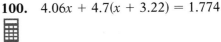
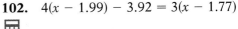

$$5x + 7 = 4x + 7$$
$$5x + 7 - 7 = 4x + 7 - 7 \quad \bullet \text{ Subtract 7 from each side of the equation.}$$
$$5x = 4x$$
$$\frac{5x}{x} = \frac{4x}{x} \quad \bullet \text{ Divide each side of the equation by } x.$$
$$5 = 4$$

106. The equation $x = x + 1$ has no solution, whereas the solution of the equation $2x + 3 = 3$ is zero. Is there a difference between no solution and a solution of zero? Explain.

11.5 Translating Verbal Expressions into Mathematical Expressions

Objective A   *To translate a verbal expression into a mathematical expression given the variable* ....

One of the major skills required in applied mathematics is to translate a verbal expression into a mathematical expression. Doing so requires recognizing the verbal phrases that translate into mathematical operations. Following is a partial list of the verbal phrases used to indicate the different mathematical operations.

Addition	more than	5 more than x	$x + 5$
	the sum of	the sum of w and 3	$w + 3$
	the total of	the total of 6 and z	$6 + z$
	increased by	x increased by 7	$x + 7$
Subtraction	less than	5 less than y	$y - 5$
	the difference between	the difference between w and 3	$w - 3$
	decreased by	8 decreased by a	$8 - a$
Multiplication	times	3 times c	$3c$
	the product of	the product of 4 and t	$4t$
	of	two-thirds of v	$\dfrac{2}{3}v$
	twice	twice d	$2d$
Division	divided by	n divided by 3	$\dfrac{n}{3}$
	the quotient of	the quotient of z and 4	$\dfrac{z}{4}$
	the ratio of	the ratio of s to 6	$\dfrac{s}{6}$

Translating phrases that contain the words *sum, difference, product,* and *quotient* can sometimes cause a problem. In the examples at the right, note where the operation symbol is placed.

the *sum* of x and y $x + y$

the *difference* of x and y $x - y$

the *product* of x and y $x \cdot y$

the *quotient* of x and y $\dfrac{x}{y}$

Note the placement of the fraction bar when translating the word *ratio*.

the *ratio* of x to y $\dfrac{x}{y}$

➡ Translate "the quotient of n and the sum of n and 6" into a mathematical expression.

the *quotient* of n and the *sum* of n and 6 $\dfrac{n}{n + 6}$

Example 1   Translate "the sum of 5 and the product of 4 and n" into a mathematical expression.

Solution $5 + 4n$

Example 2   Translate "the product of 3 and the difference between z and 4" into a mathematical expression.

Solution $3(z - 4)$

You Try It 1   Translate "the difference between 8 and twice t" into a mathematical expression.

Your solution

You Try It 2   Translate "the quotient of 5 and the product of 7 and x" into a mathematical expression.

Your solution

Solutions on p. S27

Objective B   To translate a verbal expression into a mathematical expression by assigning the variable .... (18)

In most applications that involve translating phrases into mathematical expressions, the variable to be used is not given. To translate these phrases, we must assign a variable to the unknown quantity before writing the mathematical expression.

➡ Translate "the difference between seven and twice a number" into a mathematical expression.

The difference between seven and twice a number

- Identify the phrases that indicate the mathematical operations.

The unknown number: n

- Assign a variable to one of the unknown quantities.

Twice the number: $2n$

- Use the assigned variable to write an expression for any other unknown quantity.

$7 - 2n$

- Use the identified operations to write the mathematical expression.

Example 3
Translate "the total of a number and the square of the number" into a mathematical expression.

Solution
The unknown number: c
The square of the number: c^2

$c + c^2$

You Try It 3
Translate "the product of a number and one-half of the number" into a mathematical expression.

Your solution

Solution on p. S27

11.5 Exercises

Objective A

Translate into a mathematical expression.

1. 9 less than y

2. w divided by 7

3. z increased by 3

4. the product of -2 and x

5. the sum of two-thirds of n and n

6. the difference between the square of r and r

7. the quotient of m and the difference between m and 3

8. v increased by twice v

9. the product of 9 and the sum of 4 more than x

10. the total of a and the quotient of a and 7

11. the difference between n and the product of -5 and n

12. x decreased by the quotient of x and 2

13. the product of c and one-fourth of c

14. the quotient of 3 less than z and z

15. the total of the square of m and twice the square of m

16. the product of y and the sum of y and 4

17. 2 times the sum of t and 6

18. the quotient of r and the difference between 8 and r

19. x divided by the total of 9 and x

20. the sum of z and the product of 6 and z

21. three times the sum of b and 6

22. the ratio of w to the sum of w and 8

Objective B

Translate into a mathematical expression.

23. the square of a number

24. five less than some number

25. a number divided by 20

26. the difference between a number and twelve

27. four times some number

28. the quotient of five and a number

Translate into a mathematical expression.

29. three-fourths of a number

30. the sum of a number and seven

31. four increased by some number

32. the ratio of a number to 9

33. the difference between five times a number and the number

34. six less than the total of three and a number

35. the product of a number and two more than the number

36. the quotient of six and the sum of nine and a number

37. seven times the total of a number and eight

38. the difference between ten and the quotient of a number and two

39. the square of a number plus the product of three and the number

40. a number decreased by the product of five and the number

41. the sum of three more than a number and one-half of the number

42. eight more than twice the sum of a number and seven

43. the quotient of three times a number and the number

44. the square of a number divided by the sum of a number and twelve

APPLYING THE CONCEPTS

45. Translate the expressions $2x + 3$ and $2(x + 3)$ into phrases.

46. Translate the expressions $\frac{2x}{7}$ and $\frac{2 + x}{7}$ into phrases.

47. In your own words, explain how variables are used.

48. The chemical formula for water is H_2O. This formula means that there are two hydrogen atoms and one oxygen atom in each molecule of water. If x represents the number of atoms of oxygen in a glass of pure water, express the number of hydrogen atoms in the glass of water.

49. The chemical formula for one molecule of glucose (sugar) is $C_6H_{12}O_6$, where C is carbon, H is hydrogen, and O is oxygen. If x represents the number of atoms of hydrogen in a sample of pure sugar, express the number of carbon atoms and the number of oxygen atoms in the sample in terms of x.

```
    H     O
     \   ⁄⁄
       C
       |
  H – C – OH
       |
 HO – C – H
       |
  H – C – OH
       |
  H – C – OH
       |
     CH₂OH
```

11.6 Translating Sentences into Equations and Solving

Objective A *To translate a sentence into an equation and solve* ....

POINT OF INTEREST

Number puzzle problems similar to the one on this page have appeared in textbooks for hundreds of years. Here is one from a 1st century Chinese textbook: "When a number is divided by 3, the remainder is 2; when it is divided by 5, the remainder is 3; when it is divided by 7, the remainder is 2. Find the number." There are actually an infinite number of solutions to this problem. See if you can find one of them.

An equation states that two mathematical expressions are equal. Therefore, to translate a sentence into an equation requires recognition of the words or phrases that mean "equals." Some of these phrases are

$$\left. \begin{array}{l} \text{equals} \\ \text{is} \\ \text{is equal to} \\ \text{amounts to} \\ \text{represents} \end{array} \right\} \text{translate to } =$$

Once the sentence is translated into an equation, the equation can be simplified to one of the form *variable = constant* and the solution found.

➡ Translate "three more than twice a number is seventeen" into an equation and solve.

The unknown number: n
• Assign a variable to the unknown quantity.

Three more than twice a number	is	seventeen

• Find two verbal expressions for the same value.

$$\begin{array}{rcl} 2n + 3 & = & 17 \\ 2n + 3 - 3 & = & 17 - 3 \\ 2n & = & 14 \\ \dfrac{2n}{2} & = & \dfrac{14}{2} \\ n & = & 7 \end{array}$$

• Write a mathematical expression for each verbal expression. Write the equals sign.
• Solve the resulting equation.

The number is 7.

Example 1

Translate "a number decreased by six equals fifteen" into an equation and solve.

Solution

The unknown number: x

A number decreased by six	equals	fifteen

$$x - 6 = 15$$

The number is 21.

You Try It 1

Translate "a number increased by four equals twelve" into an equation and solve.

Your solution

Solution on p. S27

Example 2

The quotient of a number and six is five. Find the number.

Solution

The unknown number: z

The quotient of a number and six	is	five

$$\frac{z}{6} = 5$$

$$6 \cdot \frac{z}{6} = 6 \cdot 5$$

$$z = 30$$

The number is 30.

You Try It 2

The product of two and a number is ten. Find the number.

Your solution

Example 3

Eight decreased by twice a number is four. Find the number.

Solution

The unknown number: t

Eight decreased by twice a number	is	four

$$8 - 2t = 4$$

$$8 - 8 - 2t = 4 - 8$$

$$-2t = -4$$

$$\frac{-2t}{-2} = \frac{-4}{-2}$$

$$t = 2$$

The number is 2.

You Try It 3

The sum of three times a number and six equals four. Find the number.

Your solution

Example 4

Three less than the ratio of a number to seven is one. Find the number.

Solution

The unknown number: x

Three less than the ratio of a number to seven	is	one

$$\frac{x}{7} - 3 = 1$$

$$\frac{x}{7} - 3 + 3 = 1 + 3$$

$$\frac{x}{7} = 4$$

$$7 \cdot \frac{x}{7} = 7 \cdot 4$$

$$x = 28$$

The number is 28.

You Try It 4

Three more than one-half of a number is nine. Find the number.

Your solution

Solutions on p. S27

Objective B   **To solve application problems** ....

Example 5

The cost of a television with remote control is $649. This amount is $125 more than the cost without remote control. Find the cost of the television without remote control.

Strategy

To find the cost of the television without remote control, write and solve an equation using C to represent the cost of the television without remote control.

Solution

| $649 | is | $125 more than the television without remote control |

$$649 = C + 125$$
$$649 - 125 = C + 125 - 125$$
$$524 = C$$

The cost of the television without remote control is $524.

Example 6

By purchasing a fleet of cars, a company receives a discount of $1972 on each car purchased. This amount is 8% of the regular price. Find the regular price.

Strategy

To find the regular price, write and solve an equation using P to represent the regular price of the car.

Solution

| $1972 | is | 8% of the regular price |

$$1972 = 0.08 \cdot P$$
$$\frac{1972}{0.08} = \frac{0.08P}{0.08}$$
$$24{,}650 = P$$

The regular price is $24,650.

You Try It 5

The sale price of a pair of slacks is $18.95. This amount is $6 less than the regular price. Find the regular price.

Your strategy

Your solution

You Try It 6

At a certain speed, the engine rpm (revolutions per minute) of a car in fourth gear is 2500. This is two-thirds of the rpm of the engine in third gear. Find the rpm of the engine when it is in third gear.

Your strategy

Your solution

Solutions on p. S28

Example 7

Ron Sierra charged $815 for plumbing repairs in an office building. This charge included $90 for parts and $25 per hour for labor. Find the number of hours he worked in the office building.

Strategy

To find the number of hours worked, write and solve an equation using N to represent the number of hours worked.

Solution

| $815 | included | $90 for parts and $25 per hour for labor |

$$815 = 90 + 25N$$
$$815 - 90 = 90 - 90 + 25N$$
$$725 = 25N$$
$$\frac{725}{25} = \frac{25N}{25}$$
$$29 = N$$

Ron worked 29 h.

You Try It 7

Natalie Adams earned $2500 last month for temporary work. This amount was the sum of a base monthly salary of $800 and an 8% commission on total sales. Find the total sales for the month.

Your strategy

Your solution

Example 8

The state income tax for Tim Fong last month was $128. This amount is $5 more than 8% of his monthly salary. Find Tim's monthly salary.

Strategy

To find Tim's monthly salary, write and solve an equation using S to represent his monthly salary.

Solution

| $128 | is | $5 more than 8% of the monthly salary |

$$128 = 0.08 \cdot S + 5$$
$$128 - 5 = 0.08 \cdot S + 5 - 5$$
$$123 = 0.08 \cdot S$$
$$\frac{123}{0.08} = \frac{0.08 \cdot S}{0.08}$$
$$1537.50 = S$$

Tim's monthly salary is $1537.50.

You Try It 8

The total cost to make a model ZY television is $300. The cost includes $100 for materials plus $12.50 per hour for labor. How many hours of labor are required to make a model ZY television?

Your strategy

Your solution

Solutions on p. S28

11.6 Exercises

· ·

Objective A

1. The sum of a number and seven is twelve. Find the number.

2. A number decreased by seven is five. Find the number.

3. The product of three and a number is eighteen. Find the number.

4. The quotient of a number and three is one. Find the number.

5. Five more than a number is three. Find the number.

6. A number divided by four is six. Find the number.

7. Six times a number is fourteen. Find the number.

8. Seven less than a number is three. Find the number.

9. Five-sixths of a number is fifteen. Find the number.

10. The total of twenty and a number is five. Find the number.

11. The sum of three times a number and four is eight. Find the number.

12. The sum of one-third of a number and seven is twelve. Find the number.

13. Seven less than one-fourth of a number is nine. Find the number.

14. The total of a number divided by four and nine is two. Find the number.

15. The ratio of a number to nine is fourteen. Find the number.

16. Five increased by the product of five and a number is equal to 30. Find the number.

17. Six less than the quotient of a number and four is equal to negative two. Find the number.

18. The product of a number plus three and two is eight. Find the number.

19. The difference between seven and twice a number is thirteen. Find the number.

20. Five more than the product of three and a number is eight. Find the number.

21. Nine decreased by the quotient of a number and two is five. Find the number.

22. The total of ten times a number and seven is twenty-seven. Find the number.

23. The sum of three-fifths of a number and eight is two. Find the number.

24. Five less than two-thirds of a number is three. Find the number.

25. The difference between a number divided by 4.186 and 7.92 is 12.529. Find the number.

26. The total of 5.68 times a number and 132.7 is the number minus 29.265. Find the number.

Objective B *Application Problems*

Write an equation and solve.

27. Sears has a shoe on sale for $72.50. This amount is $4.25 less than the shoe sells for at Target. Find the price at Target.

28. As a restaurant manager, Uechi Kim is paid a salary of $832 a week. This is $58 more a week than the salary paid last year. Find the weekly salary paid to Uechi last year.

29. The value of a sports utility vehicle this year is $16,000, which is four-fifths of what its value was last year. Find the value of the vehicle last year.

30. This year the value of a lakefront summer cottage is $175,000. This amount is twice the value of the cottage 6 years ago. What was its value 6 years ago?

31. In 1996, McDonald's Restaurants' share of the fast-food hamburger market was $16,341 million. This represented 41.9% of the total market. What was the total fast-food hamburger market in 1996?

32. Sonia Parker works the night shift at Palomar Hospital and receives a salary of $3200 per month. This is four times the salary she was making 10 years ago. Find her salary 10 years ago.

33. The Manzanares family spends $680 on the house payment and utilities, which amounts to one-fourth of the family's monthly income. Find the family's monthly income.

34. The cost of a graphics calculator is now three-fourths of what the calculator cost 5 years ago. The cost of the graphics calculator is now $72. Find the cost of the calculator 5 years ago.

Write an equation and solve.

35. Assume that the Dell Computer Corp. has increased its output of computers by 400 computers per month. This amount represents an 8% increase over last year's production. Find the monthly output last year.

36. The population of a midwestern city has decreased by 12,000 in the last 5 years. This amount represents a 3% decrease. Find the city's population 5 years ago.

37. The nutrition label on a bag of Baked Tostitos tortilla chips lists the sodium content of one serving as 200 mg, which is 8% of the recommended daily intake of sodium. What is the recommended daily intake of sodium? Express the answer in grams.

38. The price of a pair of skis at the Solitude Ski Shop is $240. This price includes the store's cost for the skis plus a markup rate of 25%. Find Solitude's cost for the skis.

39. Budget Plumbing charged $385 for a water softener and installation. The charge included $310 for the water softener and $25 per hour for labor. How many hours of labor were charged?

40. Sandy's monthly salary as a sales representative was $2580. This amount included her base monthly salary of $600 plus a 3% commission on total sales. Find the total sales for the month.

41. According to a Team Marketing Report, prices at Major League Baseball Games in 1997 were 107.1% of the prices in 1996. The average price of a ticket to a professional baseball game in 1997 was $11.98. What was the average price of a ticket in 1996? Round to the nearest cent.

42. When you use your car for business, you are able to deduct the expense on your income tax return. In 1997, the deduction was 31.5 cents per mile driven. How many business-related miles did a taxpayer who deducted a total of $1512 drive?

43. Americans spend approximately $295 million a year on remedies for cockroaches. The table at the right shows the top U.S. cities for sales of roach insecticides. What percent of the total is spent in New York? Round to the nearest tenth of a percent. (Source: IRI InfoScan for Combat)

City	Roach Insecticide Sales
Los Angeles	$16.8 million
New York	$9.8 million
Houston	$6.7 million

44. McPherson Cement charges $75 plus $24 for each yard of cement. How many yards of cement can be purchased for $363?

Write an equation and solve.

45. A water flow restrictor has reduced the flow of water to 2 gal/min. This amount is 1 gal/min less than three-fifths the original flow rate. Find the original rate.

46. The Fahrenheit temperature equals the sum of 32 and nine-fifths of the Celsius temperature. Find the Celsius temperature when the Fahrenheit temperature is 104°.

47. Assume that Paine Webber sales executives receive a base monthly salary of $600 plus an 8.25% commission on total sales per month. Find the total sales of a sales executive who receives a total of $4109.55 for the month.

The graph at the right shows the cost of lunches at the executive dining room and the employee lunch room. Use data from this graph for Exercises 48 and 49. Round to the nearest tenth of a percent.

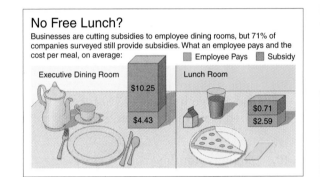

No Free Lunch?
Businesses are cutting subsidies to employee dining rooms, but 71% of companies surveyed still provide subsidies. What an employee pays and the cost per meal, on average: ■ Employee Pays ■ Subsidy

Executive Dining Room $10.25 $4.43

Lunch Room $0.71 $2.59

48. Find the amount subsidized in the executive dining room. What percent of the cost of the meal is subsidized?

49. Find the percent of the lunch room meal that is subsidized.

APPLYING THE CONCEPTS

50. A man's boyhood lasted $\frac{1}{6}$ of his life, he played football for the next $\frac{1}{8}$ of his life, and he married 5 years after quitting football. A daughter was born after he had been married $\frac{1}{12}$ of his life. The daughter lived $\frac{1}{2}$ as many years as her father. The man died 6 years after his daughter. How old was the man when he died? Use a number line to illustrate the time. Then write an equation and solve it.

51. It is always important to check the answer to an application problem to be sure the answer makes sense. Consider the following problem. "A 4-quart mixture of fruit juices is made from apple juice and cranberry juice. There are 6 more quarts of apple juice than of cranberry juice. Write and solve an equation for the number of quarts of each juice used." Does the answer to this question make sense? Explain.

52. A formula is an equation that relates variables in a known way. Find two examples of formulas that are used in your college major. Explain what each of the variables represents.

Focus on Problem Solving

From Concrete to Abstract

As you progress in your study of algebra, you will find that the problems become less concrete and more abstract. Problems that are concrete provide information pertaining to a specific instance. Abstract problems are theoretical; they are stated without reference to a specific instance. Let's look at an example of an abstract problem.

How many cents are in d dollars?

How can you solve this problem? Are you able to solve the same problem if the information given is concrete?

How many cents are in 5 dollars?

You know that there are 100 cents in 1 dollar. To find the number of cents in 5 dollars, multiply 5 by 100.

$100 \cdot 5 = 500$ There are 500 cents in 5 dollars.

Use the same procedure to find the number of cents in d dollars: multiply d by 100.

$100 \cdot d = 100d$ There are $100d$ cents in d dollars.

This problem might be taken a step further:

If one pen costs c cents, how many pens can be purchased with d dollars?

Consider the same problem using numbers in place of the variables.

If one pen costs 25 cents, how many pens can be purchased with 2 dollars?

To solve this problem, you need to calculate the number of cents in 2 dollars (multiply 2 by 100), and divide the result by the cost per pen (25 cents).

$\dfrac{100 \cdot 2}{25} = \dfrac{200}{25} = 8$ If one pen costs 25 cents, 8 pens can be purchased with 2 dollars.

Use the same procedure to solve the related abstract problem. Calculate the number of cents in d dollars (multiply d by 100), and divide the result by the cost per pen (c cents).

$\dfrac{100 \cdot d}{c} = \dfrac{100d}{c}$ If one pen costs c cents, $\frac{100d}{c}$ pens can be purchased with d dollars.

At the heart of the study of algebra is the use of variables. It is the variables in the problems above that make them abstract. But it is variables that allow us to generalize situations and state rules about mathematics.

Try the following problems.

1. How many nickels are in d dollars?

2. How long can you talk long distance on a pay phone if you have only d dollars and the call costs c cents per minute?

3. If you travel m miles on one gallon of gasoline, how far can you travel on g gallons of gasoline?

4. If you walk a mile in x minutes, how far can you walk in h hours?

5. If one photocopy costs n nickels, how many photocopies can you make for q quarters?

Projects and Group Activities

Averages We often discuss temperature in terms of average high or average low temperature. Temperatures collected over a period of time are analyzed to determine, for example, the average high temperature for a given month in your city or state. The following activity is planned to help you better understand the concept of "average."

1. Choose two cities in the United States. We will refer to them as City X and City Y. Over an eight-day period, record the daily high temperature each day in each city.

2. Determine the average high temperature for City X for the eight-day period. (Add the eight numbers, and then divide the sum by 8.) Do not round your answer.

3. Subtract the average high temperature for City X from each of the eight daily high temperatures for City X. You should have a list of eight numbers; the list should include positive numbers, negative numbers, and possibly zero.

4. Find the sum of the list of eight differences recorded in Step 3.

5. Repeat Steps 2 through 4 for City Y.

6. Compare the two sums found in Steps 4 and 5 for City X and City Y.

7. If you were to conduct this activity again, what would you expect the outcome to be? Use the results to explain what an average high temperature means. In your own words, explain what "average" means.

Addition and Multiplication Properties

The chart below is an addition table. Use it to answer Exercises 1 to 7.

+	Δ	‡	◊
Δ	‡	◊	Δ
‡	◊	Δ	‡
◊	Δ	‡	◊

1. Find the sum of Δ and ‡.

2. What is ◊ plus ◊?

3. In our number system, 0 can be added to any number without changing that number; 0 is called the **additive identity.** What is the additive identity for the system in the chart above? Explain your answer.

4. Does the Commutative Property of Addition apply to this system? Explain your answer.

5. What is −Δ (the opposite of Δ) equal to? Explain your answer.

6. What is −‡ (the opposite of ‡) equal to? Explain your answer.

7. Simplify −Δ + ‡ − ◊. Explain how you arrived at your answer.

The chart below is a multiplication table. Use it to answer Exercises 8 to 14.

×	£	¿	&
£	£	¿	&
¿	¿	¿	¿
&	&	¿	*

8. Find the product of £ and &.

9. What is ¿ times £?

10. Find the square of &.

11. Does the Commutative Property of Multiplication apply to this system? Explain your answer.

12. In our number system, the product of a number and 0 is 0. Is there an element in this system that corresponds to 0 in our system? Explain your answer.

13. In our number system, 1 can be multiplied by any number without changing that number; 1 is called the **multiplicative identity.** What is the multiplicative identity for the system in the chart above? Explain your answer.

14. Simplify & ÷ £ × ¿. Explain how you arrived at your answer.

Chapter Summary

Key Words

A *variable* is a letter that is used to stand for a quantity that is unknown.

A *variable expression* is an expression that contains one or more variables.

The *terms* of a variable expression are the addends of the expression.

A *variable term* is composed of a numerical coefficient and a variable part.

Like terms of a variable expression are the terms with the same variable part.

An *equation* expresses the equality of two mathematical expressions.

A *solution* of an equation is a value of the variable that results in a true equation.

Essential Rules

The Commutative Property of Addition
If a and b are two numbers, then $a + b = b + a$.

The Associative Property of Addition
If a, b, and c are three numbers, then $a + (b + c) = (a + b) + c$.

The Commutative Property of Multiplication
If a and b are two numbers, then $a \cdot b = b \cdot a$.

The Associative Property of Multiplication
If a, b, and c are three numbers, then $a(b \cdot c) = (a \cdot b)c$.

The Distributive Property
If a, b, and c are three numbers, then $a(b + c) = ab + ac$.

Addition Property of Zero
The sum of a term and zero is the term. $a + 0 = a$, $0 + a = a$

Addition Property of Equations
If a, b, and c are algebraic expressions, then the equation $a = b$ has the same solution as the equation $a + c = b + c$.

Multiplication Property of Equations
If a, b, and c are algebraic expressions and $c \neq 0$, then the equation $a = b$ has the same solution as the equation $ac = bc$.

Multiplication Property of One
The product of a term and 1 is the term. $a \cdot 1 = a$, $1 \cdot a = a$

Chapter Review

1. Simplify: $-2(a - b)$

2. Is -2 a solution of the equation $3x - 2 = -8$?

3. Solve: $x - 3 = -7$

4. Solve: $-2x + 5 = -9$

5. Evaluate $a^2 - 3b$ when $a = 2$ and $b = -3$.

6. Solve: $-3x = 27$

7. Solve: $\frac{2}{3}x + 3 = -9$

8. Simplify: $3x - 2(3x - 2)$

9. Solve: $6x - 9 = -3x + 36$

10. Solve: $x + 3 = -2$

11. Is 5 a solution of the equation $3x - 5 = -10$?

12. Evaluate $a^2 - (b \div c)$ when $a = -2$, $b = 8$, and $c = -4$.

13. Solve: $3(x - 2) + 2 = 11$

14. Solve: $35 - 3x = 5$

15. Simplify: $6bc - 7bc + 2bc - 5bc$

16. Solve: $7 - 3x = 2 - 5x$

17. Solve: $-\frac{3}{8}x = -\frac{15}{32}$

18. Simplify: $\frac{1}{2}x^2 - \frac{1}{3}x^2 + \frac{1}{5}x^2 + 2x^2$

19. Solve: $5x - 3(1 - 2x) = 4(2x - 1)$

20. Solve: $\frac{5}{6}x - 4 = 5$

21. A tourist drove a rental car 621 mi on 27 gal of gas. Find the number of miles per gallon of gas. Use the formula $D = M \cdot G$, where D is distance, M is miles per gallon, and G is the number of gallons.

22. Find the Celsius temperature when the Fahrenheit temperature is 100°. Use the formula $F = \frac{9}{5}C + 32$, where F is the Fahrenheit temperature and C is the Celsius temperature. Round to the nearest tenth.

23. Translate "the total of n and the quotient of n and 5" into a mathematical expression.

24. Translate "the sum of five more than a number and one-third of the number" into a mathematical expression.

25. The difference between nine and twice a number is five. Find the number.

26. The product of five and a number is fifty. Find the number.

27. A compact disk player is now on sale for $228. This is 60% of the regular price. Find the regular price of the CD player.

28. A farmer harvested 28,336 bushels of corn. This amount represents a 12% increase over last year's crop. How many bushels of corn did the farmer harvest last year?

Chapter Test

1. Solve: $\frac{x}{5} - 12 = 7$

2. Solve: $x - 12 = 14$

3. Simplify: $3y - 2x - 7y - 9x$

4. Solve: $8 - 3x = 2x - 8$

5. Solve: $3x - 12 = -18$

6. Evaluate $c^2 - (2a + b^2)$ when $a = 3$, $b = -6$, and $c = -2$.

7. Is 3 a solution of the equation $x^2 + 3x - 7 = 3x - 2$?

8. Simplify: $9 - 8ab - 6ab$

9. Solve: $-5x = 14$

10. Simplify: $3y + 5(y - 3) + 8$

11. Solve: $3x - 4(x - 2) = 8$

12. Solve: $5 = 3 - 4x$

13. Evaluate $\frac{x^2}{y} - \frac{y^2}{x}$ for $x = 3$ and $y = -2$.

14. Solve: $\frac{5}{8}x = -10$

15. Solve: $y - 4y + 3 = 12$

16. Solve: $2x + 4(x - 3) = 5x - 1$

17. A loan of \$6600 is to be paid in 48 equal monthly installments. Find the monthly payment. Use the formula $L = P \cdot N$, where L is the loan amount, P is the monthly payment, and N is the number of months.

18. A clock manufacturer's fixed costs per month are \$5000. The unit cost for each clock is \$15. Find the number of clocks made during a month in which the total cost was \$65,000. Use the formula $T = U \cdot N + F$, where T is the total cost, U is the cost per unit, N is the number of units made, and F is the fixed costs.

19. Find the time required for a falling object to increase in velocity from 24 ft/s to 392 ft/s. Use the formula $V = V_0 + 32t$, where V is the final velocity of a falling object, V_0 is the starting velocity of a falling object, and t is the time for the object to fall.

20. Translate "the sum of x and one-third of x" into a mathematical expression.

21. Translate "five times the sum of a number and three" into a mathematical expression.

22. Translate "three less than two times a number is seven" into an equation and solve.

23. The total of five and three times a number is the number minus two. Find the number.

24. Eduardo Santos earned \$3600 last month. This salary is the sum of the base monthly salary of \$1200 and a 6% commission on total sales. Find his total sales for the month.

25. Your mechanic charges you \$278 for performing a 30,000-mile checkup on your car. This charge includes \$152 for parts and \$42 per hour for labor. Find the number of hours the mechanic worked on your car.

Cumulative Review

1. Simplify $6^2 - (18 - 6) \div 4 + 8$

2. Subtract: $3\frac{1}{6} - 1\frac{7}{15}$

3. Simplify: $\left(\frac{3}{8} - \frac{1}{4}\right) \div \frac{3}{4} + \frac{4}{9}$

4. Multiply: 9.67×0.0049

5. Write "$84 earned in 20 hours" as a unit rate.

6. Solve the proportion $\frac{2}{3} = \frac{n}{40}$.
   Round to the nearest hundredth.

7. Write $5\frac{1}{3}\%$ as a fraction.

8. What percent of 30 is 42?

9. 8 is 125% of what number?

10. Multiply: 3 ft 9 in. $\times$ 5

11. Convert $1\frac{3}{8}$ lb to ounces.

12. Convert 282 mg to grams.

13. Add: $-2 + 5 + (-8) + 4$

14. Find -6 less than 13.

15. Simplify: $(-2)^2 - (-8) \div (3 - 5)^2$

16. Evaluate $3ab - 2ac$ when $a = -2$, $b = 6$, and $c = -3$.

17. Simplify: $3z - 2x + 5z - 8x$

18. Simplify: $6y - 3(y - 5) + 8$

19. Solve: $2x - 5 = -7$

20. Solve: $7x - 3(x - 5) = -10$

21. Solve: $-\dfrac{2}{3}x = 5$

22. Solve: $\dfrac{x}{3} - 5 = -12$

23. In a mathematics class of 34 students, 6 received an A grade. Find the percent of the students in the mathematics class who received an A grade. Round to the nearest tenth of a percent.

24. The manager of a pottery store used a markup rate of 40%. Find the price of a piece of pottery that cost the store $28.50.

25. A department store has a suit regularly priced at $450 on sale for $369.
   a. What is the discount?
   b. What is the discount rate?

26. A toy store borrowed $80,000 at a simple interest rate of 11% for 4 months. What is the simple interest due on the loan? Round to the nearest cent.

27. Translate "the sum of three times a number and 4" into a mathematical expression.

28. A car travels 318 mi in 6 h. Find the average speed in miles per hour. Use the formula $S = \dfrac{D}{t}$, where S is the average speed, D is the distance traveled, and t is the time of travel.

29. Sunah Yee, a sales executive, receives a base salary of $800 plus an 8% commission on total sales. Find the total sales during a month in which Sunah earned $3400. Use the formula $M = S \cdot R + B$, where M is the monthly earnings, S is the total sales, R is the commission rate, and B is the base monthly salary.

30. Three less than eight times a number is three more than five times the number. Find the number.

12

Geometry

Architects use geometric objects to design skyscrapers, homes, and shopping malls. By understanding the properties of these geometric objects, an architect can combine various geometric figures to create structures that are functional and attractive. For example, the architect I. M. Pei used a series of glass pyramids to create a new entrance to the Louvre in Paris, France.

Objectives

Section 12.1
To define and describe lines and angles
To define and describe geometric figures
To solve problems involving angles formed by intersecting lines

Section 12.2
To find the perimeter of plane geometric figures
To find the perimeter of composite geometric figures
To solve application problems

Section 12.3
To find the area of geometric figures
To find the area of composite geometric figures
To solve application problems

Section 12.4
To find the volume of geometric solids
To find the volume of composite geometric solids
To solve application problems

Section 12.5
To find the square root of a number
To find the unknown side of a right triangle using the Pythagorean Theorem
To solve application problems

Section 12.6
To solve similar and congruent triangles
To solve application problems

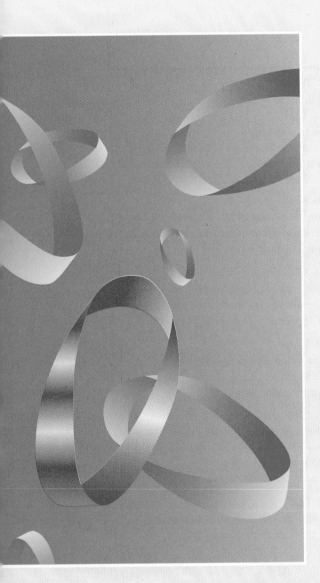

Mobius Strips and Klein Bottles

Some geometric shapes have very unusual characteristics. Among these figures are Mobius strips and Klein bottles.

A Mobius strip is formed by taking a long strip of paper and twisting it one-half turn. The resulting figure is called a "one-sided" surface. It is one-sided in the sense that if you tried to paint the strip in one continuous motion beginning at one spot, the entire surface would be painted the same color, unlike a strip that has not been twisted.

Another remarkable result of its being one-sided can be demonstrated by making a Mobius strip and sealing the junction with tape. Now cut the strip by cutting along the center of the strip. Try this; you will be amazed at the result.

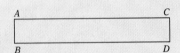

A second interesting surface is called a Klein bottle, which is a one-sided surface with no edges and no "inside" or "outside." A Klein bottle is formed by pulling the small open end of a tapering tube through the side of the tube and joining the ends of the small open end to the ends of the larger open end.

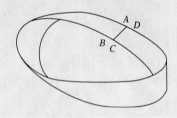

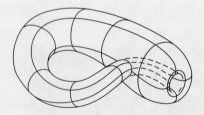

12.1 Angles, Lines, and Geometric Figures

Objective A *To define and describe lines and angles* ....

The word *geometry* comes from the Greek words for "earth" (*geo*) and "measure." The original purpose of geometry was to measure land. Today geometry is used in many sciences, such as physics, chemistry, and geology, and in applied fields such as mechanical drawing and astronomy. Geometric form is used in art and design.

Two basic geometric concepts are plane and space.

A **plane** is a flat surface, such as a table-top or a blackboard. Figures that can lie totally in a plane are called **plane figures.**

Space extends in all directions. Objects in space, such as trees, ice cubes, and doors, are called **solids.**

A **line** extends indefinitely in two directions in a plane. A line has no width.

A **line segment** is part of a line and has two endpoints. The line segment *AB* is shown in the figure.

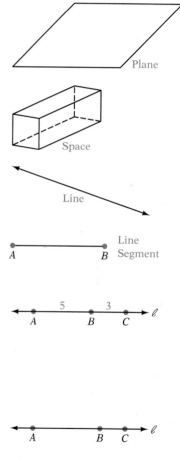

The length of a line segment is the distance between the endpoints of the line segment. The length of a line segment may be expressed as the sum of two or more shorter line segments, as shown. For this example, $AB = 5$, $BC = 3$, and $AC = AB + BC = 5 + 3 = 8$.

➡ Given that $AB = 22$ and $AC = 31$, find the length of *BC.*

$$AC = AB + BC$$
$$31 = 22 + BC$$
$$31 - 22 = 22 - 22 + BC$$
$$9 = BC$$

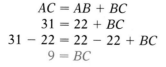

• Substitute 22 for *AB* and 31 for *AC*, and solve for *BC.*

Lines in a plane can be parallel or intersecting. **Parallel lines** never meet; the distance between them is always the same. **Intersecting lines** cross at a point in the plane.

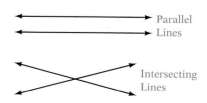

The symbol ‖ means "is parallel to." In the accompanying figure, $AB \parallel CD$ and $p \parallel q$. Note that line p contains line segment AB and that line q contains line segment CD. Parallel lines contain parallel line segments.

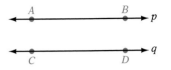

A **ray** starts at a point and extends indefinitely in one direction.

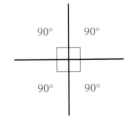

An **angle** is formed when two rays start from the same point. Rays r_1 and r_2 start from point B. The common endpoint is called the **vertex** of the angle.

If A and C are points on rays r_1 and r_2 above, respectively, then the angle is called $\angle ABC$ or $\angle B$, where $\angle$ is the symbol for angle. Note that an angle is named by giving three points, with the vertex as the second point listed, or by the point at the vertex.

An angle can also be named by a variable written between the rays close to the vertex. In the figure, $\angle x = \angle QRS = \angle SRQ$ and $\angle y = \angle SRT = \angle TRS$. Note that in this figure, more than two rays meet at the vertex. In this case, the vertex cannot be used to name the angle.

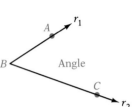

An angle is measured in **degrees.** The symbol for degree is °. One complete revolution is 360° (360 degrees).

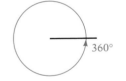

$\frac{1}{4}$ of a revolution is 90°. A 90° angle is called a **right angle.** The symbol ∟ represents a right angle.

Perpendicular lines are intersecting lines that form right angles.

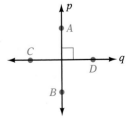

The symbol ⊥ means "is perpendicular to." In the accompanying figure, $AB \perp CD$ and $p \perp q$. Note that line p contains line segment AB and line q contains line segment CD. Perpendicular lines contain perpendicular line segments.

Complementary angles are two angles whose sum is 90°.

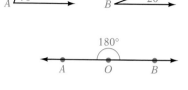

$\angle A + \angle B = 70° + 20° = 90°$
$\angle A$ and $\angle B$ are complementary angles.

$\frac{1}{2}$ of a revolution is 180°. A 180° angle is called a **straight angle.** $\angle AOB$ in the figure is a straight angle.

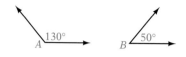

Supplementary angles are two angles whose sum is 180°.

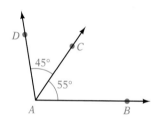

$\angle A + \angle B = 130° + 50° = 180°$
$\angle A$ and $\angle B$ are supplementary angles.

An **acute angle** is an angle whose measure is between 0° and 90°. $\angle B$ in the figure above is an acute angle. An **obtuse angle** is an angle whose measure is between 90° and 180°. $\angle A$ in the figure above is an obtuse angle.

In the accompanying figure, $\angle DAC = 45°$ and $\angle CAB = 55°$.

$\angle DAB = \angle DAC + \angle CAB$
$\quad\quad = 45° + 55° = 100°$

Example 1

Given that $MN = 15$, $NO = 18$, and $MP = 48$, find the length of OP.

Solution

$MP = MN + NO + OP$
$48 = 15 + 18 + OP$
$48 = 33 + OP$
$48 - 33 = 33 - 33 + OP$
$\quad\quad 15 = OP$

Example 2

Find the complement of a 32° angle.

Solution

Let x represent the complement of 32°.

$\quad\quad x + 32° = 90°$
$x + 32° - 32° = 90° - 32°$
$\quad\quad\quad\quad x = 58°$

• The sum of complementary angles is 90°.

58° is the complement of 32°.

You Try It 1

Given that $QR = 24$, $ST = 17$, and $QT = 62$, find the length of RS.

Your solution

You Try It 2

Find the supplement of a 32° angle.

Your solution

Solutions on p. S28

Example 3
Find the measure
of ∠x.

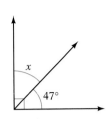

Solution

$$\angle x + 47° = 90°$$
$$\angle x + 47° - 47° = 90° - 47°$$
$$\angle x = 43°$$

You Try It 3
Find the measure
of ∠a.

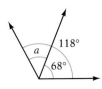

Your solution

Solution on p. S28

Objective B   To define and describe geometric figures ....

A **triangle** is a closed three-sided plane figure.
Figure *ABC* is a triangle. *AB* is called the **base.**
The line *CD*, perpendicular to the base, is called
the **height.**

The sum of the three angles in a triangle is 180°.

$$\angle A + \angle B + \angle C = 180°$$

➡ In triangle *DEF*, ∠D = 32° and ∠E = 88°. Find the measure of ∠F.

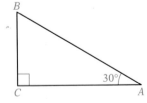

$\angle D + \angle E + \angle F = 180°$	• The sum of the three angles in a triangle is 180°.
$32° + 88° + \angle F = 180°$	• $\angle D = 32°$ and $\angle E = 88°$.
$120° + \angle F = 180°$	• Solve for $\angle F$.
$120° - 120° + \angle F = 180° - 120°$	
$\angle F = 60°$	

A **right triangle** contains one right angle. The side
opposite the right angle is called the **hypotenuse.**
The other two sides are called **legs.** In a right triangle, the two acute angles are complementary.

$$\angle A + \angle B = 90°$$

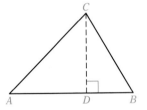

➡ In the right triangle at the left, ∠A = 30°. Find the measure of ∠B.

$\angle A + \angle B = 90°$	• The two acute angles are complementary.
$30° + \angle B = 90°$	• $\angle A = 30°$.
$30° - 30° + \angle B = 90° - 30°$	• Solve for $\angle B$.
$\angle B = 60°$	

A **quadrilateral** is a closed four-sided plane figure. Three quadrilaterals with
special characteristics are described here.

A **parallelogram** has opposite sides parallel and
equal. The distance *AE* between the parallel sides
is called the **height.**

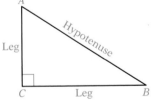

Parallelogram

A **rectangle** is a parallelogram that has four right angles.

A **square** is a rectangle that has four equal sides.

Rectangle   Square

A **circle** is a plane figure in which all points are the same distance from point O, which is called the **center** of the circle.

The **diameter** (d) is a line segment through the center of the circle with endpoints on the circle. AB is a diameter of the circle.

The **radius** (r) is a line segment from the center to a point on the circle. OC is a radius of the circle.

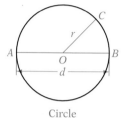

Circle

$$d = 2r \qquad \text{or} \qquad r = \frac{1}{2}d$$

➡ The line segment AB is a diameter of the circle shown. Find the radius of the circle.

The radius is one-half the diameter. Therefore,

$$r = \frac{1}{2}d$$

$$= \frac{1}{2}(8 \text{ in.}) \qquad \bullet \ d = 8 \text{ in.}$$

$$= 4 \text{ in.}$$

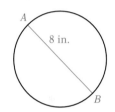

Geometric solids are figures in space, or space figures. Four common space figures are the rectangular solid, cube, sphere, and cylinder.

A **rectangular solid** is a solid in which all six faces are rectangles.

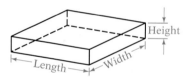

Rectangular Solid

A **cube** is a rectangular solid in which all six faces are squares.

Cube

A **sphere** is a solid in which all points on the surface are the same distance from point O, which is called the **center** of the sphere.

The **diameter** of the sphere is a line segment going through the center with endpoints on the sphere. AB is a diameter of the sphere.

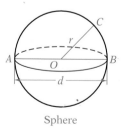

Sphere

The **radius** of the sphere is a line segment from the center to a point on the sphere. OC is a radius of the sphere.

$$r = \frac{1}{2}d \qquad \text{or} \qquad d = 2r$$

➡ The radius of the sphere shown at the right is 5 cm. Find the diameter of the sphere.

$d = 2r$ • **The diameter equals twice the radius.**
$= 2(5 \text{ cm})$ • $r = 5$ cm.
$= 10 \text{ cm}$

The diameter is 10 cm.

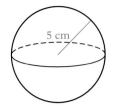

The most common **cylinder** is one in which the bases are circles and are perpendicular to the height.

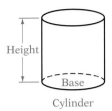

Cylinder

Example 4
One angle in a right triangle is equal to 50°. Find the measure of the other angles.

Solution
In a right triangle, the two acute angles are complementary.

$\angle A + \angle B = 90°$
$\angle A + 50° = 90°$
$\angle A + 50° - 50° = 90° - 50°$
$\angle A = 40°$

The other angles measure 90° and 40°.

Example 5
Two angles of a triangle measure 42° and 103°. Find the measure of the third angle.

Solution
The sum of the three angles of a triangle is 180°.

$\angle A + \angle B + \angle C = 180°$
$\angle A + 42° + 103° = 180°$
$\angle A + 145° = 180°$
$\angle A + 145° - 145° = 180° - 145°$
$\angle A = 35°$

The measure of the third angle is 35°.

Example 6
A circle has a radius of 8 cm. Find the diameter.

Solution
$d = 2r$
$= 2 \cdot 8 \text{ cm} = 16 \text{ cm}$

The diameter is 16 cm.

You Try It 4
A right triangle has one angle equal to 7°. Find the measure of the other angles.

Your solution

You Try It 5
Two angles of a triangle measure 62° and 45°. Find the measure of the other angle.

Your solution

You Try It 6
A circle has a diameter of 8 in. Find the radius.

Your solution

Solutions on p. S29

Objective C   ***To solve problems involving angles formed***
             by intersecting lines ....

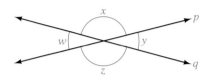

Four angles are formed by the intersection of two lines. If the two lines are perpendicular, each of the four angles is a right angle. If the two lines are not perpendicular, then two of the angles formed are acute angles and two of the angles are obtuse angles. The two acute angles are always opposite each other, and the two obtuse angles are always opposite each other.

In the figure, $\angle w$ and $\angle y$ are acute angles. $\angle x$ and $\angle z$ are obtuse angles. Two angles that are on opposite sides of the intersection of two lines are called **vertical angles.** Vertical angles have the same measure. $\angle w$ and $\angle y$ are vertical angles. $\angle x$ and $\angle z$ are vertical angles.

$$\angle w = \angle y$$
$$\angle x = \angle z$$

Two angles that share a common side are called **adjacent angles.** In the previous figure, $\angle x$ and $\angle y$ are adjacent angles, as are $\angle y$ and $\angle z$, $\angle z$ and $\angle w$, and $\angle w$ and $\angle x$. Adjacent angles of intersecting lines are supplementary angles.

$$\angle x + \angle y = 180°$$
$$\angle y + \angle z = 180°$$
$$\angle z + \angle w = 180°$$
$$\angle w + \angle x = 180°$$

➡ In the figure at the left, $\angle c = 65°$. Find the measures of angles a, b, and d.

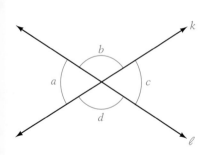

$\angle a = 65°$

• $\angle c = \angle a$ because $\angle c$ and $\angle a$ are vertical angles.

$$\angle b + \angle c = 180°$$

• $\angle c$ is supplementary to $\angle b$ because $\angle c$ and $\angle b$ are adjacent angles.

$$\angle b + 65° = 180°$$
$$\angle b + 65° - 65° = 180° - 65°$$
$$\angle b = 115°$$

• $\angle c = 65°$.

$\angle d = 115°$

• $\angle b = \angle d$ because $\angle b$ and $\angle d$ are vertical angles.

A line intersecting two other lines at two different points is called a **transversal.**

If the lines cut by a transversal are parallel lines and the transversal is perpendicular to the parallel lines, all eight angles formed are right angles.

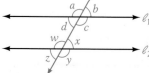

If the lines cut by a transversal are parallel lines and the transversal is not perpendicular to the parallel lines, all four acute angles have the same measure and all four obtuse angles have the same measure. For the accompanying figure:

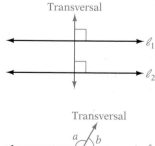

$$\angle a = \angle c = \angle w = \angle y \quad \text{and} \quad \angle b = \angle d = \angle x = \angle z$$

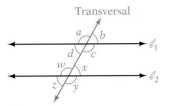

Transversal

Alternate interior angles are two angles that are on opposite sides of the transversal and between the parallel lines. For the figure at the left, $\angle c$ and $\angle w$ are alternate interior angles. $\angle d$ and $\angle x$ are alternate interior angles. Alternate interior angles have the same measure.

Alternate exterior angles are two angles that are on opposite sides of the transversal and outside the parallel lines. For the figure at the left, $\angle a$ and $\angle y$ are alternate exterior angles. $\angle b$ and $\angle z$ are alternate exterior angles. Alternate exterior angles have the same measure.

Corresponding angles are two angles that are on the same side of the transversal and are both acute angles or are both obtuse angles. For the figure at the top left, the following pairs of angles are corresponding angles: $\angle a$ and $\angle w$, $\angle d$ and $\angle z$, $\angle b$ and $\angle x$, $\angle c$ and $\angle y$. Corresponding angles have the same measure.

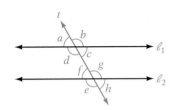

➡ In the figure at the left, $\ell_1 \parallel \ell_2$ and $\angle c = 58°$. Find the measures of $\angle f$, $\angle h$, and $\angle g$.

$\angle f = 58°$ • $\angle c = \angle f$ because $\angle f$ and $\angle c$ are alternate interior angles.

$\angle h = 58°$ • $\angle c = \angle h$ because $\angle c$ and $\angle h$ are corresponding angles.

$\angle g + \angle h = 180°$ • $\angle g$ is supplementary to $\angle h$.
$\angle g + 58° = 180°$ • $\angle h = 58°$.
$\angle g = 122°$ • Subtract 58° from each side.

Example 7
In the figure,
$\angle a = 75°$.
Find $\angle b$.

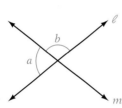

Solution
$\angle a + \angle b = 180°$ • $\angle a$ and $\angle b$ are supplementary.

$75° + \angle b = 180°$ • $\angle a = 75°$.
$\angle b = 105°$ • Subtract 75° from each side.

You Try It 7
In the figure,
$\angle a = 125°$.
Find $\angle b$.

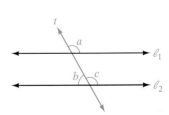

Your solution

Example 8
In the figure,
$\ell_1 \parallel \ell_2$ and
$\angle a = 70°$.
Find $\angle b$.

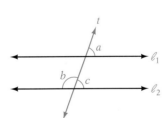

Solution
$\angle c = \angle a = 70°$ • Corresponding angles are equal.

$\angle b + \angle c = 180°$ • $\angle b$ and $\angle c$ are supplementary.

$\angle b + 70° = 180°$ • $\angle c = 70°$.
$\angle b = 110°$ • Subtract 70° from each side.

You Try It 8
In the figure,
$\ell_1 \parallel \ell_2$ and
$\angle a = 120°$.
Find $\angle b$.

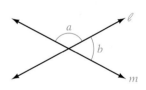

Your solution

Solutions on p. S29

12.1 Exercises

· ·

Objective A

1. The measure of an acute angle is between ___ and ___.

2. The measure of an obtuse angle is between ___ and ___.

3. How many degrees are in a straight angle?

4. Two lines that intersect at right angles are ___ lines.

5. In the figure, $EF = 20$ and $FG = 10$. Find the length of EG.

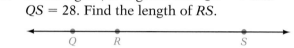

6. In the figure, $EF = 18$ and $FG = 6$. Find the length of EG.

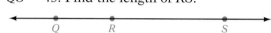

7. In the figure, it is given that $QR = 7$ and $QS = 28$. Find the length of RS.

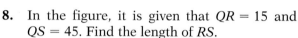

8. In the figure, it is given that $QR = 15$ and $QS = 45$. Find the length of RS.

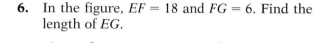

9. In the figure, it is given that $AB = 12$, $CD = 9$, and $AD = 35$. Find the length of BC.

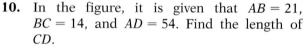

10. In the figure, it is given that $AB = 21$, $BC = 14$, and $AD = 54$. Find the length of CD.

11. Find the complement of a 31° angle.

12. Find the complement of a 62° angle.

13. Find the supplement of a 72° angle.

14. Find the supplement of a 162° angle.

15. Find the complement of a 13° angle.

16. Find the complement of an 88° angle.

17. Find the supplement of a 127° angle.

18. Find the supplement of a 7° angle.

In Exercises 19 and 20, find the measure of angle *AOB*.

19.

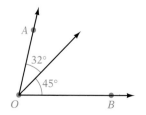

20.

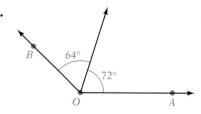

In Exercises 21 to 24, find the measure of angle *a*.

21.

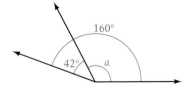

22.

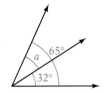

23.

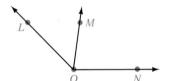

24.

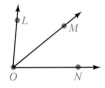

25. In the figure, it is given that ∠*LOM* = 53° and ∠*LON* = 139°. Find the measure of ∠*MON*.

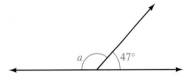

26. In the figure, it is given that ∠*MON* = 38° and ∠*LON* = 85°. Find the measure of ∠*LOM*.

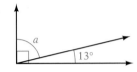

Objective B

27. What is the sum of the three angles of a triangle?

28. Name the side opposite the right angle in a right triangle.

29. Name a parallelogram with four right angles.

30. Name the rectangle with four equal sides.

31. Name a rectangular solid in which all six faces are squares.

32. Name the solid in which all points are the same distance from the center.

33. Name a quadrilateral in which opposite sides are parallel and equal.

34. Name the plane figure in which all points are the same distance from the center.

35. Name the solid in which the bases are circular and perpendicular to the height.

36. Name the solid in which all the faces are rectangles.

37. A triangle has a 13° angle and a 65° angle. Find the measure of the other angle.

38. A triangle has a 105° angle and a 32° angle. Find the measure of the other angle.

39. A right triangle has a 45° angle. Find the measure of the other two angles.

40. A right triangle has a 62° angle. Find the measure of the other two angles.

41. A triangle has a 62° angle and a 104° angle. Find the measure of the other angle.

42. A triangle has a 30° angle and a 45° angle. Find the measure of the other angle.

43. A right triangle has a 25° angle. Find the measure of the other two angles.

44. Two angles of a triangle are 42° and 105°. Find the measure of the other angle.

45. Find the radius of a circle with a diameter of 16 in.

46. Find the radius of a circle with a diameter of 9 ft.

47. Find the diameter of a circle with a radius of $2\frac{1}{3}$ ft.

48. Find the diameter of a circle with a radius of 24 cm.

49. The radius of a sphere is 3.5 cm. Find the diameter.

50. The radius of a sphere is $1\frac{1}{2}$ ft. Find the diameter.

51. The diameter of a sphere is 4 ft 8 in. Find the radius.

52. The diameter of a sphere is 1.2 m. Find the radius.

Objective C

In Exercises 53 to 56, find the measures of angles a and b.

53.
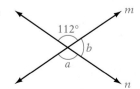

54.
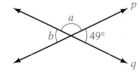

55.
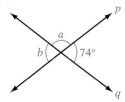

56.
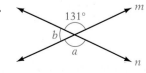

In Exercises 57 to 64, it is given that $\ell_1 \parallel \ell_2$. Find the measures of angles a and b.

57.

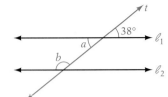

58.

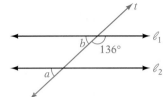

59.

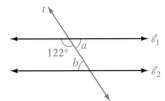

60.

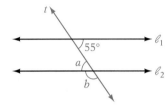

61.

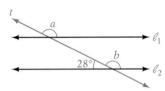

62.

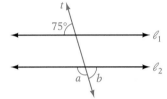

63.

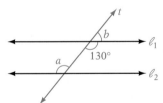

64.

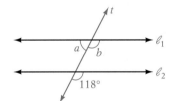

APPLYING THE CONCEPTS

65. **a.** What is the smallest possible whole number of degrees in an angle of a triangle?
   b. What is the largest possible whole number of degrees in an angle of a right triangle?

66. Determine whether the statement is always true, sometimes true, or never true.
   a. Two lines that are both parallel to a third line are parallel to each other.
   b. A triangle contains at least two acute angles.
   c. Vertical angles are complementary angles.

67. If AB and CD intersect at point O, and $\angle AOC = \angle BOC$, explain why AB is perpendicular to CD.

12.2   Plane Geometric Figures

Objective A   *To find the perimeter of plane geometric figures* ....

A **polygon** is a closed figure determined by three or more line segments that lie in a plane. The line segments that form the polygon are called its **sides.** The figures below are examples of polygons.

 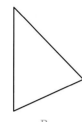 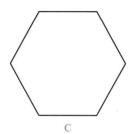 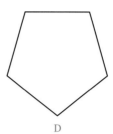 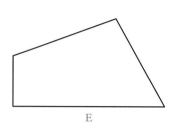

A   B   C   D   E

A **regular polygon** is one in which each side has the same length and each angle has the same measure. The polygons in Figures A, C, and D above are regular polygons.

The name of a polygon is based on the number of its sides. The table below lists the names of polygons that have from 3 to 10 sides.

Number of Sides	Name of the Polygon
3	Triangle
4	Quadrilateral
5	Pentagon
6	Hexagon
7	Heptagon
8	Octagon
9	Nonagon
10	Decagon

Triangles and quadrilaterals are two of the most common types of polygons. Triangles are distinguished by the number of equal sides and also by the measures of their angles.

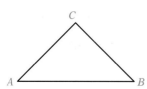 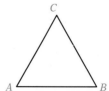 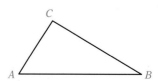

An **isosceles triangle** has two sides of equal length. The angles opposite the equal sides are of equal measure.

$AC = BC$
$\angle A = \angle B$

The three sides of an **equilateral triangle** are of equal length. The three angles are of equal measure.

$AB = BC = AC$
$\angle A = \angle B = \angle C$

A **scalene triangle** has no two sides of equal length. No two angles are of equal measure.

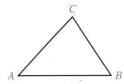

An acute triangle has three acute angles.

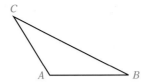

An obtuse triangle has one obtuse angle.

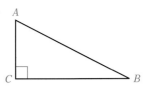

A right triangle has a right angle.

Quadrilaterals are also distinguished by their sides and angles, as shown below. Note that a rectangle, a square, and a rhombus are different forms of a parallelogram.

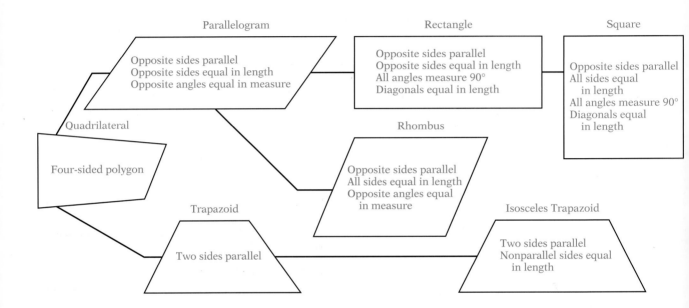

Parallelogram
Opposite sides parallel
Opposite sides equal in length
Opposite angles equal in measure

Rectangle
Opposite sides parallel
Opposite sides equal in length
All angles measure 90°
Diagonals equal in length

Square
Opposite sides parallel
All sides equal in length
All angles measure 90°
Diagonals equal in length

Quadrilateral
Four-sided polygon

Rhombus
Opposite sides parallel
All sides equal in length
Opposite angles equal in measure

Trapazoid
Two sides parallel

Isosceles Trapazoid
Two sides parallel
Nonparallel sides equal in length

The **perimeter** of a plane geometric figure is a measure of the distance around the figure. Perimeter is used in buying fencing for a lawn or determining how much baseboard is needed for a room.

The perimeter of a triangle is the sum of the lengths of the three sides.

Perimeter of a Triangle
$$P = a + b + c$$

➡ Find the perimeter of the triangle shown at the right.

$$P = a + b + c$$
$$= 3 \text{ cm} + 5 \text{ cm} + 6 \text{ cm}$$
$$= 14 \text{ cm}$$

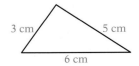

The perimeter of the triangle is 14 cm.

The perimeter of a square is the sum of the four equal sides.

Perimeter of a Square

$$P = 4s$$

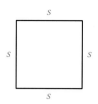

➡ Find the perimeter of the square shown at the right.

$P = 4s$
  $= 4(3 \text{ ft})$ • $s = 3$ ft.
  $= 12 \text{ ft}$

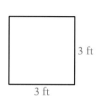

The perimeter of the square is 12 ft.

The perimeter of a quadrilateral is the sum of the lengths of the four sides.

A rectangle is a quadrilateral with opposite sides of equal length. The length of a rectangle refers to the longer side, and the width refers to the length of the shorter side.

Perimeter of a Rectangle

$$P = 2L + 2W$$

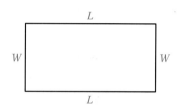

➡ Find the perimeter of the rectangle shown at the right.

$P = 2L + 2W$
  $= 2(6 \text{ m}) + 2(3 \text{ m})$ • $L = 6$ m, $W = 3$ m.
  $= 12 \text{ m} + 6 \text{ m}$
  $= 18 \text{ m}$

The perimeter of the rectangle is 18 m.

The distance around a circle is called the **circumference.** The circumference of a circle is equal to the product of π (pi) and the diameter.

Circumference of a Circle

$$C = \pi d$$
     or
$$C = 2\pi r$$ Because diameter $= 2r$

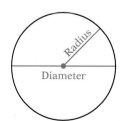

The formula for circumference uses the number π (pi). The value of π can be approximated by a fraction or a decimal.

$$\pi \approx 3.14 \qquad \pi \approx \frac{22}{7}$$

The π key on a calculator gives a closer approximation of π than 3.14.

➡ Find the circumference of the circle shown at the right.

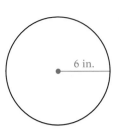

$C = 2\pi r$
$\approx 2 \cdot 3.14 \cdot 6$ in.   • $r = 6$ in.
$= 37.68$ in.

The circumference of the circle is approximately 37.68 in.

Example 1
Find the perimeter of a rectangle with a width of $\frac{2}{3}$ ft and a length of 2 ft.

Solution

$P = 2L + 2W$
$= 2(2 \text{ ft}) + 2\left(\frac{2}{3} \text{ ft}\right)$ • $L = 2$ ft, $W = \frac{2}{3}$ ft
$= 4 \text{ ft} + \frac{4}{3} \text{ ft}$
$= 5\frac{1}{3}$ ft

The perimeter of the rectangle is $5\frac{1}{3}$ ft.

Example 2
Find the perimeter of a triangle with sides 5 in., 7 in., and 8 in.

Solution

5 in. ╱╲ 7 in.
8 in.

$P = a + b + c$
$= 5 \text{ in.} + 7 \text{ in.} + 8 \text{ in.}$
$= 20$ in.

The perimeter of the triangle is 20 in.

Example 3
Find the circumference of a circle with a radius of 18 cm. Use 3.14 for π.

Solution

18 cm

$C = 2\pi r$
$\approx 2 \cdot 3.14 \cdot 18$ cm
$= 113.04$ cm

The circumference is approximately 113.04 cm.

You Try It 1
Find the perimeter of a rectangle with a length of 2 m and a width of 0.85 m.

Your solution

You Try It 2
Find the perimeter of a triangle with sides 12 cm, 15 cm, and 18 cm.

Your solution

You Try It 3
Find the circumference of a circle with a diameter of 6 in. Use 3.14 for π.

Your solution

Solutions on p. S29

Objective B   **To find the perimeter of composite geometric figures** ....

Composite geometric figures are figures made from two or more geometric figures. The following composite is made from part of a rectangle and part of a circle:

$$\text{Perimeter of the composite figure} = 3 \text{ sides of a rectangle} + \frac{1}{2} \text{ the circumference of a circle}$$

$$\text{Perimeter of the composite figure} = 2L + W + \frac{1}{2}\pi d$$

The perimeter of the composite figure below is found by adding the measures of twice the length plus the width plus one-half the circumference of the circle.

$$P = 2L + W + \frac{1}{2}\pi d$$

$$\approx 2(12 \text{ m}) + 4 \text{ m} + \frac{1}{2}(3.14)(4 \text{ m}) \qquad \bullet \ L = 12 \text{ m}, W = 4 \text{ m}, d = 4 \text{ m}.$$

$$= 34.28 \text{ m}$$

The perimeter is approximately 34.28 m.

Example 4
Find the perimeter of the composite figure.

Use $\frac{22}{7}$ for π.

Solution

$$\begin{array}{ccc} \text{Perimeter of composite figure} & = & \underbrace{\text{sum of lengths of the 4 sides}} + \underbrace{\frac{1}{2} \text{ the circumference of the circle}} \end{array}$$

$$P = 4s + \frac{1}{2}\pi d$$

$$\approx 4(5 \text{ cm}) + \frac{1}{2}\left(\frac{22}{7}\right)(7 \text{ cm})$$

$$= 20 \text{ cm} + 11 \text{ cm} = 31 \text{ cm}$$

The perimeter is approximately 31 cm.

You Try It 4
Find the perimeter of the composite figure.
Use 3.14 for π.

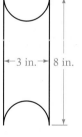

Your solution

Solution on p. S29

Objective C   To solve application problems .... 20 CT

Example 5

The dimensions of a triangular sail are 18 ft, 11 ft, and 15 ft. What is the perimeter of the sail?

Strategy

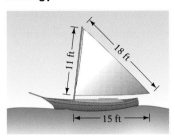

To find the perimeter, use the formula for the perimeter of a triangle.

Solution
$$P = a + b + c$$
$$= 18 \text{ ft} + 11 \text{ ft} + 15 \text{ ft}$$
$$= 44 \text{ ft}$$

The perimeter of the sail is 44 ft.

You Try It 5

What is the perimeter of a standard piece of computer paper that measures $8\frac{1}{2}$ in. by 11 in.?

Your strategy

Your solution

Example 6

If fencing costs $2.75 per foot, how much will it cost to fence a rectangular lot that is 108 ft wide and 240 ft long?

Strategy

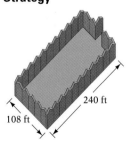

To find the cost of the fence:
- Find the perimeter of the lot.
- Multiply the perimeter by the per-foot cost of fencing.

Solution
$$P = 2L + 2W$$
$$= 2(240 \text{ ft}) + 2(108 \text{ ft})$$
$$= 480 \text{ ft} + 216 \text{ ft}$$
$$= 696 \text{ ft}$$

Cost $= 696 \times 2.75 = 1914$

The cost is $1914.

You Try It 6

A metal strip is being installed around a workbench that is 0.74 m wide and 3 m long. At $1.76 per meter, find the cost of the metal stripping. Round to the nearest cent.

Your strategy

Your solution

Solutions on p. S29

12.2 Exercises

· ·

Objective A

In Exercises 1 to 8, find the perimeter or circumference of the given figures. Use 3.14 for π.

1.

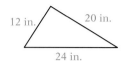

12 in.   20 in.

24 in.

2.

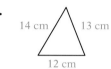

14 cm   13 cm

12 cm

3.

5 ft

5 ft

4.

2 m

2 m

5.

14 cm

32 cm

6.

5 ft

18 ft

7.

15 cm

8.

4 in.

9. Find the perimeter of a triangle with sides 2 ft 4 in., 3 ft, and 4 ft 6 in.

10. Find the perimeter of a rectangle with a length of 2 m and a width of 0.8 m.

11. Find the circumference of a circle with a radius of 8 cm. Use 3.14 for π.

12. Find the circumference of a circle with a diameter of 14 in. Use $\frac{22}{7}$ for π.

13. Find the perimeter of a square in which each side is equal to 60 m.

14. Find the perimeter of a triangle in which each side is $1\frac{2}{3}$ ft.

15. Find the perimeter of a five-sided figure with sides of 22 cm, 47 cm, 29 cm, 42 cm, and 17 cm.

16. Find the perimeter of a rectangular farm that is $\frac{1}{2}$ mi wide and $\frac{3}{4}$ mi long.

Objective B

In the figures accompanying Exercises 17 to 24, find the perimeter. Use 3.14 for π.

17.
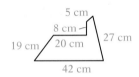

18.
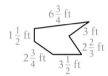

19.
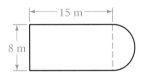

20.

21.

22.

23.
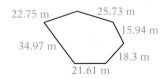

24.

___

Objective C   *Application Problems*

25. How many feet of fencing should be purchased for a rectangular garden that is 18 ft long and 12 ft wide?

26. Wall-to-wall carpeting is installed in a room that is 12 ft long and 10 ft wide. The edges of the carpet are nailed to the floor. Along how many feet must the carpet be nailed down?

27. How many meters of binding are required to bind the edge of a rectangular quilt that measures 3.5 m by 8.5 m?

28. Find the length of molding needed to put around a circular table that is 3.8 ft in diameter. Use 3.14 for π.

29. The rectangular lot shown in the figure at the right is being fenced. The fencing along the road is to cost $4.20 per foot. The rest of the fencing costs $3.85 per foot. Find the total cost to fence the lot.

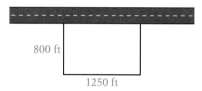

30. Bias binding is to be sewed around the edge of a rectangular tablecloth measuring 72 in. by 45 in. Each package of bias binding costs $3.50 and contains 15 ft of binding. How many packages of bias binding are needed for the tablecloth?

31. A bicycle tire has a diameter of 24 in. How many feet does the bicycle travel when the wheel makes 5 revolutions? Use 3.14 for π.

32. A tricycle tire has a diameter of 12 in. How many feet does the tricycle travel when the wheel makes 8 revolutions? Use 3.14 for π.

33. The floor plan of a roller rink is shown in the figure at the right.
　　a. Use estimation to determine whether the perimeter of the rink is more than 70 m or less than 70 m.
　　b. Calculate the perimeter of the roller rink. Use 3.14 for π.

34. A rain gutter is being installed on a home that has the dimensions shown in the figure at the right. At a cost of $11.30 per meter, how much will it cost to install the rain gutter?

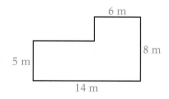

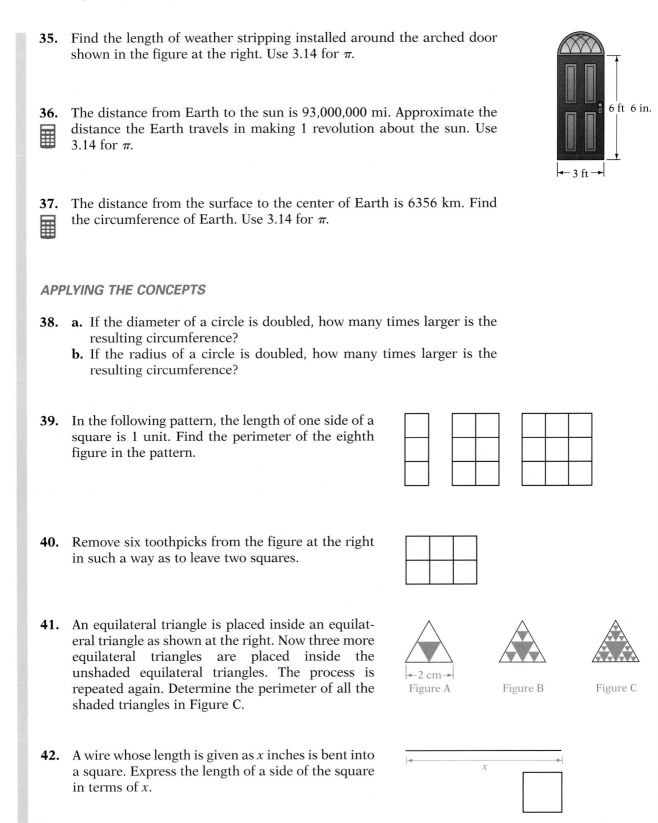

35. Find the length of weather stripping installed around the arched door shown in the figure at the right. Use 3.14 for π.

36. The distance from Earth to the sun is 93,000,000 mi. Approximate the distance the Earth travels in making 1 revolution about the sun. Use 3.14 for π.

37. The distance from the surface to the center of Earth is 6356 km. Find the circumference of Earth. Use 3.14 for π.

6 ft 6 in.

3 ft

APPLYING THE CONCEPTS

38. a. If the diameter of a circle is doubled, how many times larger is the resulting circumference?
   b. If the radius of a circle is doubled, how many times larger is the resulting circumference?

39. In the following pattern, the length of one side of a square is 1 unit. Find the perimeter of the eighth figure in the pattern.

40. Remove six toothpicks from the figure at the right in such a way as to leave two squares.

41. An equilateral triangle is placed inside an equilateral triangle as shown at the right. Now three more equilateral triangles are placed inside the unshaded equilateral triangles. The process is repeated again. Determine the perimeter of all the shaded triangles in Figure C.

2 cm

Figure A   Figure B   Figure C

42. A wire whose length is given as x inches is bent into a square. Express the length of a side of the square in terms of x.

x

43. A forest ranger must determine the diameter of a redwood tree. Explain how the ranger could do this without cutting down the tree.

12.3 Area

Objective A *To find the area of geometric figures* ....

Area is a measure of the amount of surface in a region. Area can be used to describe the size of a rug, a parking lot, a farm, or a national park. Area is measured in square units.

A square that measures 1 in. on each side has an area of 1 square inch, written 1 in^2.

A square that measures 1 cm on each side has an area of 1 square centimeter, written 1 cm^2.

Larger areas can be measured in square feet (ft^2), square meters (m^2), square miles (mi^2), acres ($43{,}560 \text{ ft}^2$), or any other square unit.

The area of a geometric figure is the number of squares that are necessary to cover the figure. In the figures below, two rectangles have been drawn and covered with squares. In the figure on the left, 12 squares, each of area 1 cm^2, were used to cover the rectangle. The area of the rectangle is 12 cm^2. In the figure on the right, 6 squares, each of area 1 in^2, were used to cover the rectangle. The area of the rectangle is 6 in^2.

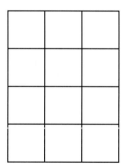

The area of the rectangle is 12 cm^2.

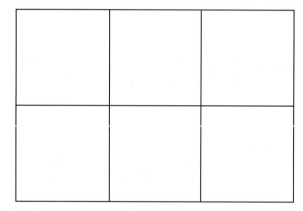

The area of the rectangle is 6 in^2.

Note from the above figures that the area of a rectangle can be found by multiplying the length of the rectangle by its width.

Area of a Rectangle

$A = LW$

➡ Find the area of the rectangle shown at the right.

$A = LW$
$ = (8 \text{ ft})(5 \text{ ft})$ • $L = 8 \text{ ft}, W = 5 \text{ ft}.$
$ = 40 \text{ ft}^2$

The area of the rectangle is 40 ft^2.

A square is a rectangle in which all sides are the same length. Therefore, both the length and width can be represented by a side.

Area of a Square

$A = s \cdot s = s^2$

➡ Find the area of the square shown at the right.

$A = s^2$
   $= (14 \text{ cm})^2$ • $s = 14$ **cm.**
   $= 196 \text{ cm}^2$

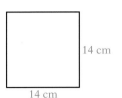

The area of the square is 196 cm².

The area of a circle is equal to the product of π and the square of the radius.

Area of a Circle

$A = \pi r^2$

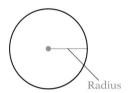

➡ Find the area of the circle shown at the right.

$A = \pi r^2$
   $= \pi (8 \text{ in.})^2 = 64\pi \text{ in}^2$
   $\approx 64 \cdot 3.14 \text{ in}^2 = 200.96 \text{ in}^2$

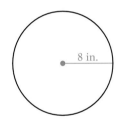

The area is exactly 64π in².
The area is approximately 200.96 in².

In the figure below, *AB* is the base of the triangle, and *CD*, which is perpendicular to the base, is the height. The area of a triangle is one-half the product of the base and the height.

Area of a Triangle

$A = \frac{1}{2}bh$

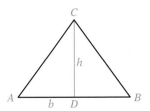

➡ Find the area of the triangle shown at the right.

$A = \frac{1}{2}bh$

   $= \frac{1}{2}(20 \text{ m})(5 \text{ m})$ • $b = 20$ **m,** $h = 5$ **m.**

   $= 50 \text{ m}^2$

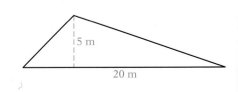

The area of the triangle is 50 m².

Example 1 Find the area of a circle with a diameter of 9 cm. Use 3.14 for π.

Solution $r = \dfrac{1}{2}d = \dfrac{1}{2}(9 \text{ cm}) = 4.5 \text{ cm}$

$A = \pi r^2$
$\approx 3.14(4.5 \text{ cm})^2 = 63.585 \text{ cm}^2$

The area is approximately 63.585 cm².

You Try It 1 Find the area of a triangle with a base of 24 in. and a height of 14 in.

Your solution

Solution on p. S30

Objective B   *To find the area of composite geometric figures* ....

The area of the composite figure shown below is found by calculating the area of the rectangle and then subtracting the area of the triangle.

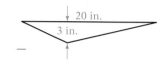

$A = LW - \dfrac{1}{2}bh$

$= (20 \text{ in.})(8 \text{ in.}) - \dfrac{1}{2}(20 \text{ in.})(3 \text{ in.}) = 160 \text{ in}^2 - 30 \text{ in}^2 = 130 \text{ in}^2$

Example 2
Find the area of the shaded portion of the figure. Use 3.14 for π.

Solution

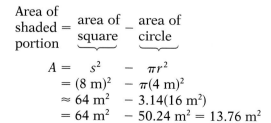

$\underbrace{\text{Area of shaded portion}} = \underbrace{\text{area of square}} - \underbrace{\text{area of circle}}$

$A = s^2 - \pi r^2$
$= (8 \text{ m})^2 - \pi(4 \text{ m})^2$
$\approx 64 \text{ m}^2 - 3.14(16 \text{ m}^2)$
$= 64 \text{ m}^2 - 50.24 \text{ m}^2 = 13.76 \text{ m}^2$

The area is approximately 13.76 m².

You Try It 2
Find the area of the composite figure.

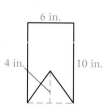

Your solution

Solution on p. S30

Objective C   To solve application problems .... (20) CT

Example 3

A walkway 2 m wide is built along the front and along both sides of a building, as shown in the figure. Find the area of the walkway.

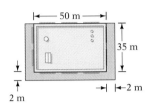

Strategy

To find the area of the walkway, add the area of the front section (54 m · 2 m) and the area of the two side sections (each 35 m · 2 m).

Solution

$$\text{Area of walkway} = \underbrace{\text{area of front section}} + \underbrace{2(\text{area of one side section})}$$

$$A = (54 \text{ m})(2 \text{ m}) + 2(35 \text{ m})(2 \text{ m})$$
$$= 108 \text{ m}^2 \quad + 140 \text{ m}^2$$
$$= 248 \text{ m}^2$$

The area of the walkway is 248 m².

You Try It 3

New carpet is installed in a room measuring 9 ft by 12 ft. Find the area of the room in square yards. (9 ft² = 1 yd²)

Your strategy

Your solution

Solution on p. S30

12.3 Exercises

· ·

Objective A

In Exercises 1 to 8, find the area of the given figures. Use 3.14 for π.

1.

6 ft
24 ft

2.

8 in.
18 in.

3.

9 in.
9 in.

4.
4 in.
4 in.

5.

4 ft

6.
3 cm

7.
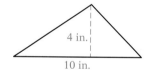
4 in.
10 in.

8.

6 m
7 m

9. Find the area of a right triangle with a base of 3 cm and a height of 1.42 cm.

10. Find the area of a triangle with a base of 3 ft and a height of $\frac{2}{3}$ ft.

11. Find the area of a square with a side of 4 ft.

12. Find the area of a square with a side of 10 cm.

13. Find the area of a rectangle with a length of 43 in. and a width of 19 in.

14. Find the area of a rectangle with a length of 82 cm and a width of 20 cm.

15. Find the area of a circle with a radius of 7 in. Use $\frac{22}{7}$ for π.

16. Find the area of a circle with a diameter of 40 cm. Use 3.14 for π.

───────────

Objective B

Find the area. Use 3.14 for π.

17.

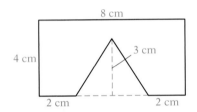

18.

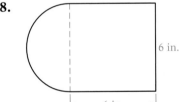

19.

20.

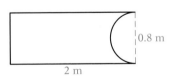

21.

22.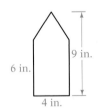

23.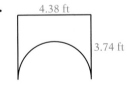

24.

Objective C *Application Problems*

25. Artificial turf is being used to cover a playing field. If the field is rectangular with a length of 100 yd and a width of 75 yd, how much artificial turf must be purchased to cover the field?

26. The telescope lens of the Hale telescope at Mount Palomar, California, has a diameter of 200 in. Find the area of the lens. Leave the answer in terms of π.

27. An irrigation system waters a circular field that has a 50-foot radius. Find the area watered by the irrigation system. Use 3.14 for π.

28. A fabric wall hanging is to fill a space that measures 5 m by 3.5 m. Allowing for 0.1 m of the fabric to be folded back along each edge, how much fabric must be purchased for the wall hanging?

29. You plan to stain the wooden deck attached to your house. The deck measures 10 ft by 8 ft. A quart of stain will cost $6.95 and will cover 50 ft^2. How many quarts of stain should you buy?

30. A carpet is to be installed in one room and a hallway, as shown in the diagram at the right. At a cost of $18.50 per square meter, how much will it cost to carpet the area?

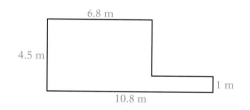

31. Find the area of a concrete driveway with the measurements shown in the figure.

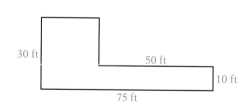

32. You want to tile your kitchen floor. The floor measures 12 ft by 9 ft. How many tiles, each a square with side $1\frac{1}{2}$ ft, should you purchase for the job?

33. You are wallpapering two walls of a child's room. One wall measures 9 ft by 8 ft, and the other measures 11 ft by 8 ft. The wallpaper costs $18.50 per roll, and each roll of the wallpaper will cover 40 ft^2. What is the cost to wallpaper the two walls?

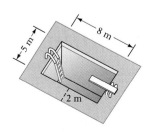

34. Find the area of the 2-meter boundary around the swimming pool shown in the figure.

35. An urban renewal project involves reseeding a park that is in the shape of a square, 60 ft on each side. Each bag of grass seed costs $5.75 and will seed 1200 ft². How much money should be budgeted for buying grass seed for the park?

36. The roller rink shown in the figure at the right is to be covered with hardwood floor.
   a. Without doing the calculations, is the area of the rink more than 8000 ft² or less than 8000 ft²?
   b. Calculate how much hardwood floor is needed to cover the roller rink. Use 3.14 for π.

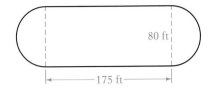

37. Find the total area of the national park with the dimensions shown in the figure. Use 3.14 for π.

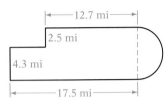

38. Find the cost of plastering the walls of a room 22 ft long, 25 ft 6 in. wide, and 8 ft high. Subtract 120 ft² for windows and doors. The cost is $1.50 per square foot.

39. **a.** A circle has a radius of 8 in. Find the increase in area when the radius is increased by 2 in. Use 3.14 for π.
   b. A circle has a radius of 5 cm. Find the increase in area when the radius is doubled. Use 3.14 for π.

APPLYING THE CONCEPTS

40. What fractional part of the area of the larger of the two squares is the shaded area? Write your answer as a fraction in simplest form. This problem appeared in *Math Teacher*, vol. 86, No. 3 (September 1993).

41. **a.** If both the length and width of a rectangle are doubled, how many times larger is the area of the resulting rectangle?
   b. If the radius of a circle is doubled, what happens to the area?
   c. If the diameter of a circle is doubled, what happens to the area?

42. The circles at the right are identical. Is the area in the circles to the left of the line equal to, less than, or greater than the area in the circles to the right of the line? Explain your answer.

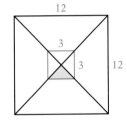

43. Determine whether the statement is always true, sometimes true, or never true.
   a. If two triangles have the same perimeter, then they have the same area.
   b. If two rectangles have the same area, then they have the same perimeter.
   c. If two squares have the same area, then the sides of the squares have the same length.

44. All of these dots are equally spaced, horizontally and vertically, 1 inch apart. What is the area of the triangle?

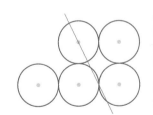

12.4 Volume

Objective A *To find the volume of geometric solids* ....

Volume is a measure of the amount of space inside a figure in space. Volume can be used to describe the amount of heating gas used for cooking, the amount of concrete delivered for the foundation of a house, or the amount of water in storage for a city's water supply.

A cube that is 1 ft on each side has a volume of 1 cubic foot, which is written 1 ft^3.

A cube that measures 1 cm on each side has a volume of 1 cubic centimeter, written 1 cm^3.

The volume of a solid is the number of cubes that are necessary to fill the solid exactly. The volume of the rectangular solid at the right is 24 cm^3 because it will hold exactly 24 cubes, each 1 cm on a side. Note that the volume can be found by multiplying the length times the width times the height.

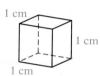

Volume of a Rectangular Solid

$V = LWH$

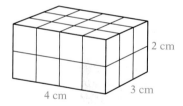

➡ Find the volume of a rectangular solid with a length of 9 in., a width of 3 in., and a height of 4 in.

$V = LWH$
$ = (9 \text{ in.})(3 \text{ in.})(4 \text{ in.})$ • $L = 9$ in., $W = 3$ in.,
$ = 108 \text{ in}^3$ $H = 4$ in.

The volume of the rectangular solid is 108 in^3.

The length, width, and height of a cube have the same measure. The volume of a cube is found by multiplying the side of the cube times itself three times (side cubed).

Volume of a Cube

$V = s^3$

➡ Find the volume of the cube shown at the right.

$V = s^3$
    $= (3 \text{ ft})^3$ • $s = 3$ ft.
    $= 27 \text{ ft}^3$

The volume of the cube is 27 ft³.

The volume of a sphere is found by multiplying four-thirds times pi (π) times the radius cubed.

Volume of a Sphere

$V = \dfrac{4}{3}\pi r^3$

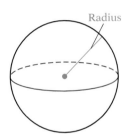

➡ Find the volume of the sphere shown below. Use 3.14 for π. Round to the nearest hundredth.

$V = \dfrac{4}{3}\pi r^3$

$\approx \dfrac{4}{3}(3.14)(2 \text{ in.})^3$ • $r = 2$ in.

$= \dfrac{4}{3}(3.14)(8 \text{ in}^3)$

$\approx 33.49 \text{ in}^3$

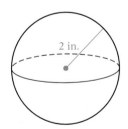

The volume is approximately 33.49 in³.

The volume of a cylinder is found by multiplying the area of the base of the cylinder (a circle) times the height.

Volume of a Cylinder

$V = \pi r^2 h$

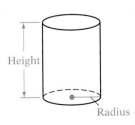

➡ Find the volume of the cylinder shown at the right. Use 3.14 for π.

$V = \pi r^2 h$
   $\approx 3.14(3 \text{ cm})^2(8 \text{ cm})$ • $r = 3$ cm; $h = 8$ cm.
   $= 3.14(9 \text{ cm}^2)(8 \text{ cm})$
   $= 226.08 \text{ cm}^3$

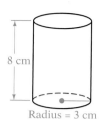

8 cm

Radius = 3 cm

The volume of the cylinder is 226.08 cm³.

Example 1

Find the volume of a rectangular solid with a length of 3 ft, a width of 1.5 ft, and a height of 2 ft.

Solution
$V = LWH$
   $= (3 \text{ ft})(1.5 \text{ ft})(2 \text{ ft})$
   $= 9 \text{ ft}^3$

The volume is 9 ft³.

You Try It 1

Find the volume of a rectangular solid with a length of 8 cm, a width of 3.5 cm, and a height of 4 cm.

Your solution

Example 2

Find the volume of a cube that has a side measuring 2.5 in.

Solution
$V = s^3$
   $= (2.5 \text{ in.})^3$
   $= 15.625 \text{ in}^3$

The volume is 15.625 in³.

You Try It 2

Find the volume of a cube with a side of 5 cm.

Your solution

Example 3

Find the volume of a cylinder with a radius of 12 cm and a height of 65 cm. Use 3.14 for π.

Solution
$V = \pi r^2 h$
   $\approx 3.14(12 \text{ cm})^2(65 \text{ cm})$
   $= 3.14(144 \text{ cm}^2)(65 \text{ cm})$
   $= 29{,}390.4 \text{ cm}^3$

The volume is approximately 29,390.4 cm³.

You Try It 3

Find the volume of a cylinder with a diameter of 14 in. and a height of 15 in. Use $\frac{22}{7}$ for π.

Your solution

Solutions on p. S30

Example 4
Find the volume of a sphere with a diameter of 12 in. Use 3.14 for π.

Solution

$r = \dfrac{1}{2}d = \dfrac{1}{2}(12 \text{ in.}) = 6 \text{ in.}$

$V = \dfrac{4}{3}\pi r^3$

$ \approx \dfrac{4}{3} \cdot (3.14)(6 \text{ in.})^3$

$ = \dfrac{4}{3}(3.14)(216 \text{ in}^3)$

$ = 904.32 \text{ in}^3$

The volume is approximately 904.32 in³.

You Try It 4
Find the volume of a sphere with a radius of 3 m. Use 3.14 for π.

Your solution

Solution on p. S30

Objective B   *To find the volume of composite geometric solids* ....

Composite geometric solids are solids made from two or more geometric solids. The solid shown is made from a cylinder and one-half of a sphere.

Volume of the composite solid = volume of the cylinder + $\dfrac{1}{2}$ the volume of the sphere

➡ Find the volume of the composite solid shown above if the radius of the base of the cylinder is 3 in. and the height of the cylinder is 10 in. Use 3.14 for π.

The volume equals the volume of a cylinder plus one-half the volume of a sphere. The radius of the sphere equals the radius of the base of the cylinder.

$V = \pi r^2 h + \dfrac{1}{2}\left(\dfrac{4}{3}\pi r^3\right)$

$ \approx 3.14(3 \text{ in.})^2(10 \text{ in.}) + \dfrac{1}{2}\left(\dfrac{4}{3}\right)(3.14)(3 \text{ in.})^3$

$ = 3.14(9 \text{ in}^2)(10 \text{ in.}) + \dfrac{1}{2}\left(\dfrac{4}{3}\right)(3.14)(27 \text{ in}^3)$

$ = 282.6 \text{ in}^3 + 56.52 \text{ in}^3$

$ = 339.12 \text{ in}^3$

The volume is approximately 339.12 in³.

Example 5
Find the volume of the solid in the figure.
Use 3.14 for π.

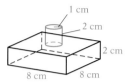

Solution

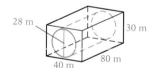

| Volume
of the
solid | = | volume of
rectangu-
lar solid | + | volume of
cylinder |

$V = LWH + \pi r^2 h$
$\approx (8 \text{ cm})(8 \text{ cm})(2 \text{ cm}) + 3.14(1 \text{ cm})^2(2 \text{ cm})$
$= 128 \text{ cm}^3 + 6.28 \text{ cm}^3$
$= 134.28 \text{ cm}^3$

The volume is approximately 134.28 cm³.

You Try It 5
Find the volume of the solid in the figure.
Use 3.14 for π.

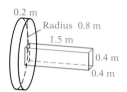

Your solution

Example 6
Find the volume of the solid in the figure.
Use 3.14 for π.

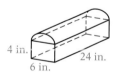

Solution

| Volume
of the
solid | = | volume of
rectangu-
lar solid | − | volume of
cylinder |

$V = LWH - \pi r^2 h$
$\approx (80 \text{ m})(40 \text{ m})(30 \text{ m}) - 3.14(14 \text{ m})^2(80 \text{ m})$
$= 96,000 \text{ m}^3 - 49,235.2 \text{ m}^3$
$= 46,764.8 \text{ m}^3$

The volume is approximately 46,764.8 m³.

You Try It 6
Find the volume of the solid in the figure.
Use 3.14 for π.

Your solution

Solutions on p. S30

Objective C *To solve application problems* ....

Example 7
An aquarium is 28 in. long, 14 in. wide, and 16 in. high. Find the volume of the aquarium.

Strategy
To find the volume of the aquarium, use the formula for the volume of a rectangular solid.

Solution
$V = LWH$
$= (28 \text{ in.})(14 \text{ in.})(16 \text{ in.})$
$= 6272 \text{ in}^3$

The volume of the aquarium is 6272 in³.

You Try It 7
Find the volume of a freezer that is 7 ft long, 3 ft high, and 2.5 ft wide.

Your strategy

Your solution

Example 8
Find the volume of the bushing shown in the figure below. Use 3.14 for π.

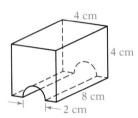

Strategy
To find the volume of the bushing, subtract the volume of the half-cylinder from the volume of the rectangular solid.

Solution

 = −

$$\begin{array}{l} \text{Volume} \\ \text{of the} \\ \text{bushing} \end{array} = \begin{array}{l} \text{volume of the} \\ \text{rectangu-} \\ \text{lar solid} \end{array} - \begin{array}{l} \frac{1}{2}\text{ the} \\ \text{volume of} \\ \text{cylinder} \end{array}$$

$V = LWH - \frac{1}{2}\pi r^2 h$

$\approx (8 \text{ cm})(4 \text{ cm})(4 \text{ cm}) - \frac{1}{2}(3.14)(1 \text{ cm})^2(8 \text{ cm})$

$= 128 \text{ cm}^3 - 12.56 \text{ cm}^3$

$= 115.44 \text{ cm}^3$

The volume of the bushing is approximately 115.44 cm³.

You Try It 8
Find the volume of the channel iron shown in the figure below.

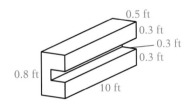

Your strategy

Your solution

Solutions on p. S30

12.4 Exercises

. . . .

Objective A

In Exercises 1 to 8, find the volume. Round to the nearest hundredth. Use 3.14 for π.

1.

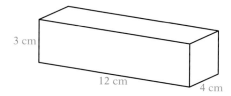

3 cm

12 cm

4 cm

2.

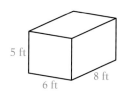

5 ft

6 ft

8 ft

3.

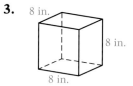

8 in.

8 in.

8 in.

4.

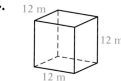

12 m

12 m

12 m

5.

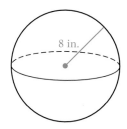

8 in.

6.

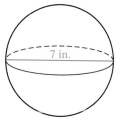

7 in.

7.

12 cm

2 cm

8.

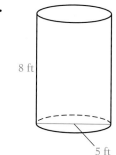

8 ft

5 ft

In Exercises 9 to 16, find the volume.

9. Find the volume of a rectangular solid with a length of 2 m, a width of 80 cm, and a height of 4 m.

10. Find the volume of a cylinder with a radius of 7 cm and a height of 14 cm. Use $\frac{22}{7}$ for π.

11. Find the volume of a sphere with a 11-millimeter radius. Use 3.14 for π. Round to the nearest hundredth.

12. Find the volume of a cube with a side of 2.14 m. Round to the nearest tenth.

13. Find the volume of a cylinder with a diameter of 12 ft and a height of 30 ft. Use 3.14 for π.

14. Find the volume of a sphere with a 6-foot diameter. Use 3.14 for π.

15. Find the volume of a cube with a side of $3\frac{1}{2}$ ft.

16. Find the volume of a rectangular solid with a length of 1.15 m, a width of 60 cm, and a height of 25 cm.

Objective B

In Exercises 17 to 22, find the volume. Use 3.14 for π.

17.

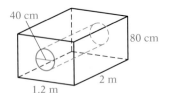

18.

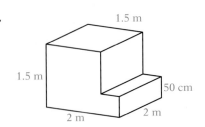

19.

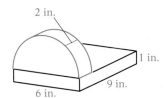

20.

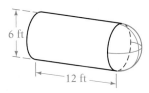

21.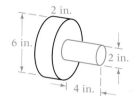

22.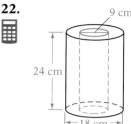

Objective C   *Application Problems*

Solve. Use 3.14 for π.

23. A rectangular tank at the fish hatchery is 9 m long, 3 m wide, and 1.5 m deep. Find the volume of the water in the tank when the tank is full.

24. A fuel tank in a booster rocket is a cylinder 10 ft in diameter and 52 ft high. Find the volume of the fuel tank.

25. A hot air balloon is in the shape of a sphere. Find the volume of a hot air balloon that is 32 ft in diameter. Round to the nearest hundredth.

26. A storage tank for propane is in the shape of a sphere that has a diameter of 9 m. Find the volume of the tank.

27. An oil tank, which is in the shape of a cylinder, is 4 m high and has a diameter of 6 m. The oil tank is two-thirds full. Find the number of cubic meters of oil in the tank. Round to the nearest hundredth.

28. A silo, which is in the shape of a cylinder, is 16 ft in diameter and has a height of 30 ft. The silo is three-fourths full. Find the volume of the portion of the silo that is not being used for storage. Round to the nearest hundredth.

29. An architect is designing the heating system for an auditorium and needs to know the volume of the structure. Find the volume of the auditorium with the measurements shown in the figure.

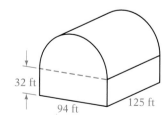

30. A swimming pool 50 ft long and 13 ft wide contains water to a depth of 10 ft. Find the total weight of the water in the swimming pool. (1 ft^3 weighs 62.4 lb.)

31. Find the volume of the bushing shown at the right.

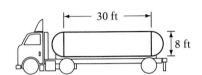

32. How many gallons of water will fill an aquarium that is 12 in. wide, 18 in. long, and 16 in. high? Round to the nearest tenth. (1 gal = 231 in^3.)

33. How many gallons of water will fill a fish tank that is 12 in. long, 8 in. wide, and 9 in. high? Round to the nearest tenth. (1 gal = 231 in^3.)

34. A truck carrying an oil tank is shown in the figure at the right.
   a. Without doing the calculations, is the volume of the oil tank more than 240 ft^3 or less than 240 ft^3?
   b. If the tank is half full, how many cubic feet of oil is the truck carrying? Round to the nearest hundredth.

35. The concrete floor of a building is shown in the figure at the right. At a cost of $3.85 per cubic foot, find the cost of having the floor poured. Round to the nearest cent.

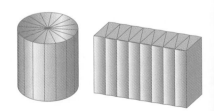

APPLYING THE CONCEPTS

36. Half a sphere is called a hemisphere. Derive a formula for the volume of a hemisphere.

37. a. If both the length and the width of a rectangular solid are doubled, how many times larger is the resulting rectangular solid?
   b. If the length, width, and height of a rectangular solid are all doubled, how many times larger is the resulting rectangular solid?
   c. If the side of a cube is doubled, how many times larger is the resulting cube?

38. Explain how you could cut through a cube so that the face of the resulting solid is **(a)** a square, **(b)** an equilateral triangle, **(c)** a trapezoid, **(d)** a hexagon.

39. Suppose a cylinder is cut into 16 equal pieces, which are then arranged as shown at the right. The figure resembles a rectangular solid. What variable expressions could be used to represent the length, width, and height of the rectangular solid? Explain how the formula for the volume of a cylinder is derived from this approach.

12.5 The Pythagorean Theorem

Objective A *To find the square root of a number* ....

The area of a square is 36 in². What is the length of one side?

Area of the square = (side)²
$$36 = \text{side} \cdot \text{side}$$

What number multiplied times itself equals 36?
$$36 = 6 \cdot 6$$

The side of the square is 6 in.

Area =
36 in²

The **square root** of a number is one of two identical factors of that number. The square root symbol is $\sqrt{}$.

The square root of 36 is 6.
$$\sqrt{36} = 6$$

POINT OF INTEREST

There is evidence of irrational numbers as early as 500 B.C. These numbers were not very well understood, and they were given the name *numerus surdus*. This phrase comes from the Latin word *surdus,* which means deaf or mute. Thus irrational numbers were "inaudible numbers."

A **perfect square** is the product of a whole number times itself.

1, 4, 9, 16, 25, and 36 are perfect squares.

$1 \cdot 1 = 1$	$\sqrt{1} = 1$
$2 \cdot 2 = 4$	$\sqrt{4} = 2$
$3 \cdot 3 = 9$	$\sqrt{9} = 3$
$4 \cdot 4 = 16$	$\sqrt{16} = 4$
$5 \cdot 5 = 25$	$\sqrt{25} = 5$
$6 \cdot 6 = 36$	$\sqrt{36} = 6$

The square root of a perfect square is a whole number.

If a number is not a perfect square, its square root can only be approximated. The approximate square roots of numbers can be found using a calculator. For example:

Number	Square Root
33	$\sqrt{33} \approx 5.745$
34	$\sqrt{34} \approx 5.831$
35	$\sqrt{35} \approx 5.916$

Example 1 Find the square roots of the perfect squares 49 and 81.

Solution $\sqrt{49} = 7$ $\sqrt{81} = 9$

You Try It 1 Find the square roots of the perfect squares 16 and 169.

Your solution

Solution on p. S31

Example 2   Find the square roots, to the nearest thousandth, of 27 and 108.

Solution $\sqrt{27} \approx 5.196$ $\sqrt{108} \approx 10.392$

You Try It 2   Find the square roots, to the nearest thousandth, of 32 and 162.

Your solution

Solution on p. S31

Objective B   *To find the unknown side of a right triangle using the Pythagorean Theorem* ....

POINT OF INTEREST

The first known proof of the Pythagorean Theorem is in a Chinese textbook that dates from 150 B.C. The book is called the *Nine Chapters on the Mathematical Art.* The diagram below is from that book and was used in the proof of the theorem.

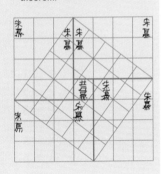

The Greek mathematician Pythagoras is generally credited with the discovery that the square of the hypotenuse of a right triangle is equal to the sum of the squares of the two legs. This is called the **Pythagorean Theorem.** However, the Babylonians used this theorem more than 1000 years before Pythagoras lived.

Square of the hypotenuse	equals	sum of the squares of the two legs
5^2	=	$3^2 + 4^2$
25	=	9 + 16
25	=	25

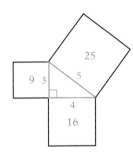

If the length of one side of a right triangle is unknown, one of the following formulas can be used to find its length.

If the hypotenuse is unknown, use

$$\textbf{Hypotenuse} = \sqrt{\textbf{(leg)}^2 + \textbf{(leg)}^2}$$
$$= \sqrt{(3)^2 + (4)^2}$$
$$= \sqrt{9 + 16}$$
$$= \sqrt{25}$$
$$= 5$$

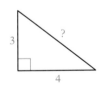

If the length of a leg is unknown, use

$$\textbf{Leg} = \sqrt{\textbf{(hypotenuse)}^2 - \textbf{(leg)}^2}$$
$$= \sqrt{(5)^2 - (4)^2}$$
$$= \sqrt{25 - 16}$$
$$= \sqrt{9}$$
$$= 3$$

By using the Pythagorean Theorem and several facts from geometry, a relationship among the sides of two special right triangles can be found.

The first special right triangle has two 45° angles and is called a **45°–45°–90° triangle.** The sides opposite the 45° angles are equal.

In a 45°–45°–90° triangle:

hypotenuse $= \sqrt{2} \times$ **(length of a leg)**

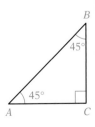

⇒ Find the length of the hypotenuse for a 45°–45°–90° triangle in which the length of one leg is 26 m. Round to the nearest thousandth.

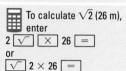
Hypotenuse = $\sqrt{2}$ × (length of a leg)

= $\sqrt{2}$(26 m)

≈ 36.770

The hypotenuse is approximately 36.770 m.

The second special right triangle is the **30°–60°–90° triangle.**

For a 30°–60°–90° triangle, the length of the leg opposite the 30° angle is one-half the length of the hypotenuse.

$$BC = \frac{1}{2} \times AB$$

⇒ Find the length of the two legs of a 30°–60°–90° triangle that has a hypotenuse 16 cm in length. Round to the nearest thousandth.

Leg = $\frac{1}{2}$ × hypotenuse

= $\frac{1}{2}$(16 cm) = 8 cm

Leg = $\sqrt{(\text{hypotenuse})^2 - (\text{leg})^2}$

= $\sqrt{16^2 - 8^2}$

= $\sqrt{256 - 64}$

= $\sqrt{192}$ ≈ 13.856

- Because the right triangle is a 30°–60°–90° triangle, the leg opposite the 30° angle is one-half the hypotenuse.

- Use the Pythagorean Theorem to find the other leg.

The lengths of the legs are 8 cm and 13.856 cm.

Example 3
Find the hypotenuse of the triangle in the figure. Round to the nearest thousandth.

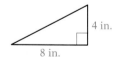

Solution
Hypotenuse = $\sqrt{(\text{leg})^2 + (\text{leg})^2}$

= $\sqrt{8^2 + 4^2}$

= $\sqrt{64 + 16}$

= $\sqrt{80}$ ≈ 8.944

The hypotenuse is approximately 8.944 in.

You Try It 3
Find the hypotenuse of the triangle in the figure. Round to the nearest thousandth.

Your solution

Solution on p. S31

Example 4

Find the length of the leg of the triangle in the figure. Round to the nearest thousandth.

12 cm
9 cm

Solution

$$\text{Leg} = \sqrt{(\text{hypotenuse})^2 - (\text{leg})^2}$$
$$= \sqrt{12^2 - 9^2}$$
$$= \sqrt{144 - 81}$$
$$= \sqrt{63} \approx 7.937$$

The length of the leg is approximately 7.937 cm.

You Try It 4

Find the length of the leg of the triangle in the figure. Round to the nearest thousandth.

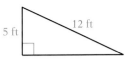

5 ft   12 ft

Your solution

Solution on p. S31

Objective C   To solve application problems ....

Example 5

A 25-foot ladder is placed against a building at a point 21 ft from the ground, as shown in the figure. Find the distance from the base of the building to the base of the ladder. Round to the nearest thousandth.

25 ft
21 ft

Strategy

To find the distance from the base of the building to the base of the ladder, use the Pythagorean Theorem. The hypotenuse is the length of the ladder (25 ft). One leg is the distance along the building from the ground to the top of the ladder (21 ft). The distance from the base of the building to the base of the ladder is the unknown leg.

Solution

$$\text{Leg} = \sqrt{(\text{hypotenuse})^2 - (\text{leg})^2}$$
$$= \sqrt{25^2 - 21^2}$$
$$= \sqrt{625 - 441}$$
$$= \sqrt{184} \approx 13.565$$

The distance is approximately 13.565 ft.

You Try It 5

Find the distance between the centers of the holes in the metal plate in the figure. Round to the nearest thousandth.

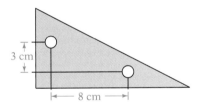

3 cm
8 cm

Your strategy

Your solution

Solution on p. S31

12.5 Exercises

· ·

Objective A

Find the square root. Round to the nearest thousandth.

1. 7

2. 34

3. 42

4. 64

5. 165

6. 144

7. 189

8. 130

Objective B

Find the unknown side of the triangle in the figures in Exercises 9 to 17.

9.

3 in.
4 in.

10.

5 in.
12 in.

11.
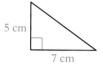
5 cm
7 cm

12.

7 cm
9 cm

13.

15 ft
10 ft

14.
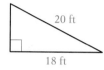
20 ft
18 ft

15.

4 cm   6 cm

16.

9 m   12 m

17.

9 yd
9 yd

Find the lengths of the two legs in the figures in Exercises 18 to 20.

18.

20 cm
30°

19.

12 ft
30°

20.

16 cm
30°

Find the hypotenuse of the triangle in the figures in Exercises 21 to 26.

21.

15 cm
45°
15 cm

22.

6 in.   6 in.
45°   45°

23.

4 m
30°   60°

24.

4.3 cm
30°

25.

45°
8 yd

26.
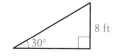
8 ft
30°

Objective C *Application Problems*

27. Find the length of the ramp used to roll barrels up to the loading dock, which is 3.5 ft high. Round to the nearest hundredth.

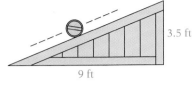

3.5 ft

9 ft

28. Find the distance between the holes in the metal plate in the figure at the right. Round to the nearest hundredth.

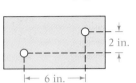

2 in.

6 in.

29. If you travel 18 mi east and then 12 mi north, how far are you from your starting point? Round to the nearest tenth.

30. A fence is built around the plot shown in the figure at the right. At $8.40 per meter, how much did it cost to fence the plot? (*Hint:* Use the Pythagorean Theorem to find the unknown length.)

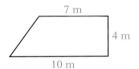

7 m

4 m

10 m

31. Four holes are drilled in the circular plate shown at the right. The centers of the holes are 3 in. from the center. Find the distance between the centers of adjacent holes. Round to the nearest thousandth.

32. Find the offset distance, d, of the length of pipe shown in the diagram at the right. The total length of the pipe is 62 in.

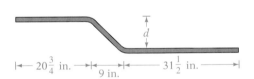

d

$20\frac{3}{4}$ in.   9 in. $31\frac{1}{2}$ in.

APPLYING THE CONCEPTS

33. Determine whether the statement is always true, sometimes true, or never true.
  a. The sum of the lengths of two sides of a triangle is greater than the length of the third side of the triangle.
  b. The hypotenuse is the longest side of a right triangle.

34. What is a Pythagorean triple? Provide at least three examples of Pythagorean triples.

35. Buildings *A* and *B* are situated on opposite sides of a river. A construction company must lay a pipeline between the two buildings. The plan is to connect the buildings as shown. What is the total length of the pipe needed to connect the buildings?

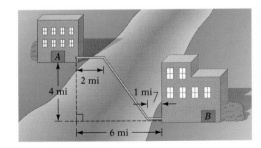

12.6 Similar and Congruent Triangles

Objective A   ***To solve similar and congruent triangles*** ....

Similar objects have the same shape but not necessarily the same size. A baseball is similar to a basketball. A model airplane is similar to an actual airplane.

Similar objects have corresponding parts; for example, the propellers on the model airplane correspond to the propellers on the actual airplane. The relationship between the sizes of each of the corresponding parts can be written as a ratio, and all such ratios will be the same. If the propellers on the model plane are $\frac{1}{50}$ the size of the propellers on the actual plane, then the model wing is $\frac{1}{50}$ the size of the actual wing, the model fuselage is $\frac{1}{50}$ the size of the actual fuselage, and so on.

The two triangles *ABC* and *DEF* shown are similar. The ratios of corresponding sides are equal.

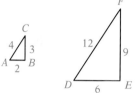

$$\frac{AB}{DE} = \frac{2}{6} = \frac{1}{3}, \frac{BC}{EF} = \frac{3}{9} = \frac{1}{3}, \text{ and } \frac{AC}{DF} = \frac{4}{12} = \frac{1}{3}$$

The ratio of corresponding sides $= \frac{1}{3}$.

Because the ratios of corresponding sides are equal, three proportions can be formed:

$$\frac{AB}{DE} = \frac{BC}{EF}, \frac{AB}{DE} = \frac{AC}{DF}, \text{ and } \frac{BC}{EF} = \frac{AC}{DF}$$

The ratio of corresponding heights equals the ratio of corresponding sides, as shown in the figure.

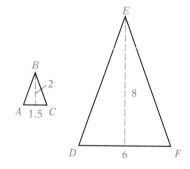

Ratio of corresponding sides $= \frac{1.5}{6} = \frac{1}{4}$

Ratio of heights $= \frac{2}{8} = \frac{1}{4}$

Congruent objects have the same shape *and* the same size.

The two triangles shown are congruent. They have exactly the same size.

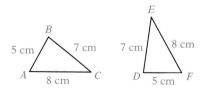

For triangles, congruent means that the corresponding sides *and* angles of the triangle are equal, unlike similar triangles, which have corresponding angles equal but corresponding sides are not necessarily equal.

Here are two major rules that can be used to determine whether two triangles are congruent.

> **Side-Side-Side Rule (SSS)**
>
> Two triangles are congruent if three sides of one triangle equal the corresponding sides of the second triangle.

In the two triangles at the right, $AB = DE$, $AC = DF$, and $BC = EF$. The corresponding sides of triangles ABC and DEF are equal. The triangles are congruent by the SSS rule.

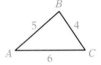

> **Side-Angle-Side Rule (SAS)**
>
> Two triangles are congruent if two sides and the included angle of one triangle equal the corresponding sides and included angle of the second triangle.

In the two triangles at the right, $AB = EF$, $AC = DE$, and angle BAC = angle DEF. The triangles are congruent by the SAS rule.

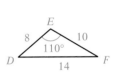

➡ Determine whether the two triangles in the adjacent figure are congruent.

Because $AC = DF$, $AB = FE$, and $BC = DE$, all three sides of one triangle equal the corresponding sides of the second triangle. The triangles are congruent by the SSS rule.

Example 1
Find the ratio of corresponding sides for the similar triangles ABC and DEF in the figure.

Solution
$$\frac{7 \text{ m}}{12 \text{ m}} = \frac{7}{12}$$

You Try It 1
Find the ratio of corresponding sides for the similar triangles ABC and DEF in the figure.

Your solution

Solution on p. S31

Example 2

Triangles *ABC* and *DEF* in the figure are similar. Find *x*, the length of side *EF*.

Solution

$$\frac{AB}{DE} = \frac{BC}{x}$$ • The ratios of corresponding sides of similar triangles are equal.

$$\frac{8 \text{ m}}{12 \text{ m}} = \frac{6 \text{ m}}{x}$$

$$8x = 12 \cdot 6 \text{ m}$$

$$8x = 72 \text{ m}$$

$$\frac{8x}{8} = \frac{72 \text{ m}}{8}$$

$$x = 9 \text{ m}$$

Side *EF* is 9 m.

Example 3

Determine whether triangle *ABC* in the figure is congruent to triangle *DEF*.

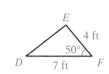

Solution

Because *AB* = *DF*, *AC* = *EF*, and angle *BAC* = angle *DFE*, the triangles are congruent by the SAS rule.

Example 4

Triangles *ABC* and *DEF* in the figure are similar. Find *h*, the height of triangle *DEF*.

Solution

$$\frac{8 \text{ cm}}{12 \text{ cm}} = \frac{4 \text{ cm}}{h}$$

$$8h = 12 \cdot 4 \text{ cm}$$ • The ratios of corresponding sides of similar triangles equal the ratio of corresponding heights.

$$8h = 48 \text{ cm}$$

$$\frac{8h}{8} = \frac{48 \text{ cm}}{8}$$

$$h = 6 \text{ cm}$$

The height of *DEF* is 6 cm.

You Try It 2

Triangles *ABC* and *DEF* in the figure are similar. Find *x*, the length of side *DF*.

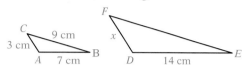

Your solution

You Try It 3

Determine whether triangle *ABC* in the figure is congruent to triangle *DEF*.

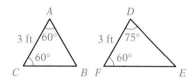

Your solution

You Try It 4

Triangles *ABC* and *DEF* in the figure are similar. Find *h*, the height of triangle *DEF*.

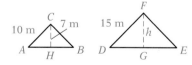

Your solution

Solutions on p. S31

Objective B **To solve application problems** .... CT

Example 5
Triangles *ABC* and *DEF* in the figure are similar. Find the area of triangle *DEF*.

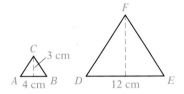

Strategy
To find the area of triangle *DEF*:

- Solve a proportion to find the height of triangle *DEF*. Let h = the height.

- Use the formula $A = \frac{1}{2}bh$.

Solution

$$\frac{AB}{DE} = \frac{\text{height of triangle } ABC}{\text{height of triangle } DEF}$$

$$\frac{4 \text{ cm}}{12 \text{ cm}} = \frac{3 \text{ cm}}{h}$$

$$4h = 12 \cdot 3 \text{ cm}$$

$$4h = 36 \text{ cm}$$

$$\frac{4h}{4} = \frac{36 \text{ cm}}{4}$$

$$h = 9 \text{ cm}$$

$$A = \frac{1}{2}bh$$

$$= \frac{1}{2}(12 \text{ cm})(9 \text{ cm})$$

$$= 54 \text{ cm}^2$$

The area is 54 cm².

You Try It 5
Triangles *ABC* and *DEF* in the figure are similar right triangles. Find the perimeter of triangle *ABC*.

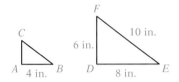

Your strategy

Your solution

Solution on p. S31

12.6 Exercises

· ·

Objective A

Find the ratio of corresponding sides for the similar triangles in Exercises 1 to 4.

1.

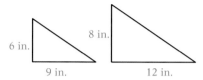

2.

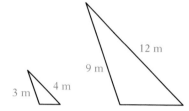

3.

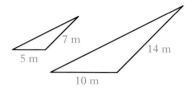

4.

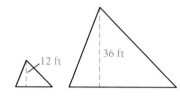

Determine whether the two triangles in Exercises 5 to 8 are congruent.

5.

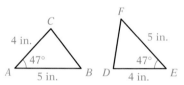

6.

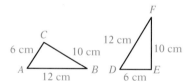

7.

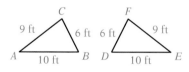

8.

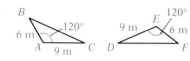

Triangles *ABC* and *DEF* in Exercises 9 to 12 are similar. Find the indicated distance. Round to the nearest tenth.

9. Find side *DE*.

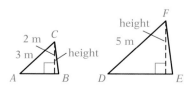

10. Find side *DE*.

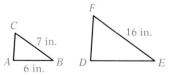

11. Find the height of triangle *DEF*.

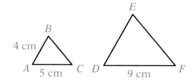

12. Find the height of triangle *ABC*.

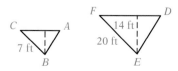

Objective B   *Application Problems*

The sun's rays, objects on earth, and the shadows cast by them form similar triangles.

13. Find the height of the building shown.

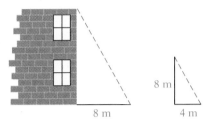

14. Find the height of the building shown.

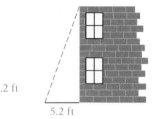

In Exercises 15 to 18, triangles *ABC* and *DEF* are similar.

15. Find the perimeter of triangle *ABC*.

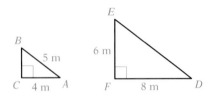

16. Find the perimeter of triangle *DEF*.

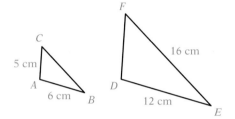

17. Find the area of triangle *ABC*.

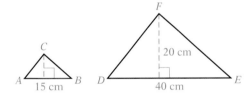

18. Find the area of triangle *DEF*.

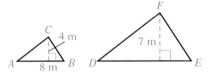

APPLYING THE CONCEPTS

19. Determine whether the statement is always true, sometimes true, or never true.
   a. If two angles of one triangle are equal to two angles of a second triangle, then the triangles are similar triangles.
   b. Two isosceles triangles are similar triangles.
   c. Two equilateral triangles are similar triangles.

20. Are all squares similar? Are all rectangles similar? Explain. Use a drawing in your explanation.

21. Figure *ABC* is a right triangle and *DE* is parallel to *AB*. What is the perimeter of the trapezoid *ABED*?

22. Explain how, by using only a yardstick, you could determine the approximate height of a tree without climbing it.

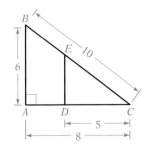

Focus on Problem Solving

Trial and Error   Some problems in mathematics are solved by using **trial and error.** The trial-and-error method of arriving at a solution to a problem involves repeated tests or experiments until a satisfactory conclusion is reached.

Many of the Applying the Concepts exercises in this text require a trial and error method of solution. For example, an exercise in Section 12.4 reads:

Explain how you could cut through a cube so that the face of the resulting solid is **(a)** a square, **(b)** an equilateral triangle, **(c)** a trapezoid, **(d)** a hexagon.

There is no formula to apply to this problem; there is no computation to perform. This problem requires picturing a cube and the results after cutting through it at different places on its surface and at different angles. For part (a), cutting perpendicular to the top and bottom of the cube and parallel to two of its sides will result in a square. The other shapes may prove more difficult.

When solving problems of this type, keep an open mind. Sometimes when using the trial-and-error method, we are hampered by narrowness of vision; we cannot expand our thinking to include other possibilities. Then when we see someone else's solution, it appears so obvious to us! For example, for the Applying the Concepts question above, it is necessary to conceive of cutting through the cube at places other than the top surface; we need to be open to the idea of beginning the cut at one of the corner points of the cube.

A topic of the Projects and Group Activities in this chapter is symmetry. Here again, trial and error is used to determine the lines of symmetry inherent in an object. For example, in determining lines of symmetry for a square, begin by drawing a square. The horizontal line of symmetry and the vertical line of symmetry may be immediately obvious to you.

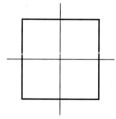

But there are two others. Do you see that a line drawn through opposite corners of the square is also a line of symmetry?

Many of the questions in this text that require an answer of "always true, sometimes true, or never true" are best solved by the trial-and-error method. For example, consider the statement presented in Section 3 of this chapter.

If two rectangles have the same area, then they have the same perimeter.

Try some numbers. Each of two rectangles, one measuring 6 units by 2 units and another measuring 4 units by 3 units, has an area of 12 square units, but the perimeter of the first is 16 units and the perimeter of the second is 14 units. So the answer "always true" has been eliminated. We still need to determine whether there is a case when it is true. After experimenting with a lot of numbers, you may come to realize that we are trying to determine if it is possible for two different pairs of factors of a number to have the same sum. Is it?

Don't be afraid to make many experiments, and remember that *errors*, or tests that "don't work," are a part of the trial-and-*error* process.

Projects and Group Activities

Investigating Perimeter

The perimeter of the square at the right is 4 units.

If two squares are joined along one of the sides, the perimeter is 6 units. Note that it does not matter which sides are joined; the perimeter is still 6 units.

If three squares are joined, the perimeter of the resulting figure is 8 units for each possible placement of the squares.

Four squares can be joined in five different ways as shown. There are two possible perimeters, 10 units for A, B, C, and D, and 8 for E.

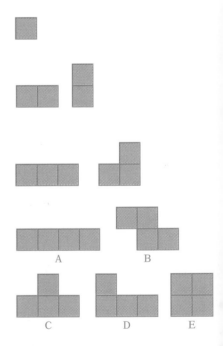

1. If five squares are joined, what is the maximum perimeter possible?

2. If five squares are joined, what is the minimum perimeter possible?

3. If six squares are joined, what is the maximum perimeter possible?

4. If six squares are joined, what is the minimum perimeter possible?

Symmetry   Look at the letter A printed at the left. If the letter were folded along line ℓ, the two sides of the letter would match exactly. This letter has **symmetry** with respect to line ℓ. Line ℓ is called the **axis of symmetry.**

Now consider the letter H printed below at the left. Both lines ℓ_1 and ℓ_2 are axes of symmetry for this letter; the letter could be folded along either line and the two sides would match exactly.

1. Does the letter A have more than one axis of symmetry?

2. Find axes of symmetry for other capital letters of the alphabet.

3. Which lowercase letters have one axis of symmetry?

4. Do any of the lowercase letters have more than one axis of symmetry?

5. Find the number of axes of symmetry for each of the plane geometric figures presented in this chapter.

6. There are other types of symmetry. Look up the meaning of point symmetry and rotational symmetry. Which plane geometric figures provide examples of these types of symmetry?

7. Find examples of symmetry in nature, art, and architecture.

Chapter Summary

Key Words   An *angle* is formed when two rays start from the same point. An angle is measured in *degrees*.

A 90° angle is called a *right angle*.

Perpendicular lines are intersecting lines that form right angles.

Complementary angles are two angles whose sum is 90°.

Supplementary angles are two angles whose sum is 180°.

A *right triangle* contains one right angle. The side opposite the right angle in a right triangle is called the *hypotenuse*. The other two sides are called *legs*.

A *45°–45°–90° triangle* is a special right triangle in which the sides opposite the 45° angles are equal and the hypotenuse is equal to $\sqrt{2} \times$ (length of a leg).

A *30°–60°–90° triangle* is a special right triangle in which the length of the leg opposite the 30° angle is one-half the length of the hypotenuse.

A *quadrilateral* is a four-sided plane figure.

A *rectangle* is a parallelogram that has four right angles.

A *square* is a rectangle that has four equal sides.

A *circle* is a plane figure in which all points are the same distance from the center of the circle. The *diameter* is a line segment across a circle going through the center. The *radius* is equal to one-half the diameter.

A *rectangular solid* is a solid in which all six faces are rectangles.

A *cube* is a rectangular solid in which all six faces are squares.

A *sphere* is a solid in which all points on the surface are the same distance from the center of the sphere.

Perimeter is the distance around a plane figure.

Area is a measure of the amount of surface in a region.

Volume is a measure of the amount of space inside a closed surface.

Composite geometric solids are solids made from two or more geometric solids.

The *square root* of a number is one of two identical factors of that number.

Similar objects have the same shape but not necessarily the same size.

Congruent objects have the same shape and the same size.

Essential Rules   *Perimeter Equations*

Triangle: $P = a + b + c$
Square: $P = 4s$
Rectangle: $P = 2L + 2W$
Circle: $C = 2\pi r$ or $C = \pi d$

Area Equations

Triangle: $A = \frac{1}{2}bh$

Square: $A = s^2$
Rectangle: $A = LW$
Circle: $A = \pi r^2$

Volume Equations

Rectangular solid: $V = LWH$
Cube: $V = s^3$

Sphere: $V = \frac{4}{3}\pi r^3$

Cylinder: $V = \pi r^2 h$

Pythagorean Theorem

Hypotenuse $= \sqrt{(\text{leg})^2 + (\text{leg})^2}$ Leg $= \sqrt{(\text{hypotenuse})^2 - (\text{leg})^2}$

Side-Side-Side (SSS)

Two triangles are congruent when three sides of one triangle equal the corresponding sides of the second triangle.

Side-Angle-Side (SAS)

Two triangles are congruent when two sides and the included angle of one triangle equal the corresponding sides and included angle of the second triangle.

Chapter Review

1. The diameter of a sphere is 1.5 m. Find the radius of the sphere.

2. Find the circumference of a circle with a radius of 5 cm. Use 3.14 for π.

3. Find the perimeter of the rectangle in the figure below.

5 ft

8 ft

4. Given $AB = 15$, $CD = 6$, and $AD = 24$, find the length of BC.

5. Find the volume of the rectangular solid shown below.

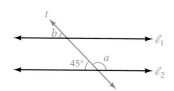

4 ft

5 ft   10 ft

6. Find the unknown side of the triangle in the figure below.

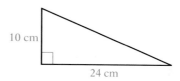

10 cm

24 cm

7. Find the supplement of a 105° angle.

8. Find the square root of 15. Round to the nearest thousandth.

9. Triangles *ABC* and *DEF* are similar. Find the height of triangle *DEF*.

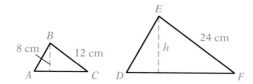

E

B   24 cm

8 cm   12 cm   h

A   C   D   F

10. Find the area of the circle shown below. Use 3.14 for π.

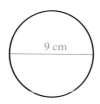

9 cm

11. Given that $\ell_1 \parallel \ell_2$, find the measures of angles *a* and *b*.

t

b ℓ_1

45°   a ℓ_2

12. Find the area of the rectangle shown below.

5 m

11 m

13. Find the volume of the composite figure shown below.

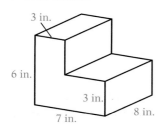

3 in.

6 in.

3 in.

7 in.   8 in.

14. Find the area of the composite figure shown below. Use 3.14 for π.

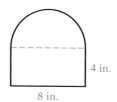

4 in.

8 in.

15. Find the volume of a sphere with a diameter of 8 ft. Use 3.14 for π. Round to the nearest tenth.

16. Triangles *ABC* and *DEF* are similar. Find the area of triangle *DEF*.

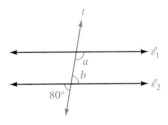

17. Find the perimeter of the composite figure shown below. Use 3.14 for π.

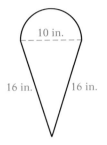

18. Given that $\ell_1 \parallel \ell_2$, find the measures of angles *a* and *b*.

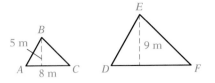

19. How high on a building will a 17-foot ladder reach when the bottom of the ladder is 8 ft from the building?

20. A right triangle has a 32° angle. Find the measures of the other two angles.

21. A bicycle tire has a diameter of 28 in. How many feet does the bicycle travel if the wheel makes 10 revolutions? Use 3.14 for π. Round to the nearest tenth of a foot.

22. New carpet is installed in a room measuring 18 ft by 14 ft. Find the area of the room in square yards. ($9 \text{ ft}^2 = 1 \text{ yd}^2$)

23. A silo, which is in the shape of a cylinder, is 9 ft in diameter and has a height of 18 ft. Find the volume of the silo. Use 3.14 for π.

24. Find the area of a right triangle with a base of 8 m and a height of 2.75 m.

25. If you travel 20 mi west and then 21 mi south, how far are you from your starting point?

Chapter Test

1. Find the volume of a cylinder with a height of 6 m and a radius of 3 m. Use 3.14 for π.

2. Find the perimeter of a rectangle that has a length of 2 m and a width of 1.4 m.

3. Find the volume of the composite figure. Use 3.14 for π.

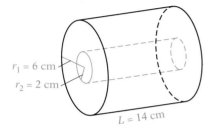

$r_1 = 6$ cm
$r_2 = 2$ cm
$L = 14$ cm

4. Triangles *ABC* and *DEF* are congruent right triangles. Find the length of *FE*.

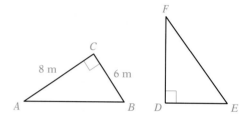

8 m   6 m

5. Find the complement of a 32° angle.

6. Find the area of a circle that has a diameter of 2 m. Use $\frac{22}{7}$ for π.

7. In the figure below, lines ℓ_1 and ℓ_2 are parallel. Angle x measures 30°. Find the measure of angle y.

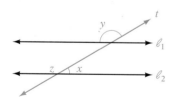

8. Find the perimeter of the composite figure. Use 3.14 for π.

$2\frac{1}{2}$ ft

4 ft

9. Find the square root of 189. Round to the nearest thousandth.

10. Find the unknown side of the triangle shown below. Round to the nearest thousandth.

12 ft

7 ft

11. Find the area of the composite figure.

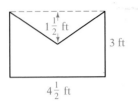

12. In the figure below, lines ℓ_1 and ℓ_2 are parallel. Angle x measures 45°. Find the measures of angles a and b.

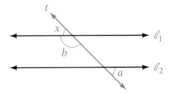

13. Triangles ABC and DEF are similar. Find side BC.

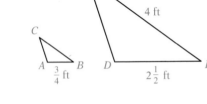

14. A right triangle has a 40° angle. Find the measures of the other two angles.

15. Find the width of the canal shown in the figure at the right.

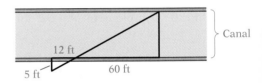

16. How much more pizza is contained in a pizza with radius 10 in. than in one with radius 8 in.? Use 3.14 for π.

17. A carpet is to be placed as shown in the diagram at the right. At $26.80 per square yard, how much will it cost to carpet the area? Round to the nearest cent. ($9 \text{ ft}^2 = 1 \text{ yd}^2$)

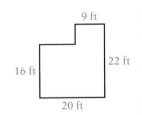

18. Find the cross-sectional area of a redwood tree that is 11 ft 6 in. in diameter. Use 3.14 for π. Round to the nearest hundredth.

19. Find the length of the rafter needed for the roof shown in the figure.

20. A toolbox is 1 ft 2 in. long, 9 in. wide, and 8 in. high. The sides and bottom of the toolbox are $\frac{1}{2}$ in. thick. Find the volume of the interior of the toolbox in cubic inches.

Cumulative Review

1. Find the GCF of 96 and 144.

2. Add: $3\frac{5}{12} + 2\frac{9}{16} + 1\frac{7}{8}$

3. Find the quotient of $4\frac{1}{3}$ and $6\frac{2}{9}$.

4. Simplify: $\left(\frac{2}{3}\right)^2 \div \left(\frac{1}{3} + \frac{1}{2}\right) - \frac{2}{5}$

5. Simplify: $-\frac{2}{3} - \left(-\frac{5}{8}\right)$

6. Write "$348.80 earned in 40 hours" as a unit rate.

7. Solve the proportion $\frac{3}{8} = \frac{n}{100}$.

8. Write $37\frac{1}{2}\%$ as a fraction.

9. Evaluate $a^2 - (b^2 - c)$ when $a = 2$, $b = -2$, and $c = -4$.

10. 30.94 is 36.4% of what number?

11. Solve: $\frac{x}{3} + 3 = 1$

12. Solve: $2(x - 3) + 2 = 5x - 8$

13. Convert 32.5 km to meters.

14. Subtract: $32 \text{ m} - 42 \text{ cm}$

15. Solve: $\frac{2}{3}x = -10$

16. Solve: $2x - 4(x - 3) = 8$

17. You bought a car for $17,488 and made a down payment of $1000. You paid the balance in 36 equal monthly installments. Find the monthly payment.

18. The sales tax on a suit costing $175 is $6.75. At the same rate, find the sales tax on a stereo system costing $1220.

19. A heavy equipment operator receives an hourly wage of $16.06 an hour after receiving a 10% wage increase. Find the operator's hourly wage before the increase.

20. An after-Christmas sale has a markdown rate of 55%. Find the sale price of a dress that had a regular price of $120.

21. An IRA pays 10% annual interest compounded daily. What would be the value of an investment of $25,000 after 20 years? Use the table in the Appendix.

22. A square tile measuring 4 in. by 4 in. weighs 6 oz. Find the weight, in pounds, of a package of 144 such tiles.

23. Twenty-five rivets are used to fasten two steel plates together. The plates are 5.4 m long, and the rivets are equally spaced with a rivet at each end. Find the distance in centimeters between the rivets.

24. The total of four times a number and two is negative six. Find the number.

25. The lines ℓ_1 and ℓ_2 in the figure below are parallel. Find angles a and b.

26. Find the perimeter of the composite figure. Use 3.14 for π.

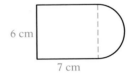

6 cm

7 cm

27. Find the area of the composite figure.

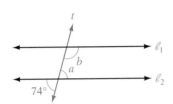

4 in.

5 in.

16 in.

28. Find the volume of the composite figure. Use 3.14 for π.

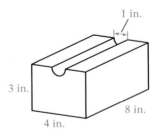

1 in.

3 in.

4 in.

8 in.

29. Find the unknown side of the triangle shown in the figure below. Round to the nearest hundredth.

8 ft

7 ft

30. Triangles ABC and DEF below are similar. Find the perimeter of DEF.

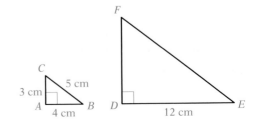

F

C

3 cm

5 cm

A B D

4 cm

12 cm E

Final Examination

1. Subtract: $100,914 - 97,655$

2. Find 34,821 divided by 657.

3. Simplify: $3^2 \cdot (5 - 3)^2 \div 3 + 4$

4. Find the LCM of 9, 12, and 16.

5. Add: $\dfrac{3}{8} + \dfrac{5}{6} + \dfrac{1}{5}$

6. Subtract: $7\dfrac{5}{12} - 3\dfrac{13}{16}$

7. Find the product of $3\dfrac{5}{8}$ and $1\dfrac{5}{7}$.

8. Divide: $1\dfrac{2}{3} \div 3\dfrac{3}{4}$

9. Simplify: $\left(\dfrac{2}{3}\right)^3 \cdot \left(\dfrac{3}{4}\right)^2$

10. Simplify: $\left(\dfrac{2}{3}\right)^2 \div \left(\dfrac{3}{4} + \dfrac{1}{3}\right) - \dfrac{1}{3}$

11. Add:
$$\begin{array}{r} 4.972 \\ 28.6 \\ 1.88 \\ + 128.725 \\ \hline \end{array}$$

12. Find 90,001 decreased by 29,796.

13. Multiply:
$$\begin{array}{r} 2.97 \\ \times\, 0.0094 \\ \hline \end{array}$$

14. Divide: $0.062\overline{)0.0426}$
Round to the nearest hundredth.

15. Convert 0.45 to a fraction in simplest form.

16. Write "323.4 miles on 13.2 gallons of gas" as a unit rate.

17. Solve the proportion $\dfrac{12}{35} = \dfrac{n}{160}$.
Round to the nearest tenth.

18. Write $22\dfrac{1}{2}\%$ as a fraction.

19. Write 1.35 as a percent.

20. Write $\frac{5}{4}$ as a percent.

21. Find 120% of 30.

22. 12 is what percent of 9?

23. 42 is 60% of what number?

24. Convert $1\frac{2}{3}$ ft to inches.

25. Subtract: 3 ft 2 in. − 1 ft 10 in.

26. Convert 40 oz to pounds.

27. Find the sum of 3 lb 12 oz and 2 lb 10 oz.

28. Convert 18 pt to gallons.

29. Divide: $3\overline{)5\text{ gal }1\text{ qt}}$

30. Convert 2.48 m to centimeters.

31. Convert 4 m 62 cm to meters.

32. Convert 1 kg 614 g to kilograms.

33. Convert 2 L 67 ml to milliliters.

34. Convert 55 mi to kilometers. Round to the nearest hundredth. (1.61 km ≈ 1 mi.)

35. How much does it cost to run a 2400-watt air conditioner for 6 h at 8¢ per kilowatt-hour? Round to the nearest cent.

36. Write 0.0000000679 in scientific notation.

37. Find the perimeter of a rectangle with a length of 1.2 m and a width of 0.75 m.

38. Find the area of a rectangle with a length of 9 in. and a width of 5 in.

39. Find the volume of a box with a length of 20 cm, a width of 12 cm, and a height of 5 cm.

40. Add: $-2 + 8 + (-10)$

41. Subtract: $-30 - (-15)$

42. Multiply: $2\frac{1}{2} \times \left(-\frac{1}{5}\right)$

43. Find the quotient of $-1\frac{3}{8}$ and $5\frac{1}{2}$.

44. Simplify: $(-4)^2 \div (1 - 3)^2 - (-2)$

45. Simplify: $2x - 3(x - 4) + 5$

46. Solve: $\frac{2}{3}x = -12$

47. Solve: $3x - 5 = 10$

48. Solve: $8 - 3x = x + 4$

49. You have $872.48 in your checking account. You write checks of $321.88 and $34.23 and then make a deposit of $443.56. Find your new checking account balance.

50. In a pre-election survey, it is estimated that 5 out of 8 eligible voters will vote in an election. How many people will vote in an election with 102,000 eligible voters?

51. This month a company is paying its stockholders a dividend of $1.60 per share. This is 80% of what the dividend per share was one year ago. What was the dividend per share one year ago?

52. A sales executive received commissions of $4320, $3572, $2864, and $4420 during a 4-month period. Find the average income for the 4 months.

53. A contractor borrows $120,000 for 9 months at an annual interest rate of 10%. What is the simple interest due on the loan?

54. The circle graph shows the population of the five most populous countries. Find what percent the population of China is of the total population of the top five countries. Round to the nearest tenth of a percent.

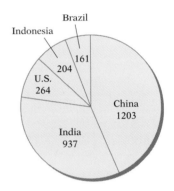

Population in Millions of People

55. A compact disk player that regularly sells for $314.00 is on sale for $226.08. What is the discount rate?

56. A square tile measuring 8 in. by 8 in. weighs 9 oz. Find the weight in pounds of a box containing 144 tiles.

57. Find the perimeter of the composite figure. Use 3.14 for π.

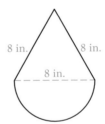

58. Find the area of the composite figure. Use 3.14 for π.

59. Five less than the quotient of a number and two is equal to three. Find the number.

Appendix

Compound Interest Table

Compounded Annually

	4%	5%	6%	7%	8%	9%	10%
1 year	1.04000	1.05000	1.06000	1.07000	1.08000	1.09000	1.10000
5 years	1.21665	1.27628	1.33823	1.40255	1.46933	1.53862	1.61051
10 years	1.48024	1.62890	1.79085	1.96715	2.15893	2.36736	2.59374
15 years	1.80094	2.07893	2.39656	2.75903	3.17217	3.64248	4.17725
20 years	2.19112	2.65330	3.20714	3.86968	4.66095	5.60441	6.72750

Compounded Semiannually

	4%	5%	6%	7%	8%	9%	10%
1 year	1.04040	1.05062	1.06090	1.07123	1.08160	1.09203	1.10250
5 years	1.21899	1.28008	1.34392	1.41060	1.48024	1.55297	1.62890
10 years	1.48595	1.63862	1.80611	1.98979	2.19112	2.41171	2.65330
15 years	1.81136	2.09757	2.42726	2.80679	3.24340	3.74531	4.32194
20 years	2.20804	2.68506	3.26204	3.95926	4.80102	5.81634	7.03999

Compounded Quarterly

	4%	5%	6%	7%	8%	9%	10%
1 year	1.04060	1.05094	1.06136	1.07186	1.08243	1.09308	1.10381
5 years	1.22019	1.28204	1.34686	1.41478	1.48595	1.56051	1.63862
10 years	1.48886	1.64362	1.81402	2.00160	2.20804	2.43519	2.68506
15 years	1.81670	2.10718	2.44322	2.83182	3.28103	3.80013	4.39979
20 years	2.21672	2.70148	3.29066	4.00639	4.87544	5.93015	7.20957

Compounded Daily

	4%	5%	6%	7%	8%	9%	10%
1 year	1.04080	1.05127	1.06183	1.07250	1.08328	1.09416	1.10516
5 years	1.22139	1.28400	1.34983	1.41902	1.49176	1.56823	1.64861
10 years	1.49179	1.64866	1.82203	2.01362	2.22535	2.45933	2.71791
15 years	1.82206	2.11689	2.45942	2.85736	3.31968	3.85678	4.48077
20 years	2.22544	2.71810	3.31979	4.05466	4.95217	6.04830	7.38703

To use this table:
1. Locate the section which gives the desired compounding period.
2. Locate the interest rate in the top row of that section.
3. Locate the number of years in the left-hand column of that section.
4. Locate the number where the interest-rate column and the number-of-years row meet. This is the compound interest factor.

Example   An investment yields an annual interest rate of 10% compounded quarterly for 5 years.
The compounding period is "compounded quarterly."
The interest rate is 10%.
The number of years is 5.
The number where the row and column meet is 1.63862. This is the compound interest factor.

Compound Interest Table

| | Compounded Annually | | | | | | |
	11%	12%	13%	14%	15%	16%	17%
1 year	1.11000	1.12000	1.13000	1.14000	1.15000	1.16000	1.17000
5 years	1.68506	1.76234	1.84244	1.92542	2.01136	2.10034	2.19245
10 years	2.83942	3.10585	3.39457	3.70722	4.04556	4.41144	4.80683
15 years	4.78459	5.47357	6.25427	7.13794	8.13706	9.26552	10.53872
20 years	8.06239	9.64629	11.52309	13.74349	16.36654	19.46076	23.10560

| | Compounded Semiannually | | | | | | |
	11%	12%	13%	14%	15%	16%	17%
1 year	1.11303	1.12360	1.13423	1.14490	1.15563	1.16640	1.17723
5 years	1.70814	1.79085	1.87714	1.96715	2.06103	2.15893	2.26098
10 years	2.91776	3.20714	3.52365	3.86968	4.24785	4.66096	5.11205
15 years	4.98395	5.74349	6.61437	7.61226	8.75496	10.06266	11.55825
20 years	8.51331	10.28572	12.41607	14.97446	18.04424	21.72452	26.13302

| | Compounded Quarterly | | | | | | |
	11%	12%	13%	14%	15%	16%	17%
1 year	1.11462	1.12551	1.13648	1.14752	1.15865	1.16986	1.18115
5 years	1.72043	1.80611	1.89584	1.98979	2.08815	2.19112	2.29891
10 years	2.95987	3.26204	3.59420	3.95926	4.36038	4.80102	5.28497
15 years	5.09225	5.89160	6.81402	7.87809	9.10513	10.51963	12.14965
20 years	8.76085	10.64089	12.91828	15.67574	19.01290	23.04980	27.93091

| | Compounded Daily | | | | | | |
	11%	12%	13%	14%	15%	16%	17%
1 year	1.11626	1.12747	1.13880	1.15024	1.16180	1.17347	1.18526
5 years	1.73311	1.82194	1.91532	2.01348	2.11667	2.22515	2.33918
10 years	3.00367	3.31946	3.66845	4.05411	4.48031	4.95130	5.47178
15 years	5.20569	6.04786	7.02625	8.16288	9.48335	11.01738	12.79950
20 years	9.02203	11.01883	13.45751	16.43582	20.07316	24.51534	29.94039

Monthly Payment Table

	4%	5%	6%	7%	8%	9%
1 year	0.0851499	0.0856075	0.0860664	0.0865267	0.0869884	0.0874515
2 years	0.0434249	0.0438714	0.0443206	0.0447726	0.0452273	0.0456847
3 years	0.0295240	0.0299709	0.0304219	0.0308771	0.0313364	0.0317997
4 years	0.0225791	0.0230293	0.0234850	0.0239462	0.0244129	0.0248850
5 years	0.0184165	0.0188712	0.0193328	0.0198012	0.0202764	0.0207584
20 years	0.0060598	0.0065996	0.0071643	0.0077530	0.0083644	0.0089973
25 years	0.0052784	0.0058459	0.0064430	0.0070678	0.0077182	0.0083920
30 years	0.0047742	0.0053682	0.0059955	0.0066530	0.0073376	0.0080462

	10%	11%	12%	13%
1 year	0.0879159	0.0883817	0.0888488	0.0893173
2 years	0.0461449	0.0466078	0.0470735	0.0475418
3 years	0.0322672	0.0327387	0.0332143	0.0336940
4 years	0.0253626	0.0258455	0.0263338	0.0268275
5 years	0.0212470	0.0217424	0.0222445	0.0227531
20 years	0.0096502	0.0103219	0.0110109	0.0117158
25 years	0.0090870	0.0098011	0.0105322	0.0112784
30 years	0.0087757	0.0095232	0.0102861	0.0110620

To use this table:
1. Locate the desired interest rate in the top row.
2. Locate the number of years in the left-hand column.
3. Locate the number where the interest-rate column and the number-of-years row meet. This is the monthly payment factor.

Example   A home has a 30-year mortgage at an annual interest rate of 12%.
The interest rate is 12%.
The number of years is 30.
The number where the row and column meet is 0.0102861. This is the monthly payment factor.

Solutions to Chapter 1 "You Try It"

SECTION 1.1

You Try It 1

You Try It 2   **a.** $45 > 29$ **b.** $27 > 0$

You Try It 3   Thirty-six million four hundred sixty-two thousand seventy-five

You Try It 4   452,007

You Try It 5 $60,000 + 8000 + 200 + 80 + 1$

You Try It 6 $100,000 + 9000 + 200 + 7$

You Try It 7   370,000

You Try It 8   4000

SECTION 1.2

You Try It 1

$$\begin{array}{r} 347 \\ + 12{,}453 \\ \hline 12{,}800 \end{array}$$

347 increased by 12,453 is 12,800.

You Try It 2

$$\begin{array}{r} {\scriptstyle 2} \\ 95 \\ 88 \\ + 67 \\ \hline 250 \end{array}$$

You Try It 3

$$\begin{array}{r} {\scriptstyle 1\ 1\ \ 2\ 1} \\ 392 \\ 4{,}079 \\ 89{,}035 \\ + \ \ 4{,}992 \\ \hline 98{,}498 \end{array}$$

You Try It 4

Strategy   To find the total amount budgeted for the three items each month, add the three amounts ($475, $275, and $120).

Solution

$$\begin{array}{r} \$475 \\ 275 \\ + 120 \\ \hline \$870 \end{array}$$

The total amount budgeted for the three items is $870.

SECTION 1.3

You Try It 1

$$\begin{array}{r} 8925 \\ - 6413 \\ \hline 2512 \end{array} \qquad \begin{array}{l} \textit{Check:} \\ \ \end{array} \begin{array}{r} 6413 \\ + 2512 \\ \hline 8925 \end{array}$$

You Try It 2

$$\begin{array}{r} 17{,}504 \\ - \ \ 9{,}302 \\ \hline 8{,}202 \end{array} \qquad \begin{array}{l} \textit{Check:} \\ \ \end{array} \begin{array}{r} 9{,}302 \\ + \ 8{,}202 \\ \hline 17{,}504 \end{array}$$

You Try It 3

$$\begin{array}{r} {\scriptstyle 2\ \ 14\ \ 7\ \ 11} \\ 3\ 4\ 8\ 1 \\ - \ \ \ 8\ 6\ 5 \\ \hline 2\ 6\ 1\ 6 \end{array} \qquad \begin{array}{l} \textit{Check:} \\ \ \end{array} \begin{array}{r} 865 \\ + 2616 \\ \hline 3481 \end{array}$$

You Try It 4

$$\begin{array}{r} {\scriptstyle 15} \\ {\scriptstyle 4\ \ 5\ \ 12} \\ 5\ 4{,}3\ 6\ 2 \\ - \ 1\ 4{,}4\ 8\ 5 \\ \hline 4\ 0{,}0\ 7\ 7 \end{array} \qquad \begin{array}{l} \textit{Check:} \\ \ \end{array} \begin{array}{r} 14{,}485 \\ + 40{,}077 \\ \hline 54{,}562 \end{array}$$

You Try It 5

$$\begin{array}{r} {\scriptstyle 13\ \ 9\ \ 9} \\ {\scriptstyle 5\ \ 3\ \ 10\ \ 10\ \ 13} \\ 6\ 4{,}0\ 0\ 3 \\ - \ 5\ 4{,}9\ 3\ 6 \\ \hline 9{,}0\ 6\ 7 \end{array} \qquad \begin{array}{l} \textit{Check:} \\ \ \end{array} \begin{array}{r} 54{,}936 \\ + \ \ 9{,}067 \\ \hline 64{,}003 \end{array}$$

You Try It 6

Strategy   To find the difference, subtract the number of residents who migrated to Montana in 1996 (5250) from the number who migrated to Colorado in 1996 (30,049).

Solution

$$\begin{array}{r} 30{,}049 \\ - \ \ 5{,}250 \\ \hline 24{,}799 \end{array}$$

24,799 more residents migrated to Colorado than to Montana in 1996.

You Try It 7

Strategy   To find your take-home pay:
• Add to find the total of the deductions ($127 + $18 + $35).
• Subtract the total of the deductions from your total salary ($638).

Solution

$$\begin{array}{r} 127 \\ 18 \\ + \ 35 \\ \hline 180 \end{array} \text{ deductions} \qquad \begin{array}{r} 638 \\ - 180 \\ \hline 458 \end{array}$$

Your take-home pay is $458.

SECTION 1.4

You Try It 1

$$\begin{array}{r} {\scriptstyle 3\,5} \\ 648 \\ \times \quad 7 \\ \hline 4536 \end{array}$$

You Try It 2

$$\begin{array}{r} 756 \\ \times\ 305 \\ \hline 3780 \\ 22680 \quad\ \\ \hline 230{,}580 \end{array}$$

You Try It 3

Strategy To find the number of cars the dealer will receive in 12 months, multiply the number of months (12) by the number of cars received each month (37).

Solution

$$\begin{array}{r} 37 \\ \times\ \ 12 \\ \hline 74 \\ 37\ \ \\ \hline 444 \end{array}$$

The dealer will receive 444 cars in 12 months.

You Try It 4

Strategy To find the total cost of the order:
• Find the cost of the sports jackets by multiplying the number of jackets (25) by the cost for each jacket ($23).
• Add the product to the cost for the suits ($4800).

Solution

$$\begin{array}{r} \$23 \\ \times\ 25 \\ \hline 115 \\ 46\ \ \\ \hline \$575 \end{array}\quad \text{cost for jackets}$$

$$\begin{array}{r} \$4800 \\ +\ \ \ 575 \\ \hline \$5375 \end{array}$$

The total cost of the order is $5375.

SECTION 1.5

You Try It 1

$$\begin{array}{r} 7 \\ 9\overline{)63} \end{array}$$

Check: $7 \times 9 = 63$

You Try It 2

$$\begin{array}{r} 453 \\ 9\overline{)\,4077} \\ -36\quad \\ \hline 47\quad \\ -45\quad \\ \hline 27 \\ -27 \\ \hline 0 \end{array}$$

Check: $453 \times 9 = 4077$

You Try It 3

$$\begin{array}{r} 705 \\ 9\overline{)\,6345} \\ -63\quad\ \\ \hline 04\quad\ \\ -\ 0\quad\ \\ \hline 45 \\ -45 \\ \hline 0 \end{array}$$

Check: $705 \times 9 = 6345$

You Try It 4

$$\begin{array}{r} 870\ \text{r}5 \\ 6\overline{)\,5225} \\ -48\quad\ \\ \hline 42\quad\ \\ -42\quad\ \\ \hline 05 \\ -\ 0 \\ \hline 5 \end{array}$$

Check: $(870 \times 6) + 5 =$
$5220 + 5 = 5225$

You Try It 5

$$\begin{array}{r} 3{,}058\ \text{r}3 \\ 7\overline{)\,21{,}409} \\ -21\quad\quad \\ \hline 0\,4\quad\ \\ -\ 0\quad\ \\ \hline 40\quad \\ -35\quad \\ \hline 59 \\ -56 \\ \hline 3 \end{array}$$

Check: $(3058 \times 7) + 3 =$
$21{,}406 + 3 = 21{,}409$

You Try It 6

$$\begin{array}{r} 109 \\ 42\overline{)\,4578} \\ -42\quad\ \\ \hline 37\quad\ \\ -\ 0\quad\ \\ \hline 378 \\ -378 \\ \hline 0 \end{array}$$

Check: $109 \times 42 = 4578$

You Try It 7

$$\begin{array}{r} 470 \text{ r}29 \\ 39\overline{)\ 18{,}359} \\ -15\ 6 \\ \hline 2\ 75 \\ -2\ 73 \\ \hline 29 \\ -\ 0 \\ \hline 29 \end{array}$$

Check: $(470 \times 39) + 29 =$
$18{,}330 + 29 = 18{,}359$

You Try It 8

$$\begin{array}{r} 62 \text{ r}111 \\ 534\overline{)\ 33{,}219} \\ -32\ 04 \\ \hline 1\ 179 \\ -1\ 068 \\ \hline 111 \end{array}$$

Check: $(62 \times 534) + 111 =$
$33{,}108 + 111 = 33{,}219$

You Try It 9

$$\begin{array}{r} 421 \text{ r}33 \\ 515\overline{)\ 216{,}848} \\ -206\ 0 \\ \hline 10\ 84 \\ -10\ 30 \\ \hline 548 \\ -515 \\ \hline 33 \end{array}$$

Check: $(421 \times 515) + 33 =$
$216{,}815 + 33 = 216{,}848$

You Try It 10

Strategy   To find the number of tires that can be stored on each shelf, divide the number of tires (270) by the number of shelves (15).

Solution

$$\begin{array}{r} 18 \\ 15\overline{)\ 270} \\ -15 \\ \hline 120 \\ -120 \\ \hline 0 \end{array}$$

Each shelf can store 18 tires.

You Try It 11

Strategy   To find the number of cases produced in 8 hours:
• Find the number of cases produced in one hour by dividing the number of cans produced (12,600) by the number of cans to a case (24).
• Multiply the number of cases produced in one hour by 8.

Solution

$$\begin{array}{r} 525 \\ 24\overline{)\ 12{,}600} \\ -12\ 0 \\ \hline 60 \\ -48 \\ \hline 120 \\ -120 \\ \hline 0 \end{array}$$ cases produced in one hour

$$\begin{array}{r} 525 \\ \times\ \ \ 8 \\ \hline 4200 \end{array}$$

In 8 hours, 4200 cases are produced.

SECTION 1.6

You Try It 1 $2^4 \cdot 3^3$

You Try It 2 10^7

You Try It 3 $2^3 \cdot 5^2 = (2 \cdot 2 \cdot 2) \cdot (5 \cdot 5) = 8 \cdot 25$
$= 200$

You Try It 4 $5 \cdot (8 - 4)^2 \div 4 - 2$
$= 5 \cdot 4^2 \div 4 - 2$
$= 5 \cdot 16 \div 4 - 2$
$= 80 \div 4 - 2$
$= 20 - 2$
$= 18$

SECTION 1.7

You Try It 1   1, 2, 4, 5, 8, 10, 20, and 40 are factors of 40.

You Try It 2 $44 = 2 \cdot 2 \cdot 11$

You Try It 3 $177 = 3 \cdot 59$

Solutions to Chapter 2 "You Try It"

SECTION 2.1

You Try It 1

	2	3	5	7
50 =	2		(5 · 5)	
84 =	(2 · 2)	3		(7)
135 =		(3 · 3 · 3)	5	

The LCM = 2 · 2 · 3 · 3 · 3 · 5 · 5 · 7
$$= 18{,}900$$

You Try It 2

	2	3	5
36 =	(2 · 2)	3 · 3	
60 =	2 · 2	(3)	5
72 =	2 · 2 · 2	3 · 3	

The GCF = 2 · 2 · 3 = 12.

You Try It 3

	2	3	5	11
11 =				11
24 =	2 · 2 · 2	3		
30 =	2	3	5	

Since no numbers are circled, the GCF = 1.

SECTION 2.2

You Try It 1 $4\dfrac{1}{4}$

You Try It 2 $\dfrac{17}{4}$

You Try It 3

$$5\overline{)22} \quad \begin{array}{r} 4 \\ -20 \\ \hline 2 \end{array} \qquad \dfrac{22}{5} = 4\dfrac{2}{5}$$

You Try It 4

$$7\overline{)28} \quad \begin{array}{r} 4 \\ -28 \\ \hline 0 \end{array} \qquad \dfrac{28}{7} = 4$$

You Try It 5 $14\dfrac{5}{8} = \dfrac{112 + 5}{8} = \dfrac{117}{8}$

SECTION 2.3

You Try It 1 $45 \div 5 = 9 \qquad \dfrac{3}{5} = \dfrac{3 \cdot 9}{5 \cdot 9} = \dfrac{27}{45}$

$\dfrac{27}{45}$ is equivalent to $\dfrac{3}{5}$.

You Try It 2 Write 6 as $\dfrac{6}{1}$.

$$18 \div 1 = 18 \qquad 6 = \dfrac{6 \cdot 18}{1 \cdot 18} = \dfrac{108}{18}$$

$\dfrac{108}{18}$ is equivalent to 6.

You Try It 3 $\dfrac{16}{24} = \dfrac{\cancel{2} \cdot \cancel{2} \cdot \cancel{2} \cdot 2}{\cancel{2} \cdot \cancel{2} \cdot \cancel{2} \cdot 3} = \dfrac{2}{3}$

You Try It 4 $\dfrac{8}{56} = \dfrac{\cancel{2} \cdot \cancel{2} \cdot \cancel{2}}{\cancel{2} \cdot \cancel{2} \cdot \cancel{2} \cdot 7} = \dfrac{1}{7}$

You Try It 5 $\dfrac{15}{32} = \dfrac{3 \cdot 5}{2 \cdot 2 \cdot 2 \cdot 2 \cdot 2} = \dfrac{15}{32}$

You Try It 6 $\dfrac{48}{36} = \dfrac{\cancel{2} \cdot \cancel{2} \cdot 2 \cdot 2 \cdot \cancel{3}}{\cancel{2} \cdot \cancel{2} \cdot \cancel{3} \cdot 3} = \dfrac{4}{3} = 1\dfrac{1}{3}$

SECTION 2.4

You Try It 1

$$\begin{array}{r} \dfrac{3}{8} \\ + \dfrac{7}{8} \\ \hline \dfrac{10}{8} = \dfrac{5}{4} = 1\dfrac{1}{4} \end{array}$$

You Try It 2

$$\begin{array}{r} \dfrac{5}{12} = \dfrac{20}{48} \\ + \dfrac{9}{16} = \dfrac{27}{48} \\ \hline \dfrac{47}{48} \end{array}$$

You Try It 3

$$\begin{array}{r} \dfrac{7}{8} = \dfrac{105}{120} \\ + \dfrac{11}{15} = \dfrac{88}{120} \\ \hline \dfrac{193}{120} = 1\dfrac{73}{120} \end{array}$$

You Try It 4

$$\frac{3}{4} = \frac{30}{40}$$
$$\frac{4}{5} = \frac{32}{40}$$
$$+\ \frac{5}{8} = \frac{25}{40}$$
$$\overline{\qquad\qquad}$$
$$\frac{87}{40} = 2\frac{7}{40}$$

You Try It 5 $7 + \dfrac{6}{11} = 7\dfrac{6}{11}$

You Try It 6

$$29$$
$$+\ 17\frac{5}{12}$$
$$\overline{\qquad\quad}$$
$$46\frac{5}{12}$$

You Try It 7

$$7\frac{4}{5} = 7\frac{24}{30}$$
$$6\frac{7}{10} = 6\frac{21}{30}$$
$$+\ 13\frac{11}{15} = 13\frac{22}{30}$$
$$\overline{\qquad\qquad\qquad}$$
$$26\frac{67}{30} = 28\frac{7}{30}$$

You Try It 8

$$9\frac{3}{8} = 9\frac{45}{120}$$
$$17\frac{7}{12} = 17\frac{70}{120}$$
$$+\ 10\frac{14}{15} = 10\frac{112}{120}$$
$$\overline{\qquad\qquad\qquad}$$
$$36\frac{227}{120} = 37\frac{107}{120}$$

You Try It 9

Strategy   To find the total time spent on the activities, add the three times $\left(4\frac{1}{2}, 3\frac{3}{4}, 1\frac{1}{3}\right)$.

Solution

$$4\frac{1}{2} = 4\frac{6}{12}$$
$$3\frac{3}{4} = 3\frac{9}{12}$$
$$+\ 1\frac{1}{3} = 1\frac{4}{12}$$
$$\overline{\qquad\qquad}$$
$$8\frac{19}{12} = 9\frac{7}{12}$$

The total time spent on the three activities was $9\frac{7}{12}$ hours.

You Try It 10

Strategy   To find the overtime pay:
- Find the total number of overtime hours $\left(1\frac{2}{3} + 3\frac{1}{3} + 2\right)$.
- Multiply the total number of hours by the overtime hourly wage ($24).

Solution

$$1\frac{2}{3}$$
$$3\frac{1}{3}$$
$$+\ 2$$
$$\overline{\qquad}$$
$$6\frac{3}{3} = 7 \text{ hours}$$

$$\begin{array}{r} \$24 \\ \times\ \ 7 \\ \hline \$168 \end{array}$$

Jeff earned $168 in overtime pay.

SECTION 2.5

You Try It 1

$$\frac{16}{27}$$
$$-\ \frac{7}{27}$$
$$\overline{\quad\ }$$
$$\frac{9}{27} = \frac{1}{3}$$

You Try It 2

$$\frac{13}{18} = \frac{52}{72}$$
$$-\ \frac{7}{24} = \frac{21}{72}$$
$$\overline{\qquad\qquad}$$
$$\frac{31}{72}$$

You Try It 3

$$17\frac{5}{9} = 17\frac{20}{36}$$
$$-\ 11\frac{5}{12} = 11\frac{15}{36}$$
$$\overline{\qquad\qquad\qquad}$$
$$6\frac{5}{36}$$

You Try It 4

$$8 = 7\frac{13}{13}$$
$$-\ 2\frac{4}{13} = 2\frac{4}{13}$$
$$\overline{\qquad\qquad}$$
$$5\frac{9}{13}$$

You Try It 5

$$21\frac{7}{9} = 21\frac{28}{36} = 20\frac{64}{36}$$
$$-\ 7\frac{11}{12} = 7\frac{33}{36} = 7\frac{33}{36}$$
$$\overline{\qquad\qquad\qquad\qquad}$$
$$13\frac{31}{36}$$

You Try It 6

Strategy To find the time remaining before the plane lands, subtract the number of hours already in the air $\left(2\frac{3}{4}\right)$ from the total time of the trip $\left(5\frac{1}{2}\right)$.

Solution

$$5\frac{1}{2} = 5\frac{2}{4} = 4\frac{6}{4}$$
$$-\,2\frac{3}{4} = 2\frac{3}{4} = 2\frac{3}{4}$$
$$\overline{\qquad\qquad 2\frac{3}{4}\text{ hours}}$$

The plane will land in $2\frac{3}{4}$ hours.

You Try It 7

Strategy To find the amount of weight to be lost during the third month:
- Find the total weight loss during the first two months $\left(7\frac{1}{2} + 5\frac{3}{4}\right)$.
- Subtract the total weight loss from the goal (24 pounds).

Solution

$$7\frac{1}{2} = 7\frac{2}{4}$$
$$+\,5\frac{3}{4} = 5\frac{3}{4}$$
$$\overline{\qquad 12\frac{5}{4} = 13\frac{1}{4}\text{ pounds lost}}$$

$$24 = 23\frac{4}{4}$$
$$-\,13\frac{1}{4} = 13\frac{1}{4}$$
$$\overline{\qquad 10\frac{3}{4}\text{ pounds}}$$

The patient must lose $10\frac{3}{4}$ pounds to achieve the goal.

SECTION 2.6

You Try It 1 $\dfrac{4}{21} \times \dfrac{7}{44} = \dfrac{4 \cdot 7}{21 \cdot 44}$

$$= \dfrac{\overset{1}{\cancel{2}} \cdot \overset{1}{\cancel{2}} \cdot \overset{1}{\cancel{7}}}{3 \cdot \cancel{7} \cdot \cancel{2} \cdot \cancel{2} \cdot 11} = \dfrac{1}{33}$$

You Try It 2 $\dfrac{2}{21} \times \dfrac{10}{33} = \dfrac{2 \cdot 10}{21 \cdot 33}$

$$= \dfrac{2 \cdot 2 \cdot 5}{3 \cdot 7 \cdot 3 \cdot 11} = \dfrac{20}{693}$$

You Try It 3 $\dfrac{16}{5} \times \dfrac{15}{24} = \dfrac{16 \cdot 15}{5 \cdot 24}$

$$= \dfrac{\overset{1}{\cancel{2}} \cdot \overset{1}{\cancel{2}} \cdot \overset{1}{\cancel{2}} \cdot 2 \cdot \overset{1}{\cancel{3}} \cdot \overset{1}{\cancel{5}}}{\cancel{5} \cdot \cancel{2} \cdot \cancel{2} \cdot 2 \cdot \cancel{3}} = 2$$

You Try It 4 $5\dfrac{2}{5} \times \dfrac{5}{9} = \dfrac{27}{5} \times \dfrac{5}{9} = \dfrac{27 \cdot 5}{5 \cdot 9}$

$$= \dfrac{\overset{1}{\cancel{3}} \cdot \overset{1}{\cancel{3}} \cdot 3 \cdot \overset{1}{\cancel{5}}}{\cancel{5} \cdot \cancel{3} \cdot \cancel{3}} = 3$$

You Try It 5 $3\dfrac{2}{5} \times 6\dfrac{1}{4} = \dfrac{17}{5} \times \dfrac{25}{4} = \dfrac{17 \cdot 25}{5 \cdot 4}$

$$= \dfrac{17 \cdot \overset{1}{\cancel{5}} \cdot 5}{\underset{1}{\cancel{5}} \cdot 2 \cdot 2} = \dfrac{85}{4} = 21\dfrac{1}{4}$$

You Try It 6 $3\dfrac{2}{7} \times 6 = \dfrac{23}{7} \times \dfrac{6}{1} = \dfrac{23 \cdot 6}{7 \cdot 1}$

$$= \dfrac{23 \cdot 3 \cdot 2}{7 \cdot 1} = \dfrac{138}{7} = 19\dfrac{5}{7}$$

You Try It 7

Strategy To find the value of the house today, multiply the old value of the house ($30,000) by $3\frac{1}{2}$.

Solution $30{,}000 \times 3\dfrac{1}{2} = \dfrac{30{,}000}{1} \times \dfrac{7}{2}$

$$= \dfrac{30{,}000 \cdot 7}{1 \cdot 2}$$
$$= 105{,}000$$

The value of the house today is $105,000.

You Try It 8

Strategy To find the cost of the air compressor:
- Multiply to find the value of the drying chamber $\left(\dfrac{4}{5} \times \$60{,}000\right)$.
- Subtract the value of the drying chamber from the total value of the two items ($60,000).

Solution $\dfrac{4}{5} \times \dfrac{\$60{,}000}{1} = \dfrac{\$240{,}000}{5}$

$$= \$48{,}000$$

$$\begin{array}{r} \$60{,}000 \\ -\ 48{,}000 \\ \hline \$12{,}000 \end{array}$$

The cost of the air compressor was $12,000.

SECTION 2.7

You Try It 1 $\dfrac{3}{7} \div \dfrac{2}{3} = \dfrac{3}{7} \times \dfrac{3}{2} = \dfrac{3 \cdot 3}{7 \cdot 2} = \dfrac{9}{14}$

You Try It 2 $\dfrac{3}{4} \div \dfrac{9}{10} = \dfrac{3}{4} \times \dfrac{10}{9}$

$= \dfrac{3 \cdot 10}{4 \cdot 9} = \dfrac{\cancel{3} \cdot \cancel{2} \cdot 5}{2 \cdot 2 \cdot \cancel{3} \cdot 3} = \dfrac{5}{6}$

You Try It 3 $\dfrac{5}{7} \div 6 = \dfrac{5}{7} \div \dfrac{6}{1}$

$= \dfrac{5}{7} \times \dfrac{1}{6} = \dfrac{5 \cdot 1}{7 \cdot 6}$

$= \dfrac{5}{7 \cdot 2 \cdot 3} = \dfrac{5}{42}$

You Try It 4 $12\dfrac{3}{5} \div 7 = \dfrac{63}{5} \div \dfrac{7}{1} = \dfrac{63}{5} \times \dfrac{1}{7}$

$= \dfrac{63 \cdot 1}{5 \cdot 7} = \dfrac{3 \cdot 3 \cdot \cancel{7}}{5 \cdot \cancel{7}} = \dfrac{9}{5} = 1\dfrac{4}{5}$

You Try It 5 $3\dfrac{2}{3} \div 2\dfrac{2}{5} = \dfrac{11}{3} \div \dfrac{12}{5}$

$= \dfrac{11}{3} \times \dfrac{5}{12} = \dfrac{11 \cdot 5}{3 \cdot 12}$

$= \dfrac{11 \cdot 5}{3 \cdot 2 \cdot 2 \cdot 3} = \dfrac{55}{36} = 1\dfrac{19}{36}$

You Try it 6 $2\dfrac{5}{6} \div 8\dfrac{1}{2} = \dfrac{17}{6} \div \dfrac{17}{2}$

$= \dfrac{17}{6} \times \dfrac{2}{17} = \dfrac{17 \cdot 2}{6 \cdot 17}$

$= \dfrac{\cancel{17} \cdot \cancel{2}}{2 \cdot 3 \cdot \cancel{17}} = \dfrac{1}{3}$

You Try It 7 $6\dfrac{2}{5} \div 4 = \dfrac{32}{5} \div \dfrac{4}{1}$

$= \dfrac{32}{5} \times \dfrac{1}{4} = \dfrac{32 \cdot 1}{5 \cdot 4}$

$= \dfrac{2 \cdot 2 \cdot 2 \cdot \cancel{2} \cdot \cancel{2}}{5 \cdot \cancel{2} \cdot \cancel{2}} = \dfrac{8}{5} = 1\dfrac{3}{5}$

You Try It 8

Strategy To find the price of one ounce of gold, divide the total price of the coin ($195) by the number of ounces $\left(\dfrac{1}{2}\right)$.

Solution $195 \div \dfrac{1}{2} = \dfrac{195}{1} \div \dfrac{1}{2}$

$= \dfrac{195}{1} \times \dfrac{2}{1} = \dfrac{195 \cdot 2}{1 \cdot 1} = 390$

The price of one ounce of gold is $390.

You Try It 9

Strategy To find the length of the remaining piece:
- Divide the total length of the board (16 feet) by the length of each shelf $\left(3\dfrac{1}{3} \text{ feet}\right)$.
- Multiply the fraction left over by the length of one shelf to determine the length of the remaining piece.

Solution $16 \div 3\dfrac{1}{3} = 16 \div \dfrac{10}{3}$

$= \dfrac{16}{1} \times \dfrac{3}{10} = \dfrac{16 \cdot 3}{1 \cdot 10}$

$= \dfrac{\cancel{2} \cdot 2 \cdot 2 \cdot 2 \cdot 3}{\cancel{2} \cdot 5} = \dfrac{24}{5}$

$= 4\dfrac{4}{5}$

$\dfrac{4}{5} \times 3\dfrac{1}{3} = \dfrac{4}{5} \times \dfrac{10}{3}$

$= \dfrac{4 \cdot 10}{5 \cdot 3} = \dfrac{8}{3} = 2\dfrac{2}{3}$

The length of the piece remaining is $2\dfrac{2}{3}$ feet.

SECTION 2.8

You Try It 1 $\dfrac{9}{14} = \dfrac{27}{42} \qquad \dfrac{13}{21} = \dfrac{26}{42} \qquad \dfrac{9}{14} > \dfrac{13}{21}$

You Try It 2 $\left(\dfrac{7}{11}\right)^2 \cdot \left(\dfrac{2}{7}\right) = \left(\dfrac{7}{11} \cdot \dfrac{7}{11}\right) \cdot \left(\dfrac{2}{7}\right)$

$= \dfrac{\cancel{7} \cdot 7 \cdot 2}{11 \cdot 11 \cdot \cancel{7}} = \dfrac{14}{121}$

You Try It 3

$$\left(\frac{1}{13}\right)^2 \cdot \left(\frac{1}{4} + \frac{1}{6}\right) \div \frac{5}{13}$$

$$\left(\frac{1}{13}\right)^2 \cdot \left(\frac{5}{12}\right) \div \frac{5}{13}$$

$$\left(\frac{1}{169}\right) \cdot \left(\frac{5}{12}\right) \div \frac{5}{13}$$

$$\left(\frac{1 \cdot 5}{13 \cdot 13 \cdot 12}\right) \div \frac{5}{13}$$

$$\left(\frac{1 \cdot 5}{13 \cdot 13 \cdot 12}\right) \times \frac{13}{5}$$

$$\frac{1 \cdot \overset{1}{\cancel{5}} \cdot \overset{1}{\cancel{13}}}{\underset{1}{\cancel{13}} \cdot 13 \cdot 12 \cdot \underset{1}{\cancel{5}}}$$

$$\frac{1}{156}$$

Solutions to Chapter 3 "You Try It"

SECTION 3.1

You Try It 1   Two hundred nine and five thousand eight hundred thirty-eight hundred-thousandths

You Try It 2   42,000.000207

You Try It 3   4.35

You Try It 4   3.29053

SECTION 3.2

You Try It 1

$$\begin{array}{r} \overset{1\ 2}{}\\ 4.62\\ 27.9\\ +\ \ 0.62054\\ \hline 33.14054 \end{array}$$

You Try It 2

$$\begin{array}{r} \overset{1}{}\\ 6.05\\ 12.\\ +\ \ 0.374\\ \hline 18.424 \end{array}$$

You Try It 3

Strategy   To find the total, add the cost of each kind and number of tulip. ($16.40 + $5.80 + $16.40).

Solution
$$\begin{array}{r} \$16.40\\ 5.80\\ +\ \ 16.40\\ \hline \$38.60 \end{array}$$

The cost of the tulips is $38.60.

You Try It 4

Strategy   To find the total income, add the four commissions ($485.60, $599.46,

$326.75, and $725.42) to the salary ($425.00).

Solution
$$\begin{array}{r} \$485.60\\ 599.46\\ 326.75\\ 725.42\\ +\ \ 425.00\\ \hline \$2562.23 \end{array}$$

Anita's total income was $2562.23.

SECTION 3.3

You Try It 1

$$\begin{array}{r} \overset{\ \ \ \ \ \ 11\ \ 9}{\overset{6\ \ \cancel{7}\ \cancel{10}\ 13}{\cancel{7}\ \cancel{2}.\cancel{0}\ \cancel{3}\ 9}}\\ -\ \ \ \ 8.4\ 7\\ \hline 6\ 3.5\ 6\ 9 \end{array}$$

Check:
$$\begin{array}{r} \overset{1\ 1\ \ 1}{8.47}\\ +\ 63.569\\ \hline 72.039 \end{array}$$

You Try It 2

$$\begin{array}{r} \overset{\ \ \ 14\ \ 9}{\overset{2\ \cancel{4}\ \cancel{10}\ 10}{\cancel{3}\ \cancel{5}.\cancel{0}\ \cancel{0}}}\\ -\ \ \ 9.6\ 7\\ \hline 2\ 5.3\ 3 \end{array}$$

Check:
$$\begin{array}{r} \overset{1\ 1\ \ 1}{9.67}\\ +\ 25.33\\ \hline 35.00 \end{array}$$

You Try It 3

$$\begin{array}{r} \overset{\ \ \ 16\ 9\ \ 9}{\overset{2\ \cancel{6}\ \cancel{10}\ \cancel{10}\ 10}{\cancel{3}.\cancel{7}\ \cancel{0}\ \cancel{0}\ \cancel{0}}}\\ -\ 1.9\ 7\ 1\ 5\\ \hline 1.7\ 2\ 8\ 5 \end{array}$$

Check:
$$\begin{array}{r} \overset{1\ 1\ 1\ 1}{1.9715}\\ +\ 1.7285\\ \hline 3.7000 \end{array}$$

You Try It 4

Strategy   To find the amount of change, subtract the amount paid ($3.85) from $5.00.

Solution
$$\begin{array}{r} \$5.00\\ -\ 3.85\\ \hline \$1.15 \end{array}$$

Your change was $1.15.

You Try It 5

Strategy   To find the new balance:
  • Add to find the total of the three
    checks
    ($1025.60 + $79.85 + $162.47).
  • Subtract the total from the
    previous balance ($2472.69).

Solution

$1025.60 $2472.69
   79.85   − 1267.92
+ 162.47 $1204.77
$1267.92

The new balance is $1204.77.

SECTION 3.4

You Try It 1

    870
×   4.6
   522 0
  3480
  4002.0

You Try It 2

      0.000086
×   0.057
        602
        430
    0.000004902

You Try It 3

     4.68
×   6.03
    1404
   28 080
   28.2204

You Try It 4 $6.9 \times 1000 = 6900$

You Try It 5 $4.0273 \times 10^2 = 402.73$

You Try It 6

Strategy   To find the total bill:
  • Find the number of gallons of
    water used by multiplying the
    number of gallons used per day
    (5000) by the number of days (62).
  • Find the cost of water by
    multiplying the cost per 1000
    gallons ($1.39) by the number of
    1000-gallon units used.
  • Add the cost of the water to the
    meter fee ($133.70).

Solution

Number of gallons = 5000(62) = 310,000

Cost of water $= \dfrac{310,000}{1000} \times 1.39 = 430.90$

Total cost = 133.70 + 430.90 = 564.60

The total bill is $564.60.

You Try It 7

Strategy   To find the cost of running the
             freezer for 210 hours, multiply the
             hourly cost ($.035) by the number of
             hours the freezer has run (210).

Solution

   $.035
×   210
   $7.35

The cost of running the freezer for
210 hours is $7.35.

You Try It 8

Strategy   To find the total cost of the stereo:
  • Multiply the monthly payment
    ($37.18) by the number of months
    (18).
  • Add the total to the down payment
    ($175.00).

Solution

   $37.18 $669.24
×   18   + 175.00
  $669.24 $844.24

The total cost of the stereo is
$844.24.

SECTION 3.5

You Try It 1

$$0.052.\overline{)0.140.4}$$

          2.7
0.052.)0.140.4
       −104
         36 4
        −36 4
            0

You Try It 2

       0.4873 ≈ 0.487
76)37.0420
  −30 4
    6 64
   −6 08
      562
     −532
       300
      −228

You Try It 3

$$5.09. \overline{)370.20.00} \approx 72.7 \quad 72.73$$

$$-356\ 3$$
$$13\ 90$$
$$10\ 18$$
$$3\ 720$$
$$-3\ 563$$
$$1570$$
$$-1527$$

You Try It 4 $309.21 \div 10{,}000 = 0.030921$

You Try It 5 $42.93 \div 10^4 = 0.004293$

You Try It 6

Strategy   To find the amount she paid in gasoline taxes:
- Find the total number of gallons of gas used by dividing the total number of miles driven (9675) by the number of miles driven per gallon of gas (22.5).
- Multiply the state tax ($.875) by the total number of gallons of gas used.

Solution $9675 \div 22.5 = 430$
$0.875 \times 430 = 376.25$

Susan paid $376.25 in gasoline taxes.

You Try It 7

Strategy   To find the average number of people watching TV:
- Add the number of people watching each day of the week.
- Divide the total number of people watching by 7.

Solution $91.9 + 89.8 + 90.6 + 93.9 + 78.0 +$
$77.1 + 87.7 = 609$

$$\frac{609}{7} = 87$$

An average of 87 million people watch television per day.

SECTION 3.6

You Try It 1

$$16 \overline{)9.00} \quad 0.56 \approx 0.6$$

You Try It 2 $4\dfrac{1}{6} = \dfrac{25}{6}$

$$6 \overline{)25.00} \quad 4.166 \approx 4.17$$

You Try It 3 $0.56 = \dfrac{56}{100} = \dfrac{14}{25}$

$5.35 = 5\dfrac{35}{100} = 5\dfrac{7}{20}$

You Try It 4 $0.12\dfrac{7}{8} = \dfrac{12\dfrac{7}{8}}{100} = 12\dfrac{7}{8} \div 100$

$= \dfrac{103}{8} \times \dfrac{1}{100} = \dfrac{103}{800}$

You Try It 5 $\dfrac{5}{8} = 0.625$

$0.63 > 0.625$

$0.63 > \dfrac{5}{8}$

Solutions to Chapter 4 "You Try It"

SECTION 4.1

You Try It 1 $\dfrac{20 \text{ pounds}}{24 \text{ pounds}} = \dfrac{20}{24} = \dfrac{5}{6}$

20 pounds : 24 pounds = 20 : 24 = 5 : 6

20 pounds to 24 pounds = 20 to 24
= 5 to 6

You Try It 2 $\dfrac{64 \text{ miles}}{8 \text{ miles}} = \dfrac{64}{8} = \dfrac{8}{1}$

64 miles : 8 miles = 64 : 8 = 8 : 1

64 miles to 8 miles = 64 to 8 = 8 to 1

You Try It 3

Strategy   To find the ratio, write the ratio of board feet of cedar (12,000) to board feet of ash (18,000) in simplest form.

Solution $\dfrac{12{,}000}{18{,}000} = \dfrac{2}{3}$

The ratio is $\dfrac{2}{3}$.

You Try It 4

Strategy   To find the ratio, write the ratio of the amount spent on radio advertising ($15,000) to the amount spent on radio and television advertising ($15,000 + $20,000) in simplest form.

Solution

$$\frac{\$15,000}{\$15,000 + \$20,000} = \frac{\$15,000}{\$35,000} = \frac{3}{7}$$

The ratio is $\frac{3}{7}$.

SECTION 4.2

You Try It 1 $\dfrac{15 \text{ pounds}}{12 \text{ trees}} = \dfrac{5 \text{ pounds}}{4 \text{ trees}}$

You Try It 2 $\dfrac{260 \text{ miles}}{8 \text{ hours}}$

$$8)\overline{260.0} \quad 32.5$$

32.5 miles/hour

You Try It 3

Strategy   To find Erik's profit per ounce:
  • Find the total profit by subtracting the cost ($1625) from the selling price ($1720).
  • Divide the total profit by the number of ounces (5).

Solution

$$\begin{array}{r} 1720 \\ -\ 1625 \\ \hline 95 \text{ total profit} \end{array} \qquad \begin{array}{r} 19 \\ 5)\overline{95} \end{array}$$

The profit is $19 per ounce.

SECTION 4.3

You Try It 1 $\dfrac{6}{10} \diagup\!\!\!\!\diagdown \dfrac{9}{15} \begin{array}{l} \rightarrow 10 \times 9 = 90 \\ \rightarrow 6 \times 15 = 90 \end{array}$

The proportion is true.

You Try It 2 $\dfrac{32}{6} \diagup\!\!\!\!\diagdown \dfrac{90}{8} \begin{array}{l} \rightarrow 6 \times 90 = 540 \\ \rightarrow 32 \times 8 = 256 \end{array}$

The proportion is not true.

You Try It 3 $\dfrac{n}{14} = \dfrac{3}{7}$

$$n \times 7 = 14 \times 3$$
$$n \times 7 = 42$$
$$n = 42 \div 7$$
$$n = 6$$

Check: $\dfrac{6}{14} \diagup\!\!\!\!\diagdown \dfrac{3}{7} \begin{array}{l} \rightarrow 14 \times 3 = 42 \\ \rightarrow 6 \times 7 = 42 \end{array}$

You Try It 4 $5 \times 20 = 8 \times n$
$$100 = 8 \times n$$
$$100 \div 8 = n$$
$$12.5 = n$$

You Try It 5 $15 \times n = 20 \times 12$
$$15 \times n = 240$$
$$n = 240 \div 15$$
$$n = 16$$

Check: $\dfrac{15}{20} \diagup\!\!\!\!\diagdown \dfrac{12}{16} \begin{array}{l} \rightarrow 20 \times 12 = 240 \\ \rightarrow 15 \times 16 = 240 \end{array}$

You Try It 6 $12 \times 4 = 7 \times n$
$$48 = 7 \times n$$
$$48 \div 7 = n$$
$$6.86 \approx n$$

You Try It 7 $n \times 1 = 12 \times 4$
$$n \times 1 = 48$$
$$n = 48 \div 1$$
$$n = 48$$

Check: $\dfrac{48}{12} \diagup\!\!\!\!\diagdown \dfrac{4}{1} \begin{array}{l} \rightarrow 12 \times 4 = 48 \\ \rightarrow 48 \times 1 = 48 \end{array}$

You Try It 8 $3 \times n = 12 \times 8$
$$3 \times n = 96$$
$$n = 96 \div 3$$
$$n = 32$$

Check: $\dfrac{3}{8} \diagup\!\!\!\!\diagdown \dfrac{12}{32} \begin{array}{l} \rightarrow 8 \times 12 = 96 \\ \rightarrow 3 \times 32 = 96 \end{array}$

You Try It 9

Strategy   To find the number of jars that can be packed in 15 boxes, write and solve a proportion, using n to represent the number of jars.

Solution

$$\frac{24 \text{ jars}}{6 \text{ boxes}} = \frac{n \text{ jars}}{15 \text{ boxes}}$$

$$24 \times 15 = 6 \times n$$
$$360 = 6 \times n$$
$$360 \div 6 = n$$
$$60 = n$$

60 jars can be packed in 15 boxes.

You Try It 10

Strategy   To find the number of tablespoons of fertilizer needed, write and solve a proportion, using n to represent the number of tablespoons of fertilizer.

Solution

$$\frac{3 \text{ tablespoons}}{4 \text{ gallons}} = \frac{n \text{ tablespoons}}{10 \text{ gallons}}$$

$$3 \times 10 = 4 \times n$$
$$30 = 4 \times n$$
$$30 \div 4 = n$$
$$7.5 = n$$

For 10 gallons of water, 7.5 tablespoons of fertilizer are required.

Solutions to Chapter 5 "You Try It"

SECTION 5.1

You Try It 1 $125\% = 125 \times \dfrac{1}{100} = \dfrac{125}{100} = 1\dfrac{1}{4}$

$125\% = 125 \times 0.01 = 1.25$

You Try It 2 $33\dfrac{1}{3}\% = 33\dfrac{1}{3} \times \dfrac{1}{100}$

$= \dfrac{100}{3} \times \dfrac{1}{100}$

$= \dfrac{100}{300} = \dfrac{1}{3}$

You Try It 3 $0.25\% = 0.25 \times 0.01 = 0.0025$

You Try It 4 $0.048 = 0.048 \times 100\% = 4.8\%$

You Try It 5 $3.67 = 3.67 \times 100\% = 367\%$

You Try It 6 $0.62\dfrac{1}{2} = 0.62\dfrac{1}{2} \times 100\%$

$= 62\dfrac{1}{2}\%$

You Try It 7 $\dfrac{5}{6} = \dfrac{5}{6} \times 100\% = \dfrac{500\%}{6} = 83\dfrac{1}{3}\%$

You Try It 8 $1\dfrac{4}{9} = \dfrac{13}{9} = \dfrac{13}{9} \times 100\%$

$= \dfrac{1300\%}{9} \approx 144.4\%$

SECTION 5.2

You Try It 1 $n = 0.063 \times 150$
$n = 9.45$

You Try It 2 $n = \dfrac{1}{6} \times 66$

$n = 11$

You Try It 3

Strategy   To find the new hourly wage:
- Find the amount of the raise. Write and solve a basic percent equation, using n to represent the amount of the raise (amount). The percent is 8%. The base is $13.50.
- Add the amount of the raise to the old wage.

Solution
$8\% \times \$13.50 = n$
$0.08 \times \$13.50 = n$
$\$1.08 = n$

$$\begin{array}{r} \$13.50 \\ +\ \ \ 1.08 \\ \hline \$14.58 \end{array}$$

The new hourly wage is $14.58.

SECTION 5.3

You Try It 1 $n \times 32 = 16$
$n = 16 \div 32$
$n = 0.50$
$n = 50\%$

You Try It 2 $n \times 15 = 48$
$n = 48 \div 15$
$n = 3.20$
$n = 320\%$

You Try It 3 $30 = n \times 45$
$30 \div 45 = n$
$\dfrac{2}{3} = n$
$66\dfrac{2}{3}\% = n$

You Try It 4

Strategy   To find what percent of the income the income tax is, write and solve a basic percent equation, using n to represent the percent. The base is $33,500 and the amount is $5025.

Solution $n \times 33{,}500 = \$5025$
$$n = \$5025 \div \$33{,}500$$
$$n = 0.15 = 15\%$$

The income tax is 15% of the income.

You Try It 5

Strategy   To find the percent that are under the age of 30:
- Subtract to find the number of people that are under the age of 30 $(1{,}300{,}000 - 416{,}000)$.
- Write and solve a basic percent equation, using n to represent the percent. The base is 1,300,000 and the amount is the number of people who are under the age of 30.

Solution $1{,}300{,}000 - 416{,}000 = 884{,}000$

$$n \times 1{,}300{,}000 = 884{,}000$$
$$n = 884{,}000 \div 1{,}300{,}000$$
$$n = 0.68 = 68\%$$

68% of the people are under the age of 30.

SECTION 5.4

You Try It 1 $0.86 \times n = 215$
$$n = 215 \div 0.86$$
$$n = 250$$

You Try It 2 $0.025 \times n = 15$
$$n = 15 \div 0.025$$
$$n = 600$$

You Try It 3 $\dfrac{1}{6} \times n = 5$
$$n = 5 \div \dfrac{1}{6}$$
$$n = 30$$

You Try It 4

Strategy   To find the original value of the car, write and solve a basic percent equation, using n to represent the original value (base). The percent is 42%. The amount is $5229.

Solution $42\% \times n = \$5229$
$$0.42 \times n = \$5229$$
$$n = \$5229 \div 0.42$$
$$n = 12{,}450$$

The original value of the car was $12,450.

You Try It 5

Strategy   To find the difference between the original price and the sale price:
- Find the original price. Write and solve a basic percent equation, using n to represent the original price (base). The percent is 80%. The amount is $44.80.
- Subtract the sale price ($44.80) from the original price.

Solution $80\% \times n = \$44.80$
$$0.80 \times n = \$44.80$$
$$n = \$44.80 \div 0.80$$
$$n = \$56.00 \text{ original price}$$

$$\$56.00 - \$44.80 = \$11.20$$

The difference between the original price and the sale price is $11.20.

SECTION 5.5

You Try It 1 $\dfrac{26}{100} = \dfrac{22}{n}$
$$26 \times n = 100 \times 22$$
$$26 \times n = 2200$$
$$n = 2200 \div 26$$
$$n \approx 84.62$$

You Try It 2 $\dfrac{16}{100} = \dfrac{n}{132}$
$$16 \times 132 = 100 \times n$$
$$2112 = 100 \times n$$
$$2112 \div 100 = n$$
$$21.12 = n$$

You Try It 3

Strategy   To find the number of days it snowed, write and solve a proportion, using n to represent the number of days (amount). The percent is 64%. The base is 150.

Solution $\dfrac{64}{100} = \dfrac{n}{150}$
$$64 \times 150 = 100 \times n$$
$$9600 = 100 \times n$$
$$9600 \div 100 = n$$
$$96 = n$$

It snowed 96 days.

You Try It 4

Strategy   To find the percent of pens that were not defective:

- Subtract to find the number of pens that were not defective $(200 - 5)$.
- Write and solve a proportion, using n to represent the percent of pens that were not defective. The base is 200, and the amount is the number of pens not defective.

Solution

$200 - 5 = 195$ number of pens not defective

$$\frac{n}{100} = \frac{195}{200}$$

$200 \times n = 195 \times 100$
$200 \times n = 19{,}500$
$\qquad n = 19{,}500 \div 200$
$\qquad n = 97.5\%$

97.5% of the pens were not defective.

Solutions to Chapter 6 "You Try It"

SECTION 6.1

You Try It 1

Strategy   To find the unit cost, divide the total cost by the number of units.

Solution   **a.** $5.59 \div 8 = 0.69875$
$.699 for each battery
b. $1.89 \div 15 = 0.126$
$.126 per ounce

You Try It 2

Strategy   To find the more economical purchase, compare the unit costs.

Solution $2.52 \div 6 = 0.42$
$1.66 \div 4 = 0.415$
$.415 < $.42

The more economical purchase is 4 cans for $1.66.

You Try It 3

Strategy   To find the total cost, multiply the unit cost ($4.96) by the number of units (7).

Solution $4.96 \times 7 = 34.72$

The total cost is $34.72.

SECTION 6.2

You Try It 1

Strategy   To find the percent increase:
- Find the amount of the increase.
- Solve the basic percent equation for *percent*.

Solution

$$\begin{array}{r} 150 \\ -\ \ 80 \\ \hline 70 \end{array}$$

$n \times 80 = 70$
$n = 70 \div 80$
$n = 0.875 = 87.5\%$

The percent increase was 87.5%.

You Try It 2

Strategy   To find the new hourly wage:
- Solve the basic percent equation for *amount*.
- Add the amount of the increase to the original wage.

Solution $0.14 \times 8.50 = n$
$\qquad\quad 1.19 = n$
$8.50 + 1.19 = 9.69$

The new hourly wage is $9.69.

You Try It 3

Strategy   To find the markup, solve the basic percent equation for *amount*.

Solution $0.20 \times 8 = n$
$\qquad 1.60 = n$

The markup is $1.60.

You Try It 4

Strategy   To find the selling price:
- Find the markup by solving the basic percent equation for *amount*.
- Add the markup to the cost.

Solution $0.55 \times 72 = n$
$\qquad\ 39.60 = n$
$72 + 39.60 = 111.60$

The selling price is $111.60.

You Try It 5

Strategy   To find the percent decrease:
- Find the amount of the decrease.
- Solve the basic percent equation for *percent*.

Solution $6670 - 3100 = 3570$
$n \times 6670 = 3570$
$\qquad\quad n = 3570 \div 6670$
$\qquad\quad n \approx 0.535$

The percent decrease is 54%.

You Try It 6

Strategy   To find the visibility:
* Find the amount of decrease by solving the basic percent equation for *amount*.
* Subtract the amount of decrease from the original visibility.

Solution $0.40 \times 5 = n$
$2 = n$

$5 - 2 = 3$

The visibility was 3 miles.

You Try It 7

Strategy   To find the discount rate:
* Find the discount.
* Solve the basic percent equation for *percent*.

Solution $4.25 - 3.75 = 0.50$
$n \times 4.25 = 0.50$
$n = 0.50 \div 4.25$
$n \approx 0.1176$

The discount rate is 11.8%.

You Try It 8

Strategy   To find the sale price:
* Find the discount by solving the basic percent equation for *amount*.
* Subtract the find the sale price.

Solution $0.15 \times 110 = n$
$16.5 = n$

$110 - 16.5 = 93.5$

The sale price is $93.50.

SECTION 6.3

You Try It 1

Strategy   To find the simple interest, multiply the principal by the annual interest rate by the time (in years).

Solution $15,000 \times 0.08 \times 1.5 = 1800$

The interest due is $1800.

You Try It 2

Strategy   To find the interest due, multiply the principal by the monthly interest rate by the time (in months).

Solution $400 \times 0.012 \times 2 = 9.60$

The interest charge is $9.60.

You Try It 3

Strategy   To find the interest earned:
* Find the new principal by multiplying the original principal by the factor (3.29066) found in the compound interest table.
* Subtract the original principal from the new principal.

Solution $1000 \times 3.29066 = 3290.66$

The new principal is $3290.66.

$3290.66 - 1000 = 2290.66$

The interest earned is $2290.66.

SECTION 6.4

You Try It 1

Strategy   To find the mortgage:
* Find the down payment by solving the basic percent equation for *amount*.
* Subtract the down payment from the purchase price.

Solution $0.25 \times 216,000 = n$
$54,000 = n$

The down payment is $54,000.

$216,000 - 54,000 = 162,000$

The mortgage is $162,000.

You Try It 2

Strategy   To find the loan origination fee, solve the basic percent equation for *amount*.

Solution $0.045 \times 80,000 = n$
$3600 = n$

The loan origination fee was $3600.

You Try It 3

Strategy   To find the monthly mortgage payment:
* Subtract the down payment from the purchase price to find the mortgage.
* Multiply the mortgage by the factor found in the monthly payment table.

Solution $75,000 - 15,000 = 60,000$
The mortgage is $60,000.
$60,000 \times 0.0089973 = 539.838$

The monthly mortgage payment is $539.84.

You Try It 4

Strategy To find the interest:
- Multiply the mortgage by the factor found in the monthly payment table to find the monthly mortgage payment.
- Subtract the principal from the monthly mortgage payment.

Solution $125,000 \times 0.0083920 = 1049$

The monthly mortgage payment is $1049.

$1049 - 492.65 = 556.35$

The interest on the mortgage is $556.35.

You Try It 5

Strategy To find the monthly payment:
- Divide the annual property tax by 12 to find the monthly property tax.
- Add the monthly property tax to the monthly mortgage payment.

Solution $744 \div 12 = 62$

The monthly property tax is $62.

$415.20 + 62 = 477.20$

The total monthly payment is $477.20.

SECTION 6.5

You Try It 1

Strategy To find the amount financed:
- Find the down payment by solving the basic percent equation for *amount*.
- Subtract the down payment from the purchase price.

Solution $0.20 \times 9200 = n$
$ 1840 = n$

The down payment is $1840.

$9200 - 1840 = 7360$

The amount financed is $7360.

You Try It 2

Strategy To find the license fee, solve the basic percent equation for *amount*.

Solution $0.015 \times 7350 = n$
$ 110.25 = n$

The license fee is $110.25.

You Try It 3

Strategy To find the cost of operating the car, multiply the cost per mile by the number of miles driven.

Solution $23,000 \times 0.22 = 5060$

The cost of operating the car is $5060.

You Try It 4

Strategy To find the cost per mile for the car insurance, divide the cost for insurance by the number of miles driven.

Solution $360 \div 15,000 = 0.024$

The cost per mile for insurance is $.024.

You Try It 5

Strategy To find the monthly payment:
- Subtract the down payment from the purchase price to find the amount financed.
- Multiply the amount financed by the factor found in the monthly payment table.

Solution $15,900 - 3975 = 11,925$

The amount financed is $11,925.

$11,925 \times 0.0244129 \approx 291.123$

The monthly payment is $291.12.

SECTION 6.6

You Try It 1

Strategy To find the worker's earnings:
- Find the worker's overtime wage by multiplying the hourly wage by 2.
- Multiply the number of overtime hours worked by the overtime wage.

Solution $8.50 \times 2 = 17$

The hourly wage for overtime is $17.

$17 \times 8 = 136$

The construction worker earns $136.

You Try It 2

Strategy To find the salary per month, divide the annual salary by the number of months in a year (12).

Solution $28,224 \div 12 = 2352$

The contractor's monthly salary is $2352.

You Try It 3

Strategy To find the total earnings:
- Find the commission earned by multiplying the commission rate by the sales over $50,000.
- Add the commission to the annual salary.

Solution $175,000 - 50,000 = 125,000$

Sales over $50,000 totaled $125,000.

$125,000 \times 0.095 = 11,875$

Earnings from commissions totaled $11,875.

$12,000 + 11,875 = 23,875$

The insurance agent earned $23,875.

SECTION 6.7

You Try It 1

Strategy To find the current balance:
- Subtract the amount of the check from the old balance.
- Add the amount of each deposit.

Solution
$$\begin{array}{rl} 302.46 & \\ -\ \ 20.59 & \text{check} \\ \hline 281.87 & \\ 176.86 & \text{first deposit} \\ +\ \ 94.73 & \text{second deposit} \\ \hline 553.46 & \end{array}$$

The current checking account balance is $553.46.

You Try It 2

$$\begin{array}{lr} \text{Current checkbook} & \\ \text{balance:} & 653.41 \\ \text{Check: 237} & +\ \ 48.73 \\ \hline & 702.14 \\ \text{Interest:} & +\ \ \ \ 2.11 \\ \hline & 704.25 \\ \text{Deposit:} & -523.84 \\ \hline & 180.41 \end{array}$$

Closing bank balance from bank statement: $180.41.

Checkbook balance: $180.41.

The bank statement and checkbook balance.

Solutions to Chapter 7 "You Try It"

SECTION 7.1

You Try It 1

Strategy To find what percent of the total number of cellular phone purchases the number of March cellular phone purchases represents:
- Read the pictograph to determine the number of cellular phones purchased for each month.
- Find the total cellular phone purchases for the 4-month period.
- Solve the basic percent equation for percent (n). Amount = 3000; the base is the total sales for the 4-month period.

Solution
$$\begin{array}{r} 4,500 \\ 3,500 \\ 3,000 \\ \underline{1,500} \\ 12,500 \end{array}$$

$n \times 12,500 = 3000$
$$n = 3000 \div 12,500$$
$$n = 0.24$$

The March purchases of cellular phones were 24% of the purchases for the 4-month period.

You Try It 2

Strategy To find the ratio of the annual cost of fuel to the annual cost of

maintenance:
- Locate the annual fuel cost and annual maintenance cost in the circle graph.
- Write the ratio of the annual fuel cost to the annual maintenance cost as a ratio in simplest form.

Solution   Annual fuel cost: $700
Annual maintenance cost: $500

$$\frac{700}{500} = \frac{7}{5}$$

The ratio is $\frac{7}{5}$.

You Try It 3

Strategy   To find the amount paid for medical/dental insurance:
- Locate the percent of the distribution that is medical/dental insurance.
- Solve the basic percent equation for amount.

Solution   Percent medical/dental insurance: 6%

Percent × base = amount
0.06 × 2900 = 174

The amount paid for medical/dental insurance was $174.

SECTION 7.2

You Try It 1

Strategy   To find the company that had the largest decrease in sales from June 1996 to June 1997:
- Subtract the June sales for 1997 from the June sales for 1996 for each company that had a decrease in sales.
- Compare the decreases for the companies.

Solution   GM: 435,000 − 375,000 = 60,000
Ford: Ford's sales increased.
Chrysler:
230,000 − 220,000 = 10,000
Toyota: 100,000 − 95,000 = 5000

GM had the largest decrease in sales from June 1996 to June 1997.

You Try It 2

Strategy   To determine between which two years the net income of Math Associates increased the most:

- Read the line graph to determine the net income of Math Associates for each of the years shown.
- Subtract to find the difference between each two years.

Solution   1994: $1 million
1995: $3 million
1996: $5 million
1997: $8 million
1998: $11 million

Between 1994 and 1995: 3 − 1 = 2
Between 1995 and 1996: 5 − 3 = 2
Between 1996 and 1997: 8 − 5 = 3
Between 1997 and 1998: 11 − 8 = 3

The net income of Math Associates increased the most between the years 1996 and 1997, and 1997 and 1998.

SECTION 7.3

You Try It 1

Strategy   To find the number of employees:
- Read the histogram to find the number of employees whose hourly wage is between $8 and $10 and the number whose hourly wage is between $10 and $12.
- Add the two numbers.

Solution   Number whose wage is between $8 and $10: 7; between $10 and $12: 15.

7 + 15 = 22

22 employees earn between $8 and $12.

You Try It 2

Strategy   To find the number of people who scored between 1200 and 1400 on the exam:
- Read the frequency polygon to find the number of people who scored between 1200 and 1300 and the number of people who scored between 1300 and 1400.
- Add the two numbers.

Solution   Between 1200 and 1300: 110,000
Between 1300 and 1400: 60,000

110,000 + 60,000 = 170,000

170,000 people scored between 1200 and 1400.

SECTION 7.4

You Try It 1

Strategy To find the mean amount spent by the 12 customers:
- Find the sum of the amounts.
- Divide the sum by the number of customers (12).

Solution 5.26 + 7.23 + 4.09 + 7.11 + 6.50 + 5.69 + 4.66 + 3.89 + 4.25 + 8.36 + 5.75 + 6.05 = 68.84

$$\bar{x} = \frac{68.84}{12} = 5.73\bar{6}$$

The mean amount spent by the 12 customers was $5.74.

You Try It 2

Strategy To find the median weight loss:
- Arrange the weight losses from smallest to largest.
- Because there is an even number of values, the median is the mean of the middle two numbers.

Solution 10, 14, 16, 16, 22, 27, 29, 31, 31, 40

$$\text{Median} = \frac{22 + 27}{2} = 24.5$$

The median weight loss was 24.5 pounds.

You Try It 3

Strategy To draw the box-and-whiskers plot:
- Arrange the data from smallest to largest. Then find the median.
- Find Q_1, the median of the lower half of the data.
- Find Q_3, the median of the upper half of the data.
- Find the range by subtracting the smallest number from the largest number.
- Graph the box-and-whiskers plot.

Solution

24	30	35	38	38	40	43
45	46	48	53	54	62	64

$$\text{Median} = \frac{43 + 45}{2} = 44$$

$Q_1 = 38$ • The median of the top row of data.

$Q_3 = 53$ • The median of the bottom row of data.

Range = 64 − 24 = 40

The range is 40 people.

Solutions to Chapter 8 "You Try It"

SECTION 8.1

You Try It 1 60 in. = 60 i̶n̶. × $\dfrac{1 \text{ ft}}{12 \text{ i̶n̶.}}$ = 5 ft

You Try It 2 14 ft = 14 f̶t̶ × $\dfrac{1 \text{ yd}}{3 \text{ f̶t̶}}$ = $4\dfrac{2}{3}$ yd

You Try It 3 9800 ft = 9800 f̶t̶ × $\dfrac{1 \text{ mi}}{5280 \text{ f̶t̶}}$

$$= 1\dfrac{113}{132} \text{ mi}$$

You Try It 4

$$\begin{array}{r} 3 \text{ ft } 6 \text{ in.} \\ 12\overline{)\ 42} \\ -36 \\ \hline 6 \end{array}$$

42 in. = 3 ft 6 in.

You Try It 5

$$\begin{array}{r} 4 \text{ yd } 2 \text{ ft} \\ 3\overline{)\ 14} \\ -12 \\ \hline 2 \end{array}$$

14 ft = 4 yd 2 ft

You Try It 6

$$\begin{array}{r} 3 \text{ ft } 5 \text{ in.} \\ +\ 4 \text{ ft } 9 \text{ in.} \\ \hline 7 \text{ ft } 14 \text{ in.} = 8 \text{ ft } 2 \text{ in.} \end{array}$$

You Try It 7

$$\begin{array}{r} {\scriptstyle 3 \text{ ft} \quad 14 \text{ in.}} \\ \cancel{4 \text{ ft } 2 \text{ in.}} \\ -\ 1 \text{ ft } 8 \text{ in.} \\ \hline 2 \text{ ft } 6 \text{ in.} \end{array}$$

You Try It 8

$$\begin{array}{r} 4 \text{ yd } 1 \text{ ft} \\ \times \qquad 8 \\ \hline 32 \text{ yd } 8 \text{ ft} = 34 \text{ yd } 2 \text{ ft} \end{array}$$

You Try It 9

$$\begin{array}{r} 3 \text{ yd} \quad 2 \text{ ft} \\ 2)\overline{7 \text{ yd} \quad 1 \text{ ft}} \\ -6 \text{ yd} \\ \hline 1 \text{ yd} = 3 \text{ ft} \\ 4 \text{ ft} \\ -4 \text{ ft} \\ \hline 0 \end{array}$$

You Try It 10

$$6\frac{1}{4} \text{ ft} = 6\frac{3}{12} \text{ ft} = 5\frac{15}{12} \text{ ft}$$
$$-3\frac{2}{3} \text{ ft} = 3\frac{8}{12} \text{ ft} = 3\frac{8}{12} \text{ ft}$$
$$\overline{2\frac{7}{12} \text{ ft}}$$

You Try It 11

Strategy To find the width of the storage room:
- Multiply the number of tiles (8) by the width of each tile (9 in.).
- Divide the result by the number of inches in one foot (12) to find the width in feet.

Solution 9 in. × 8 = 72 in.

72 ÷ 12 = 6

The width is 6 ft.

You Try It 12

Strategy To find the length of each piece, divide the total length (9 ft 8 in.) by the number of pieces (4).

Solution
$$\begin{array}{r} 2 \text{ ft} \quad 5 \text{ in.} \\ 4)\overline{9 \text{ ft} \quad 8 \text{ in.}} \\ -8 \text{ ft} \\ \hline 1 \text{ ft} = 12 \text{ in.} \\ 20 \text{ in.} \\ -20 \text{ in.} \\ \hline 0 \text{ in.} \end{array}$$

Each piece is 2 ft 5 in. long.

SECTION 8.2

You Try It 1

$$3 \text{ lb} = 3 \cancel{\text{lb}} \times \frac{16 \text{ oz}}{1 \cancel{\text{lb}}} = 48 \text{ oz}$$

You Try It 2

$$4200 \text{ lb} = 4200 \cancel{\text{lb}} \times \frac{1 \text{ ton}}{2000 \cancel{\text{lb}}}$$
$$= 2\frac{1}{10} \text{ tons}$$

You Try It 3

$$\begin{array}{r} 6 \text{ lb} \quad 17 \text{ oz} \\ \cancel{7 \text{ lb}} \quad \cancel{1 \text{ oz}} \\ -3 \text{ lb} \quad 4 \text{ oz} \\ \hline 3 \text{ lb } 13 \text{ oz} \end{array}$$

You Try It 4

$$\begin{array}{r} 3 \text{ lb} \quad 6 \text{ oz} \\ \times 4 \\ \hline 12 \text{ lb } 24 \text{ oz} = 13 \text{ lb } 8 \text{ oz} \end{array}$$

You Try It 5

Strategy To find the weight of 12 bars of soap:
- Multiply the number of bars (12) by the weight of each bar (9 oz).
- Convert the number of ounces to pounds.

Solution
$$\begin{array}{r} 12 \\ \times 9 \text{ oz} \\ \hline 108 \text{ oz} \end{array} \qquad 108 \cancel{\text{oz}} \times \frac{1 \text{ lb}}{16 \cancel{\text{oz}}} = 6\frac{3}{4} \text{ lb}$$

The 12 bars of soap weigh $6\frac{3}{4}$ lb.

SECTION 8.3

You Try It 1

$$18 \text{ pt} = 18 \cancel{\text{pt}} \times \frac{1 \cancel{\text{qt}}}{2 \cancel{\text{pt}}} \times \frac{1 \text{ gal}}{4 \cancel{\text{qt}}}$$
$$= \frac{18 \text{ gal}}{8} = 2\frac{1}{4} \text{ gal}$$

You Try It 2

$$\begin{array}{r} 1 \text{ gal} \quad 2 \text{ qt} \\ 3)\overline{4 \text{ gal} \quad 2 \text{ qt}} \\ -3 \text{ gal} \\ \hline 1 \text{ gal} = 4 \text{ qt} \\ 6 \text{ qt} \\ -6 \text{ qt} \\ \hline 0 \end{array}$$

You Try It 3

Strategy To find the number of gallons of water needed:
- Find the number of quarts required by multiplying the number of quarts one student needs (3) by the number of students (5) by the number of days (3).
- Convert the number of quarts to gallons.

Solution 3 × 5 × 3 = 45 qt

$$45 \text{ qt} \cdot \frac{1 \text{ gal}}{4 \text{ qt}} = 11\frac{1}{4} \text{ gal}$$

The students should take $11\frac{1}{4}$ gal of water.

SECTION 8.4

You Try It 1 $4.5 \text{ Btu} = 4.5 \text{ Btu} \times \dfrac{778 \text{ ft} \cdot \text{lb}}{1 \text{ Btu}}$

$$= 3501 \text{ ft} \cdot \text{lb}$$

You Try It 2 $800 \text{ lb} \times 16 \text{ ft} = 12{,}800 \text{ ft} \cdot \text{lb}$

You Try It 3 $56{,}000 \text{ Btu} =$

$$56{,}000 \text{ Btu} \times \frac{778 \text{ ft} \cdot \text{lb}}{1 \text{ Btu}} =$$

$$43{,}568{,}000 \text{ ft} \cdot \text{lb}$$

You Try It 4 $\text{Power} = \dfrac{90 \text{ ft} \times 1200 \text{ lb}}{24 \text{ s}}$

$$= 4500 \frac{\text{ft} \cdot \text{lb}}{\text{s}}$$

You Try It 5 $\dfrac{3300}{550} = 6 \text{ hp}$

Solutions to Chapter 9 "You Try It"

SECTION 9.1

You Try It 1 $3.07 \text{ m} = 307 \text{ cm}$

You Try It 2 $750 \text{ m} = 0.750 \text{ km}$

$$3 \text{ km } 750 \text{ m} = 3 \text{ km} + 0.750 \text{ km}$$
$$= 3.750 \text{ km}$$

You Try It 3

Strategy   To find the cost of the shelves:
- Multiply the length of the bookcase (175 cm) by the number of shelves (4).
- Convert centimeters to meters.
- Multiply the number of meters by the cost per meter ($15.75).

Solution
$$\begin{array}{r} 175 \text{ cm} \\ \times \quad 4 \\ \hline 700 \text{ cm} \end{array}$$

$$700 \text{ cm} = 7 \text{ m}$$

$$\begin{array}{r} \$15.75 \\ \times \quad 7 \\ \hline \$110.25 \end{array}$$

The cost of the shelves is $110.25.

SECTION 9.2

You Try It 1 $42.3 \text{ mg} = 0.0423 \text{ g}$

You Try It 2 $54 \text{ mg} = 0.054 \text{ g}$

$$3 \text{ g } 54 \text{ mg} = 3 \text{ g} + 0.054 \text{ g}$$
$$= 3.054 \text{ g}$$

You Try It 3

Strategy   To find how much fertilizer is required:
- Convert 300 g to kilograms.
- Multiply the number of kilograms by the number of trees (400).

Solution $300 \text{ g} = 0.3 \text{ kg}$

$$\begin{array}{r} 400 \\ \times \quad 0.3 \text{ kg} \\ \hline 120.0 \text{ kg} \end{array}$$

To fertilize the trees, 120 kg of fertilizer are required.

SECTION 9.3

You Try It 1 $2 \text{ kl} = 2000 \text{ L}$

$$2 \text{ kl } 167 \text{ L} = 2000 \text{ L} + 167 \text{ L}$$
$$= 2167 \text{ L}$$

You Try It 2 $325 \text{ cm}^3 = 325 \text{ ml} = 0.325 \text{ L}$

You Try It 3

Strategy   To find the profit:
- Convert 5 L to milliliters.
- Find the number of jars by dividing the number of milliliters by 125 (the number of milliliters in each jar).
- Multiply the number of jars by the cost per jar ($.35).
- Find the total cost by adding the cost of the jars to the cost for the moisturizer ($99.50).

- Find the income by multiplying the number of jars by the selling price per jar ($5.95).
- Subtract the total cost from the income.

Solution   5 L = 5000 ml

$$5000 \div 125 = 40 \quad \text{This is the number of jars.}$$

$$
\begin{array}{r}
\$.35 \\
\times \quad 40 \\
\hline
\$14.00
\end{array}
\quad \text{This is the cost of the jars.}
$$

$$
\begin{array}{r}
\$99.50 \\
+ \quad 14.00 \\
\hline
\$113.50
\end{array}
\quad \text{This is the total cost.}
$$

$$
\begin{array}{r}
\$5.95 \\
\times \quad 40 \\
\hline
\$238.00
\end{array}
\quad \text{This is the income from sales.}
$$

$$
\begin{array}{r}
\$238.00 \\
- \quad 113.50 \\
\hline
\$124.50
\end{array}
$$

The profit on the 5 L of moisturizer is $124.50.

SECTION 9.4

You Try It 1

Strategy   To find the number of Calories burned off, multiply the number of hours spent doing housework $\left(4\frac{1}{2}\right)$ by the Calories used per hour (240).

Solution $4\dfrac{1}{2} \times 240 = \dfrac{9}{2} \times 240 = 1080$

Doing $4\frac{1}{2}$ h of housework burns off 1080 Calories.

You Try It 2

Strategy   To find the number of kilowatt-hours used, multiply to find the number of watt-hours used. Convert the watt-hours to kilowatt-hours.

Solution   150 W × 200 h = 30,000 Wh
                                  = 30 kWh

30 kWh of energy are used.

You Try It 3

Strategy   To find the cost:
- Convert 20 min to hours.

- Multiply to find the total number of hours the oven is used.
- Multiply the number of hours used by the number of watts to find the watt-hours.
- Convert to kilowatt-hours.
- Multiply the number of kilowatt-hours by the cost per kilowatt-hour.

Solution $20 \text{ min} = 20 \text{ min} \times \dfrac{1 \text{ h}}{60 \text{ min}}$

$$= \dfrac{20}{60} \text{ h} = \dfrac{1}{3} \text{ h}$$

$$\dfrac{1}{3} \text{ h} \times 30 = 10 \text{ h}$$

$$10 \text{ h} \times 500 \text{ W} = 5000 \text{ Wh}$$

$$5000 \text{ Wh} = 5 \text{ kWh}$$

$$5 \times 8.7¢ = 43.5¢$$

The cost is 43.5¢.

SECTION 9.5

You Try It 1 $\dfrac{60 \text{ ft}}{\text{s}} \approx \dfrac{60 \text{ ft}}{\text{s}} \times \dfrac{1 \text{ m}}{3.28 \text{ ft}}$

$$= \dfrac{60 \text{ m}}{3.28 \text{ s}} = 18.29 \text{ m/s}$$

60 ft/s ≈ 18.29 m/s

You Try It 2 $\dfrac{\$2.19}{\text{gal}} \approx \dfrac{\$2.19}{\text{gal}} \times \dfrac{1 \text{ gal}}{3.79 \text{ L}}$

$$= \dfrac{\$2.19}{3.79 \text{ L}} \approx \dfrac{\$.58}{\text{L}}$$

$2.19/gal ≈ $.58/L

You Try It 3 $45 \text{ cm} = \dfrac{45 \text{ cm}}{1} \times \dfrac{1 \text{ in.}}{2.54 \text{ cm}}$

$$= \dfrac{45 \text{ in.}}{2.54} \approx 17.72 \text{ in.}$$

45 cm ≈ 17.72 in.

You Try It 4 $\dfrac{75 \text{ km}}{\text{h}} \approx \dfrac{75 \text{ km}}{\text{h}} \times \dfrac{1 \text{ mi}}{1.61 \text{ km}}$

$$= 46.58 \text{ mi/h}$$

75 km/h ≈ 46.58 mi/h

You Try It 5 $\dfrac{\$1.75}{\text{L}} \approx \dfrac{\$1.75}{\text{L}} \times \dfrac{3.79 \text{ L}}{1 \text{ gal}}$

$$= \dfrac{\$6.6325}{1 \text{ gal}} \approx \$6.63/\text{gal}$$

$1.75/L ≈ $6.63/gal

Solutions to Chapter 10 "You Try It"

SECTION 10.1

You Try It 1 -232 ft

You Try It 2

You Try It 3   **a.** $-12 < -8$
b. $-5 < 0$

You Try It 4 $|-7| = 7$
$|21| = 21$

You Try It 5 $|2| = 2$
$|-9| = 9$

You Try It 6 $-|-12| = -12$

SECTION 10.2

You Try It 1 $-154 + (-37) = -191$

You Try It 2 $-5 + (-2) + 9 + (-3)$
$\quad = -7 + 9 + (-3)$
$\quad = 2 + (-3)$
$\quad = -1$

You Try It 3 $-8 - 14$
$\quad = -8 + (-14)$
$\quad = -22$

You Try It 4 $3 - (-15)$
$\quad = 3 + 15$
$\quad = 18$

You Try It 5 $4 - (-3) - 12 - (-7) - 20$
$\quad = 4 + 3 + (-12) + 7 + (-20)$
$\quad = 7 + (-12) + 7 + (-20)$
$\quad = -5 + 7 + (-20)$
$\quad = 2 + (-20)$
$\quad = -18$

You Try It 6

Strategy   To find the temperature, add the increase (12) to the previous temperature (-10).

Solution $-10 + 12 = 2$

After an increase of 12°C, the temperature is 2°C.

SECTION 10.3

You Try It 1 $(-3)(-5) = 15$

You Try It 2 $-38 \cdot 51 = -1938$

You Try It 3 $-7(-8)(9)(-2) = 56(9)(-2)$
$\qquad\qquad\qquad = 504(-2)$
$\qquad\qquad\qquad = -1008$

You Try It 4 $(-135) \div (-9) = 15$

You Try It 5 $84 \div (-6) = -14$

You Try It 6 $-72 \div 4 = -18$

You Try It 7   Division by zero is undefined.
$-39 \div 0$ is undefined.

You Try It 8

Strategy   To find the melting point of argon, multiply the melting point of mercury ($-38°$) by 5.

Solution $5(-38) = -190$

The melting point of argon is $-190°$C.

You Try It 9

Strategy   To find the average daily low temperature:
• Add the seven temperature readings.
• Divide by 7.

Solution
$-6 + (-7) + 1 + 0 + (-5) + (-10) + (-1)$
$\quad = -13 + 1 + 0 + (-5) + (-10) + (-1)$
$\quad = -12 + 0 + (-5) + (-10) + (-1)$
$\quad = -12 + (-5) + (-10) + (-1)$
$\quad = -17 + (-10) + (-1)$
$\quad = -27 + (-1)$
$\quad = -28$

$\qquad -28 \div 7 = -4$

The average daily low temperature was $-4°$.

SECTION 10.4

You Try It 1 The LCM of 9 and 12 is 36.

$$\frac{5}{9} - \frac{11}{12} = \frac{20}{36} - \frac{33}{36} = \frac{20}{36} + \frac{-33}{36}$$

$$= \frac{20 + (-33)}{36} = \frac{-13}{36}$$

$$= -\frac{13}{36}$$

You Try It 2 The LCM of 8, 6 and 3 is 24.

$$-\frac{7}{8} - \frac{5}{6} + \frac{2}{3}$$

$$= -\frac{21}{24} - \frac{20}{24} + \frac{16}{24}$$

$$= \frac{-21}{24} + \frac{-20}{24} + \frac{16}{24}$$

$$= \frac{-21 + (-20) + 16}{24}$$

$$= -\frac{25}{24} = -1\frac{1}{24}$$

You Try It 3
$$\begin{array}{r} 67.910 \\ -16.127 \\ \hline 51.783 \end{array}$$

$$16.127 - 67.91 = -51.783$$

You Try It 4
$$2.7 + (-9.44) + 6.2$$
$$= -6.74 + 6.2$$
$$= -0.54$$

You Try It 5 The product is positive.

$$\left(-\frac{2}{3}\right)\left(-\frac{9}{10}\right) = \frac{2 \cdot 9}{3 \cdot 10}$$

$$= \frac{3}{5}$$

You Try It 6 The quotient is negative.

$$-\frac{5}{8} \div \frac{5}{40} = -\frac{5}{8} \cdot \frac{40}{5}$$

$$= -\frac{5 \cdot 40}{8 \cdot 5}$$

$$= -5$$

You Try It 7
$$\begin{array}{r} 5.44 \\ \times 3.8 \\ \hline 4352 \\ 1632 \\ \hline 20.672 \end{array}$$

$$-5.44 \times 3.8 = -20.672$$

You Try It 8 $3.44 \times (-1.7) \times 0.6$
$$= (-5.848) \times 0.6$$
$$= -3.5088$$

You Try It 9
$$\begin{array}{r} 0.231 \\ 1.7\overline{)0.3.940} \\ -3\ 4 \\ \hline 54 \\ -51 \\ \hline 30 \\ -17 \\ \hline 13 \end{array}$$

$$-0.394 \div 1.7 \approx -0.23$$

You Try It 10

Strategy To find how many degrees the temperature fell, subtract the lower temperature (-13.33) from the higher temperature (12.78).

Solution $12.78 - (-13.33) = 12.78 + 13.33$
$$= 26.11$$

The temperature fell 26.11°C in the 15-minute period.

SECTION 10.5

You Try It 1 The number is less than 1. Move the decimal point 7 places to the right. The exponent on 10 is -7.

$$0.000000961 = 9.61 \times 10^{-7}$$

You Try It 2 The exponent on 10 is positive. Move the decimal point 6 places to the right.

$$7.329 \times 10^6 = 7,329,000$$

You Try It 3 $9 - 9 \div (-3)$
$$= 9 - (-3)$$
$$= 9 + 3$$
$$= 12$$

You Try It 4 $8 \div 4 \cdot 4 - (-2)^2$
$$= 8 \div 4 \cdot 4 - 4$$
$$= 2 \cdot 4 - 4$$
$$= 8 - 4$$
$$= 8 + (-4)$$
$$= 4$$

You Try It 5 $8 - (-15) \div (2 - 7)$
$$= 8 - (-15) \div (-5)$$
$$= 8 - 3$$
$$= 8 + (-3)$$
$$= 5$$

You Try It 6

$$(-2)^2 \times (3 - 7)^2 - (-16) \div (-4)$$
$$= (-2)^2 \times (-4)^2 - (-16) \div (-4)$$
$$= 4 \times 16 - (-16) \div (-4)$$
$$= 64 - (-16) \div (-4)$$
$$= 64 - 4$$
$$= 64 + (-4)$$
$$= 60$$

You Try It 7

$$7 \div \left(\frac{1}{7} - \frac{3}{14}\right) - 9$$
$$= 7 \div \left(-\frac{1}{14}\right) - 9 = 7(-14) - 9$$
$$= -98 - 9$$
$$= -98 + (-9)$$
$$= -107$$

Solutions to Chapter 11 "You Try It"

SECTION 11.1

You Try It 1 $6a - 5b$

$$6(-3) - 5(4) = -18 - 20$$
$$= -18 + (-20)$$
$$= -38$$

You Try It 2 $-3s^2 - 12 \div t$

$$-3(-2)^2 - 12 \div 4 = -3(4) - 12 \div 4$$
$$= -12 - 12 \div 4$$
$$= -12 - 3$$
$$= -12 + (-3)$$
$$= -15$$

You Try It 3 $-\frac{2}{3}m + \frac{3}{4}n^3$

$$-\frac{2}{3}(6) + \frac{3}{4}(2)^3 = -\frac{2}{3}(6) + \frac{3}{4}(8)$$
$$= -4 + 6$$
$$= 2$$

You Try It 4 $-3yz - z^2 + y^2$

$$-3\left(-\frac{2}{3}\right)\left(\frac{1}{3}\right) - \left(\frac{1}{3}\right)^2 + \left(-\frac{2}{3}\right)^2$$
$$= -3\left(-\frac{2}{3}\right)\left(\frac{1}{3}\right) - \frac{1}{9} + \frac{4}{9}$$
$$= \frac{2}{3} - \frac{1}{9} + \frac{4}{9} = \frac{6}{9} - \frac{1}{9} + \frac{4}{9} = \frac{9}{9}$$
$$= 1$$

You Try It 5 $5a^2 - 6b^2 + 7a^2 - 9b^2$

$$= 5a^2 + (-6)b^2 + 7a^2 + (-9)b^2$$
$$= 5a^2 + 7a^2 + (-6)b^2 + (-9)b^2$$
$$= 12a^2 + (-15)b^2$$
$$= 12a^2 - 15b^2$$

You Try It 6 $-6x + 7 + 9x - 10$

$$= (-6)x + 7 + 9x + (-10)$$
$$= (-6)x + 9x + 7 + (-10)$$
$$= 3x + (-3)$$
$$= 3x - 3$$

You Try It 7 $\frac{3}{8}w + \frac{1}{2} - \frac{1}{4}w - \frac{2}{3}$

$$= \frac{3}{8}w - \frac{1}{4}w + \frac{1}{2} - \frac{2}{3}$$
$$= \frac{3}{8}w - \frac{2}{8}w + \frac{3}{6} - \frac{4}{6}$$
$$= \frac{1}{8}w - \frac{1}{6}$$

You Try It 8 $5(a - 2) = 5a - 5(2)$
$$= 5a - 10$$

You Try It 9 $8s - 2(3s - 5)$
$$= 8s + (-2)(3s) - (-2)(5)$$
$$= 8s + (-6s) + 10$$
$$= 2s + 10$$

You Try It 10 $4(x - 3) - 2(x + 1)$
$$= 4x - 4(3) - 2x - 2(1)$$
$$= 4x - 12 - 2x - 2$$
$$= 4x - 2x - 12 - 2$$
$$= 2x - 14$$

SECTION 11.2

You Try It 1

$$\frac{x(x + 3) = 4x + 6}{\begin{array}{c|c} (-2)(-2 + 3) & 4(-2) + 6 \\ (-2)(1) & (-8) + 6 \\ \end{array}}$$
$$-2 = -2$$

Yes, -2 is a solution.

You Try It 2

$$\frac{x^2 - x = 3x + 7}{\begin{array}{c|c} (-3)^2 - (-3) & 3(-3) + 7 \\ 9 + 3 & -9 + 7 \\ \end{array}}$$
$$12 \neq -2$$

No, -3 is not a solution.

You Try It 3

$$-2 + y = -5$$
$$-2 + 2 + y = -5 + 2$$
$$0 + y = -3$$
$$y = -3$$

The solution is -3.

You Try It 4

$$7 = y + 8$$
$$7 - 8 = y + 8 - 8$$
$$-1 = y + 0$$
$$-1 = y$$

The solution is -1.

You Try It 5

$$\frac{1}{5} = z + \frac{4}{5}$$
$$\frac{1}{5} - \frac{4}{5} = z + \frac{4}{5} - \frac{4}{5}$$
$$-\frac{3}{5} = z + 0$$
$$-\frac{3}{5} = z$$

The solution is $-\frac{3}{5}$.

You Try It 6

$$4z = -20$$
$$\frac{4z}{4} = \frac{-20}{4}$$
$$1z = -5$$
$$z = -5$$

The solution is -5.

You Try It 7

$$8 = \frac{2}{5}n$$
$$\left(\frac{5}{2}\right)(8) = \left(\frac{5}{2}\right)\frac{2}{5}n$$
$$20 = 1n$$
$$20 = n$$

The solution is 20.

You Try It 8

$$\frac{2}{3}t - \frac{1}{3}t = -2$$
$$\frac{1}{3}t = -2$$
$$\left(\frac{3}{1}\right)\frac{1}{3}t = \left(\frac{3}{1}\right)(-2)$$
$$1t = -6$$
$$t = -6$$

The solution is -6.

You Try It 9

Strategy   To find the regular price, replace the variables S and D in the formula by the given values and solve for R.

Solution
$$S = R - D$$
$$22 = R - 8$$
$$22 + 8 = R - 8 + 8$$
$$30 = R$$

The regular price is $30.

You Try It 10

Strategy   To find the monthly payment, replace the variables A and N in the formula by the given values and solve for M.

Solution
$$A = MN$$
$$6840 = M \cdot 24$$
$$6840 = 24M$$
$$\frac{6840}{24} = \frac{24M}{24}$$
$$285 = M$$

The monthly payment is $285.

SECTION 11.3

You Try It 1

$$5x + 8 = 6$$
$$5x + 8 - 8 = 6 - 8$$
$$5x = -2$$
$$\frac{5x}{5} = \frac{-2}{5}$$
$$x = -\frac{2}{5}$$

The solution is $-\frac{2}{5}$.

You Try It 2

$$7 - x = 3$$
$$7 - 7 - x = 3 - 7$$
$$-x = -4$$
$$(-1)(-x) = (-1)(-4)$$
$$x = 4$$

The solution is 4.

You Try It 3

Strategy   To find the Celsius temperature, replace the variable F in the formula by the given value and solve for C.

Solution
$$F = \frac{9}{5}C + 32$$
$$-22 = \frac{9}{5}C + 32$$
$$-22 - 32 = \frac{9}{5}C + 32 - 32$$
$$-54 = \frac{9}{5}C$$
$$\left(\frac{5}{9}\right)(-54) = \left(\frac{5}{9}\right)\frac{9}{5}C$$
$$-30 = C$$

The Celsius temperature is $-30°$.

You Try It 4

Strategy   To find the cost per unit, replace the variables T, N, and F in the formula by the given values and solve for U.

Solution

$$T = U \cdot N + F$$
$$4500 = U \cdot 250 + 1500$$
$$4500 = 250U + 1500$$
$$4500 - 1500 = 250U + 1500 - 1500$$
$$3000 = 250U$$
$$\frac{3000}{250} = \frac{250U}{250}$$
$$12 = U$$

The cost per unit is $12.

SECTION 11.4

You Try It 1

$$\frac{1}{5}x - 2 = \frac{2}{5}x + 4$$
$$\frac{1}{5}x - \frac{2}{5}x - 2 = \frac{2}{5}x - \frac{2}{5}x + 4$$
$$-\frac{1}{5}x - 2 = 4$$
$$-\frac{1}{5}x - 2 + 2 = 4 + 2$$
$$-\frac{1}{5}x = 6$$
$$(-5)\left(-\frac{1}{5}x\right) = (-5)6$$
$$x = -30$$

The solution is -30.

You Try It 2

$$4(x - 1) - x = 5$$
$$4x - 4 - x = 5$$
$$3x - 4 = 5$$
$$3x - 4 + 4 = 5 + 4$$
$$3x = 9$$
$$\frac{3x}{3} = \frac{9}{3}$$
$$x = 3$$

The solution is 3.

SECTION 11.5

You Try It 1 $8 - 2t$

You Try It 2 $\dfrac{5}{7x}$

You Try It 3   The product of a number and one-half of the number.
The unknown number: n

One-half the number: $\dfrac{n}{2}$

$$(n)\left(\frac{n}{2}\right)$$

SECTION 11.6

You Try It 1   The unknown number: x

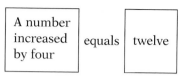

$$x + 4 = 12$$
$$x + 4 - 4 = 12 - 4$$
$$x = 8$$

The number is 8.

You Try It 2   The unknown number: x

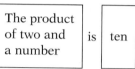

$$2x = 10$$
$$\frac{2x}{2} = \frac{10}{2}$$
$$x = 5$$

The number is 5.

You Try It 3   The unknown number: x

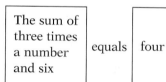

$$3x + 6 = 4$$
$$3x + 6 - 6 = 4 - 6$$
$$3x = -2$$
$$\frac{3x}{3} = \frac{-2}{3}$$
$$x = -\frac{2}{3}$$

The number is $-\dfrac{2}{3}$.

You Try It 4   The unknown number: x

$$\boxed{\text{Three more than one-half of a number}}\ \ \text{is}\ \ \boxed{\text{nine}}$$

$$\frac{1}{2}x + 3 = 9$$
$$\frac{1}{2}x + 3 - 3 = 9 - 3$$
$$\frac{1}{2}x = 6$$

$$2 \cdot \frac{1}{2}x = 2 \cdot 6$$
$$x = 12$$

The number is 12.

You Try It 5

Strategy To find the regular price, write and solve an equation using R to represent the regular price of the slacks.

Solution

$$\boxed{\$18.95} \text{ is } \boxed{\$6 \text{ less than} \atop \text{the regular price}}$$

$$18.95 = R - 6$$
$$18.95 + 6 = R - 6 + 6$$
$$24.95 = R$$

The regular price of the slacks is $24.95.

You Try It 6

Strategy To find the rpm of the engine when it is in third gear, write and solve an equation using R to represent the rpm of the engine in third gear.

Solution

$$\boxed{2500} \text{ is } \boxed{\text{two-thirds of the} \atop \text{rpm of the engine} \atop \text{in third gear}}$$

$$2500 = \frac{2}{3}R$$
$$\frac{3}{2}(2500) = \left(\frac{3}{2}\right)\frac{2}{3}R$$
$$3750 = R$$

The rpm of the engine when in third gear is 3750.

You Try It 7

Strategy To find the total sales, write and solve an equation using S to represent the total sales.

Solution

$$\boxed{\$2500} \text{ is } \boxed{\text{the sum of \$800 and} \atop \text{an 8\% commission} \atop \text{on total sales}}$$

$$2500 = 800 + 0.08S$$
$$2500 - 800 = 800 - 800 + 0.08S$$
$$1700 = 0.08S$$
$$\frac{1700}{0.08} = \frac{0.08S}{0.08}$$
$$21,250 = S$$

Natalie's total sales for the month were $21,250.

You Try It 8

Strategy To find the number of hours of labor, write and solve an equation using H to represent the number of hours of labor required.

Solution

$$\boxed{\$300} \text{ includes } \boxed{\$100 \text{ for} \atop \text{materials plus} \atop \$12.50 \text{ per hour} \atop \text{of labor}}$$

$$300 = 100 + 12.50H$$
$$300 - 100 = 100 - 100 + 12.50H$$
$$200 = 12.50H$$
$$\frac{200}{12.50} = \frac{12.50H}{12.50}$$
$$16 = H$$

The number of hours of labor required is 16.

Solutions to Chapter 12 "You Try It"

SECTION 12.1

You Try It 1
$$QT = QR + RS + ST$$
$$62 = 24 + RS + 17$$
$$62 = 41 + RS$$
$$62 - 41 = 41 - 41 + RS$$
$$21 = RS$$

You Try It 2 Let x represent the supplement of a $32°$ angle.

$$x + 32° = 180$$
$$x + 32° - 32° = 180° - 32°$$
$$x = 148°$$

$148°$ is the supplement of $32°$.

You Try It 3
$$\angle a + 68° = 118°$$
$$\angle a + 68° - 68° = 118° - 68°$$
$$\angle a = 50°$$

You Try It 4   In a right triangle, the two acute angles are complementary.

$$\angle A + \angle B = 90°$$
$$\angle A + 7° = 90°$$
$$\angle A + 7° - 7° = 90° - 7°$$
$$\angle A = 83°$$

The other angles measure 90° and 83°.

You Try It 5   The sum of the three angles of a triangle is 180°.

$$\angle A + \angle B + \angle C = 180°$$
$$\angle A + 62° + 45° = 180°$$
$$\angle A + 107° = 180°$$
$$\angle A = 73°$$

The measure of the other angle is 73°.

You Try It 6 $r = \dfrac{1}{2}d$

$r = \dfrac{1}{2}(8 \text{ in.}) = 4 \text{ in.}$

The radius is 4 in.

You Try It 7   Angles a and b are supplementary angles.

$$\angle a + \angle b = 180°$$
$$125° + \angle b = 180°$$
$$125° - 125° + \angle b = 180° - 125°$$
$$\angle b = 55°$$

You Try It 8 $\angle c$ and $\angle a$ are corresponding angles. Corresponding angles are equal.

$$\angle c = \angle a = 120°$$

$\angle b$ and $\angle c$ are supplementary angles.

$$\angle b + \angle c = 180°$$
$$\angle b + 120° = 180°$$
$$\angle b + 120° - 120° = 180° - 120°$$
$$\angle b = 60°$$

SECTION 12.2

You Try It 1 $P = 2L + 2W$
$$= 2(2 \text{ m}) + 2(0.85 \text{ m})$$
$$= 4 \text{ m} + 1.7 \text{ m}$$
$$= 5.7 \text{ m}$$

The perimeter of the rectangle is 5.7 m.

You Try It 2 $P = a + b + c$
$$= 12 \text{ cm} + 15 \text{ cm} + 18 \text{ cm}$$
$$= 45 \text{ cm}$$

The perimeter of the triangle is 45 cm.

You Try It 3 $C = \pi d$
$$\approx 3.14 \cdot 6 \text{ in.}$$
$$= 18.84 \text{ in.}$$

The circumference is approximately 18.84 in.

You Try It 4 $\begin{array}{ccc} \text{Perimeter} & \text{two} & \text{the} \\ \text{of} & \text{lengths} & \text{circumference} \\ \text{composite} = & \text{of a} & + \text{of a} \\ \text{figure} & \text{rectangle} & \text{circle} \end{array}$

$P = 2L + \pi d$
$$\approx 2(8 \text{ in.}) + 3.14(3 \text{ in.})$$
$$= 16 \text{ in.} + 9.42 \text{ in.}$$
$$= 25.42 \text{ in.}$$

The perimeter is approximately 25.42 in.

You Try It 5

Strategy   To find the perimeter, use the formula for the perimeter of a rectangle.

Solution $P = 2L + 2W$
$$= 2(11 \text{ in.}) + 2\left(8\dfrac{1}{2} \text{ in.}\right)$$
$$= 22 \text{ in.} + 17 \text{ in.}$$
$$= 39 \text{ in.}$$

The perimeter of the computer paper is 39 in.

You Try It 6

Strategy   To find the cost:
• Find the perimeter of the workbench.
• Multiply the perimeter by the perimeter cost of the stripping.

Solution $P = 2L + 2W$
$$= 2(3 \text{ m}) + 2(0.74 \text{ m})$$
$$= 6 \text{ m} + 1.48 \text{ m}$$
$$= 7.48 \text{ m}$$

$$\$1.76 \times 7.48 = \$13.1648$$

The cost is \$13.16.

SECTION 12.3

You Try It 1 $A = \frac{1}{2}bh = \frac{1}{2}(24 \text{ in.})(14 \text{ in.}) = 168 \text{ in}^2$

The area is 168 in².

You Try It 2

$A = \text{area of rectangle} - \text{area of triangle}$

$A = LW - \frac{1}{2}bh$

$= (10 \text{ in.} \times 6 \text{ in.}) - \left(\frac{1}{2} \times 6 \text{ in.} \times 4 \text{ in.}\right)$

$= 60 \text{ in}^2 - 12 \text{ in}^2$

$= 48 \text{ in}^2$

The area is 48 in².

You Try It 3

Strategy   To find the area of the room:
- Find the area in square feet.
- Convert to square yards.

Solution $A = LW$

$= 12 \text{ ft} \cdot 9 \text{ ft}$

$= 108 \text{ ft}^2$

$108 \text{ ft}^2 \times \frac{1 \text{ yd}^2}{9 \text{ ft}^2} = \frac{108}{9} \text{ yd}^2$

$= 12 \text{ yd}^2$

The area of the room is 12 yd².

SECTION 12.4

You Try It 1 $V = LWH$

$= (8 \text{ cm})(3.5 \text{ cm})(4 \text{ cm})$

$= 112 \text{ cm}^3$

The volume is 112 cm³.

You Try It 2 $V = s^3$

$= (5 \text{ cm})^3$

$= 125 \text{ cm}^3$

The volume is 125 cm³.

You Try It 3 $r = \frac{1}{2}d = \frac{1}{2}(14 \text{ in.}) = 7 \text{ in.}$

$V = \pi r^2 h$

$= \frac{22}{7}(7 \text{ in.})^2(15 \text{ in.})$

$= 2310 \text{ in}^3$

The volume is approximately 2310 in³.

You Try It 4 $V = \frac{4}{3}\pi r^3$

$\approx \frac{4}{3}(3.14)(3 \text{ m})^3$

$= 113.04 \text{ m}^3$

The volume is approximately 113.04 m³.

You Try It 5 $V = \text{volume of rectangular solid}$
$\qquad\qquad + \text{volume of cylinder}$

$V = LWH + \pi r^2 h$

$\approx (1.5 \text{ m})(0.4 \text{ m})(0.4 \text{ m}) + 3.14(0.8 \text{ m})^2(0.2 \text{ m})$

$= 0.24 \text{ m}^3 + 0.40192 \text{ m}^3$

$= 0.64192 \text{ m}^3$

The volume is approximately 0.64192 m³.

You Try It 6 $V = \text{volume of rectangular solid}$
$\qquad\qquad + \frac{1}{2} \text{ the volume of cylinder}$

$V = LWH + \frac{1}{2}\pi r^2 h$

$\approx (24 \text{ in.})(6 \text{ in.})(4 \text{ in.}) + \frac{1}{2}(3.14)(3 \text{ in.})^2(24 \text{ in.})$

$= 576 \text{ in}^3 + 339.12 \text{ in}^3$

$= 915.12 \text{ in}^3$

The volume is approximately 915.12 in³.

You Try It 7

Strategy   To find the volume of the freezer, use the formula for the volume of a rectangular solid.

Solution $V = LWH$

$= (7 \text{ ft})(2.5 \text{ ft})(3 \text{ ft})$

$= 52.5 \text{ ft}^3$

The volume of the freezer is 52.5 ft³.

You Try It 8

Strategy   To find the volume of the channel iron, add the volumes of the three rectangular solids.

Solution

$V = 2LWH + LWH$

$= 2(10 \text{ ft})(0.5 \text{ ft})(0.3 \text{ ft}) + (10 \text{ ft})(0.2 \text{ ft})(0.2 \text{ ft})$

$= 3 \text{ ft}^3 + 0.4 \text{ ft}^3$

$= 3.4 \text{ ft}^3$

The volume of the channel iron is 3.4 ft³.

SECTION 12.5

You Try It 1 $\sqrt{16} = 4$
$\sqrt{169} = 13$

You Try It 2 $\sqrt{32} \approx 5.657$
$\sqrt{162} \approx 12.728$

You Try It 3   Hypotenuse $= \sqrt{(\text{leg})^2 + (\text{leg})^2}$
$= \sqrt{8^2 + 11^2}$
$= \sqrt{64 + 121}$
$= \sqrt{185}$
≈ 13.601

The hypotenuse is approximately 13.601 in.

You Try It 4   Leg $= \sqrt{(\text{hypotenuse})^2 - (\text{leg})^2}$
$= \sqrt{12^2 - 5^2}$
$= \sqrt{144 - 25}$
$= \sqrt{119}$
≈ 10.909

The length of the leg is approximately 10.909 ft.

You Try It 5

Strategy   To find the distance between the holes, use the Pythagorean Theorem. The hypotenuse is the distance between the holes. The length of each leg is given (3 cm and 8 cm).

Solution   Hypotenuse $= \sqrt{(\text{leg})^2 + (\text{leg})^2}$
$= \sqrt{3^2 + 8^2}$
$= \sqrt{9 + 64}$
$= \sqrt{73}$
≈ 8.544

The distance is approximately 8.544 cm.

SECTION 12.6

You Try It 1 $\dfrac{4 \text{ cm}}{7 \text{ cm}} = \dfrac{4}{7}$

You Try It 2 $\dfrac{AB}{DE} = \dfrac{AC}{x}$

$\dfrac{7 \text{ cm}}{14 \text{ cm}} = \dfrac{3 \text{ cm}}{x}$

$7x = 14 \cdot 3 \text{ cm}$
$7x = 42 \text{ cm}$
$\dfrac{7x}{7} = \dfrac{42 \text{ cm}}{7}$
$x = 6 \text{ cm}$

Side DF is 6 cm.

You Try It 3 $AC = DF$, Angle $ACB =$ Angle DFE, but $CB \neq EF$ because $\angle CAB \neq \angle FDE$. Therefore the triangles are not congruent.

You Try It 4 $\dfrac{AC}{DF} = \dfrac{\text{height } CH}{\text{height } FG}$

$\dfrac{10 \text{ m}}{15 \text{ m}} = \dfrac{7 \text{ cm}}{h}$

$10h = 15 \cdot 7 \text{ m}$
$10h = 105 \text{ m}$
$\dfrac{10h}{10} = \dfrac{105 \text{ m}}{10}$
$h = 10.5 \text{ m}$

The height FG is 10.5 m.

You Try It 5

Strategy   To find the perimeter of triangle ABC:
- Solve a proportion to find the lengths of sides BC and AC.
- Use the formula Perimeter $=$ side $AB +$ side $BC +$ side AC.

Solution $\dfrac{BC}{EF} = \dfrac{AB}{DE}$

$\dfrac{BC}{10 \text{ in.}} = \dfrac{4 \text{ in.}}{8 \text{ in.}}$

$8BC = 10 \text{ in.} \cdot 4$
$8BC = 40 \text{ in.}$
$\dfrac{8BC}{8} = \dfrac{40 \text{ in.}}{8}$
$BC = 5 \text{ in.}$

$\dfrac{AC}{DF} = \dfrac{AB}{DE}$

$\dfrac{AC}{6 \text{ in.}} = \dfrac{4 \text{ in.}}{8 \text{ in.}}$

$8AC = 6 \text{ in.} \cdot 4$
$8AC = 24 \text{ in.}$
$\dfrac{8AC}{8} = \dfrac{24 \text{ in.}}{8}$
$AC = 3 \text{ in.}$

Perimeter $= 4 \text{ in.} + 5 \text{ in.} + 3 \text{ in.}$
$= 12 \text{ in.}$

The perimeter of triangle ABC is 12 in.

Answers to Chapter 1 Odd-Numbered Exercises

SECTION 1.1

1. [number line: 0 1 2 3 4 5 6 7 8 9 10 11 12 with point at 3] **3.** [number line: 0 1 2 3 4 5 6 7 8 9 10 11 12 with point at 9] **5.** $37 < 49$ **7.** $101 > 87$
9. $245 > 158$ **11.** $0 < 45$ **13.** $815 < 928$ **15.** Three thousand seven hundred ninety
17. Fifty-eight thousand four hundred seventy three **19.** Four hundred ninety-eight thousand five hundred twelve
21. Six million eight hundred forty-two thousand seven hundred fifteen **23.** 357 **25.** 63,780 **27.** 7,024,709
29. $6000 + 200 + 90 + 5$ **31.** $400,000 + 50,000 + 3000 + 900 + 20 + 1$ **33.** $300,000 + 1000 + 800 + 9$
35. $3,000,000 + 600 + 40 + 2$ **37.** 850 **39.** 4000 **41.** 53,000 **43.** 250,000 **45.** 999; 10,000
47. No. Round 3846 to the nearest hundred.

SECTION 1.2

1. 28 **3.** 125 **5.** 102 **7.** 154 **9.** 1489 **11.** 828 **13.** 1584 **15.** 1219 **17.** 102,317 **19.** 79,326
21. 1804 **23.** 1579 **25.** 19,740 **27.** 7420 **29.** 120,570 **31.** 207,453 **33.** 24,218 **35.** 11,974
37. 9323 **39.** 77,139 **41.** 14,383 **43.** 9473 **45.** 33,247 **47.** 5058 **49.** 1992 **51.** 68,263
53. Est.: 17,700 **55.** Est.: 2900 **57.** Est.: 101,000 **59.** Est.: 158,000 **61.** Est.: 260,000 **63.** Est.: 940,000
  Cal.: 17,754   Cal.: 2872   Cal.: 101,712   Cal.: 158,763   Cal.: 261,595   Cal.: 946,718
65. Est.: 33,000,000 **67.** Est.: 34,000,000 **69.** The total amount of trade with the United States was $603 billion.
  Cal.: 32,691,621   Cal.: 34,420,922
71. The total number of yards gained by passing was 307. **73.** The total income from the five Disney productions was
$900,600,000 **75.** Yes, the total income from the two productions with the lowest box-office incomes does exceed the
income from *Aladdin*. **77a.** 1285 miles will be driven. **b.** The odometer will read 69,977 miles. **79.** The total
average amount for Americans ages 16 to 34 in checking accounts, savings accounts, and U.S. Savings Bonds is $1796.
81. The sum of the average amounts invested in home equity and retirement is greater for all Americans than that same sum
for Americans between the ages of 16 and 34. **83.** 11 different sums **85.** No. $0 + 0 = 0$ **87.** 10 numbers

SECTION 1.3

1. 4 **3.** 4 **5.** 10 **7.** 4 **9.** 9 **11.** 22 **13.** 60 **15.** 66 **17.** 31 **19.** 901 **21.** 791 **23.** 1125
25. 3131 **27.** 47 **29.** 925 **31.** 4561 **33.** 3205 **35.** 1222 **37.** 3021 **39.** 3022 **41.** 3040
43. 212 **45.** 60,245 **47.** 65 **49.** 17 **51.** 23 **53.** 456 **55.** 57 **57.** 375 **59.** 3139 **61.** 3621
63. 738 **65.** 3545 **67.** 749 **69.** 5343 **71.** 66,463 **73.** 16,590 **75.** 52,404 **77.** 38,777 **79.** 4638
81. 3612 **83.** 2913 **85.** 2583 **87.** 5268 **89.** 71,767 **91.** 11,239 **93.** 8482 **95.** 625 **97.** 76,725
99. Est.: 30,000 **101.** Est.: 40,000 **103.** Est.: 100,000
  Cal.: 29,837   Cal.: 36,668   Cal.: 101,998
105. Sam saved $2479 off the sticker price. **107.** The amount that remains to be paid is $4775. **109.** The national debt
increased $220,000,000,000 in one year. **111.** Florida has lost 9,286,713 acres of wetlands over the past 200 years.
113. The Chevrolet with all the options will cost more. **115.** It will take 27 more months to withdraw principal and
interest in 2012 than it did in 1992. **117.** Answers will vary.

SECTION 1.4

1. 12 **3.** 35 **5.** 25 **7.** 0 **9.** 72 **11.** 198 **13.** 335 **15.** 2492 **17.** 5463 **19.** 4200 **21.** 6327
23. 1896 **25.** 5056 **27.** 1685 **29.** 46,963 **31.** 59,976 **33.** 19,120 **35.** 19,790 **37.** 108
39. 3664 **41.** 20,036 **43.** 71,656 **45.** 432 **47.** 1944 **49.** 41,832 **51.** 43,620 **53.** 335,195
55. 594,625 **57.** 321,696 **59.** 342,171 **61.** 279,220 **63.** 191,800 **65.** 463,712 **67.** 180,621
69. 478,800 **71.** 158,422 **73.** 4,696,714 **75.** 5,542,452 **77.** 51,443 **79.** 18,834 **81.** 260,178
83. 315,109,895 **85.** Est.: 450,000 **87.** Est.: 4,200,000 **89.** Est.: 6,300,000 **91.** Est.: 18,000,000
    Cal.: 440,076   Cal.: 4,315,403   Cal.: 6,491,166   Cal.: 18,728,744
93. Est.: 54,000,000 **95.** Est.: 56,000,000 **97.** The plane used 5190 gallons of fuel on a 6-hour flight.
  Cal.: 57,691,192   Cal.: 56,324,340

99. The machine can fill and cap 168,000 bottles in 40 hours.   **101.** The estimated attendance for the 11 home games is 300,000. The total attendance for the 15 games is 397,159.   **103.** The lighting designer can save $84.   **105.** The total wages of the four plumbers are $1380.   **107a.** Always true   **b.** Always true   **c.** Sometimes true; c is a true statement except in the cases described in parts a and b.   **109.** 17,112 acres are deforested each day. 513,360 acres are deforested each month. 6,245,880 acres are deforested each year.   **111.** Answers will vary.

SECTION 1.5

1. 2   **3.** 6   **5.** 7   **7.** 16   **9.** 210   **11.** 44   **13.** 703   **15.** 910   **17.** 21,560   **19.** 3580   **21.** 482   **23.** 1075   **25.** 2 rl   **27.** 5 r2   **29.** 13 rl   **31.** 10 r3   **33.** 90 r2   **35.** 230 rl   **37.** 204 r3   **39.** 1347 r3   **41.** 1720 r2   **43.** 409 r2   **45.** 6214 r2   **47.** 8708 r2   **49.** 1080 r2   **51.** 4200   **53.** 19,600   **55.** 1 r38   **57.** 1 r26   **59.** 21 r21   **61.** 30 r22   **63.** 5 r40   **65.** 9 r17   **67.** 200 r21   **69.** 303 r1   **71.** 67 r13   **73.** 176 r13   **75.** 1086 r7   **77.** 403   **79.** 12 r456   **81.** 4 r160   **83.** 160 r27   **85.** 1669 r14   **87.** 7950   **89.** Est.: 2000 Cal.: 2225   **91.** Est.: 10,000 Cal.: 11,016   **93.** Est.: 30,000 Cal.: 26,656   **95.** Est.: 500 Cal.: 504   **97.** Est.: 500 Cal.: 541   **99.** Est.: 20,000 Cal.: 20,621   **101.** The average number of miles traveled on each gallon of gas was 27.   **103.** Belle receives $156,250 for each home run.   **105.** The number of bytes of information on 1 disk is 368,640.   **107. a.** The remaining balance to be paid is $8976.   **b.** The monthly payment is $187.   **109.** Lemieux's hourly wage is $5660.   **111.** Belle's average salary per game is $61,728. Aikman's average salary per game is $335,625. Aikman's per game salary is approximately 5 times Belle's per game salary.   **113.** The smallest four-digit palindromic number is 2112.   **115a.** False; division by zero is not allowed.   **b.** False; division by zero is not allowed.   **c.** True

SECTION 1.6

1. 2^3 **3.** $6^3 \cdot 7^4$ **5.** $2^3 \cdot 3^3$ **7.** $5 \cdot 7^5$ **9.** $3^3 \cdot 6^4$ **11.** $3^3 \cdot 5 \cdot 9^3$ **13.** 8   **15.** 400   **17.** 900   **19.** 972   **21.** 120   **23.** 360   **25.** 0   **27.** 90,000   **29.** 540   **31.** 4050   **33.** 11,025   **35.** 25,920   **37.** 4,320,000   **39.** 5   **41.** 10   **43.** 47   **45.** 8   **47.** 5   **49.** 8   **51.** 6   **53.** 53   **55.** 44   **57.** 19   **59.** 67   **61.** 168   **63.** 27   **65.** 14   **67.** 10   **69.** 9   **71.** 12   **73.** 32   **75.** 39   **77.** 1024   **79.** Yes. Answers will vary.

SECTION 1.7

1. 1, 2, 4   **3.** 1, 2, 5, 10   **5.** 1, 7   **7.** 1, 3, 9   **9.** 1, 13   **11.** 1, 2, 3, 6, 9, 18   **13.** 1, 2, 4, 7, 8, 14, 28, 56   **15.** 1, 3, 5, 9, 15, 45   **17.** 1, 29   **19.** 1, 2, 11, 22   **21.** 1, 2, 4, 13, 26, 52   **23.** 1, 2, 41, 82   **25.** 1, 3, 19, 57   **27.** 1, 2, 3, 4, 6, 8, 12, 16, 24, 48   **29.** 1, 5, 19, 95   **31.** 1, 2, 3, 6, 9, 18, 27, 54   **33.** 1, 2, 3, 6, 11, 22, 33, 66   **35.** 1, 2, 4, 5, 8, 10, 16, 20, 40, 80   **37.** 1, 2, 3, 4, 6, 8, 12, 16, 24, 32, 48, 96   **39.** 1, 2, 3, 5, 6, 9, 10, 15, 18, 30, 45, 90   **41.** $2 \cdot 3$ **43.** Prime   **45.** $2 \cdot 2 \cdot 2 \cdot 3$ **47.** $3 \cdot 3 \cdot 3$ **49.** $2 \cdot 2 \cdot 3 \cdot 3$ **51.** Prime   **53.** $2 \cdot 3 \cdot 3 \cdot 5$ **55.** $5 \cdot 23$ **57.** $2 \cdot 3 \cdot 3$ **59.** $2 \cdot 2 \cdot 7$ **61.** Prime   **63.** $2 \cdot 31$ **65.** $2 \cdot 11$ **67.** Prime   **69.** $2 \cdot 3 \cdot 11$ **71.** $2 \cdot 37$ **73.** Prime   **75.** $5 \cdot 11$ **77.** $2 \cdot 2 \cdot 2 \cdot 3 \cdot 5$ **79.** $2 \cdot 2 \cdot 2 \cdot 2 \cdot 2 \cdot 5$ **81.** $2 \cdot 2 \cdot 2 \cdot 3 \cdot 3 \cdot 3$ **83.** $5 \cdot 5 \cdot 5 \cdot 5$ **85.** 3 and 5, 5 and 7, 11 and 13. Other answers are possible.   **87.** Answers will vary.

CHAPTER REVIEW

1. 600 [1.6A]   **2.** $10,000 + 300 + 20 + 7$ [1.1C]   **3.** 1, 2, 3, 6, 9, 18 [1.7A]   **4.** 12,493 [1.2A]   **5.** 1749 [1.3B]   **6.** 2135 [1.5A]   **7.** $101 > 87$ [1.1A]   **8.** $5^2 \cdot 7^5$ [1.6A]   **9.** 619,833 [1.4B]   **10.** 5409 [1.3B]   **11.** 1081 [1.2A]   **12.** 2 [1.6B]   **13.** $2 \cdot 3 \cdot 7$ [1.7B]   **14.** Two hundred seventy-six thousand fifty-seven [1.1B]   **15.** 1306 r59 [1.5C]   **16.** 2,011,044 [1.1B]   **17.** 1, 2, 3, 5, 6, 10, 15, 30 [1.7A]   **18.** 17 [1.6B]   **19.** 32 [1.6B]   **20.** $2 \cdot 2 \cdot 2 \cdot 3 \cdot 3$ [1.7B]   **21.** $2^4 \cdot 5^3$ [1.6A]   **22.** 22,761 [1.4B]   **23.** Vincent's total pay for the last week was $384. [1.4C]   **24.** He drove 27 miles per gallon of gasoline. [1.5D]   **25.** The monthly car payment is $155. [1.5D]   **26.** The total income from commissions was $2567. [1.2B]   **27.** The total amount deposited was $301. The new checking account balance is $817. [1.2B]   **28.** The total of the car payments is $1476. [1.4C]   **29.** A U.S. company spends $1985 per person more than an Italian company. [1.3C]   **30.** A U.S. company spends $563 more for business travel and entertainment. [1.3C]   **31.** No [1.3C]

CHAPTER TEST

1. 432 [1.6A]   **2.** Two hundred seven thousand sixty-eight [1.1B]   **3.** 9333 [1.3A]   **4.** 1, 2, 4, 5, 10, 20 [1.7A]
5. 6,854,144 [1.4B]   **6.** 9 [1.6B]   **7.** 900,000 + 6000 + 300 + 70 + 8 [1.1C]   **8.** 75,000 [1.1D]
9. 1121 r27 [1.5C]   **10.** $3^3 \cdot 7^2$ [1.6A]   **11.** 135,915 [1.2A]   **12.** $2 \cdot 2 \cdot 3 \cdot 7$ [1.7B]   **13.** 4 [1.6B]
14. 726,104 [1.4A]   **15.** 1,204,006 [1.1B]   **16.** 8710 r2 [1.5B]   **17.** 21 > 19 [1.1A]   **18.** 703 [1.5A]
19. 96,798 [1.2A]   **20.** 19,922 [1.3B]   **21.** The salary difference between mechanical engineers and industrial
engineers is $2120. [1.3C]   **22.** The average salary of the degree candidates is $39,788. [1.5D]   **23.** The farmer
needed 3000 boxes. [1.5D]   **24.** The investor will receive $2844 over 12 months. [1.4C]   **25a.** They drove
855 miles. [1.2B]   **b.** The odometer reading was 48,481. [1.2B]

Answers to Chapter 2 Odd-Numbered Exercises

SECTION 2.1

1. 40   **3.** 24   **5.** 30   **7.** 12   **9.** 24   **11.** 60   **13.** 56   **15.** 9   **17.** 32   **19.** 36   **21.** 660
23. 9384   **25.** 24   **27.** 30   **29.** 24   **31.** 576   **33.** 1680   **35.** 1   **37.** 3   **39.** 5   **41.** 25   **43.** 1
45. 4   **47.** 4   **49.** 6   **51.** 4   **53.** 1   **55.** 7   **57.** 5   **59.** 8   **61.** 1   **63.** 25   **65.** 7   **67.** 8
69. Numbers with no common factors except the factor 1. 4, 5; 8, 9; 16, 21 (Answers will vary.)   **71.** The LCM of 2 and 3
is 6, of 5 and 7 is 35, of 11 and 19 is 209. The LCM of two prime numbers is the product of the two numbers. The LCM of
three prime numbers is the product of the three numbers.   **73.** Yes. Each number contains all the factors of the GCF.
75. 44 solar years; 73 ritual years

SECTION 2.2

1. $\frac{3}{4}$ **3.** $\frac{7}{8}$ **5.** $1\frac{1}{2}$ **7.** $2\frac{5}{8}$ **9.** $3\frac{3}{5}$ **11.** $\frac{5}{4}$ **13.** $\frac{8}{3}$ **15.** $\frac{28}{8}$ **17.** ⊘   **19.** ⊘⊘

21. ⊘⊘   **23.** $2\frac{3}{4}$ **25.** 5   **27.** $1\frac{1}{8}$ **29.** $2\frac{3}{10}$ **31.** 3   **33.** $1\frac{1}{7}$ **35.** $2\frac{1}{3}$ **37.** 16   **39.** $2\frac{1}{8}$

41. $2\frac{2}{5}$ **43.** 1   **45.** 9   **47.** $\frac{7}{3}$ **49.** $\frac{13}{2}$ **51.** $\frac{41}{6}$ **53.** $\frac{37}{4}$ **55.** $\frac{21}{2}$ **57.** $\frac{73}{9}$ **59.** $\frac{58}{11}$ **61.** $\frac{21}{8}$

63. $\frac{13}{8}$ **65.** $\frac{100}{9}$ **67.** $\frac{27}{8}$ **69.** $\frac{85}{13}$ **71.** $\frac{8}{50}; \frac{8}{50}$ **73.** Answers will vary.

SECTION 2.3

1. $\frac{5}{10}$ **3.** $\frac{9}{48}$ **5.** $\frac{12}{32}$ **7.** $\frac{9}{51}$ **9.** $\frac{12}{16}$ **11.** $\frac{27}{9}$ **13.** $\frac{20}{60}$ **15.** $\frac{44}{60}$ **17.** $\frac{12}{18}$ **19.** $\frac{35}{49}$ **21.** $\frac{10}{18}$

23. $\frac{21}{3}$ **25.** $\frac{35}{45}$ **27.** $\frac{60}{64}$ **29.** $\frac{21}{98}$ **31.** $\frac{30}{48}$ **33.** $\frac{15}{42}$ **35.** $\frac{102}{144}$ **37.** $\frac{153}{408}$ **39.** $\frac{340}{800}$ **41.** $\frac{1}{3}$ **43.** $\frac{1}{2}$

45. $\frac{1}{6}$ **47.** $1\frac{1}{9}$ **49.** 0   **51.** $\frac{9}{22}$ **53.** 3   **55.** $\frac{4}{21}$ **57.** $\frac{12}{35}$ **59.** $\frac{7}{11}$ **61.** $1\frac{1}{3}$ **63.** $\frac{3}{5}$ **65.** $\frac{1}{11}$

67. 4   **69.** $\frac{1}{3}$ **71.** $\frac{3}{5}$ **73.** $2\frac{1}{4}$ **75.** $\frac{1}{5}$ **77.** Answers will vary. Examples are $\frac{12}{4}, \frac{15}{5}, \frac{21}{7}, \frac{24}{8}$, and $\frac{30}{10}$.
79. Answers will vary.

SECTION 2.4

1. $\frac{3}{7}$ **3.** 1   **5.** $1\frac{4}{11}$ **7.** $3\frac{2}{5}$ **9.** $2\frac{4}{5}$ **11.** $2\frac{1}{4}$ **13.** $1\frac{3}{8}$ **15.** $1\frac{7}{15}$ **17.** $\frac{15}{16}$ **19.** $1\frac{4}{11}$ **21.** 1

23. $1\frac{7}{8}$ **25.** $1\frac{1}{6}$ **27.** $\frac{13}{14}$ **29.** $\frac{53}{60}$ **31.** $1\frac{1}{56}$ **33.** $\frac{23}{60}$ **35.** $\frac{56}{57}$ **37.** $1\frac{17}{18}$ **39.** $1\frac{11}{48}$ **41.** $1\frac{9}{20}$

43. $1\frac{109}{180}$ **45.** $1\frac{91}{144}$ **47.** $2\frac{5}{72}$ **49.** $\frac{39}{40}$ **51.** $1\frac{19}{24}$ **53.** $1\frac{65}{72}$ **55.** $3\frac{2}{3}$ **57.** $10\frac{1}{12}$ **59.** $9\frac{2}{7}$ **61.** $6\frac{7}{40}$

63. $9\frac{47}{48}$ **65.** $8\frac{22}{39}$ **67.** $16\frac{29}{120}$ **69.** $24\frac{29}{40}$ **71.** $33\frac{7}{24}$ **73.** $10\frac{5}{36}$ **75.** $10\frac{5}{12}$ **77.** $14\frac{73}{90}$ **79.** $10\frac{13}{48}$

81. $42\frac{13}{54}$ **83.** $8\frac{1}{36}$ **85.** $14\frac{1}{12}$ **87.** $9\frac{37}{72}$ **89.** The fractional amount of income spent on these three items is $\frac{17}{24}$.

91. The value of the stock after the increase is $\$84\frac{3}{4}$.   **93.** The length of the shaft is $8\frac{9}{16}$ inches.   **95a.** The total number of overtime hours worked was 12.   **b.** The overtime pay is $264.   **97.** The value of the stock at the end of the three months is $\$30\frac{5}{8}$.   **99.** Answers will vary.   **101.** No. These activities account for only 22 hours.

SECTION 2.5

1. $\frac{2}{17}$ **3.** $\frac{1}{3}$ **5.** $\frac{1}{10}$ **7.** $\frac{5}{13}$ **9.** $\frac{1}{3}$ **11.** $\frac{4}{7}$ **13.** $\frac{1}{4}$ **15.** $\frac{9}{23}$ **17.** $\frac{1}{4}$ **19.** $\frac{1}{2}$ **21.** $\frac{19}{56}$ **23.** $\frac{1}{2}$

25. $\frac{11}{60}$ **27.** $\frac{15}{56}$ **29.** $\frac{37}{51}$ **31.** $\frac{17}{70}$ **33.** $\frac{49}{120}$ **35.** $\frac{8}{45}$ **37.** $\frac{11}{21}$ **39.** $\frac{23}{60}$ **41.** $\frac{1}{18}$ **43.** $5\frac{1}{5}$ **45.** $10\frac{9}{17}$

47. $4\frac{7}{8}$ **49.** $\frac{16}{21}$ **51.** $5\frac{1}{2}$ **53.** $5\frac{4}{7}$ **55.** $7\frac{5}{24}$ **57.** $48\frac{31}{70}$ **59.** $85\frac{2}{9}$ **61.** $9\frac{5}{13}$ **63.** $15\frac{11}{20}$ **65.** $4\frac{23}{24}$

67. $2\frac{11}{15}$ **69.** $9\frac{1}{2}$ inches.   **71.** Meyfarth jumped $9\frac{3}{8}$ inches farther than Coachman. Kostadinova jumped $5\frac{1}{4}$ inches farther than Meyfarth.   **73a.** It is $7\frac{17}{24}$ miles to the second checkpoint.   **b.** It is $4\frac{7}{24}$ miles from the second checkpoint to the finish line.   **75a.** Yes.   **b.** The wrestler must lose $3\frac{1}{4}$ pounds in the third week.   **77.** The difference in price is $\$45\frac{5}{8}$.   **79.** $2\frac{5}{6}$ **81.**

$\frac{3}{8}$	$\frac{3}{4}$	$\frac{3}{4}$
1	$\frac{5}{8}$	$\frac{1}{4}$
$\frac{1}{2}$	$\frac{1}{2}$	$\frac{7}{8}$

SECTION 2.6

1. $\frac{7}{12}$ **3.** $\frac{7}{48}$ **5.** $\frac{1}{48}$ **7.** $\frac{11}{14}$ **9.** $\frac{1}{7}$ **11.** $\frac{1}{8}$ **13.** 6 **15.** $\frac{5}{12}$ **17.** 6 **19.** $\frac{2}{3}$ **21.** $\frac{3}{16}$ **23.** $\frac{3}{80}$

25. 10 **27.** $\frac{1}{15}$ **29.** $\frac{2}{3}$ **31.** $\frac{7}{26}$ **33.** 4 **35.** $\frac{100}{357}$ **37.** $\frac{5}{24}$ **39.** $\frac{1}{12}$ **41.** $\frac{4}{15}$ **43.** $1\frac{1}{2}$ **45.** 4

47. $\frac{4}{9}$ **49.** $\frac{1}{2}$ **51.** $16\frac{1}{2}$ **53.** 10 **55.** $6\frac{3}{7}$ **57.** $18\frac{1}{3}$ **59.** $1\frac{5}{7}$ **61.** $3\frac{1}{2}$ **63.** $25\frac{5}{8}$ **65.** $1\frac{11}{16}$ **67.** 16

69. 3 **71.** $8\frac{37}{40}$ **73.** $6\frac{19}{28}$ **75.** $7\frac{2}{5}$ **77.** 16 **79.** $32\frac{4}{5}$ **81.** $28\frac{1}{2}$ **83.** 9 **85.** $\frac{5}{8}$ **87.** $3\frac{1}{40}$

89. The salmon cost $22.   **91.** The Honda Civic can travel 361 miles on $9\frac{1}{2}$ gallons of gasoline.   **93.** 535,000 gallons of propellant is used before burnout.   **95a.** 30 students passed the chemistry course.   **b.** 6 of the chemistry students received an A grade.   **97.** $267,000 of the monthly income remained.   **99.** The weight is $54\frac{19}{36}$ pounds.   **101.** $\frac{3}{5}$ of the park is heavily wooded.   **103.** $\frac{1}{2}$ **105.** Yes   **107.** *A*

SECTION 2.7

1. $\frac{5}{6}$ **3.** 1 **5.** 0 **7.** $\frac{1}{2}$ **9.** $2\frac{73}{256}$ **11.** $1\frac{1}{9}$ **13.** $\frac{1}{6}$ **15.** $\frac{7}{10}$ **17.** 2 **19.** 2 **21.** $\frac{1}{6}$ **23.** 6

25. $\frac{1}{15}$ **27.** 2 **29.** $2\frac{1}{2}$ **31.** 3 **33.** 6 **35.** $\frac{1}{2}$ **37.** $1\frac{1}{6}$ **39.** $3\frac{1}{3}$ **41.** $\frac{1}{30}$ **43.** $1\frac{4}{5}$ **45.** 13

47. $\dfrac{25}{288}$ **49.** 3   **51.** $\dfrac{1}{5}$ **53.** $\dfrac{11}{28}$ **55.** $\dfrac{5}{86}$ **57.** 120   **59.** $\dfrac{11}{40}$ **61.** $\dfrac{33}{40}$ **63.** $4\dfrac{4}{9}$ **65.** $\dfrac{13}{32}$ **67.** $10\dfrac{2}{3}$

69. $9\dfrac{39}{40}$ **71.** $\dfrac{12}{53}$ **73.** $4\dfrac{62}{191}$ **75.** 68   **77.** $8\dfrac{2}{7}$ **79.** $3\dfrac{13}{49}$ **81.** 4   **83.** $1\dfrac{3}{5}$ **85.** $\dfrac{9}{34}$ **87.** The package

contains twelve $1\dfrac{1}{3}$-ounce servings.   **89.** Each acre cost \$24,000.   **91.** The nut makes 12 turns to move $1\dfrac{7}{8}$ inches.

93a. The total weight of the fat and bone is $1\dfrac{5}{12}$ pounds.   **b.** There will be 28 servings.   **95a.** The actual length of wall

a is $12\dfrac{1}{2}$ feet.   **b.** The actual length of wall b is 18 feet.   **c.** The actual length of wall c is $15\dfrac{3}{4}$ feet.   **97.** No. For

example, $4 \div \dfrac{1}{2} = 8$. Answers will vary.   **99.** Each column is $2\dfrac{1}{4}$ inches wide.   **101a.** $2\dfrac{1}{2}$ **b.** $\dfrac{2}{3}$ **c.** $\dfrac{1}{3}$ **d.** $2\dfrac{1}{2}$

SECTION 2.8

1. $\dfrac{11}{40} < \dfrac{19}{40}$ **3.** $\dfrac{2}{3} < \dfrac{5}{7}$ **5.** $\dfrac{5}{8} > \dfrac{7}{12}$ **7.** $\dfrac{7}{9} < \dfrac{11}{12}$ **9.** $\dfrac{13}{14} > \dfrac{19}{21}$ **11.** $\dfrac{7}{24} < \dfrac{11}{30}$ **13.** $\dfrac{9}{64}$ **15.** $\dfrac{8}{729}$ **17.** $\dfrac{1}{24}$

19. $\dfrac{8}{245}$ **21.** $\dfrac{1}{121}$ **23.** $\dfrac{81}{625}$ **25.** $\dfrac{7}{36}$ **27.** $\dfrac{27}{49}$ **29.** $\dfrac{16}{75}$ **31.** $\dfrac{5}{6}$ **33.** $1\dfrac{5}{12}$ **35.** $1\dfrac{1}{5}$ **37.** $\dfrac{7}{48}$ **39.** $\dfrac{29}{36}$

41. $\dfrac{55}{72}$ **43.** $\dfrac{35}{54}$ **45.** 2   **47.** $\dfrac{9}{19}$ **49.** $\dfrac{7}{32}$ **51.** $\dfrac{64}{75}$ **53.** Answers will vary.

CHAPTER REVIEW

1. $\dfrac{2}{3}$ [2.3B]   **2.** $\dfrac{5}{16}$ [2.8B]   **3.** $\dfrac{13}{4}$ [2.2A]   **4.** $1\dfrac{13}{18}$ [2.4B]   **5.** $\dfrac{11}{18} < \dfrac{17}{24}$ [2.8A]   **6.** $14\dfrac{19}{42}$ [2.5C]

7. $\dfrac{5}{36}$ [2.8C]   **8.** $9\dfrac{1}{24}$ [2.6B]   **9.** 2 [2.7B]   **10.** $\dfrac{25}{48}$ [2.5B]   **11.** $3\dfrac{1}{3}$ [2.7B]   **12.** 4 [2.1B]

13. $\dfrac{24}{36}$ [2.3A]   **14.** $\dfrac{3}{4}$ [2.7A]   **15.** $\dfrac{32}{44}$ [2.3A]   **16.** $16\dfrac{1}{2}$ [2.6B]   **17.** 36 [2.1A]   **18.** $\dfrac{4}{11}$ [2.3B]

19. $1\dfrac{1}{8}$ [2.4A]   **20.** $10\dfrac{1}{8}$ [2.5C]   **21.** $18\dfrac{13}{54}$ [2.4C]   **22.** 5 [2.1B]   **23.** $3\dfrac{2}{5}$ [2.2B]   **24.** $\dfrac{1}{15}$ [2.8C]

25. $5\dfrac{7}{8}$ [2.4C]   **26.** 54 [2.1A]   **27.** $\dfrac{1}{3}$ [2.5A]   **28.** $\dfrac{19}{7}$ [2.2B]   **29.** 2 [2.7A]   **30.** $\dfrac{1}{15}$ [2.6A]

31. $\dfrac{1}{8}$ [2.6A]   **32.** $1\dfrac{7}{8}$ [2.2A]   **33.** The total rainfall was $21\dfrac{7}{24}$ inches. [2.4D]   **34.** Each acre cost \$36,000. [2.7C]

35. The second checkpoint is $4\dfrac{3}{4}$ miles from the finish line. [2.5D]   **36.** The car can travel 243 miles. [2.6C]

CHAPTER TEST

1. $\dfrac{4}{9}$ [2.6A]   **2.** 8 [2.1B]   **3.** $1\dfrac{3}{7}$ [2.7A]   **4.** $\dfrac{7}{24}$ [2.8C]   **5.** $\dfrac{49}{5}$ [2.2B]   **6.** 8 [2.6B]   **7.** $\dfrac{5}{8}$ [2.3B]

8. $\dfrac{3}{8} < \dfrac{5}{12}$ [2.8A]   **9.** $\dfrac{5}{6}$ [2.8C]   **10.** 120 [2.1A]   **11.** $\dfrac{1}{4}$ [2.5A]   **12.** $3\dfrac{3}{5}$ [2.2B]   **13.** $2\dfrac{2}{19}$ [2.7B]

14. $\dfrac{45}{72}$ [2.3A]   **15.** $1\dfrac{61}{90}$ [2.4B]   **16.** $13\dfrac{81}{88}$ [2.5C]   **17.** $\dfrac{7}{48}$ [2.5B]   **18.** $\dfrac{1}{6}$ [2.8B]   **19.** $1\dfrac{11}{12}$ [2.4A]

20. $22\dfrac{4}{15}$ [2.4C]   **21.** $\dfrac{11}{4}$ [2.2A]   **22.** The electrician's total earnings are \$420. [2.6C]   **23.** There were 11 lots

available for sale. [2.7C]   **24.** The value of one share is $27\dfrac{7}{8}$. [2.5D]   **25.** The total rainfall was $21\dfrac{11}{24}$ inches. [2.4D]

CUMULATIVE REVIEW

1. 290,000 [1.1D]   **2.** 291,278 [1.3B]   **3.** 73,154 [1.4B]   **4.** 540 r12 [1.5C]   **5.** 1 [1.6B]

6. $2 \cdot 2 \cdot 11$ [1.7B]   **7.** 210 [2.1A]   **8.** 20 [2.1B]   **9.** $\dfrac{23}{3}$ [2.2B]   **10.** $6\dfrac{1}{4}$ [2.2B]   **11.** $\dfrac{15}{48}$ [2.3A]

12. $\frac{2}{5}$ [2.3B]   **13.** $1\frac{7}{48}$ [2.4B]   **14.** $14\frac{11}{48}$ [2.4C]   **15.** $\frac{13}{24}$ [2.5B]   **16.** $1\frac{7}{9}$ [2.5C]   **17.** $\frac{7}{20}$ [2.6A]

18. $7\frac{1}{2}$ [2.6B]   **19.** $1\frac{1}{20}$ [2.7A]   **20.** $2\frac{5}{8}$ [2.7B]   **21.** $\frac{1}{9}$ [2.8B]   **22.** $5\frac{5}{24}$ [2.8C]

23. There is \$862 in the checking account at the end of the week. [1.3C]   **24.** The total income is \$705. [1.4C]

25. The total weight is $12\frac{1}{24}$ pounds. [2.4D]   **26.** The length of the remaining piece is $4\frac{17}{24}$ feet. [2.5D]

27. The car traveled 225 miles. [2.6C]   **28.** 25 parcels can be sold from the remaining land. [2.7C]

Answers to Chapter 3 Odd-Numbered Exercises

SECTION 3.1

1. Twenty-seven hundredths   **3.** One and five thousandths   **5.** Thirty-six and four tenths   **7.** Thirty-five hundred-thousandths   **9.** Ten and seven thousandths   **11.** Fifty-two and ninety-five hundred-thousandths   **13.** Two hundred ninety-three ten-thousandths   **15.** Six and three hundred twenty-four thousandths   **17.** Two hundred seventy-six and three thousand two hundred ninety-seven ten-thousandths   **19.** Two hundred sixteen and seven hundred twenty-nine ten-thousandths   **21.** Four thousand six hundred twenty-five and three hundred seventy-nine ten-thousandths   **23.** One and one hundred-thousandth   **25.** 0.762   **27.** 0.000062   **29.** 8.0304   **31.** 304.07   **33.** 362.048   **35.** 3048.2002   **37.** 7.4   **39.** 23.0   **41.** 22.68   **43.** 7.073   **45.** 62.009   **47.** 0.0123   **49.** 2.07924   **51.** 0.100975   **53.** Answers will vary.   **55a.** 5.5 and 6.4   **b.** 10.15 and 10.24

SECTION 3.2

1. 150.1065   **3.** 95.8446   **5.** 69.644   **7.** 92.883   **9.** 113.205   **11.** 0.69   **13.** 16.305   **15.** 110.7666   **17.** 104.4959   **19.** Est.: 234   Cal.: 234.192   **21.** Est.: 782   Cal.: 781.943   **23.** The length of the shaft is 5.65 inches.   **25.** The total amount of gas used is 47.8 gallons.   **27.** The amount in the checking account is \$3664.20.   **29.** The total number of television viewers is 366.2 million.   **31.** No, the customer does not have enough money.   **33.** No, the rope cannot be wrapped around the box.

SECTION 3.3

1. 5.627   **3.** 113.6427   **5.** 6.7098   **7.** 215.697   **9.** 53.8776   **11.** 72.7091   **13.** 4.685   **15** 10.0365   **17.** 0.7727   **19.** 3.273   **21.** 791.247   **23.** 547.951   **25.** 403.8557   **27.** 22.479   **29.** Est.: 600   Cal.: 590.25   **31.** Est.: 30   Cal.: 35.194   **33.** Est.: 3   Cal.: 2.74506   **35.** Est.: 7   Cal.: 7.14925   **37.** The missing dimension is 7.55 inches.   **39a.** The total amount of the checks is \$607.36.   **b.** Your new balance is \$422.38.   **41.** The rainfall was 0.86 inch below normal.   **43.** The difference in average speed was 40.124 mph.   **45.** \$167.61 would be saved by buying from Waterhouse Securities.

SECTION 3.4

1. 0.36   **3.** 0.30   **5.** 0.25   **7.** 0.45   **9.** 6.93   **11.** 1.84   **13.** 4.32   **15.** 0.74   **17.** 39.5   **19.** 2.72   **21.** 0.603   **23.** 0.096   **25.** 13.50   **27.** 79.80   **29.** 4.316   **31.** 1.794   **33.** 0.06   **35.** 0.072   **37.** 0.1323   **39.** 0.03568   **41.** 0.0784   **43.** 0.076   **45.** 34.48   **47.** 580.5   **49.** 20.148   **51.** 0.04255   **53.** 0.17686   **55.** 0.19803   **57.** 14.8657   **59.** 0.0006608   **61.** 53.9961   **63.** 0.536335   **65.** 0.429   **67.** 2.116   **69.** 0.476   **71.** 1.022   **73.** 37.96   **75.** 2.318   **77.** 3.2   **79** 6.5   **81.** 6285.6   **83.** 3200   **85.** 35,700   **87.** 6.3   **89.** 3.9   **91.** 49,000   **93.** 6.7   **95.** 0.012075   **97.** 0.0117796   **99.** 0.31004   **101.** 0.082845   **103.** 5.175   **105.** Est.: 90   Cal.: 91.2   **107.** Est.: 0.8   Cal.: 1.0472   **109.** Est.: 4.5   Cal.: 3.897   **111.** Est.: 12   Cal.: 11.2406   **113.** Est.: 0.32   Cal.: 0.371096   **115.** Est.: 30   Cal.: 31.8528

117. Est.: 2000   **119.** Est.: 0.00005   **121.** The cost to rent the car is $188.40.
Cal.: 1941.069459   Cal.: 0.000043512

123. The amount received from recycling is $14.06.   **125.** The broker's fee is $173.25.   **127a.** The amount of the payments is $4590.   **b.** The total cost of the car is $6590.   **129.** The total cost to rent the car is $64.20.
131. Grade 1 of steel costs $21.12, Grade 2 costs $29.84, and Grade 3 costs $201.66.   **133a.** The cost is $52.90.
b. The cost is $79.60.   **c.** The cost is $61.45.   **135.** The complete solution is in the Solutions Manual.   **137.** The total cost for labor is $1029.88.   **139.** Answers will vary.   **141.** $1.3 \times 2.31 = \dfrac{13}{10} \times \dfrac{231}{100} = \dfrac{3003}{1000} = 3.003$

SECTION 3.5

1. 0.82   **3.** 4.8   **5.** 89   **7.** 60   **9.** 84.3   **11.** 32.3   **13.** 5.06   **15.** 1.3   **17.** 0.11   **19.** 3.8   **21.** 6.3
23. 0.6   **25.** 2.5   **27.** 1.1   **29.** 130.6   **31.** 0.81   **33.** 42.40   **35.** 40.70   **37.** 0.46   **39.** 0.019
41. 0.087   **43.** 0.360   **45.** 0.103   **47.** 0.009   **49.** 1   **51.** 3   **53.** 1   **55.** 57   **57.** 0.407   **59.** 4.267
61. 0.01037   **63.** 0.008295   **65.** 0.82537   **67.** 0.032   **69.** 0.23627   **71.** 0.000053   **73.** 0.0018932
75. 18.42   **77.** 16.07   **79.** 0.0135   **81.** 0.023678   **83.** 0.112   **85.** Est.: 10   **87.** Est.: 1000
Cal.: 11.1632   Cal.: 884.0909

89. Est.: 1.5   **91.** Est.: 50   **93.** Est.: 100   **95.** Est.: 0.0025   **97.** Ramon averaged 6.23 yards per carry.
Cal.: 1.8269   Cal.: 58.8095   Cal.: 72.3053   Cal.: 0.0023

99. The car travels 25.5 miles on 1 gallon of gasoline.   **101.** Three shelves can be cut from the board.   **103.** The amount of the dividend is $1.72.   **105a.** The amount to be paid in monthly payments is $842.58.   **b.** The monthly payment is $46.81.   **107.** The possible answers are 1¢, 3¢, 5¢, 9¢, 15¢, or 45¢.   **109.** Answers will vary.   **111.** ×   **113.** ×
115. ÷   **117.** 2.53

SECTION 3.6

1. 0.625   **3.** 0.667   **5.** 0.167   **7.** 0.417   **9.** 1.750   **11.** 1.500   **13.** 4.000   **15.** 0.003   **17.** 7.080
19. 37.500   **21.** 0.375   **23.** 0.208   **25.** 3.333   **27.** 5.444   **29.** 0.313   **31.** $\dfrac{4}{5}$ **33.** $\dfrac{8}{25}$ **35.** $\dfrac{1}{8}$
37. $1\dfrac{1}{4}$ **39.** $16\dfrac{9}{10}$ **41.** $8\dfrac{2}{5}$ **43.** $8\dfrac{437}{1000}$ **45.** $2\dfrac{1}{4}$ **47.** $\dfrac{23}{150}$ **49.** $\dfrac{703}{800}$ **51.** $1\dfrac{17}{25}$ **53.** $\dfrac{9}{200}$ **55.** $16\dfrac{18}{25}$
57. $\dfrac{33}{100}$ **59.** $\dfrac{1}{3}$ **61.** $0.15 < 0.5$ **63.** $6.65 > 6.56$ **65.** $2.504 > 2.054$ **67.** $\dfrac{3}{8} > 0.365$ **69.** $\dfrac{2}{3} > 0.65$
71. $\dfrac{5}{9} > 0.55$ **73.** $0.62 > \dfrac{7}{15}$ **75.** $0.161 > \dfrac{1}{7}$ **77.** $0.86 > 0.855$ **79.** $1.005 > 0.5$ **81a.** False   **b.** False
c. True   **83.** No. 0.0402 rounded to hundredths is 0.04, to thousandths is 0.040.   **85.** Answers will vary.

CHAPTER REVIEW

1. 54.5 [3.5A]   **2.** 833.958 [3.2A]   **3.** $0.055 < 0.1$ [3.6C]   **4.** Twenty-two and ninety-two ten-thousandths [3.1A]
5. 0.05678 [3.1B]   **6.** 2.33 [3.6A]   **7.** $\dfrac{3}{8}$ [3.6B]   **8.** 36.714 [3.2A]   **9.** 34.025 [3.1A]   **10.** $\dfrac{5}{8} > 0.62$ [3.6C]
11. 0.778 [3.6A]   **12.** $\dfrac{2}{3}$ [3.6B]   **13.** 22.8635 [3.3A]   **14.** 7.94 [3.1B]   **15.** 8.932 [3.4A]
16. Three hundred forty-two and thirty-seven hundredths [3.1A]   **17.** 3.06753 [3.1A]   **18.** 25.7446 [3.4A]
19. 6.594 [3.5A]   **20.** 4.8785 [3.3A]   **21.** The new checking account balance is $661.51. [3.3B]
22. The amount of income tax paid was $5600. [3.4B]   **23.** The amount of each monthly payment is $123.45. [3.5B]
24. The checking account balance is $478.02. [3.2B]

CHAPTER TEST

1. $0.66 < 0.666$ [3.6C]   **2.** 4.087 [3.3A]   **3.** Forty-five and three hundred two ten-thousandths [3.1A]
4. 0.692 [3.6A]   **5.** $\dfrac{33}{40}$ [3.6B]   **6.** 0.0740 [3.1B]   **7.** 1.538 [3.5A]   **8.** 27.76626 [3.3A]   **9.** 7.095 [3.1B]

10. 232 [3.5A]   **11.** 458.581 [3.2A]   **12.** 1.37 inches [3.3B]   **13.** 0.00548 [3.4A]   **14.** 255.957 [3.2A]
15. 209.07086 [3.1A]   **16.** The amount of each monthly payment is $142.85. [3.5B]   **17.** Your total income was
$1543.57. [3.2B]   **18.** The cost of the long-distance call is $4.63. [3.4B]   **19.** The cost of mailing the 55 pieces of mail
was $19.11. [3.4B]   **20.** The cost of mailing the 112 pieces of mail was $50.47. [3.4B]

CUMULATIVE REVIEW

1. 235 r17 [1.5C]   **2.** 128 [1.6A]   **3.** 3 [1.6B]   **4.** 72 [2.1A]   **5.** $4\frac{2}{5}$ [2.2B]   **6.** $\frac{37}{8}$ [2.2B]

7. $\frac{25}{60}$ [2.3A]   **8.** $1\frac{17}{48}$ [2.4B]   **9.** $8\frac{35}{36}$ [2.4C]   **10.** $5\frac{23}{36}$ [2.5C]   **11.** $\frac{1}{12}$ [2.6A]   **12.** $9\frac{1}{8}$ [2.6B]

13. $1\frac{2}{9}$ [2.7A]   **14.** $\frac{19}{20}$ [2.7B]   **15.** $\frac{3}{16}$ [2.8B]   **16.** $2\frac{5}{18}$ [2.8C]   **17.** Sixty-five and three hundred nine

ten-thousandths [3.1A]   **18.** 504.6991 [3.2A]   **19.** 21.0764 [3.3A]   **20.** 55.26066 [3.4A]   **21.** 2.154 [3.5A]

22. 0.733 [3.6A]   **23.** $\frac{1}{6}$ [3.6B]   **24.** $\frac{8}{9} < 0.98$ [3.6C]   **25.** There were 234 passengers on the continuing

flight. [1.3C]   **26.** The value of each share is $32\frac{7}{8}$. [2.5D]   **27.** The checking account balance was $617.38. [3.3B]

28. The resulting thickness of the bushing was 1.395 inches. [3.3B]   **29.** The amount of income tax paid last year was
$6008.80. [3.4B]   **30.** The monthly payment is $23.87. [3.5B]

Answers to Chapter 4 Odd-Numbered Exercises

SECTION 4.1

1. $\frac{1}{5}$ 1:5   1 to 5   **3.** $\frac{2}{1}$ 2:1   2 to 1   **5.** $\frac{3}{8}$ 3:8   3 to 8   **7.** $\frac{37}{24}$ 37:24   37 to 24   **9.** $\frac{1}{1}$ 1:1   1 to 1

11. $\frac{7}{10}$ 7:10   7 to 10   **13.** $\frac{1}{2}$ 1:2   1 to 2   **15.** $\frac{2}{1}$ 2:1   2 to 1   **17.** $\frac{3}{4}$ 3:4   3 to 4   **19.** $\frac{5}{3}$ 5:3   5 to 3

21. $\frac{2}{3}$ 2:3   2 to 3   **23.** $\frac{2}{1}$ 2:1   2 to 1   **25.** The ratio of housing cost to total expenses is $\frac{1}{3}$.   **27.** The ratio of

utilities cost to food cost is $\frac{3}{8}$.   **29.** The ratio of first-year college basketball players to high school senior basketball

players is $\frac{2}{77}$.   **31.** The ratio of the turns in the primary coil to the turns in the secondary coil is $\frac{1}{12}$.   **33a.** The amount

of increase is $20,000.   **b.** The ratio of the increase to the original value is $\frac{2}{9}$.   **35.** The ratio of the increase in price to

the original price is $\frac{5}{16}$.   **37.** No. $\frac{265}{778}$ is greater than $\frac{1}{3}$.   **39.** No. Answers will vary.

SECTION 4.2

1. $\frac{3 \text{ pounds}}{4 \text{ people}}$ **3.** $\frac{\$20}{3 \text{ boards}}$ **5.** $\frac{20 \text{ miles}}{1 \text{ gallon}}$ **7.** $\frac{5 \text{ children}}{2 \text{ families}}$ **9.** $\frac{8 \text{ gallons}}{1 \text{ hour}}$ **11.** 2.5 feet/second   **13.** $325/week
15. 110 trees/acre   **17.** $4.71/hour   **19.** 52.4 miles/hour   **21.** 28 miles/gallon   **23.** $1.65/pound   **25.** The car
was driven 28.4 miles per gallon of gas.   **27.** The rocket uses 213,600 gallons of fuel per minute.   **29a.** The estimated
cost is $40 per share.   **b.** The actual cost is $42.25 per share.   **31a.** There were 4878 compact disks meeting company
standards.   **b.** The cost was $5.44 per disk.   **33.** The profit was $.60 per box of strawberries.   **35.** The pay scale of
$18 per hour gives you the highest yearly income.

SECTION 4.3

1. True   **3.** Not true   **5.** Not true   **7.** True   **9.** True   **11.** Not true   **13.** True   **15.** True   **17.** True
19. Not true   **21.** True   **23.** Not true   **25.** 3   **27.** 6   **29.** 9   **31.** 5.67   **33.** 4   **35.** 4.38   **37.** 88

39. 3.33 **41.** 26.25 **43.** 96 **45.** 9.78 **47.** 3.43 **49.** 1.34 **51.** 50.4 **53.** There are 50 calories in the serving of cereal. **55.** There were 50 pounds of fertilizer used. **57.** There were 375 wooden bats produced. **59.** The distance between the two cities is 16 miles. **61.** 1.25 ounces of medication are required. **63.** There would be 160,000 people voting in the election. **65.** The monthly cost of the life insurance is $176.75. **67.** You will own 400 shares of stock. **69.** Students used the computer 300 hours. **71.** No. $\frac{2}{5} + \frac{3}{4} = \frac{23}{20}$, which is more than the number of voters. **73.** The length of the door on the car is 3.25 feet. **75.** Answers will vary.

CHAPTER REVIEW

1. True [4.3A] **2.** $\frac{2}{5}$ 2:5 2 to 5 [4.1A] **3.** 62.5 miles/hour [4.2B] **4.** True [4.3A] **5.** 68 [4.3B]

6. $7.50/hour [4.2B] **7.** $1.75/pound [4.2B] **8.** $\frac{2}{7}$ 2:7 2 to 7 [4.1A] **9.** 36 [4.3B] **10.** 19.44 [4.3B]

11. $\frac{2}{5}$ 2:5 2 to 5 [4.1A] **12.** Not true [4.3A] **13.** $\frac{\$15}{4 \text{ hours}}$ [4.2A] **14.** 27.2 miles/gallon [4.2B]

15. $\frac{1}{1}$ 1:1 1 to 1 [4.1A] **16.** True [4.3A] **17.** 65.45 [4.3B] **18.** $\frac{100 \text{ miles}}{3 \text{ hours}}$ [4.2A] **19.** The ratio of the decrease in price to the original price is $\frac{2}{5}$. [4.1B] **20.** The property tax is $2400. [4.3C] **21.** The ratio of the high temperature to the low temperature is 2:1. [4.1B] **22.** The cost per radio is $37.50. [4.2C] **23.** It would take 1344 blocks to build the wall. [4.3C] **24.** The ratio of TV advertising to newspaper advertising is $\frac{5}{2}$. [4.1B] **25.** The cost is $.68/pound. [4.2C] **26.** Mahesh drove an average of 56.8 miles/hour. [4.2C] **27.** The cost of the insurance is $193.50. [4.3C] **28.** The cost is $44.75 per share. [4.2C] **29.** There were 22.5 pounds of fertilizer used. [4.3C] **30.** The ratio of the increase to the original value is $\frac{1}{2}$. [4.1B]

CHAPTER TEST

1. $1836.40/month [4.2B] **2.** $\frac{1}{6}$ 1:6 1 to 6 [4.1A] **3.** $\frac{9 \text{ supports}}{4 \text{ feet}}$ [4.2A] **4.** Not true [4.3A]

5. $\frac{3}{2}$ 3:2 3 to 2 [4.1A] **6.** 144 [4.3B] **7.** 30.5 miles/gallon [4.2B] **8.** $\frac{1}{3}$ 1:3 1 to 3 [4.1A]

9. True [4.3A] **10.** 40.5 [4.3B] **11.** $\frac{\$27}{4 \text{ boards}}$ [4.2A] **12.** $\frac{3}{5}$ 3:5 3 to 5 [4.1A] **13.** The dividend would be $625. [4.3C] **14.** The ratio of the city temperature to the desert temperature is $\frac{43}{56}$. [4.1B] **15.** The speed is 538 miles/hour. [4.2C] **16.** The number of pounds of water is 132. [4.3C] **17.** The per-foot cost is $1.73. [4.2C] **18.** The amount of medication needed is 0.875 ounce. [4.3C] **19.** The ratio of the cost of radio advertising to the total cost of advertising is $\frac{8}{13}$. [4.1B] **20.** The property tax is $1200. [4.3C]

CUMULATIVE REVIEW

1. 9158 [1.3B] **2.** $2^4 \cdot 3^3$ [1.6A] **3.** 3 [1.6B] **4.** $2 \cdot 2 \cdot 2 \cdot 2 \cdot 2 \cdot 5$ [1.7B] **5.** 36 [2.1A] **6.** 14 [2.1B]

7. $\frac{5}{8}$ [2.3B] **8.** $8\frac{3}{10}$ [2.4C] **9.** $5\frac{11}{18}$ [2.5C] **10.** $2\frac{5}{6}$ [2.6B] **11.** $4\frac{2}{3}$ [2.7B] **12.** $\frac{23}{30}$ [2.8C]

13. Four and seven hundred nine ten-thousandths [3.1A] **14.** 2.10 [3.1B] **15.** 1.990 [3.5A] **16.** $\frac{1}{15}$ [3.6B]

17. $\frac{1}{8}$ [4.1A] **18.** $\frac{29¢}{2 \text{ bars}}$ [4.2A] **19.** 33.4 miles/gallon [4.2B] **20.** 4.25 [4.3B] **21.** 57.2 miles/hour [4.2C]

22. 36 [4.3B] **23.** The new balance is $744. [1.3C] **24.** The monthly payment is $370. [1.5D] **25.** There are 105 pages remaining to be read. [2.6C] **26.** The cost for each acre is $36,000. [2.7C] **27.** The amount of change is $19.62. [3.3B] **28.** The player's batting average is 0.271. [3.5B] **29.** There will be 25 inches eroded. [4.3C] **30.** The person needs 1.6 ounces of medication. [4.3C]

Answers to Chapter 5 Odd-Numbered Exercises

SECTION 5.1

1. $\frac{1}{4}$, 0.25   **3.** $1\frac{3}{10}$, 1.30   **5.** 1, 1.00   **7.** $\frac{73}{100}$, 0.73   **9.** $3\frac{83}{100}$, 3.83   **11.** $\frac{7}{10}$, 0.70   **13.** $\frac{22}{25}$, 0.88

15. $\frac{8}{25}$, 0.32   **17.** $\frac{2}{3}$ **19.** $\frac{5}{6}$ **21.** $\frac{1}{9}$ **23.** $\frac{5}{11}$ **25.** $\frac{3}{70}$ **27.** $\frac{1}{15}$ **29.** 0.065   **31.** 0.0055   **33.** 0.0825

35. 0.0675   **37.** 0.0045   **39.** 0.804   **41.** 16%   **43.** 5%   **45.** 1%   **47.** 70%   **49.** 124%   **51.** 0.4%

53. 0.6%   **55.** 310.6%   **57.** 54%   **59.** 33.3%   **61.** 62.5%   **63.** 16.7%   **65.** 17.5%   **67.** 177.8%

69. 30%   **71.** $23\frac{1}{3}$%   **73.** $237\frac{1}{2}$%   **75.** $216\frac{2}{3}$%   **77a.** False; 4(200%) = 8   **b.** False; $\frac{4}{200\%}$ = 2   **c.** True

d. False; 125% = 1.25   **79.** Answers will vary.   **81.** $\frac{1}{2}$ **83.** No; 0.495   **85.** The fraction is less than $\frac{1}{100}$.

SECTION 5.2

1. 8   **3.** 10.8   **5.** 0.075   **7.** 80   **9.** 51.895   **11.** 7.5   **13.** 13   **15.** 3.75   **17.** 20   **19.** 210
21. 5% of 95   **23.** 79% of 16   **25.** 72% of 40   **27.** 25,805.0324   **29.** The invoice cost was $16,750.80.
31. The average number of hours to build a car was 25.2 hours.   **33.** The rebate was $822.50.
35a. The sales tax was $570.   **b.** The total cost was $10,070.   **37.** A total of 671 employees was needed.
39. The actual number of hours spent with family and friends is 48.2 hours.   **41.** The difference is 3.4 hours.

SECTION 5.3

1. 32%   **3.** $16\frac{2}{3}$%   **5.** 200%   **7.** 37.5%   **9.** 18%   **11.** 0.25%   **13.** 20%   **15.** 400%   **17.** 2.5%

19. 37.5%   **21.** 0.25%   **23.** 2.4%   **25.** 9.6%   **27.** Microsoft's revenues were 52.8% of the total revenues.
29. The percent of wasted vegetables was 25.4%.   **31.** Women were 13.7% of the total number of people in the Army.

33a. The speed of the chip was increased by 75 megahertz.   **b.** The speed of the chip was increased by $33\frac{1}{3}$%.

35. 98.5% of the slabs met the safety requirements.   **37.** The percent spent on veterinary care was 26.7%.
39. The cost to refurbish the Statue of Liberty is 3250% of the original cost.   **41.** Answers will vary.

SECTION 5.4

1. 75   **3.** 50   **5.** 100   **7.** 85   **9.** 1200   **11.** 19.2   **13.** 7.5   **15.** 32   **17.** 200   **19.** 80   **21.** 9
23. 504   **25.** 108   **27.** 7122.15   **29.** The average size of a house in 1977 was 1680 square feet.   **31.** The selling price of the car was $16,400.   **33.** The amount spent in 2000 will be $92 billion.   **35a.** The number of computer boards tested was 3000.   **b.** The number of nondefective boards was 2976.   **37.** There is 0.45 milligram of thiamine in one serving.   **39.** No. Answers will vary.

SECTION 5.5

1. 65   **3.** 25%   **5.** 75   **7.** 12.5%   **9.** 400   **11.** 19.5   **13.** 14.8%   **15.** 62.62   **17.** 5   **19.** 45
21. 15   **23.** The club collected $24,500.   **25.** The cost of the calculator 8 years ago was $71.25.
27. Her average golf score per round in 1977 was 73.27.   **29.** The mail order price was 68.3% of the retail price.
31. There were 495 people who worried somewhat about privacy on the Internet.   **33.** The projected percent increase in demand is 3.3%.   **35.** The approximate total land area is 58,750,000 square miles.   **37.** The potency has decreased by 93.75% after 60 hours.

CHAPTER REVIEW

1. 60 [5.2A]   **2.** 20% [5.3A]   **3.** 175% [5.1B]   **4.** 75 [5.4A]   **5.** $\frac{3}{25}$ [5.1A]   **6.** 19.36 [5.2A]

7. 150% [5.3A]   **8.** 504 [5.4A]   **9.** 0.42 [5.1A]   **10.** 5.4 [5.2A]   **11.** 157.5 [5.4A]   **12.** 0.076 [5.1A]

13. 77.5 [5.2A]   **14.** $\frac{1}{6}$ [5.1A]   **15.** 160% [5.5A]   **16.** 75 [5.5A]   **17.** 38% [5.1B]   **18.** 10.9 [5.4A]

19. 7.3% [5.3A]   **20.** 613.3% [5.3A]   **21.** Trent answered 85% of the questions correctly. [5.5B]
22. The company spent $4500 for TV advertising. [5.2B]   **23.** The population increased by 6.25%. [5.3B]
24. The total cost of the camera was $1041.25. [5.2B]   **25.** 78.6% of the women wore sunscreen often. [5.3B]
26. The world's population in 1997 was 5,800,000,000 people. [5.4B]   **27.** The cost of the computer 4 years ago was
$3000. [5.5B]   **28.** The team scored 110 points. [5.4B]

CHAPTER TEST

1. 0.973 [5.1A]   **2.** $\frac{5}{6}$ [5.1A]   **3.** 30% [5.1B]   **4.** 163% [5.1B]   **5.** 150% [5.1B]   **6.** $66\frac{2}{3}$% [5.1B]

7. 50.05 [5.2A]   **8.** 61.36 [5.2A]   **9.** 76% of 13 [5.2A]   **10.** 212% of 12 [5.2A]   **11.** The company spends
$4500 for advertising. [5.2B]   **12.** There were 1170 pounds of vegetables unspoiled. [5.2B]   **13.** One serving provides
14.7% of the daily recommended amount of potassium. [5.3B]   **14.** One serving provides 9.1% of the daily recommended
number of calories. [5.3B]   **15.** The store's temporary employees were 16% of the permanent employees. [5.3B]
16. Conchita answered 91.3% of the questions correctly. [5.3B]   **17.** 80 [5.4A]   **18.** 28.3 [5.4A]   **19.** There were
32,000 transistors tested. [5.4B]   **20.** The increase was 60% of the original price. [5.3B]   **21.** 143.0 [5.5A]
22. 1000% [5.5A]   **23.** The increase in the hourly wage is $1.02. [5.5B]   **24.** The population now is 220% of the
population 10 years ago. [5.5B]   **25.** The value of the car is $6500. [5.5B]

CUMULATIVE REVIEW

1. 4 [1.6B]   **2.** 240 [2.1A]   **3.** $10\frac{11}{24}$ [2.4C]   **4.** $12\frac{41}{48}$ [2.5C]   **5.** $12\frac{4}{7}$ [2.6B]   **6.** $\frac{7}{24}$ [2.7B]

7. $\frac{1}{3}$ [2.8B]   **8.** $\frac{13}{36}$ [2.8C]   **9.** 3.08 [3.1B]   **10.** 1.1196 [3.3A]   **11.** 34.2813 [3.5A]   **12.** 3.625 [3.6A]

13. $1\frac{3}{4}$ [3.6B]   **14.** $\frac{3}{8} < 0.87$ [3.6C]   **15.** 53.3 [4.3B]   **16.** $9.60/hour [4.2B]   **17.** $\frac{11}{60}$ [5.1A]

18. $83\frac{1}{3}$% [5.1B]   **19.** 19.56 [5.2A]   **20.** $133\frac{1}{3}$% [5.3A]   **21.** 9.92 [5.4A]   **22.** 342.9% [5.5A]

23. Sergio's take-home pay is $592. [2.6C]   **24.** The monthly payment is $92.25. [3.5B]   **25.** There were 420 gallons
of gasoline used during the month. [3.5B]   **26.** The real estate tax is $3000. [4.3C]   **27.** The sales tax was 6% of the
purchase price. [5.3B]   **28.** 45% of the people surveyed did not favor the candidate. [5.3B]   **29.** The 1990 value is
250% of the 1985 value. [5.5B]   **30.** 18% of the children tested had levels of lead that exceeded federal standards. [5.5B]

Answers to Chapter 6 Odd-Numbered Exercises

SECTION 6.1

1. The unit cost is $.073 per ounce.   **3.** The unit cost is $.374 per ounce.   **5.** The unit cost is $.040 per tablet.
7. The unit cost is $4.975 per clamp.   **9.** The unit cost is $.153 per ounce.   **11.** The unit cost is $.119 per screw.
13. The more economical purchase is Sutter Home.   **15.** The more economical purchase is La Victoria.   **17.** The more
economical purchase is 400 tablets.   **19.** The more economical purchase is Land to Lake.   **21.** The more economical
purchase is Maxwell House.   **23.** The more economical purchase is Friskies Chef's Blend.   **25.** The total cost is $7.77.
27. The total cost is $1.84.   **29.** The total cost is $6.37.   **31.** The total cost is $1.24.   **33.** The total cost is $5.96.
35. Answers will vary.

SECTION 6.2

1. The percent increase is 20%.   **3.** The percent increase is 62.0%.   **5.** The percent increase is 80%.   **7.** The percent
increase is 87.0%.   **9.** The percent increase is 5852%.   **11.** The markup is $71.25.   **13.** The markup is $24.
15. The markup rate is 30%.   **17a.** The markup is $77.76.   **b.** The selling price is $239.76.   **19a.** The markup is

$25.60. **b.** The selling price is $57.60. **21.** The selling price is $227.20. **23.** The percent decrease is 40%. **25.** The percent decrease is 40%. **27.** The car loses $3360 in value. **29a.** The amount of the decrease is 12 cameras. **b.** The percent decrease is 60%. **31a.** The amount of the decrease is $15.20. **b.** The average monthly gasoline bill is now $60.80. **33.** The percent decrease is 20%. **35.** The discount rate is $33\frac{1}{3}\%$. **37.** The discount is $67.50. **39.** The discount rate is 25%. **41a.** The discount is $.17 per pound. **b.** The sale price is $.68 per pound. **43a.** The discount is $4 per gallon. **b.** The discount rate is 25%. **45.** Yes. **47.** No. 50% off the regular price.

SECTION 6.3

1. The simple interest due is $6750. **3.** The simple interest due is $16. **5a.** The interest on the loan is $72,000. **b.** The monthly payment is $6187.50. **7a.** The simple interest is $1080. **b.** The monthly payment is $545. **9.** The monthly payment is $1332.50. **11.** The value will be $1414.78. **13.** The value will be $12,380.43. **15.** The value will be $28,212. **17a.** The value of the investment will be $6040.86. **b.** The interest earned on the investment will be $3040.86. **19.** Answers will vary. **21a.** The value after the deposit will be $200.50. **b.** The value on March 1 will be $301.50.

SECTION 6.4

1. The mortgage is $82,450. **3.** The down payment is $7500. **5.** The down payment was $212,500. **7.** The loan origination fee is $3750. **9a.** The down payment is $7500. **b.** The mortgage is $142,500. **11.** The mortgage is $189,000. **13.** The monthly mortgage payment is $1157.73. **15.** No, the couple cannot afford to buy the home. **17.** The monthly property tax is $112.35. **19a.** The monthly mortgage payment is $1678.40. **b.** The interest is $736.68 during that month. **21.** The total monthly payment (mortgage and property tax) is $982.70. **23.** The monthly mortgage payment is $1430.83. **25.** $63,408 of interest can be saved.

SECTION 6.5

1. Amanda does not have enough money for the down payment. **3.** The sales tax was $742.50. **5.** The license fee is $250. **7a.** The sales tax is $420. **b.** The total cost of the sales tax and the license fee is $595. **9a.** The down payment is $550. **b.** The amount financed is $1650. **11.** The amount financed is $28,000. **13.** The monthly truck payment is $348.39. **15.** The cost to operate the car is $5120. **17.** The cost per mile is $.11. **19.** The interest is $74.75. **21a.** The amount financed is $76,600. **b.** The monthly truck payment is $1590.09. **23.** The monthly car payment is $709.88. **25.** The 10% loan with the application fee has a lower loan cost.

SECTION 6.6

1. Lewis earns $300. **3.** The commission earned is $3930. **5.** The commission received was $84. **7.** Keisha receives $3244 per month. **9.** The electrician's overtime hourly wage is $31.60. **11.** The commission earned is $112.50. **13.** The typist earns $393.75. **15.** The consultant's hourly wage is $85. **17a.** Mark's hourly wage is $19.35. **b.** Mark earns $154.80 on Saturday. **19a.** The increase in pay is $1.65 per hour. **b.** The nurse's hourly pay is $18.15. **21.** Nicole earned $375. **23.** The starting salary was $36,281. **25.** Liberal arts majors received the smaller amount of increase in starting salary.

SECTION 6.7

1. The new balance is $486.32. **3.** The balance in the account is $1222.47. **5.** The current balance is $825.27. **7.** The current balance is $3000.82. **9.** Yes, there is enough money to purchase a refrigerator. **11.** Yes, there is enough money to make both purchases. **13.** The bank statement and checkbook balance. **15.** The bank statement and checkbook balance. **17.** Added **19.** Subtract

CHAPTER REVIEW

1. The unit cost is 14.5¢ per ounce. [6.1A] **2.** The cost per mile was 12.1¢. [6.5B] **3.** The percent increase was 30.4%. [6.2A] **4.** The markup is $72. [6.2B] **5.** The simple interest due on the loan is $6750. [6.3A] **6.** The value of the investment will be $45,550.75. [6.3B] **7.** The percent increase was 15%. [6.2A] **8.** The monthly

payment for mortgage and property tax is $578.53.   [6.4B]   **9.** The monthly payment is $330.82.   [6.5B]
10. The value of the investment will be $53,593.   [6.3B]   **11.** The down payment is $18,750.   [6.4A]   **12.** The total
of the sales tax and license fee is $1158.75.   [6.5A]   **13.** The selling price is $2079.   [6.2B]   **14.** The amount of
interest is $97.33.   [6.5B]   **15.** The commission is $3240.   [6.6A]   **16.** The sale price was $141.   [6.2D]   **17.** The
current balance is $943.68.   [6.7A]   **18.** The simple interest due is $1200.   [6.3A]   **19.** The loan origination fee
is $1875.   [6.4A]   **20.** The more economical purchase is 60 ounces for $8.40.   [6.1B]   **21.** The monthly mortgage
payment is $934.08.   [6.4B]   **22.** The total income was $655.20.   [6.6A]   **23.** The current checkbook balance is
$8866.58.   [6.7A]   **24.** The percent increase was 200%.   [6.2A]

CHAPTER TEST

1. The cost per foot is $6.92.   [6.1A]   **2.** The more economical purchase is 5 pounds for $1.65.   [6.1B]
3. The cost is $14.53.   [6.1C]   **4.** The percent increase is 20%.   [6.2A]   **5.** The percent increase was 150%.   [6.2A]
6. The selling price is $301.   [6.2B]   **7.** The selling price is $6.25.   [6.2B]   **8.** The percent decrease was 7.7%.   [6.2C]
9. The percent decrease was 20%.   [6.2C]   **10.** The sale price is $209.30.   [6.2D]   **11.** The discount rate is 40%.   [6.2D]
12. The simple interest due is $2000.   [6.3A]   **13.** The interest earned was $24,420.60.   [6.3B]   **14.** The loan
origination fee is $3350.   [6.4A]   **15.** The monthly mortgage payment is $1713.44.   [6.4B]   **16.** The amount financed
is $19,000.   [6.5A]   **17.** The monthly truck payment is $482.68.   [6.5B]   **18.** The nurse earns $703.50.   [6.6A]
19. The current balance is $6612.25.   [6.7A]   **20.** The bank statement and checkbook balance.   [6.7B]

CUMULATIVE REVIEW

1. 13   [1.6B]   **2.** $8\frac{13}{24}$ [2.4C]   **3.** $2\frac{37}{48}$ [2.5C]   **4.** 9   [2.6B]   **5.** 2   [2.7B]   **6.** 5   [2.8C]   **7.** 52.2   [3.5A]

8. 1.417   [3.6A]   **9.** $51.25/hour   [4.2B]   **10.** 10.94   [4.3B]   **11.** 62.5%   [5.1B]   **12.** 27.3   [5.2A]

13. 0.182   [5.1A]   **14.** 42%   [5.3A]   **15.** 250   [5.4A]   **16.** 154.76   [5.5A]   **17.** The total rainfall was $13\frac{11}{12}$

inches.   [2.4D]   **18.** The amount the family pays in taxes is $570.   [2.6C]   **19.** The ratio of decrease in price to

original price is $\frac{3}{5}$.   [4.1B]   **20.** The car was driven 33.4 miles per gallon.   [4.2C]   **21.** The unit cost is $.93/lb.   [4.2C]

22. The dividend is $280.   [4.3C]   **23.** The sale price is $720.   [6.2D]   **24.** The selling price is $119.   [6.2B]
25. The percent increase is 8%.   [6.2A]   **26.** The simple interest due is $6000.   [6.3A]   **27.** The monthly payment is
$791.81.   [6.5B]   **28.** The new balance is $2243.77.   [6.7A]   **29.** The cost per mile is $.20.   [6.5B]
30. The monthly mortgage payment is $743.18.   [6.4B]

Answers to Chapter 7 Odd-Numbered Exercises

SECTION 7.1

1. The gross revenues were $775 million.   **3.** *The Lion King* earned 38.7% of the total gross revenue.   **5.** There were
50 more people who agreed that humanity should explore planets than agreed that space exploration impacts daily life.
7. 150 children hid vegetables under a napkin.   **9.** No, the percents do not add to 100%.   **11.** The ratio of the number

of units in finance to the number of units in accounting is $\frac{1}{3}$.   **13.** 9.4% of the units required to graduate are taken in

mathematics.   **15.** The ratio of the population of Asia to the population of Africa is $\frac{60}{13}$.   **17.** The ratio of the population

of North America to the population of South America is $\frac{11}{18}$.   **19.** The amount spent on portable game machines was

$279,000,000.   **21.** Yes.   **23.** The amount spent for food is $19,600.   **25.** The total amount spent for housing and

education is $36,260.   **27.** The ratio of the land area of North America to the land area of South America is $\frac{314}{229}$.

29. Australia has 5.2% of the total world land area.   **31.** $1700 of the family's income was spent on entertainment.

33. Yes.   **35.** Answers will vary.

SECTION 7.2

1. There were 210 days when the PSI was greater than 100.   **3.** The PSI decreased the most between 1993 and 1994.

5. There were 25,000 burglaries committed in 1992.   **7.** Robbery had the greatest percent decrease of the given crime categories.   **9.** The difference in maximum salaries in New York was $16,000.   **11.** Philadelphia is the city where the difference between maximum salaries was the greatest.   **13.** There were 20 inches of snowfall during January.

15. The total snowfall during March and April was 25 inches.   **17.** The difference in the recommended number of Calories was 800 Calories.   **19.** The ratio of the Calories for 15 to 18-year-old women to the Calories for 51 to 74-year-old women is $\frac{7}{6}$.   **21.** Coal, 19%; wood, 3%; natural gas, 20%; petroleum, 45%; hydroelectric, 5%; nuclear, 10%; your estimate should total approximately 100%.   **23.** Answers will vary.

SECTION 7.3

1. There were 44 students whose tuition was between $3000 and $6000.   **3.** There were 18 students who paid more than $12,000 annually for tuition.   **5.** There were 410 cars between 6 and 12 years old.   **7.** There were 230 cars more than 12 years old.   **9.** There were 54 adults who spent between 1 and 2 hours at the mall.   **11.** 22% of the adults spent less than 1 hour at the mall.   **13.** There were 7 runners who ran the race in less than 21 seconds.   **15.** 14.3% of the runners ran the race in between 20.5 and 21 seconds.   **17.** 10.8% of the people purchased between 20 and 30 tickets each month.

19. No. A frequency polygon shows only the number of occurrences in a class, not the number of occurrences for a particular value.   **21.** 32.4% of the students scored between 800 and 1000.   **23.** There were 900,000 students who scored above 800.   **25.** Answers will vary.

SECTION 7.4

1. The mean is 19 TVs, the median is 19.5 TVs, and the mode is 20 TVs.   **3.** The mean is 10.61 seconds and the median is 10.605 seconds.   **5.** The median will give a higher average.   **7.** The mean is $403.625, the median is $404.5, and there is no mode.   **9.** The mean is $82.6525 and the median is $86.48.   **11.** The mean life expectancy is 70.8 years and the median life expectancy is 72 years.   **13.** The range is $4.15, the first quartile is $6.895, the third quartile is $8.95, and the interquartile range is $2.055.

15. The first quartile is 20 mpg and the third quartile is 30 mpg.

17. The interquartile range is 1.8 hours.   **19.** The first quartile is $29,778, the median is $33,858, and the third quartile is $36,453.   **21.** 50% of the median incomes fall between $29,788 and $36,453.   **23a.** No.   **b.** No.   **c.** No.   **25.** The median gives a better representation of his performance.

27. False. Change the word *mean* to *median*.

CHAPTER REVIEW

1. $349 million was spent on maintaining Web sites. [7.1B]   **2.** The ratio of the amount spent by the Department of Commerce to the amount spent by the EPA was $\frac{9}{8}$. [7.1B]   **3.** 8.9% of the total was spent by NASA. [7.1B]   **4.** The difference between the prices was $40. [7.2B]   **5.** The price of one ounce of gold and one ounce of platinum in 1996 was $830. [7.2B]   **6.** The ratio of the price of gold to the price of platinum in 1995 was $\frac{38}{41}$. [7.2B]   **7.** There were 54 games in which fewer than 100 points were scored. [7.3B]   **8.** The ratio of the number of games in which 90 to 100 points were scored to the number of games in which 110 to 120 points were scored was $\frac{31}{8}$. [7.3B]   **9.** There were 110 or more points scored in 11.3% of the games. [7.3B]   **10.** There were 63 athletes from Russia who won medals. [7.1A]

11. The ratio of the number of athletes receiving a gold medal to the number receiving a bronze medal was $\frac{13}{8}$.   [7.1A]

12. 33.3% of the Russian athletes received a silver medal.   [7.1A]   **13.** The difference between the numbers of days was 50.   [7.2A]   **14.** The Rocky Mountain ski areas were in full operation for 50% of the days.   [7.2A]   **15.** The Southeast had 30 days of full operation.   [7.2A]   **16.** There were 15 people who slept 8 or more hours.   [7.3A]   **17.** The ratio of the number of people who slept 6 or fewer hours to the number who slept 9 or more hours is $\frac{6}{1}$.   [7.3A]   **18.** 28.3% of the people slept 7 hours.   [7.3A]   **19.** The mean is $91.58\overline{3}$, the median is 93.5, and the mode is 96.   [7.4A]   **20.** The range is 36 and the interquartile range is 15.   [7.4B]

CHAPTER TEST

1. There were 19 students who spent between $15 and $25 per week.   [7.3B]   **2.** The ratio of the number of students who spent between $10 and $15 to the number who spent between $15 and $20 is $\frac{2}{3}$.   [7.3B]   **3.** 45% of the students spent less than $15 per week.   [7.3B]   **4.** There were 36 people surveyed.   [7.1A]   **5.** The ratio of the number of people who gave their marriage a B to those who gave it a C was $\frac{5}{2}$.   [7.1A]   **6.** 58.3% of the people surveyed gave their marriage an A.   [7.1A]   **7.** There were 6,400 thousand trucks sold in the third quarter of 1995.   [7.2A]   **8.** The difference between the number of trucks sold in the second quarter of 1996 and the number sold in the second quarter of 1995 was 500 thousand.   [7.2A]   **9.** There were more trucks sold in 1996.   [7.2A]   **10.** The population of the United States is 263 million.   [7.1B]   **11.** 17.1% of the U.S. population belongs to Generation X.   [7.1B]   **12.** The larger segment of the population is made up of those born before 1965.   [7.1B]   **13.** There are 34 states with per capita incomes between $16,000 and $22,000.   [7.3A]   **14.** 38% of the states have a per capita income between $19,000 and $22,000.   [7.3A]   **15.** 14% of the states have a per capita income that is $25,000 or more.   [7.3A]   **16.** Nordstrom's third-quarter income for 1995 was $30 million.   [7.2B]   **17.** In the 1st, 2nd, and 4th quarters Nordstrom's quarterly income in 1996 was less than its quarterly income in 1995.   [7.2B]   **18.** The difference between Nordstrom's fourth-quarter income in 1995 and its fourth-quarter income in 1996 was $10 million.   [7.2B]   **19.** The mean is 2.53 days and the median is 2.55 days.   [7.4A]

20.

[7.4B]

CUMULATIVE REVIEW

1. 540   [1.6A]   **2.** 14   [1.6B]   **3.** 120   [2.1A]   **4.** $\frac{5}{12}$ [2.3B]   **5.** $12\frac{3}{40}$ [2.4C]   **6.** $4\frac{17}{24}$ [2.5C]

7. 2   [2.6B]   **8.** $\frac{64}{85}$ [2.7B]   **9.** $8\frac{1}{4}$ [2.8C]   **10.** 209.305   [3.1A]   **11.** 2.82348   [3.4A]   **12.** 16.67   [3.6A]

13. 26.4 miles/gallon   [4.2B]   **14.** 3.2   [4.3B]   **15.** 80%   [5.1B]   **16.** 80   [5.4A]   **17.** 16.34   [5.2A]

18. 40%   [5.3A]   **19.** Tanim had $650 in income.   [6.6A]   **20.** The life insurance costs $207.50.   [4.3C]

21. The interest due is $6875.   [6.3A]   **22.** The markup rate is 55%.   [6.2B]   **23.** $570 is budgeted for food.   [7.1B]

24. The difference between the numbers of problems answered correctly was 12 problems.   [7.2B]   **25.** The mean high temperature was 69.6°.   [7.4A]   **26.** The median salary was $31,650.   [7.4A]

Answers to Chapter 8 Odd-Numbered Exercises

SECTION 8.1

1. 72 in.   **3.** $2\frac{1}{2}$ ft   **5.** 39 ft   **7.** $5\frac{1}{3}$ yd   **9.** 84 in.   **11.** $3\frac{1}{3}$ yd   **13.** 10,560 ft   **15.** $\frac{5}{8}$ ft   **17.** 1 mi 1120 ft

19. 9 ft 11 in.   **21.** 2 ft 9 in.   **23.** 14 ft 6 in.   **25.** 2 ft 8 in.   **27.** $11\frac{1}{6}$ ft   **29.** 4 mi 2520 ft   **31.** 14 tiles can be placed along one row. **33.** The missing dimension is $1\frac{5}{6}$ ft. **35.** The length of material needed is $7\frac{1}{2}$ in. **37.** Each piece is $1\frac{2}{3}$ ft long. **39.** 6 ft 6 in. of framing is needed. **41.** The wall is $33\frac{3}{4}$ ft in length. **43.** Yes, the line would reach around Earth at the equator.

SECTION 8.2

1. 4 lb **3.** 64 oz **5.** $1\frac{3}{5}$ tons **7.** 12,000 lb **9.** $4\frac{1}{8}$ lb **11.** 24 oz **13.** 2600 lb **15.** $\frac{1}{4}$ ton
17. $11\frac{1}{4}$ lb **19.** 4 tons 1000 lb **21.** 2 lb 8 oz **23.** 5 tons 400 lb **25.** 1 ton 1700 lb **27.** 33 lb
29. 14 lb **31.** 9 oz **33.** 1 lb 7 oz **35.** The load will weigh 2000 lb. **37.** The weight of 144 tiles is 63 lb.
39. The case of soft drink weighs 9 lb. **41.** 1 lb 5 oz of shampoo is in each container. **43.** The ham costs $13.50.
45. The cost of mailing the manuscript is $8.75. **47.** Answers will vary.

SECTION 8.3

1. $7\frac{1}{2}$ c **3.** 24 fl oz **5.** 4 pt **7.** 7 c **9.** $5\frac{1}{2}$ gal **11.** 9 qt **13.** $3\frac{3}{4}$ qt **15.** $1\frac{1}{4}$ pt **17.** $4\frac{1}{4}$ qt

19. 3 gal 2 qt **21.** 2 qt 1 pt **23.** 7 qt **25.** 6 fl oz **27.** $17\frac{1}{2}$ pt **29.** $\frac{7}{8}$ gal **31.** 5 gal 1 qt

33. 1 gal 2 qt **35.** $2\frac{3}{4}$ gal **37.** $7\frac{1}{2}$ gal of coffee should be prepared. **39.** There are $4\frac{1}{4}$ qt of solution.

41. The farmer used $8\frac{3}{4}$ gal of oil. **43.** 1 qt for $1.20 is the more economical purchase. **45.** $43.50 of profit
was made on each 5-quart package. **47.** grain = 0.002285 oz; dram = 0.0625 oz; furlong = 0.125 mi; rod = 16.5 ft

SECTION 8.4

1. 19,450 ft · lb **3.** 19,450,000 ft · lb **5.** 1500 ft · lb **7.** 29,700 ft · lb **9.** 30,000 ft · lb **11.** 25,500 ft · lb
13. 35,010,000 ft · lb **15.** 9,336,000 ft · lb **17.** 2 hp **19.** 8 hp **21.** $2750\frac{\text{ft} \cdot \text{lb}}{\text{s}}$ **23.** $3850\frac{\text{ft} \cdot \text{lb}}{\text{s}}$

25. $500\frac{\text{ft} \cdot \text{lb}}{\text{s}}$ **27.** $4800\frac{\text{ft} \cdot \text{lb}}{\text{s}}$ **29.** $1440\frac{\text{ft} \cdot \text{lb}}{\text{s}}$ **31.** 3 hp **33.** 12 hp

CHAPTER REVIEW

1. 48 in. [8.1A] **2.** 2 ft 6 in. [8.1B] **3.** 1600 ft · lb [8.4A] **4.** 40 fl oz [8.3A] **5.** $4\frac{2}{3}$ yd [8.1A]

6. $1\frac{1}{5}$ tons [8.2A] **7.** 2 lb 7 oz [8.2B] **8.** 54 oz [8.2A] **9.** 9 ft 3 in. [8.1B] **10.** 1 ton 1000 lb [8.2B]

11. 9 lb 3 oz [8.2B] **12.** 1 yd 2 ft [8.1B] **13.** 3 qt [8.3A] **14.** 13 ft 4 in. [8.1B] **15.** $1375\frac{\text{ft} \cdot \text{lb}}{\text{s}}$ [8.4B]

16. 44 lb [8.2B] **17.** 38,900 ft · lb [8.4A] **18.** 7 hp [8.4B] **19.** A board 3 ft 6 in. long remains. [8.1C]

20. The cost of mailing the book is $6.30. [8.2C] **21.** There are $13\frac{1}{2}$ qt in a case of 24 cans. [8.3C]

22. There were 16 gal of milk sold. [8.3C] **23.** The furnace releases 27,230,000 ft · lb in 1 h. [8.4A] **24.** The power
is $480\frac{\text{ft} \cdot \text{lb}}{\text{s}}$. [8.4B]

CHAPTER TEST

1. 30 in. [8.1A] **2.** 2 ft 5 in. [8.1B] **3.** Each piece is $1\frac{1}{3}$ ft. [8.1C] **4.** The wall is 48 ft in length. [8.1C]

5. 46 oz [8.2A] **6.** 2 lb 8 oz [8.2B] **7.** 17 lb 1 oz [8.2B] **8.** 1 lb 11oz [8.2B] **9.** The books weigh
750 lb. [8.2C] **10.** The class earned $28.13. [8.2C] **11.** $3\frac{1}{4}$ gal [8.3A] **12.** 28 pt [8.3A]

13. $12\frac{1}{4}$ gal [8.3B]   **14.** 8 gal 1 qt [8.3B]   **15.** There are 60 c of juice in 24 cans. [8.3C]   **16.** Nick made a profit of $126. [8.3C]   **17.** 3750 ft · lb [8.4A]   **18.** 31,120,000 ft · lb [8.4A]   **19.** $160\frac{\text{ft} \cdot \text{lb}}{\text{s}}$ [8.4B]
20. 4 hp [8.4B]

CUMULATIVE REVIEW

1. 180 [2.1A]   **2.** $5\frac{3}{8}$ [2.2B]   **3.** $3\frac{7}{24}$ [2.5C]   **4.** 2 [2.7B]   **5.** $4\frac{3}{8}$ [2.8C]   **6.** 2.10 [3.1B]
7. 0.038808 [3.4A]   **8.** 8.8 [4.3B]   **9.** 1.25 [5.2A]   **10.** 42.86 [5.4A]   **11.** The unit cost is $2.15/lb. [6.1A]
12. $8\frac{11}{15}$ in. [8.1B]   **13.** 1 lb 8 oz [8.2B]   **14.** 31 lb 8 oz [8.2B]   **15.** $2\frac{1}{2}$ qt [8.3B]   **16.** 1 lb 12 oz [8.2B]
17. The dividend would be $280. [4.3C]   **18.** The new checkbook balance is $642.79. [6.7A]   **19.** The monthly income is $3100. [6.6A]   **20.** 2425 lb of the shipment could be sold. [5.2B]   **21.** 18% of the class received scores between 80% and 90%. [7.3A]   **22.** The selling price is $308. [6.2B]   **23.** The interest paid was $14,666.67. [6.3A]
24. Each student received $1267. [8.2C]   **25.** The cost to mail the books was $10.80. [8.2C]   **26.** 36 oz for $2.70 is the better buy. [6.1B]   **27.** The contractor saves $1080. [8.3C]   **28.** 3200 ft · lb [8.4A]   **29.** $400\frac{\text{ft} \cdot \text{lb}}{\text{s}}$ [8.4B]

Answers to Chapter 9 Odd-Numbered Exercises

SECTION 9.1

1. 420 mm   **3.** 8.1 cm   **5.** 6.804 km   **7.** 2109 m   **9.** 4.32 m   **11.** 88 cm   **13.** 7.038 km   **15.** 3500 m
17. 2.60 m   **19.** 168.5 cm   **21.** 148 mm   **23.** 62.07 m   **25.** 31.9 cm   **27.** 8.075 km   **29.** The missing dimension is 7.8 cm.   **31.** The distance between rivets is 17.9 cm.   **33.** 15.6 m of fencing is left on the roll.
35. It takes 500 s for light from the sun to reach Earth.   **37.** Light travels 25,920,000,000 km in 1 day.
39. Answers will vary.

SECTION 9.2

1. 0.420 kg   **3.** 0.127 g   **5.** 4200 g   **7.** 450 mg   **9.** 1.856 kg   **11.** 4.057 g   **13.** 1370 g   **15.** 45.6 mg
17. 18.000 kg   **19.** 3.922 kg   **21.** 7.891 g   **23.** 4.063 kg   **25.** There are 40 g in one serving.   **27a.** There are 3.288 g of cholesterol in one dozen eggs.   **b.** There is 0.132 g of cholesterol in four glasses of milk.   **29a.** There is 0.186 kg of mix in the package.   **b.** There is 0.42 g of sodium in two servings of the corn bread.   **31.** 1.6 kg of grass seed are needed to cover 2000 m².   **33.** The profit on a container of nuts is $42.50.   **35.** 50.3% of the grain exports was corn.
37. Answers will vary.

SECTION 9.3

1. 4.2 L   **3.** 3420 ml   **5.** 423 cm³   **7.** 642 ml   **9.** 0.042 L   **11.** 435 cm³   **13.** 4620 L   **15.** 1.423 kl
17. 1267 cm³   **19.** 3.042 L   **21.** 3.004 kl   **23.** 8.200 L   **25a.** The amount of oxygen in 50 L of air is less than 25 L.
b. There are 10.5 L of oxygen in 50 L of air.   **27.** 24 L of chlorine are used in a month.   **29.** 4000 people can be immunized.   **31.** The better buy is the case of 12 one-liter bottles of apple juice.   **33.** The profit on the gasoline is $8715.   **35.** 2720 ml; 2.72 L; 2L 720 ml

SECTION 9.4

1. 3300 Calories can be eliminated from your diet.   **3a.** There are 90 Calories in $1\frac{1}{2}$ servings.   **b.** In 6 slices of bread, 30 Calories are from fat.   **5.** A 135-pound lightly active person should consume 2025 Calories per day.   **7.** You burn 10,125 Calories in 30 days.   **9.** You would have to hike for 2.6 h.   **11.** 1250 Wh of energy are used.   **13.** 0.567 kWh of energy is used.   **15.** It costs $1.58 to run the air conditioner.   **17a.** The light output of the Energy Saver Bulb is less than half that of the Long Life Soft White Bulb. **b.** The difference in cost is $.42. **19.** The cost of using the welder is $109.98. **21.** Answers will vary.

SECTION 9.5

1. 91.74 m **3.** 1.73 m **5.** 6.82 kg **7.** 235.85 ml **9.** 104.65 km/h **11.** $7.68/kg **13.** $.39/L **15.** He will lose 1 lb. **17.** The distance is 40,068.07 km. **19.** 328 ft **21.** 1.58 gal **23.** 4920 ft **25.** 6.33 gal **27.** 49.69 mi/h **29.** $1.46/gal **31.** 4.62 lb **33.** The speed is 186,335.40 mi/s. **35a.** False. **b.** False. **c.** True. **d.** True. **e.** False.

CHAPTER REVIEW

1. 1250 m [9.1A] **2.** 450 mg [9.2A] **3.** 5.6 ml [9.3A] **4.** 1090 yd [9.5B] **5.** 7.9 cm [9.1A] **6.** 5.34 m [9.1A] **7.** 0.990 kg [9.2A] **8.** 2.550 L [9.3A] **9.** 4.870 km [9.1A] **10.** 3.7 mm [9.1A] **11.** 6.829 g [9.2A] **12.** 1200 cm³ [9.3A] **13.** 4050 g [9.2A] **14.** 870 cm [9.1A] **15.** 192 cm³ [9.3A] **16.** 0.356 g [9.2A] **17.** 3.72 m [9.1A] **18.** 8300 L [9.3A] **19.** 2.089 L [9.3A] **20.** 5.410 L [9.3A] **21.** 3.792 kl [9.3A] **22.** 468 ml [9.3A] **23.** 37.2 m of wire are left on the roll. [9.1B] **24.** The cost is $6.35. [9.2B] **25.** The cost is $7.48/kg. [9.5A] **26.** 50 L of coffee should be prepared. [9.3B] **27.** 2700 Calories can be eliminated from your diet. [9.4A] **28.** It costs $3.42 to run the set. [9.4A] **29.** The weight is 4.18 lb. [9.5B] **30.** 8.75 h of cycling are necessary to lose 1 lb. [9.4A] **31.** The profit on the soap is $52.80. [9.3B] **32.** 1.120 kWh of energy are used during the week. [9.4A] **33.** 125 kg of fertilizer are required. [9.2B]

CHAPTER TEST

1. 2960 m [9.1A] **2.** 378 mg [9.2A] **3.** 46 ml [9.3A] **4.** 919 ml [9.3A] **5.** 4.26 cm [9.1A] **6.** 7.96 m [9.1A] **7.** 0.847 kg [9.2A] **8.** 3.920 L [9.3A] **9.** 5.885 km [9.1A] **10.** 15 mm [9.1A] **11.** 3.089 g [9.2A] **12.** 1600 cm³ [9.3A] **13.** 3290 g [9.2A] **14.** 420 cm [9.1A] **15.** 96 cm³ [9.3A] **16.** 1.375 g [9.2A] **17.** 4.02 m [9.1A] **18.** 8920 L [9.3A] **19.** 5038 m [9.1A] **20.** 6.020 kl [9.3A] **21.** The total length of the rafters is 114 m. [9.1B] **22.** The weight is 36 kg. [9.2B] **23.** 5.2 L of vaccine are needed. [9.3B] **24.** 35 mi/h is equivalent to 56.4 km/h. [9.5A] **25.** The distance between the rivets is 17.5 cm. [9.1B] **26.** It costs $660 to fertilize the orchard. [9.2B] **27.** It costs $16.32 to operate the air conditioner. [9.4A] **28.** 11 L of acid should be ordered. [9.3B] **29.** The distance is 166.77 m. [9.5A] **30.** The distance is 669.12 ft. [9.5B]

CUMULATIVE REVIEW

1. 6 [1.6B] **2.** $12\frac{13}{36}$ [2.4C] **3.** $\frac{29}{36}$ [2.5C] **4.** $3\frac{1}{14}$ [2.7B] **5.** 1 [2.8B] **6.** 2.0702 [3.3A] **7.** 31.3 [4.3B] **8.** 175% [5.1B] **9.** 145 [5.4A] **10.** 2.25 gal [8.3A] **11.** 8.75 m [9.1A] **12.** 3.420 km [9.1A] **13.** 5050 g [9.2A] **14.** 3.672 g [9.2A] **15.** 6000 ml [9.3A] **16.** 2400 L [9.3A] **17.** There is $1683 left after the rent is paid. [2.6C] **18.** The amount of state income tax paid is $7207.20. [3.4B] **19.** The property tax is $1500. [4.3C] **20.** The new car buyer would receive a $1620 rebate. [5.2B] **21.** The dividend is 6.5% of the investment. [5.3B] **22.** Your average grade is 76. [7.4A] **23.** The salary next year will be $25,200. [5.2B] **24.** The discount rate is 22%. [6.2D] **25.** The length of the wall is 36 ft. [8.1C] **26.** The number of quarts of apple juice is 12. [8.3C] **27.** The profit is $123.20. [8.3C] **28.** 24 L of chlorine are used during the month. [9.3B] **29.** It costs $1.89 to operate the hair dryer. [9.4A] **30.** The conversion is 96.6 km/h. [9.5A]

Answers to Chapter 10 Odd-Numbered Exercises

SECTION 10.1

1. −120 feet **3.** +2 dollars **5.** **7.** **9.** −2 > −5 **11.** −16 < 1 **13.** 3 > −7 **15.** −11 < −8 **17.** 35 > 28 **19.** −42 < 27 **21.** 21 > −34

23. $-27 > -39$ **25.** $-87 < 63$ **27.** $86 > -79$ **29.** $-62 > -84$ **31.** $-131 < 101$ **33.** -4 **35.** 2
37. -22 **39.** 31 **41.** -70 **43.** 2 **45.** 6 **47.** 8 **49.** 9 **51.** -1 **53.** 0 **55.** 19 **57.** 22
59. -20 **61.** -18 **63.** 23 **65.** -27 **67.** 25 **69.** 74 **71.** -88 **73.** The state of New York has the lowest
recorded temperature.   **75a.** -6 **b.** -8 **c.** -9 or -6

SECTION 10.2

1. $-14, -364$ **3.** -2 **5.** 20 **7.** -11 **9.** -9 **11.** -3 **13.** 1 **15.** -5 **17.** -30 **19.** 9 **21.** 1
23. -10 **25.** -28 **27.** -41 **29.** -392 **31.** -20 **33.** -23 **35.** -2 **37.** -6 **39.** -6 **41.** 8
43. -7 **45.** -9 **47.** 36 **49.** -3 **51.** 18 **53.** -9 **55.** 11 **57.** 0 **59.** 11 **61.** 2 **63.** -138
65. 86 **67.** -337 **69.** 4 **71.** -12 **73.** -12 **75.** 3 **77.** The temperature is $-1°C$.   **79.** Nick's score
was -15 points.   **81.** The change in the price of the stock was -9 dollars.   **83.** The difference is $127°F$.   **85.** The
difference in elevation is 22,965 ft.   **87.** The difference is $82°C$.   **89.** The difference is $13°C$.   **91.**

-3	2	1
4	0	-4
-1	-2	3

93. Answers will vary.

SECTION 10.3

1. 42 **3.** -24 **5.** 6 **7.** 18 **9.** -20 **11.** -16 **13.** 25 **15.** 0 **17.** -72 **19.** -102 **21.** 140
23. -228 **25.** -320 **27.** -156 **29.** -70 **31.** 162 **33.** 120 **35.** 36 **37.** 192 **39.** -108
41. -2100 **43.** 20 **45.** -48 **47.** 140 **49.** -2 **51.** 8 **53.** 0 **55.** -9 **57.** -9 **59.** 9 **61.** -24
63. -12 **65.** 31 **67.** 17 **69.** 15 **71.** -13 **73.** -18 **75.** 19 **77.** 13 **79.** -19 **81.** 17
83. 26 **85.** 23 **87.** 25 **89.** -34 **91.** 11 **93.** -13 **95.** 13 **97.** 12 **99.** -14 **101.** -14
103. -6 **105.** -4 **107.** The average daily high temperature was $-4°$.   **109.** The average score of the ten
golfers was -2.   **111.** The wind chill factor at $-15°F$ with a 20-mph wind is $-60°F$.   **113a.** 25 **b.** -17
115a. True   **b.** True

SECTION 10.4

1. $-\dfrac{5}{24}$ **3.** $-\dfrac{19}{24}$ **5.** $\dfrac{5}{26}$ **7.** $\dfrac{7}{24}$ **9.** $-\dfrac{19}{60}$ **11.** $-1\dfrac{3}{8}$ **13.** $\dfrac{3}{4}$ **15.** $-\dfrac{47}{48}$ **17.** $\dfrac{3}{8}$ **19.** $-\dfrac{7}{60}$ **21.** $\dfrac{13}{24}$
23. -3.4 **25.** -8.89 **27.** -8.0 **29.** -0.68 **31.** -181.51 **33.** 2.7 **35.** -20.7 **37.** -37.19
39. -34.99 **41.** 6.778 **43.** -8.4 **45.** $\dfrac{1}{21}$ **47.** $\dfrac{2}{9}$ **49.** $-\dfrac{2}{9}$ **51.** $-\dfrac{45}{328}$ **53.** $\dfrac{2}{3}$ **55.** $\dfrac{15}{64}$ **57.** $-\dfrac{3}{7}$
59. $-1\dfrac{1}{9}$ **61.** $\dfrac{5}{6}$ **63.** $-2\dfrac{2}{7}$ **65.** $-13\dfrac{1}{2}$ **67.** 31.15 **69.** -112.97 **71.** 0.0363 **73.** 97 **75.** 2.2
77. -4.14 **79.** -3.8 **81.** -22.70 **83.** 0.07 **85.** 0.55 **87.** The temperature fell $32.22°C$.   **89.** The
difference is $35.438°C$.   **91a.** The closing price on the previous day for Quaker Oats was $\$40\dfrac{7}{8}$.   **b.** The closing price on
the previous day for General Mills was $\$63\dfrac{7}{8}$.   **93.** Answers will vary. For example, $-\dfrac{17}{24}$.   **95.** Yes. Answers will vary.

SECTION 10.5

1. 2.37×10^6 **3.** 4.5×10^{-4} **5.** 3.09×10^5 **7.** 6.01×10^{-7} **9.** 5.7×10^{10} **11.** 1.7×10^{-8} **13.** $710,000$
15. 0.000043 **17.** $671,000,000$ **19.** 0.00000713 **21.** $5,000,000,000,000$ **23.** 0.00801 **25.** 1.6×10^{10}
27. $\$1.67 \times 10^{11}$ **29.** 3.7×10^{-6} **31.** 4 **33.** 0 **35.** 12 **37.** -6 **39.** -5 **41.** 2 **43.** -3 **45.** 1
47. 2 **49.** -3 **51.** 14 **53.** -4 **55.** 33 **57.** -13 **59.** -12 **61.** 17 **63.** 0 **65.** 30 **67.** 94
69. -8 **71.** 39 **73.** 22 **75.** 0.21 **77.** -0.96 **79.** -0.29 **81.** -1.76 **83.** 2.1 **85.** $\dfrac{3}{16}$ **87.** $\dfrac{7}{16}$
89. $-\dfrac{5}{16}$ **91.** $-\dfrac{5}{8}$ **93a.** $3.45 \times 10^{-14} > 3.45 \times 10^{-15}$ **b.** $5.23 \times 10^{18} > 5.23 \times 10^{17}$ **c.** $3.12 \times 10^{12} > 3.12 \times 10^{11}$
95a. 100 **b.** -100 **c.** 225 **d.** -225 **97.** Carl   **99.** Sun: 1.99×10^{30} kg; Neutron: 1.67×10^{-27} kg

CHAPTER REVIEW

1. -22 [10.1B]　　**2.** 1 [10.2B]　　**3.** $-\dfrac{5}{24}$ [10.4A]　　**4.** 0.21 [10.4A]　　**5.** $\dfrac{8}{25}$ [10.4B]　　**6.** -1.28 [10.4B]

7. 10 [10.5B]　　**8.** $-\dfrac{7}{18}$ [10.5B]　　**9.** 4 [10.1B]　　**10.** $0 > -3$ [10.1A]　　**11.** -6 [10.1B]　　**12.** 6 [10.3B]

13. $\dfrac{17}{24}$ [10.4A]　　**14.** $-\dfrac{1}{4}$ [10.4B]　　**15.** $1\dfrac{5}{8}$ [10.4B]　　**16.** 24 [10.5B]　　**17.** -26 [10.2A]　　**18.** 2 [10.5B]

19. 3.97×10^{-5} [10.5A]　　**20.** -0.08 [10.4B]　　**21.** $\dfrac{1}{36}$ [10.4A]　　**22.** $\dfrac{3}{40}$ [10.4B]　　**23.** -0.042 [10.4B]

24. $\dfrac{1}{3}$ [10.5B]　　**25.** 5 [10.1B]　　**26.** $-2 > -40$ [10.1A]　　**27.** -26 [10.3A]　　**28.** 1.33 [10.5B]

29. $-\dfrac{1}{4}$ [10.4A]　　**30.** -7.4 [10.4A]　　**31.** $\dfrac{15}{32}$ [10.4B]　　**32.** 240,000 [10.5A]　　**33.** $-4°$ [10.2C]

34. The student scored 98 points. [10.3C]　　**35.** The difference is 395.45°C. [10.4C]

CHAPTER TEST

1. 3 [10.2B]　　**2.** -2 [10.1B]　　**3.** $\dfrac{1}{15}$ [10.4A]　　**4.** -0.0608 [10.4B]　　**5.** $-8 > -10$ [10.1A]

6. -1.88 [10.4A]　　**7.** -26 [10.5B]　　**8.** 90 [10.3A]　　**9.** -4.014 [10.4A]　　**10.** -9 [10.3B]　　**11.** -7 [10.2A]

12. $\dfrac{7}{24}$ [10.4A]　　**13.** 8.76×10^{10} [10.5A]　　**14.** -48 [10.3A]　　**15.** 0 [10.3B]　　**16.** 10 [10.2B]

17. $-\dfrac{4}{5}$ [10.4B]　　**18.** $0 > -4$ [10.1A]　　**19.** -14 [10.2A]　　**20.** -4 [10.5B]　　**21.** $\dfrac{3}{10}$ [10.4A]

22. 0.00000009601 [10.5A]　　**23.** 3.4 [10.4B]　　**24.** $\dfrac{1}{12}$ [10.4A]　　**25.** $\dfrac{1}{12}$ [10.4B]　　**26.** 3.213 [10.4A]

27. The temperature is 7°C. [10.2C]　　**28.** The melting point of oxygen is -213°C. [10.3C]　　**29.** The temperature fell 46.62°C. [10.4C]　　**30.** The average low temperature was $-2°$. [10.3C]

CUMULATIVE REVIEW

1. 0 [1.6B]　　**2.** $4\dfrac{13}{14}$ [2.5C]　　**3.** $2\dfrac{7}{12}$ [2.7B]　　**4.** $1\dfrac{2}{7}$ [2.8C]　　**5.** 1.80939 [3.3A]　　**6.** 18.67 [4.3B]

7. 13.75 [5.4A]　　**8.** 1 gal 3 qt [8.3A]　　**9.** 6.692 L [9.3A]　　**10.** 1.28 m [9.5A]　　**11.** 57.6 [5.2A]

12. 340% [5.1B]　　**13.** -3 [10.2A]　　**14.** $-3\dfrac{3}{8}$ [10.4A]　　**15.** $-10\dfrac{13}{24}$ [10.4A]　　**16.** 19 [10.5B]

17. 3.488 [10.4B]　　**18.** $31\dfrac{1}{2}$ [10.4B]　　**19.** -7 [10.3B]　　**20.** $\dfrac{25}{42}$ [10.4B]　　**21.** -4 [10.5B]　　**22.** -4 [10.5B]

23. The length of board remaining is $2\dfrac{1}{3}$ ft. [2.5D]　　**24.** Nimisha's new checkbook balance is $803.31. [6.7A]

25. The percent decrease in price is 27.3%. [6.2C]　　**26.** There should be 10 gal of coffee prepared. [8.3C]

27. The dividend per share is $1.68. [6.2A]　　**28.** The median hourly pay is $9.40. [7.4A]　　**29.** There would be 600,000 people voting in the city election. [4.3C]　　**30.** The average high temperature was $-4°$. [10.3C]

Answers to Chapter 11 Odd-Numbered Exercises

SECTION 11.1

1. -33　　**3.** -12　　**5.** -4　　**7.** -3　　**9.** -22　　**11.** -40　　**13.** -1　　**15.** 14　　**17.** 32　　**19.** 6　　**21.** 7

23. 49　　**25.** -24　　**27.** 63　　**29.** 9　　**31.** 4　　**33.** $-\dfrac{2}{3}$　　**35.** 0　　**37.** 0　　**39.** $-3\dfrac{1}{4}$　　**41.** 8.5023

43. -18.950658　　**45.** 3.5961　　**47.** $16z$　　**49.** $9m$　　**51.** $12at$　　**53.** $3yt$　　**55.** Unlike terms　　**57.** $-2t^2$

59. $13c - 5$　　**61.** $-2t$　　**63.** $3y^2 - 2$　　**65.** $14w - 8u$　　**67.** $-23xy + 10$　　**69.** $-11v^2$　　**71.** $-8ab - 3a$

73. $4y^2 - y$ **75.** $-3a - 2b^2$ **77.** $7x^2 - 8x$ **79.** $-3s + 6t$ **81.** $-3m + 10n$ **83.** $5ab + 4ac$ **85.** $\frac{2}{3}a^2 + \frac{3}{5}b^2$

87. $6.994x$ **89.** $1.56m - 3.77n$ **91.** $5x + 20$ **93.** $4y - 12$ **95.** $-2a - 8$ **97.** $15x + 30$ **99.** $15c - 25$

101. $-3y + 18$ **103.** $7x + 14$ **105.** $4y - 8$ **107.** $5x + 24$ **109.** $y - 6$ **111.** $6n - 3$ **113.** $6y + 20$

115. $10x + 4$ **117.** $-6t - 6$ **119.** $z - 2$ **121.** $y + 6$ **123.** $9t + 15$ **125.** $5t + 24$

127a.

| 1 | 1 | 1 | x | x | | x | x | x | x | 1 | 1 | 1 | 1 | 1 | 1 | | x | x | x | 1 | 1 | | x | x | 1 | 1 | 1 | 1 |

b.

| x | x | x | 1 | 1 | 1 |

$3x + 3$ **129.** Answers will vary.

SECTION 11.2

1. Yes   **3.** No   **5.** Yes   **7.** Yes   **9.** Yes   **11.** Yes   **13.** Yes   **15.** Yes   **17.** No   **19.** No   **21.** Yes

23. -2 **25.** 14   **27.** 2   **29.** -4 **31.** -5 **33.** 0   **35.** 2   **37.** -3 **39.** 10   **41.** -5 **43.** -12

45. -7 **47.** $\frac{2}{3}$ **49.** -1 **51.** $\frac{1}{3}$ **53.** $-\frac{1}{8}$ **55.** $-\frac{3}{4}$ **57.** $-1\frac{1}{12}$ **59.** 6   **61.** -9 **63.** -5 **65.** 14

67. 8   **69.** -3 **71.** 20   **73.** -21 **75.** -15 **77.** 16   **79.** -42 **81.** 15   **83.** $-38\frac{2}{5}$ **85.** $9\frac{3}{5}$

87. $-10\frac{4}{5}$ **89.** $1\frac{17}{18}$ **91.** $-2\frac{2}{3}$ **93.** 3   **95.** The amount of the original investment was \$23,610.   **97.** The increase in value of the investment was \$1190.   **99.** You used 18.5 gal of gasoline.   **101.** Your car averages 34.2 mi/gal. **103.** The markup on each shirt is \$6.30.   **105.** The cost of a compact disk is \$10.30.   **107.** Answers will vary. **109.** Answers will vary. For example, $x + 5 = 1$.   **111.** Answers will vary.

SECTION 11.3

1. 3   **3.** 5   **5.** -1 **7.** -4 **9.** 1   **11.** 3   **13.** -2 **15.** -3 **17.** -2 **19.** -1 **21.** 3   **23.** -1

25. 7   **27.** 2   **29.** 2   **31.** 0   **33.** 2   **35.** 0   **37.** $\frac{2}{3}$ **39.** $2\frac{5}{6}$ **41.** $-2\frac{1}{2}$ **43.** $1\frac{1}{2}$ **45.** 2   **47.** -2

49. $2\frac{1}{3}$ **51.** $-1\frac{1}{2}$ **53.** 10   **55.** 5   **57.** 36   **59.** -6 **61.** -9 **63.** $-4\frac{4}{5}$ **65.** $-8\frac{3}{4}$ **67.** 36   **69.** $1\frac{1}{3}$

71. 2   **73.** 4   **75.** 9   **77.** 4   **79.** -3.125 **81.** 1   **83.** -3 **85.** -9 **87.** 4.95   **89.** -0.0862069 **91.** The Celsius temperature is $-40°C$.   **93.** The time required is 14.5 s.   **95.** There were 2500 units made.   **97.** The mechanic's monthly salary is \$1800.   **99.** The total sales were \$32,000.   **101.** Miguel's commission rate was 4.5%. **103.** Answers will vary.   **105.** No. You cannot *solve* an expression.

SECTION 11.4

1. $\frac{1}{2}$ **3.** -1 **5.** -4 **7.** -1 **9.** -4 **11.** 3   **13.** -1 **15.** 2   **17.** 3   **19.** 0   **21.** -2 **23.** -1

25. $-\frac{2}{3}$ **27.** -4 **29.** $\frac{1}{3}$ **31.** $-\frac{3}{4}$ **33.** $\frac{1}{4}$ **35.** 0   **37.** $-1\frac{3}{4}$ **39.** 1   **41.** -1 **43.** -5 **45.** $\frac{5}{12}$

47. $-\frac{4}{7}$ **49.** $2\frac{1}{3}$ **51.** 21   **53.** 21   **55.** 2   **57.** -1 **59.** -4 **61.** $-\frac{6}{7}$ **63.** 5   **65.** 3   **67.** 0

69. -1 **71.** 2   **73.** $1\frac{9}{10}$ **75.** 13   **77.** $2\frac{1}{2}$ **79.** 2   **81.** 0   **83.** $3\frac{1}{5}$ **85.** 4   **87.** $-6\frac{1}{2}$ **89.** $-\frac{3}{4}$

91. $-\frac{2}{3}$ **93.** -3 **95.** $-1\frac{1}{4}$ **97.** $2\frac{5}{8}$ **99.** 1.9936196   **101.** 13.383119   **103.** 48   **105.** The solution of the original equation is 0. Therefore, the fourth line involves division by zero, which is undefined.

SECTION 11.5

1. $y - 9$ **3.** $z + 3$ **5.** $\frac{2}{3}n + n$ **7.** $\frac{m}{m - 3}$ **9.** $9(x + 4)$ **11.** $n - (-5)n$ **13.** $c\left(\frac{1}{4}c\right)$ **15.** $m^2 + 2m^2$

17. $2(t + 6)$ **19.** $\frac{x}{9 + x}$ **21.** $3(b + 6)$ **23.** x^2 **25.** $\frac{x}{20}$ **27.** $4x$ **29.** $\frac{3}{4}x$ **31.** $4 + x$ **33.** $5x - x$

35. $x(x + 2)$ **37.** $7(x + 8)$ **39.** $x^2 + 3x$ **41.** $(x + 3) + \frac{1}{2}x$ **43.** $\frac{3x}{x}$ **45.** 3 more than twice x; twice the sum of x and 3   **47.** Answers will vary.   **49.** carbon: $\frac{1}{2}x$; oxygen: $\frac{1}{2}x$

SECTION 11.6

1. $x + 7 = 12$; 5   **3.** $3x = 18$; 6   **5.** $x + 5 = 3$; -2 **7.** $6x = 14$; $2\frac{1}{3}$ **9.** $\frac{5}{6}x = 15$; 18   **11.** $3x + 4 = 8$; $1\frac{1}{3}$

13. $\frac{1}{4}x - 7 = 9$; 64   **15.** $\frac{x}{9} = 14$; 126   **17.** $\frac{x}{4} - 6 = -2$; 16   **19.** $7 - 2x = 13$; -3 **21.** $9 - \frac{x}{2} = 5$; 8

23. $\frac{3}{5}x + 8 = 2$; -10 **25.** $\frac{x}{4.186} - 7.92 = 12.529$; 85.599514   **27.** Target's price is $76.75.   **29.** The value of the sports utility vehicle last year was $20,000.   **31.** The total fast-food hamburger market was $39,000 million.   **33.** Their monthly income is $2720.   **35.** The monthly output last year was 5000 computers.   **37.** The recommended daily intake of sodium is 2.5 g.   **39.** Budget Plumbing charged for 3 h of labor.   **41.** The average price of a ticket in 1996 was $11.19.   **43.** 3.3% of the total is spent in New York.   **45.** The original rate was 5 gal/min.   **47.** The total sales were $42,540.   **49.** The percent subsidized is 21.5%.   **51.** $x + (x + 6) = 4$. No. There are more quarts of apple juice than the total number allowed for the mixture.

CHAPTER REVIEW

1. $-2a + 2b$ [11.1C]   **2.** Yes [11.2A]   **3.** -4 [11.2B]   **4.** 7 [11.3A]   **5.** 13 [11.1A]   **6.** -9 [11.2C]
7. -18 [11.3A]   **8.** $-3x + 4$ [11.1C]   **9.** 5 [11.4A]   **10.** -5 [11.2B]   **11.** No [11.2A]   **12.** 6 [11.1A]
13. 5 [11.4B]   **14.** 10 [11.3A]   **15.** $-4bc$ [11.1B]   **16.** $-2\frac{1}{2}$ [11.4A]   **17.** $1\frac{1}{4}$ [11.2C]   **18.** $\frac{71}{30}x^2$ [11.1B]

19. $-\frac{1}{3}$ [11.4B]   **20.** $10\frac{4}{5}$ [11.3A]   **21.** The car averaged 23 mi/gal. [11.2D]   **22.** The Celsius temperature is 37.8°C. [11.3B]   **23.** $n + \frac{n}{5}$ [11.5A]   **24.** $(n + 5) + \frac{1}{3}n$ [11.5B]   **25.** The number is 2. [11.6A]   **26.** The number is 10. [11.6A]   **27.** The regular price is $380. [11.6B]   **28.** The farmer harvested 25,300 bushels of corn last year. [11.6B]

CHAPTER TEST

1. 95 [11.3A]   **2.** 26 [11.2B]   **3.** $-11x - 4y$ [11.1B]   **4.** $3\frac{1}{5}$ [11.4A]   **5.** -2 [11.3A]   **6.** -38 [11.1A]

7. No [11.2A]   **8.** $-14ab + 9$ [11.1B]   **9.** $-2\frac{4}{5}$ [11.2C]   **10.** $8y - 7$ [11.1C]   **11.** 0 [11.4B]

12. $-\frac{1}{2}$ [11.3A]   **13.** $-5\frac{5}{6}$ [11.1A]   **14.** -16 [11.2C]   **15.** -3 [11.3A]   **16.** 11 [11.4B]   **17.** The monthly payment is $137.50. [11.2D]   **18.** There were 4000 clocks made during the month. [11.3B]   **19.** The time required is 11.5 s. [11.3B]   **20.** $x + \frac{1}{3}x$ [11.5A]   **21.** $5(x + 3)$ [11.5B]   **22.** $2x - 3 = 7$; 5 [11.6A]   **23.** The number is $-3\frac{1}{2}$. [11.6A]   **24.** His total sales for the month were $40,000. [11.6B]   **25.** The mechanic worked on your car for 3 h. [11.6B]

CUMULATIVE REVIEW

1. 41 [1.6B]   **2.** $1\frac{7}{10}$ [2.5C]   **3.** $\frac{11}{18}$ [2.8C]   **4.** 0.047383 [3.4A]   **5.** $4.20/h [4.2B]   **6.** 26.67 [4.3B]

7. $\frac{4}{75}$ [5.1A]   **8.** 140% [5.3A]   **9.** 6.4 [5.4A]   **10.** 18 ft 9 in. [8.1B]   **11.** 22 oz [8.2A]

12. 0.282 g [9.2A]   **13.** -1 [10.2A]   **14.** 19 [10.2B]   **15.** 6 [10.5B]   **16.** -48 [11.1A]

17. $-10x + 8z$ [11.1B]   **18.** $3y + 23$ [11.1C]   **19.** -1 [11.3A]   **20.** $-6\frac{1}{4}$ [11.4B]   **21.** $-7\frac{1}{2}$ [11.2C]

22. -21 [11.3A]   **23.** The percent was 17.6%. [5.3B]   **24.** The price of the pottery was $39.90. [6.2B]

25a. The discount is $81.   **b.** The discount rate is 18%. [6.2D]   **26.** The simple interest due is $2933.33. [6.3A]

27. $3n + 4$ [11.5B]   **28.** The average speed is 53 mi/h. [11.6B]   **29.** The total monthly sales are $32,500. [11.6B]

30. The number is 2. [11.6A]

Answers to Chapter 12 Odd-Numbered Exercises

SECTION 12.1

1. 0°, 90°   **3.** 180°   **5.** 30   **7.** 21   **9.** 14   **11.** 59°   **13.** 108°   **15.** 77°   **17.** 53°   **19.** 77°   **21.** 118°

23. 133°   **25.** 86°   **27.** 180°   **29.** Rectangle or square   **31.** Cube   **33.** Parallelogram, rectangle, or square

35. Cylinder   **37.** 102°   **39.** 90° and 45°   **41.** 14°   **43.** 90° and 65°   **45.** 8 in.   **47.** $4\frac{2}{3}$ ft   **49.** 7 cm

51. 2 ft 4 in.   **53.** $a = 106°$, $b = 74°$ **55.** $a = 112°$, $b = 68°$ **57.** $a = 38°$, $b = 142°$ **59.** $a = 58°$, $b = 58°$

61. $a = 152°$, $b = 152°$ **63.** $a = 130°$, $b = 50°$ **65a.** 1°   **b.** 90°   **67.** $\angle AOC$ and $\angle BOC$ are supplementary. Since $\angle AOC = \angle BOC$ is given, each angle is 90° and the lines are perpendicular.

SECTION 12.2

1. 56 in.   **3.** 20 ft   **5.** 92 cm   **7.** 47.1 cm   **9.** 9 ft 10 in.   **11.** 50.24 cm   **13.** 240 m   **15.** 157 cm

17. 121 cm   **19.** 50.56 m   **21.** 3.57 ft   **23.** 139.3 m   **25.** 60 ft of fencing should be purchased.   **27.** 24 m of binding are required.   **29.** The total cost is $16,222.50.   **31.** The bicycle travels 31.4 ft.   **33a.** The perimeter is more than 70 m.   **b.** The perimeter is 81.4 m.   **35.** The length of weather stripping is 20.71 ft.   **37.** The circumference of Earth is 39,915.68 km.   **39.** The perimeter of the eighth figure is 22 units.   **41.** The perimeter of all the shaded triangles is $14\frac{1}{4}$ cm.   **43.** Answers will vary.

SECTION 12.3

1. 144 ft²   **3.** 81 in²   **5.** 50.24 ft²   **7.** 20 in²   **9.** 2.13 cm²   **11.** 16 ft²   **13.** 817 in²   **15.** 154 in²

17. 26 cm²   **19.** 2220 cm²   **21.** 150.72 in²   **23.** 8.851323 ft²   **25.** 7500 yd² of artificial turf must be purchased.

27. The area watered is 7850 ft².   **29.** You should buy 2 qt of stain.   **31.** The area is 1250 ft².   **33.** The cost is $74.

35. $17.25 should be budgeted.   **37.** The total area of the park is 125.1492 mi².   **39a.** The increase in area is 113.04 in².

b. The increase in area is 235.5 cm².   **41a.** 4 times   **b.** Quadrupled   **c.** Quadrupled   **43a.** Sometimes true

b. Sometimes true   **c.** Always true

SECTION 12.4

1. 144 cm³   **3.** 512 in³   **5.** 2143.57 in³   **7.** 150.72 cm³   **9.** 6.4 m³   **11.** 5572.45 mm³   **13.** 3391.2 ft³

15. $42\frac{7}{8}$ ft³   **17.** 82.26 in³   **19.** 1.6688 m³   **21.** 69.08 in³   **23.** The volume is 40.5 m³.   **25.** The volume is 17,148.59 ft³.   **27.** There are 75.36 m³ of oil in the tank.   **29.** The volume is 809,516.25 ft³.   **31.** The volume is 212.64 in³.   **33.** The fish tank will be filled by 3.7 gal of water.   **35.** The cost is $4295.16.   **37a.** 4 times larger

b. 8 times larger   **c.** 8 times larger   **39.** Answers will vary.

SECTION 12.5

1. 2.646   **3.** 6.481   **5.** 12.845   **7.** 13.748   **9.** 5 in.   **11.** 8.602 cm   **13.** 11.180 ft   **15.** 4.472 cm

17. 12.728 yd   **19.** 6 ft and 10.392 ft   **21.** 21.213 cm   **23.** 8 m   **25.** 11.314 yd   **27.** The length of the ramp is 9.66 ft.   **29.** You are 21.6 mi from your starting point.   **31.** The distance is 4.243 in.   **33a.** Always true

b. Always true   **35.** A total of 8 mi of pipe are needed.

SECTION 12.6

1. $\frac{1}{2}$ **3.** $\frac{3}{4}$ **5.** Yes **7.** Yes **9.** 7.2 cm **11.** 3.3 m **13.** The height of the building is 16 m.
15. The perimeter is 12 m. **17.** The area is 56.25 cm². **19a.** Always true **b.** Sometimes true **c.** Always true
21. 16.5

CHAPTER REVIEW

1. 0.75 m [12.1B] **2.** 31.4 cm [12.2A] **3.** 26 ft [12.2A] **4.** 3 [12.1A] **5.** 200 ft³ [12.4A]
6. 26 cm [12.5B] **7.** 75° [12.1A] **8.** 3.873 [12.5A] **9.** 16 cm [12.6A] **10.** 63.585 cm² [12.3A]
11. $a = 135°, b = 45°$ [12.1C] **12.** 55 m² [12.3A] **13.** 240 in³ [12.4B] **14.** 57.12 in² [12.3B]
15. 267.9 ft³ [12.4A] **16.** 64.8 m² [12.6B] **17.** 47.7 in. [12.2B] **18.** $a = 100°, b = 80°$ [12.1C]
19. The ladder reaches 15 ft up the building. [12.5C] **20.** The other two angles measure 58° and 90°. [12.1B]
21. The bicycle travels 73.3 ft. [12.2C] **22.** The area of the room is 28 yd². [12.3C] **23.** The volume is
1144.53 ft³. [12.4C] **24.** The area is 11 m². [12.3A] **25.** You are 29 mi from your starting point. [12.5C]

CHAPTER TEST

1. 169.56 m³ [12.4A] **2.** 6.8 m [12.2A] **3.** 1406.72 cm³ [12.4B] **4.** 10 m [12.6A] **5.** 58° [12.1A]
6. $3\frac{1}{7}$ m² [12.3A] **7.** 150° [12.1C] **8.** 15.85 ft [12.2B] **9.** 13.748 [12.5A] **10.** 9.747 ft [12.5B]
11. 10.125 ft² [12.3B] **12.** $\angle a = 45°, \angle b = 135°$ [12.1C] **13.** $1\frac{1}{5}$ ft [12.6A] **14.** The other two angles measure
50° and 90°. [12.1B] **15.** The width is 25 ft. [12.6B] **16.** The larger pizza contains 113.04 in² more. [12.3C]
17. The cost will be $1113.69. [12.3C] **18.** The cross-sectional area is 103.82 ft². [12.3C] **19.** The length of the
rafter is 15 ft. [12.5C] **20.** The volume is 780 in³. [12.4C]

CUMULATIVE REVIEW

1. 48 [2.1B] **2.** $7\frac{41}{48}$ [2.4C] **3.** $\frac{39}{56}$ [2.7B] **4.** $\frac{2}{15}$ [2.8C] **5.** $-\frac{1}{24}$ [10.4A] **6.** $8.72/h [4.2B]
7. 37.5 [4.3B] **8.** $\frac{3}{8}$ [5.1A] **9.** -4 [11.1A] **10.** 85 [5.4A] **11.** -6 [11.3A] **12.** $\frac{4}{3}$ [11.4B]
13. 32,500 m [9.1A] **14.** 31.58 m [9.1A] **15.** -15 [11.2C] **16.** 2 [11.4B] **17.** The monthly payment
is $458. [1.5D] **18.** The sales tax is $47.06. [4.3C] **19.** The operator's hourly wage was $14.60. [5.4B]
20. The sale price is $54. [6.2D] **21.** The value after 20 years would be $184,675.75. [6.3B] **22.** The weight of
the package is 54 lb. [8.2C] **23.** The distance between the rivets is 22.5 cm. [9.1B] **24.** -2 [11.6A]
25. $a = 74°; b = 106°$ [12.1C] **26.** 29.42 cm [12.2B] **27.** 50 in² [12.3B] **28.** 92.86 in³ [12.4B]
29. 10.63 ft [12.5B] **30.** 36 cm [12.6B]

FINAL EXAMINATION

1. 3259 [1.3B] **2.** 53 [1.5C] **3.** 16 [1.6B] **4.** 144 [2.1A] **5.** $1\frac{49}{120}$ [2.4B] **6.** $3\frac{29}{48}$ [2.5C]
7. $6\frac{3}{14}$ [2.6B] **8.** $\frac{4}{9}$ [2.7B] **9.** $\frac{1}{6}$ [2.8B] **10.** $\frac{1}{13}$ [2.8C] **11.** 164.177 [3.2A] **12.** 60,205 [1.3B]
13. 0.027918 [3.4A] **14.** 0.69 [3.5A] **15.** $\frac{9}{20}$ [3.6B] **16.** 24.5 mi/gal [4.2B] **17.** 54.9 [4.3B]
18. $\frac{9}{40}$ [5.1A] **19.** 135% [5.1B] **20.** 125% [5.1B] **21.** 36 [5.2A] **22.** $133\frac{1}{3}$% [5.3A] **23.** 70 [5.4A]
24. 20 in. [8.1A] **25.** 1 ft 4 in. [8.1B] **26.** 2.5 lb [8.2A] **27.** 6 lb 6 oz [8.2B] **28.** 2.25 gal [8.3A]
29. 1 gal 3 qt [8.3B] **30.** 248 cm [9.1A] **31.** 4.62 m [9.1A] **32.** 1.614 kg [9.2A] **33.** 2067 ml [9.3A]
34. 88.55 km [9.5A] **35.** It costs $1.15 to run the air conditioner. [9.4A] **36.** 6.79×10^{-8} [10.5A]
37. The perimeter is 3.9 m. [12.2A] **38.** The area is 45 in². [12.3A] **39.** The volume is 1200 cm³. [12.4A]

40. -4 [10.2A]   **41.** -15 [10.2B]   **42.** $-\dfrac{1}{2}$ [10.4B]   **43.** $-\dfrac{1}{4}$ [10.4B]   **44.** 6 [10.5B]

45. $-x + 17$ [11.1C]   **46.** -18 [11.2C]   **47.** 5 [11.3A]   **48.** 1 [11.4A]   **49.** Your new balance is $959.93. [6.7A]   **50.** There will be 63,750 people voting in the election. [4.3C]   **51.** One year ago the dividend per share was $2.00. [5.4B]   **52.** The average income was $3794. [7.4A]   **53.** The simple interest due is $9000. [6.3A]   **54.** The percent is 43.4%. [7.1B]   **55.** The discount rate is 28%. [6.2D]   **56.** The weight of the tiles is 81 lb. [8.2C]   **57.** The perimeter is 28.56 in. [12.2B]   **58.** The area is 16.86 cm^2. [12.3B]   **59.** The number is 16. [11.6A]

Glossary

absolute value of a number The distance between zero and the number on the number line. (Sec. 10.1)

acute angle An angle whose measure is between 0° and 90°. (Sec. 12.1)

acute triangle A triangle that has three acute angles. (Sec. 12.2)

addend In addition, one of the numbers added. (Sec. 1.2)

addition The process of finding the total of two numbers. (Sec. 1.2)

Addition Property of Zero Zero added to a number does not change the number. (Sec. 1.2)

adjacent angles Two angles that share a common side. (Sec. 12.1)

alternate exterior angles Two angles that are on opposite sides of the transversal and outside the parallel lines. (Sec. 12.1)

alternate interior angles Two angles that are on opposite sides of the transversal and between the parallel lines. (Sec. 12.1)

angle An angle is formed when two rays start at the same point; it is measured in degrees. (Sec. 12.1)

area A measure of the amount of surface in a region. (Sec. 12.3)

Associative Property of Addition Numbers to be added can be grouped (with parentheses, for example) in any order; the sum will be the same. (Sec. 1.2)

Associative Property of Multiplication Numbers to be multiplied can be grouped (with parentheses, for example) in any order; the product will be the same. (Sec. 1.4)

average value The sum of all values divided by the number of those values; also known as the mean value. (Sec. 7.4)

balancing a checkbook Determining if the checking account balance is accurate. (Sec. 6.7)

bar graph A graph that represents data by the height of the bars. (Sec. 7.2)

basic percent equation Percent times base equals amount. (Sec. 5.2)

box-and-whiskers plot A graph that shows the smallest value in a set of numbers, the first quartile, the median, the third quartile, and the greatest value. (Sec. 7.4)

British Thermal Unit A unit of energy. 1 British Thermal Unit = 778 foot-pounds. (Sec. 8.4)

broken-line graph A graph that represents data by the position of the lines and shows trends and comparisons. (Sec. 7.2)

Calorie A unit of energy in the metric system. (Sec. 9.4)

capacity A measure of liquid substances. (Sec. 8.3)

circle A plane figure in which all points are the same distance from point *O*, which is called the center of the circle. (Sec. 12.1)

circle graph A graph that represents data by the size of the sectors. (Sec. 7.1)

circumference The distance around a circle. (Sec. 12.2)

class frequency The number of occurrences of data in each class interval on a histogram; represented by the height of each bar. (Sec. 7.3)

class interval Range of numbers represented by the width of a bar on a histogram. (Sec. 7.3)

class midpoint The center of a class interval in a frequency polygon. (Sec. 7.3)

commission That part of the pay earned by a salesperson that is calculated as a percent of the salesperson's sales. (Sec. 6.6)

common factor A number that is a factor of two or more numbers is a common factor of those numbers. (Sec. 2.1)

common multiple A number that is a multiple of two or more numbers is a common multiple of those numbers. (Sec. 2.1)

Commutative Property of Addition Two numbers can be added in either order; the sum will be the same. (Sec. 1.2)

Commutative Property of Multiplication Two numbers can be multiplied in either order; the product will be the same. (Sec. 1.4)

complementary angles Two angles whose sum is 90°. (Sec. 12.1)

composite geometric figure A figure made from two or more geometric figures. (Sec. 12.2)

composite geometric solid A solid made from two or more geometric solids. (Sec. 12.4)

composite number A number that has whole-number factors besides 1 and itself. For instance, 18 is a composite number. (Sec. 1.7)

compound interest Interest computed not only on the original principal but also on interest already earned. (Sec. 6.3)

congruent objects Objects that have the same shape and the same size. (Sec. 12.6)

constant term A term that has no variables. (Sec. 11.1)

corresponding angles Two angles that are on the same side of the transversal and are both acute angles or are both obtuse angles. (Sec. 12.1)

cost The price that a business pays for a product. (Sec. 6.2)

cube A rectangular solid in which all six faces are squares. (Sec. 12.1)

cubic centimeter A unit of capacity equal to 1 milliliter. (Sec. 9.3)

cup A U.S. Customary measure of capacity. 2 cups = 1 pint. (Sec. 8.3)

data Numerical information. (Sec. 7.1)

decimal A number written in decimal notation. (Sec. 3.1)

decimal notation Notation in which a number consists of a whole-number part, a decimal point, and a decimal part. (Sec. 3.1)

decimal part In decimal notation, that part of the number that appears to the right of the decimal point. (Sec. 3.1)

decimal point In decimal notation, the point that separates the whole-number part from the decimal part. (Sec. 3.1)

degree Unit used to measure angles; one complete revolution is 360°. (Sec. 12.1)

denominator The part of a fraction that appears below the fraction bar. (Sec. 2.2)

diameter of a circle A line segment with endpoints on the circle and going through the center. (Sec. 12.1)

diameter of a sphere A line segment with endpoints on the sphere and going through the center. (Sec. 12.1)

difference In subtraction, the result of subtracting two numbers. (Sec. 1.3)

discount The difference between the regular price and the sale price. (Sec. 6.2)

discount rate The percent of a product's regular price that is represented by the discount. (Sec. 6.2)

dividend In division, the number into which the divisor is divided to yield the quotient. (Sec. 1.5)

division The process of finding the quotient of two numbers. (Sec. 1.5)

divisor In division, the number that is divided into the dividend to yield the quotient. (Sec. 1.5)

energy The ability to do work. (Sec. 8.4)

equation A statement of the equality of two mathematical expressions. (Sec. 11.2)

equilateral triangle A triangle that has three sides of equal length; the three angles are also of equal measure. (Sec. 12.2)

equivalent fractions Equal fractions with different denominators. (Sec. 2.3)

evaluating a variable expression Replacing the variable or variables and then simplifying the resulting numerical expression. (Sec. 11.1)

expanded form The number 46,208 can be written in expanded form as 40,000 + 6000 + 200 + 0 + 8. (Sec. 1.1)

exponent In exponential notation, the raised number that indicates how many times the number to which it is attached is taken as a factor. (Sec. 1.6)

exponential notation The expression of a number to some power, indicated by an exponent. (Sec. 1.6)

factors In multiplication, the numbers that are multiplied. (Sec. 1.4)

first quartile In a set of numbers, the number below which one-quarter of the data lie. (Sec. 7.4)

fluid ounce A U.S. Customary measure of capacity. 8 fluid ounces = 1 cup. (Sec. 8.3)

foot A U.S. Customary unit of length. 3 feet = 1 yard. (Sec. 8.1)

foot-pound A U.S. Customary unit of energy. One foot-pound of energy is required to lift 1 pound a distance of 1 foot. (Sec. 8.4)

foot-pounds per second A U.S. Customary unit of power. (Sec. 8.4)

fraction The notation used to represent the number of equal parts of a whole. (Sec. 2.2)

fraction bar The bar that separates the numerator of a fraction from the denominator. (Sec. 2.2)

frequency polygon A graph that displays information similarly to a histogram. A dot is placed above the center of each class interval at a height corresponding to that class's frequency. (Sec. 7.3)

gallon A U.S. Customary measure of capacity. 1 gallon = 4 quarts. (Sec. 8.3)

geometric solid A figure in space. (Sec. 12.1)

gram The basic unit of mass in the metric system. (Sec. 9.2)

graph A display that provides a pictorial representation of data. (Sec. 7.1)

graph of a whole number A heavy dot placed directly above that number on the number line. (Sec. 1.1)

greater than A number that appears to the right of a given number on the number line is greater than that given number. (Sec. 1.1)

greatest common factor The largest common factor of two or more numbers. (Sec. 2.1)

histogram A bar graph in which the width of each bar corresponds to a range of numbers called a class interval. (Sec. 7.3)

horsepower The U.S. Customary unit of power. 1 horsepower = 550 foot-pounds per second. (Sec. 8.4)

hourly wage Pay calculated on the basis of a certain amount for each hour worked. (Sec. 6.6)

hypotenuse The side opposite the right angle in a right triangle. (Sec. 12.1)

improper fraction A fraction greater than or equal to 1. (Sec. 2.2)

inch A U.S. Customary unit of length. 12 inches = 1 foot. (Sec. 8.1)

integers The integers are ..., −3, −2, −1, 0, 1, 2, 3, ... (Sec 10.1)

interest The amount of money paid for the privilege of using someone else's money. (Sec. 6.3)

interest rate The percent used to determine the amount of interest. (Sec. 6.3)

interquartile range The difference between the third quartile and the first quartile. (Sec. 7.4)

intersecting lines Lines that cross at a point in the plane. (Sec. 12.1)

inverting a fraction Interchanging the numerator and denominator. (Sec. 2.7)

isosceles triangle A triangle that has two sides of equal length; the angles opposite the equal sides are of equal measure. (Sec. 12.2)

least common denominator The least common multiple of denominators. (Sec. 2.4)

least common multiple The smallest common multiple of two or more numbers. (Sec. 2.1)

legs The two shortest sides of a right triangle. (Sec. 12.1)

less than A number that appears to the left of a given number on the number line is less than that given number. (Sec. 1.1)

like terms Terms of a variable expression that have the same variable part. (Sec. 11.1)

line A line extends indefinitely in two directions in a plane; it has no width. (Sec. 12.1)

line segment Part of a line; it has two endpoints. (Sec. 12.1)

liter The basic unit of capacity in the metric system. (Sec. 9.3)

markup The difference between selling price and cost. (Sec. 6.2)

markup rate The percent of a product's cost that is represented by the markup. (Sec. 6.2)

mass The amount of material in an object. On the surface of the earth, mass is the same as weight. (Sec. 9.2)

mean value The sum of all values divided by the number of those values; also known as the average value. (Sec. 7.4)

measurement A measurement has both a number and a unit. Examples include 7 feet, 4 ounces, and 0.5 gallon. (Sec. 8.1)

median value The value that separates a list of values in such a way that there are the same number of values below the median as above it. (Sec. 7.4)

meter The basic unit of length in the metric system. (Sec. 9.1)

metric system A system of measurement based on the decimal system. (Sec. 9.1)

mile A U.S. Customary unit of length. 5280 feet = 1 mile. (Sec. 8.1)

minuend In subtraction, the number from which another number (the subtrahend) is subtracted. (Sec. 1.3)

mixed number A number greater than 1 that has a whole-number part and a fractional part. (Sec. 2.2)

mode In a set of numbers, the value that occurs most frequently. (Sec. 7.4)

mortgage The amount borrowed to buy real estate. (Sec. 6.4)

multiples of a number The products of that number and the numbers 1, 2, 3, …. (Sec. 2.1)

multiplication The process of finding the product of two numbers. (Sec. 1.4)

Multiplication Property of One The product of a number and one is the number. (Sec. 1.4)

Multiplication Property of Zero The product of a number and zero is zero. (Sec. 1.4)

negative integers The numbers …, −5, −4, −3, −2, −1. (Sec. 10.1)

negative numbers Numbers less than zero. (Sec. 10.1)

number line A line on which a number can be graphed. (Sec. 1.1)

numerator The part of a fraction that appears above the fraction bar. (Sec. 2.2)

numerical coefficient The number part of a variable term. When the numerical coefficient is 1 or −1, the 1 is usually not written. (Sec. 11.1)

obtuse angle An angle whose measure is between 90° and 180°. (Sec. 12.1)

obtuse triangle A triangle that has one obtuse angle. (Sec. 12.2)

opposites Two numbers that are the same distance from zero on the number line, but on opposite sides. (Sec. 10.1)

Order of Operations Agreement A set of rules that tell us in what order to perform the operations that occur in a numerical expression. (Sec. 1.6)

ounce A U.S. Customary unit of weight. 16 ounces = 1 pound. (Sec. 8.2)

parallel lines Lines that never meet; the distance between them is always the same. (Sec. 12.1)

parallelogram A quadrilateral that has opposite sides equal and parallel. (Sec. 12.1)

percent Parts per hundred. (Sec. 5.1)

percent decrease A decrease of a quantity expressed as a percent of its original value. (Sec. 6.2)

percent increase An increase of a quantity expressed as a percent of its original value. (Sec. 6.2)

perfect square The product of a whole number and itself. (Sec. 12.5)

perimeter The distance around a plane figure. (Sec. 12.2)

period In a number written in standard form, each group of digits separated by a comma. (Sec. 1.1)

perpendicular lines Intersecting lines that form right angles. (Sec. 12.1)

pictograph A graph that uses symbols to represent information. (Sec. 7.1)

pint A U.S. Customary measure of capacity. 2 pints = 1 quart. (Sec. 8.3)

place value The position of each digit in a number written in standard form determines that digit's place value. (Sec. 1.1)

plane A flat surface. (Sec. 12.1)

plane figure A figure that lies totally in a plane. (Sec. 12.1)

points A term banks use to mean percent of a mortgage; used to express the loan origination fee. (Sec. 6.4)

polygon A closed figure determined by three or more line segments that lie in a plane. (Sec. 12.2)

positive integers The numbers 1, 2, 3, 4, 5, …; also called the natural numbers. (Sec. 10.1)

positive numbers Numbers greater than zero. (Sec. 10.1)

pound A U.S. Customary unit of weight. 1 pound = 16 ounces. (Sec. 8.2)

power The rate at which work is done or energy is released. (Sec. 8.4)

prime factorization The expression of a number as the product of its prime factors. (Sec. 1.7)

prime number A number whose only whole-number factors are 1 and itself. For instance, 13 is a prime number. (Sec. 1.7)

principal The amount of money originally deposited or borrowed. (Sec. 6.3)

product In multiplication, the result of multiplying two numbers. (Sec. 1.4)

proper fraction A fraction less than 1. (Sec. 2.2)

proportion An expression of the equality of two ratios or rates. (Sec. 4.3)

Pythagorean Theorem The square of the hypotenuse of a right triangle is equal to the sum of the squares of the two legs. (Sec. 12.5)

quadrilateral A four-sided closed figure. (Sec. 12.1)

quart A U.S. Customary measure of capacity. 4 quarts = 1 gallon. (Sec. 8.3)

quotient In division, the result of dividing the divisor into the dividend. (Sec. 1.5)

radius of a circle A line segment going from the center to a point on the circle. (Sec. 12.1)

radius of a sphere A line segment going from the center to a point on the sphere. (Sec. 12.1)

range In a set of numbers, the difference between the largest and smallest values. (Sec. 7.4)

rate A comparison of two quantities that have different units. (Sec. 4.2)

rate in simplest form A rate in which the numbers that form the rate have no common factors. (Sec. 4.2)

ratio A comparison of two quantities that have the same units. (Sec. 4.1)

ratio in simplest form A ratio in which the two numbers that form the ratio do not have a common factor. (Sec. 4.1)

rational number A number that can be written as the ratio of two integers, where the denominator is not zero. (Sec. 10.4)

ray A ray starts at a point and extends indefinitely in one direction. (Sec. 12.1)

reciprocal of a fraction The fraction with the numerator and denominator interchanged. (Sec. 2.7)

rectangle A parallelogram that has four right angles. (Sec. 12.1)

rectangular solid A solid in which all six faces are rectangles. (Sec. 12.1)

regular polygon A polygon in which each side has the same length and each angle has the same measure. (Sec. 12.2)

remainder In division, the quantity left over when it is not possible to separate objects or numbers into a whole number of equal groups. (Sec. 1.5)

right angle A 90° angle. (Sec. 12.1)

right triangle A triangle that contains one right angle. (Sec. 12.1)

rounding Giving an approximate value of an exact number. (Sec. 1.1)

salary Pay based on a weekly, biweekly, monthly, or annual time schedule. (Sec. 6.6)

sale price The reduced price. (Sec. 6.2)

scalene triangle A triangle that has no sides of equal length; no two of its angles are of equal measure. (Sec. 12.2)

scientific notation Notation in which a number is expressed as a product of two factors, one a number between 1 and 10 and the other a power of 10. (Sec. 10.5)

selling price The price for which a business sells a product to a customer. (Sec. 6.2)

similar objects Objects that have the same shape but not necessarily the same size. (Sec. 12.6)

simple interest Interest computed on the original principal. (Sec. 6.3)

simplest form of a fraction A fraction is in simplest form when there are no common factors in the numerator and the denominator. (Sec. 2.3)

simplifying a variable expression Combining like terms by adding their numerical coefficients. (Sec. 11.1)

solid An object in space. (Sec. 12.1)

solution of an equation A number that, when substituted for the variable, results in a true equation. (Sec. 11.2)

solving an equation Finding a solution of the equation. (Sec. 11.2)

sphere A solid in which all points are the same distance from point O, which is called the center of the sphere. (Sec. 12.1)

square A rectangle that has four equal sides. (Sec. 12.1)

square root A square root of a number is one of two identical factors of that number. (Sec. 12.5)

standard form A whole number is in standard form when it is written using the digits 0, 1, 2, …, 9. An example is 46,208. (Sec. 1.1)

statistics The branch of mathematics concerned with data, or numerical information. (Sec. 7.1)

straight angle A 180° angle. (Sec. 12.1)

subtraction The process of finding the difference between two numbers. (Sec. 1.3)

subtrahend In subtraction, the number that is subtracted from another number (the minuend). (Sec. 1.3)

sum In addition, the total of the numbers added. (Sec. 1.2)

supplementary angles Two angles whose sum is 180°. (Sec. 12.1)

terms of a variable expression The addends of the expression. (Sec. 11.1)

third quartile In a set of numbers, the number above which one-quarter of the data lie. (Sec. 7.4)

ton A U.S. Customary unit of weight. 1 ton = 2000 pounds. (Sec. 8.2)

transversal A line intersecting two other lines at two different points. (Sec. 12.1)

triangle A three-sided closed figure. (Sec. 12.1)

true proportion A proportion in which the fractions are equal. (Sec. 4.3)

unit cost The cost of one item. (Sec. 6.1)

unit rate A rate in which the number in the denominator is 1. (Sec. 4.2)

units In the quantity 3 feet, feet are the units in which the measurement is made. (Sec. 4.1)

variable A letter used to stand for a quantity that is unknown or that can change. (Sec. 11.1)

variable expression An expression that contains one or more variables. (Sec. 11.1)

variable part In a variable term, the variable or variables and their exponents. (Sec. 11.1)

variable term A term composed of a numerical coefficient and a variable part. (Sec. 11.1)

vertex The common endpoint of two rays that form an angle. (Sec. 12.1)

vertical angles Two angles that are on opposite sides of the intersection of two lines. (Sec. 12.1)

volume A measure of the amount of space inside a closed surface. (Sec. 12.4)

watt-hour A unit of electrical energy in the metric system. (Sec. 9.4)

weight A measure of how strongly the earth is pulling on an object. (Sec. 8.2)

whole numbers The whole numbers are 0, 1, 2, 3, …. (Sec. 1.1)

whole-number part In decimal notation, that part of the number that appears to the left of the decimal point. (Sec. 3.1)

yard A U.S. Customary unit of length. 36 inches = 1 yard. (Sec. 8.1)

Index